3:00 oral.

STATISTICAL PROCEDURES
AND THEIR
MATHEMATICAL BASES

The quality of the materials used in the manufacture of this book is governed by continued postwar shortages.

STATISTICAL PROCEDURES

AND THEIR

MATHEMATICAL BASES

BY

CHARLES C. PETERS, Ph.D.

Director of Educational Research,
The Pennsylvania State College

AND

WALTER R. VAN VOORHIS, M.A.

Schuylkill Administrative Head and
Assistant Professor of Mathematics,
The Pennsylvania State College

FIRST EDITION
FIFTH IMPRESSION

McGRAW-HILL BOOK COMPANY, Inc.

NEW YORK AND LONDON

1940

THE MAPLE PRESS COMPANY, YORK, PA.

PREFACE

This volume is a revision and extension of a book by the same title published privately in lithoprinted form in 1935. The wide demand for the preliminary edition showed that there was a need for the type of presentation of statistics here offered.

The characteristic feature of the book is the effort to explain the mathematical origins of the most widely used statistical formulas in terms that persons with comparatively little mathematical training can easily follow. We believe that, if statistical workers do not take their tools as magic but understand them in the light of their origins and assumptions, they will use these tools more intelligently and more safely. In order to make such understanding available to persons of little mathematical training we give the derivations in much detail. It is a well-known fact that the source of difficulty in mathematical reading by relatively untrained persons is largely the omission of steps which are supposed to be obvious. When these steps are supplied and when the use of specialized mathematical terminology is reduced to a minimum, much that would otherwise be closed to the reader is readily understandable. In order to make calculus available as a tool for those who do not have a command of it, we open this volume with a chapter on calculus. This is, of course, only "a little calculus," but it is enough to prepare the reader who has not hitherto studied calculus to follow the derivations in which we must draw upon this branch of mathematics. Our experience with this presentation, as well as that reported by some others, shows that this chapter on calculus can be mastered in about 10 per cent of the time normally allotted to a one-semester course in advanced statistics.

The title of the book is somewhat too pretentious. It might better be called *Some Statistical Procedures and a Little Insight into the Mathematical Bases of a Few of Them.* It is not, of course, a comprehensive treatment of the mathematical bases of statistics. It is intended to bridge the gap between the elementary courses, in which the formulas are given purely authoritatively,

v

and the original contributions in the monographic press, which are often highly mathematical in character. We had hoped to be able to include in this volume a section on the geometry of hyperspace, matrix algebra, and other forms of advanced mathematics basic to the reading of present-day statistical literature. We had hoped to make this parallel in simplicity our chapter on calculus. But we found that, if this were to be made really intelligible without being superficial, we would need to allot to it an amount of additional space that would not be feasible without sacrificing the other and simpler functions which this volume is intended to perform. An introduction to the geometry of hyperspace, as well as to some other forms of higher mathematics, is really indispensable to anyone who wishes to follow contemporary statistical theory. But it will probably need to be set up in a separate volume—a chatty, leisurely volume.

In this edition we have included many of the statistical techniques advocated by R. A. Fisher and have undertaken to bring them into synthesis with classical statistics. We do not believe that the Fisher techniques will prove to have the importance for research in the psychological and social sciences that they have in the biological sciences, because in the former fields it is unnecessary to work much with small samples and with rough exploratory research. Certainly the Fisher techniques will only supplement and not supplant the classical methods in the psychological and social sciences. Nevertheless, we believe that the workers for whom we are writing in these fields are entitled to know what these techniques are. We have attempted to take the magic out of them, as we did also out of classical statistics, by explaining them in very simple terms and by showing how they fit in with the older methods. In this way we hope to bring it about that the workers in the fields for which we are writing will find some useful elements in them without grasping at them as some "new magic" and unwarrantedly throwing away the vastly useful techniques of classical statistics as "antiquated."

We are glad to acknowledge our very great indebtedness to the work of Prof. Truman L. Kelley. Indeed, when this book was first begun it was intended merely as a footnote to his *Statistical Method*. Even though frequent explicit references to this book are absent, the informed reader will see that our treatment was shaped largely by Kelley's and often closely parallels his. In the further development of the work we went, of course, directly to the sources in the monographic literature, and hence we are obligated to Karl Pearson and the many other scholars who contributed to that literature, a very large portion of whom wrote under the inspiration and the guidance of Pearson. We desire to express our gratitude to members of the mathematics department of the Pennsylvania State College, especially to Clyde H. Graves, for competent counsel on technical matters given unstintedly every time we had occasion to seek such help.

We are also indebted to Prof. R. A. Fisher and his publishers, Oliver and Boyd, for permission to use the table of the distribution of t which we reproduce on page 173; to Prof. Egon S. Pearson, editor of *Biometrika* and the Biometrika Publications, for permission to use the two tables on the normal curve integral, pages 481 to 487, and the chi-square table pages 498 to 500; and to Mrs. Marjory Gosset of Oxford, England—wife and heir of William Sealy Gosset, the brilliant English scholar who signed his statistical articles "Student"—for permission to use his tables of t published in *Metron* in 1925, which tables we give on pages 488 to 493 of this volume.

C. C. P,
W. R. V.

State College, Pa.,
August, 1940.

CONTENTS

CONTENTS xi

STATISTICAL PROCEDURES AND THEIR MATHEMATICAL BASES

CHAPTER I

A LITTLE CALCULUS

This chapter is intended for persons who have not previously studied calculus. It presents, in a way that a reader who has had only a limited training in mathematics should be able to follow, practically all the calculus upon which we shall have occasion to draw in this volume on statistics, which includes many fundamental elements common also to applications in other fields. We trust that this simple presentation of the elements of differential and integral calculus may not only prove useful to the student of statistics but that it may also give to laymen in mathematics an interesting and culturally enriching insight into the nature and applications of this fascinating mathematical discipline.

In every case where one quantity varies in a manner that is definitely related to the variation in a second, the relation between the two may be represented geometrically by a curve of some shape (including a straight line). Take first the simple relation $y = x$, where x may be represented by any number and y will therefore of necessity be the same number. We may lay off this relation on the adjacent diagram.

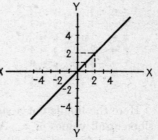

FIG. 1.—Straight line relation: Slope = 1.

When $x = 1$, $y = 1$; when $x = 2$, $y = 2$, etc. If we go to the right one unit for x and then up one unit for y, we shall have a point x_1y_1 that shows the relation between the two series at that value of x. If we go two units to the right and two units up, we shall have a second point x_2y_2; etc.

1

A straight line may be drawn through all these points. Its slope will be $\frac{1}{1}$, $\frac{2}{2}$, $\frac{3}{3}$, $\frac{4}{4}$, $\cdot$ $\cdot$ $\cdot$ $= 1$. Its slope will always be the same at all values of x.

Suppose, now, that $y = 0.4x$. We shall then have a line representing the relation as follows:

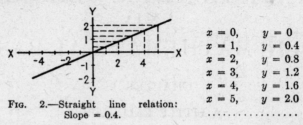

$x = 0,$	$y = 0$
$x = 1,$	$y = 0.4$
$x = 2,$	$y = 0.8$
$x = 3,$	$y = 1.2$
$x = 4,$	$y = 1.6$
$x = 5,$	$y = 2.0$
	$\dots\dots\dots\dots\dots\dots$

FIG. 2.—Straight line relation: Slope = 0.4.

Here likewise we can represent the relation by a straight line, and this line will have the same slope at every value of x; at each point a change of n units in x will be accompanied by a change of $0.4n$ units in y.

But let us now take a more complicated case, $y = x^2$.

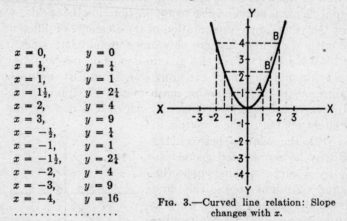

$x = 0,$	$y = 0$
$x = \frac{1}{2},$	$y = \frac{1}{4}$
$x = 1,$	$y = 1$
$x = 1\frac{1}{2},$	$y = 2\frac{1}{4}$
$x = 2,$	$y = 4$
$x = 3,$	$y = 9$
$x = -\frac{1}{2},$	$y = \frac{1}{4}$
$x = -1,$	$y = 1$
$x = -1\frac{1}{2},$	$y = 2\frac{1}{4}$
$x = -2,$	$y = 4$
$x = -3,$	$y = 9$
$x = -4,$	$y = 16$
$\dots\dots\dots\dots\dots\dots$	

FIG. 3.—Curved line relation: Slope changes with x.

Here the line is not a straight one; it does not have the same slope at all values of x. As we proceed out from the y axis, the slope is at first very small; at $x = 1$ it is moderate; and at $x = 3$ the slope is very steep. We have a similar behavior on the side where x has negative values. We have, in fact, very great difficulty in saying what the slope is, because it is always changing. We could draw a straight line between A and B, where $x = 1$ and $x = 2$, respectively, but the slope of this line would not precisely describe the slope of the curve.   If we took a smaller change in x, say that represented by the distance AB' on our scale, our secant line would more nearly coincide with the curve. We may consider A as any fixed point on the graph and allow B to move along the curve and approach A as a limiting position The changes in x would become smaller and smaller and approach zero as a limit.   The secant line drawn through A and B would turn about A, approaching the tangent line at A as its limiting position.

Now the basic task of the differential calculus (except in regions of discontinuity and other similar matters which lie beyond the scope of this chapter) is to ascertain the slope of a curve at various points by determining the slope of a secant which, in a limiting position, becomes the tangent to the curve at the point in question.   This same idea may be expressed in other terms by saying that it is the task of the differential calculus to ascertain the amount of change in a variable y that corresponds to a certain change in a related variable x as these increments in the independent variable x become so small as to approach zero in value.   At certain times in its history this discipline has been called the *infinitesimal calculus* in recognition of the fact that it deals with the relation of infinitesimal increments of one variable to infinitesimal increments of another. In operating with the calculus we are often operating algebraically with no curve in sight; but usually we can represent these algebraic operations geometrically and show that what we are seeking is something about the slope of that curve at some point.

DIFFERENTIATION

Let us proceed with that algebraic process with which we said, in our preceding paragraph, we shall often be operating with no curve before us visually.   We have the equation

$$y = x^2$$

We wish to find what change in y goes with a change in x at any value of x in which we are interested.   Let Δx be an increment to be added to x (algebraically), and Δy be the corresponding increment that would need to be added to y in order to maintain the equation.

(1) $$y + \Delta y = (x + \Delta x)^2$$

Performing the indicated square,

$$y + \Delta y = x^2 + 2x\,\Delta x + \overline{\Delta x}^2$$

But our original equation gave us $y = x^2$. We may subtract the terms of this equation from the corresponding ones of our last equation above on the basis of the axiom, "If equals be subtracted from equals the remainders are equal." We shall then have

(2) $$\Delta y = 2x\,\Delta x + \overline{\Delta x}^2$$

Dividing through by Δx, we shall have

(3) $$\frac{\Delta y}{\Delta x} = 2x + \Delta x$$

We said Δx should be an increment added to x and Δy an increment added to y, but we did not commit ourselves as to the particular size of the increment. Let us now conceive of Δx as decreasing until it becomes infinitesimal in size. It will necessarily drag Δy down with it, since the equation must continue to hold for all values of Δx. When Δx has become so small as to have approached zero as its limit let us replace $\Delta y/\Delta x$ by dy/dx. At this limit the Δx in the last term of our equation will approach zero in value and thus disappear from consideration. The reason why dy/dx can not be similarly dropped as of zero value is that both its numerator and its denominator become small together so that the fraction has a value that may be of considerable dimension. And so as the limit zero is approached by Δx we have

(4) $$\frac{dy}{dx} = 2x$$

This $2x$ is called the *derivative* of the expression $y = x^2$. The process of getting it is called *differentiation*. If the dx appears in the denominator of the fraction expressing the derivative, we say that we are differentiating "with respect to x"; if the dy appears in the denominator, as it will sometimes do in our later developments, we say we are differentiating "with respect to y." This process alone, in more or less complicated forms, constitutes essentially all there is to the differential calculus. In terms of the slope of a curve a derivative equal to $2x$ means that, at the point where $x = 1$, the slope of the curve is 2 times 1 or 2 (which means that at that point the y values are changing twice as rapidly as the x values through the infinitesimal distance to which we have shrunken our Δx at its limit). At the point where $x = 3$, the slope of the curve relating the two is 2 times 3 or 6, which means that y changes 6 units for each unit of change in x.

After a few more concrete examples we shall seek a general rule for differentiating an expression directly without going each time through a long process of algebraic manipulation. But in the meantime the reader may be interested in observing the relation of the form of the $2x$ to the x^2 of which it is the derivative. He will notice that the exponent of the x has dropped from 2 to 1, a decrease of one unit. He will also observe that the coefficient of the derivative has become 2, possibly the same 2 that was lost from the original exponent; about that we shall see later.

Let us now try differentiating the expression $y = x^3$. We shall go through the same four fundamental steps, through which we passed in our previous example, as follows: (1) Add Δy to the y and Δx to the x and perform the indicated involution. (2) Subtract from the resultant equation our original equation. (3) Divide through by Δx. (4) Let Δx approach zero as a limit, and, as the limit is approached, substitute dy/dx, the symbol for the derivative at the limit, for $\Delta y/\Delta x$; drop from the equation any of these Δx values that stand without a Δ denominator, on the ground that even in the first power their values are approximately zero and that in any of the higher powers the values are lower than in the first power.

$$y = x^3$$

Adding Δy to y and Δx to x,

(1) $$y + \Delta y = (x + \Delta x)^3$$

Expanding the second term,

$$y + \Delta y = x^3 + 3x^2\Delta x + 3x\,\overline{\Delta x}^2 + \overline{\Delta x}^3$$

Subtracting,

(2) $$\Delta y = 3x^2\Delta x + 3x\,\overline{\Delta x}^2 + \overline{\Delta x}^3$$

Dividing by Δx,

(3) $$\frac{\Delta y}{\Delta x} = 3x^2 + 3x\,\Delta x + \overline{\Delta x}^2$$

Letting Δx approach zero,

$$(4) \qquad \frac{dy}{dx} = 3x^2$$

In this last expression the $3x\,\Delta x$ dropped out in the limit because as Δx approaches zero as a limit, any product formed by multiplying it by any factor approaches zero and, in the limit, disappears from the equation. For a similar reason the $\overline{\Delta x}^2$ becomes zero in the limit. In fact since Δx becomes, as it decreases, a very small quantity (*i.e.*, a decimal quantity less than 1), when raised to any power (including 1) and multiplied by 1 or by any other factor it will approach zero and vanish from the equation as Δx approaches zero as its limit.

The derivative of $y = x^3$ is, therefore, $3x^2$. Notice that here, again, the original exponent has become the coefficient of the derivative and that the exponent of the x in the derivative is one less than that of the original quantity. Let us now take a more generalized example,

$$y = x^n$$

where n may represent any positive integer.[1] Performing in succession our four fundamental steps,

$$(1) \qquad y + \Delta y = (x + \Delta x)^n$$

Expanding,

$$y + \Delta y = x^n + nx^{n-1}\Delta x + \frac{n(n-1)}{1 \cdot 2} x^{n-2}\overline{\Delta x}^2$$
$$+ \frac{n(n-1)(n-2)}{1 \cdot 2 \cdot 3} x^{n-3}\overline{\Delta x}^3 + \cdots$$
$$y = x^n$$

was our original equation, to be subtracted,

$$(2) \quad \Delta y = nx^{n-1}\Delta x + \frac{n(n-1)}{1 \cdot 2} x^{n-2}\overline{\Delta x}^2$$
$$+ \frac{n(n-1)(n-2)}{1 \cdot 2 \cdot 3} x^{n-3}\overline{\Delta x}^3 + \cdots$$

[1] It may be shown that the rule for differentiating functions of this form will hold for any real value of n.

(3) $\dfrac{\Delta y}{\Delta x} = nx^{n-1} + \dfrac{n(n-1)}{1\cdot 2}\, x^{n-2}\Delta x$

$$+ \dfrac{n(n-1)(n-2)}{1\cdot 2\cdot 3}\, x^{n-3}\overline{\Delta x}^2 + \cdots$$

Letting Δx approach zero as limit and observing what was said above about the vanishing of all powers of Δx that stand without a Δ denominator, we have remaining

$$\dfrac{dy}{dx} = nx^{n-1} \qquad \text{(Derivative of the function } y = x^n) \quad (1)$$

From this general case it is now obvious that what we inferred as a possibility in our two previous examples is in fact the rule: *the derivative in respect to x at any power has as its coefficient the original power of x and as its exponent the original exponent decreased by* 1. This must be so because only the second term in the binomial expansion is free from the Δx after the subtraction of step (2) and the division of step (3) and because the coefficient of the second term in a binomial expansion is always the power to which the binomial is being raised and its exponent is always the original exponent less 1.

Suppose now we try the effect of a constant as coefficient of our variable x,

$$y = ax^n$$

Here a may represent any coefficient we please, whether integral or fraction, whether positive or negative. Going through our four steps,

(1) $$y + \Delta y = a(x + \Delta x)^n$$

$$y + \Delta y = ax^n + anx^{n-1}\Delta x + \dfrac{an(n-1)}{1\cdot 2}\, x^{n-2}\overline{\Delta x}^2$$

$$+ \dfrac{an(n-1)(n-2)}{1\cdot 2\cdot 3}\, x^{n-3}\overline{\Delta x}^3 + \cdots$$

(2) $\Delta y = anx^{n-1}\Delta x + \dfrac{an(n-1)}{1\cdot 2}\, x^{n-2}\overline{\Delta x}^2$

$$+ \dfrac{an(n-1)(n-2)}{1\cdot 2\cdot 3}\, x^{n-3}\overline{\Delta x}^3 + \cdots$$

(3) $\dfrac{\Delta y}{\Delta x} = anx^{n-1} + \dfrac{an(n-1)}{1\cdot 2}\, x^{n-2}\Delta x$

$$+ \dfrac{an(n-1)(n-2)}{1\cdot 2\cdot 3}\, x^{n-3}\overline{\Delta x}^2 + \cdots$$

(4) $\dfrac{dy}{dx} = anx^{n-1}$ (Derivative of a constant times a function of the form x^n)   (2)

Here the constant reappears in the derivative unchanged. Hence, since a may represent any constant, we may say: *The derivative of a constant times a function is the same constant times the derivative of the function.*

Let us now take a more complicated expression, one involving x in each of several terms with different powers in each term, the total function being the sum of these several functions.

$$y = ax^3 + bx^2 + cx$$

(1) $y + \Delta y = ax^3 + 3ax^2\Delta x + 3ax\,\overline{\Delta x}^2 + a\,\overline{\Delta x}^3 + bx^2$
$$+\, 2bx\,\Delta x + b\,\overline{\Delta x}^2 + cx + c\,\Delta x$$

 $y = ax^3 \phantom{+ 3ax^2\Delta x + 3ax\,\overline{\Delta x}^2 + a\,\overline{\Delta x}^3} + bx^2 \phantom{+ 2bx\,\Delta x + b\,\overline{\Delta x}^2} + cx$

(2) $\Delta y = 3ax^2\Delta x + 3ax\,\overline{\Delta x}^2 + a\,\overline{\Delta x}^3 + 2bx\,\Delta x + b\,\overline{\Delta x}^2 + c\,\Delta x$

(3) $\dfrac{\Delta y}{\Delta x} = 3ax^2 + 3ax\,\Delta x + a\,\overline{\Delta x}^2 + 2bx + b\,\Delta x + c$

(4) $\dfrac{dy}{dx} = 3ax^2 + 2bx + c$ (Derivative of the sum of functions)   (3)

If the reader will compare this derivative with the expression we started out to differentiate, he will observe that the derivative of the complex quantity made up of the sum of three terms is precisely the sum of the derivatives of the several terms if differentiated separately. If he will carry through on paper the generalized case or visualize to himself how it would work out, he will easily convince himself that that same conclusion would hold universally for any values for which the binomial law holds. Therefore, *the derivative of the sum of any number of functions is the sum of their derivatives.*

Let us now try differentiating a constant, $y = a$. Since $x^0 = 1$, the above equation might be written

$$y = x^0 a$$

Going through our four steps,

(1) $y + \Delta y = (x + \Delta x)^0 a = a$

Subtracting our original equation, $y = a$, we get

(2) $\Delta y = 0$.   Then (3) $\dfrac{\Delta y}{\Delta x} = 0$; and (4) $\dfrac{dy}{dx} = 0$

Thus the derivative of a constant is found to be zero. If the reader will think of the a as placed as an addend in the series above when we were generalizing about the derivative of a sum of functions, he will perceive that it would behave in the same manner there as when standing alone; *i.e.*, its derivative would be zero, and it would not appear in the sum which constitutes the derivative of the complex function. So in the process of differentiation, any constant independent of the variable with respect to which we are differentiating disappears entirely from the derivative, since its own derivative is zero.

We have now covered the s mplest cases of differentiation. We have yet to consider the complicated situations in which the term with respect to which we are differentiating occurs as an exponent, as a product, as the denominator of a fraction, etc. But before we proceed further let us draw together our findings so far, when we differentiate a function with respect to x, and make some applications of them.

1. The derivative of a simple monomial containing any power of x is another monomial containing as its coefficient the original exponent of x times the original coefficient and as its exponent the original exponent diminished by 1.

2. The derivative of a constant times a function is equal to the constant times the derivative of the function.

3. The derivative of a sum of monomials is the sum of the derivatives of these monomials.

4. Terms independent of x disappear from the derivative when we are differentiating with respect to x, since the derivatives of any such terms are zero. This is on the assumption, of course, that these terms do not contain the y or any other function of x.

On the left below we shall place certain equations to be differentiated with respect to x; on the right we shall indicate the derivatives of some of them while leaving others blank for the reader to complete as an exercise.

Function	Derivative
$y = 4x^3$	$12x^2$
$y = x^5 + 10$	$5x^4$
$y = 6x^{-2}$	$-12x^{-3}$
$y = x^2 - 3x - 5$	$2x - 3$
$y = \dfrac{x^3}{6} - \dfrac{2x^2}{3} + 5x + 7$	$\dfrac{x^2}{2} - \dfrac{4x}{3} + 5$
$y = 7x^{\frac{3}{2}} - 4x^{\frac{1}{2}}$	$\dfrac{21}{2}x^{\frac{1}{2}} - 2x^{-\frac{1}{2}}$

$y = s(3x^2)$

$y = 2x^3 - 3x^2 + 8$

$y = \dfrac{x^2}{6} - 3$

$y = 6x^{-2} + 7x^{-1} + x$

MINIMA AND MAXIMA

In order to get afresh in mind the meaning of a derivative, let us graph the equation $y = x^2 - 3x - 5$. Its derivative, as given above, is $(2x - 3)$. This indicates the rate at which y is changing when x has any given value. When put graphically, it means that at any value of x the slope of the line representing the relation of y to x is $(2x - 3)$. Let us list below some values of x and some corresponding values of y derived from the original equation. In Fig. 4 we shall locate these calculated points and shall draw through them a smooth curve. As said above, the fact that the derivative is $(2x - 3)$ indicates that the slope of the curve at any value of x is $(2x - 3)$ and that at any such value of x the y is changing $(2x - 3)$ times as rapidly as the x. Examine the curve at a few points in order to confirm this fact. When $x = -2$, the derivative is $(2 \cdot -2) - 3$,

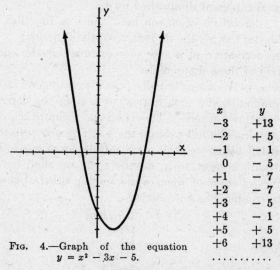

x	y
-3	$+13$
-2	$+ 5$
-1	$- 1$
0	$- 5$
$+1$	$- 7$
$+2$	$- 7$
$+3$	$- 5$
$+4$	$- 1$
$+5$	$+ 5$
$+6$	$+13$

Fig. 4.—Graph of the equation $y = x^2 - 3x - 5$.

which equals -7. This statement indicates that the y value is decreasing seven times as fast as the x is increasing—that, if one followed the graph with a pencil, the pencil would be moving

downward seven times as rapidly as it is moving across the page
toward the right. Does inspection of the curve indicate to
you that such is true? Let $x = 1\frac{1}{2}$. Then the derivative is
$(2 \cdot 1\frac{1}{2} - 3)$, which equals zero. This means that here y (the
vertical distance) does not change at all as you move along the x
(horizontal) direction—provided, of course, the distance through
which you move is an extremely short one. Does the figure
bear that out? Let x be 3. Then the derivative is

$$(2 \cdot 3 - 3) = +3.$$

The y should be increasing three times as rapidly as the x is
increasing. Does that look plausible? The reader may be
interested in making additional suppositions about x values and
in seeing how the derivative indicates the slope of the curve at
those points and consequently the relative rapidity of changes in
y as compared with changes in x at the points in question. No
matter what the connection, differentiation always has precisely
the sort of meaning and significance involved in this illustration.

Figure 4 lends itself so well to a comment about minima that
we cannot refrain from entering that topic here. That will
carry us, even at this early stage of our study, into the very
heart of one of the most important applications of the differential
calculus. We saw that when $x = 1\frac{1}{2}$, the slope of our curve was
zero. To this point the slope has been negative; *i.e.*, to this
point it has been descending for increasing values of x. From
this point on the slope is positive; *i.e.*, the curve ascends for
increasing values of x. Consequently the lowest value that y
can take lies at this point where x equals $1\frac{1}{2}$. In other words,
y is then at a minimum. To find the point in x values where y
is at a minimum is one of the most important applications of the
calculus. We chanced to take $1\frac{1}{2}$ as a value for x, and the slope
turned out to be zero. But we could easily have gotten this by
calculation. We could have set $(2x - 3)$ equal to zero and
solved the equation to find x under this special assumption that
$(2x - 3)$ is to equal zero. We would have the following simple
operation:

$$2x - 3 = 0; \; 2x = 3; \text{ therefore } x = 1\frac{1}{2}$$

Always, when we wish to find a minimum, we differentiate our
function with respect to the variable on the scale of which

we desire to know the position of the minimum in the related variable, set the derivative equal to zero, and solve for the unknown term. Since this matter of minima is so important in statistics for the sake of which we are at present studying calculus, as well as in most other areas in which calculus is employed, perhaps it will pay us to stay longer with the topic and illustrate it more fully. So let us take another example—one right out of statistics.

In the following equation y represents the errors squared in fitting a straight line to paired numbers. If we can find a value for r that will make this y a minimum, we shall have one formula for a coefficient of correlation.

$$y = 1 - 2r\frac{\Sigma z_1 z_2}{N} + r^2$$

The variables here are the y and the r; all other terms are constants. We wish to find that value for r that will make y a minimum. We must, therefore, differentiate the expression with respect to r and set the derivative equal to zero. Remember that, if a constant is independent of the variable with respect to which we are differentiating, it will disappear from the derivative because its own derivative is zero. But remember that, if it occurs as a coefficient of our variable, it will reappear as a coefficient in the derivative. Differentiating, then, according to our rules,

$$\frac{dy}{dr} = -\frac{2\Sigma z_1 z_2}{N} + 2r$$

Now set this derivative equal to zero and solve for r.

$$-2r = -\frac{2\Sigma z_1 z_2}{N}; \text{ whence } r = \frac{\Sigma z_1 z_2}{N}$$

This is the formula for the coefficient of correlation when our data are in the form of "standard measures." But we shall learn more of this later; just now our attention is focused on the method of finding that value of the one variable at which the other is a minimum.

Try next

$$y = 8x - x^2$$

Differentiating, we get

$$\frac{dy}{dx} = 8 - 2x$$

Setting the derivative equal to zero and solving for x, we have

$$8 - 2x = 0; \; -2x = -8; \text{ therefore } x = 4$$

Our minimum should be where $x = 4$. Let us see how that looks on a graph. We shall determine from the original equation some values for y from given values for x and then construct the curve passing through these points.

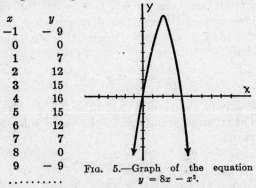

x	y
−1	− 9
0	0
1	7
2	12
3	15
4	16
5	15
6	12
7	7
8	0
9	− 9

FIG. 5.—Graph of the equation $y = 8x - x^2$.

Wait a minute! The curve is flat at $x = 4$, that is true, but y is not at its lowest point. It is at its highest point instead. So far from being a minimum at $x = 4$, y is then at a maximum. Now that we think of it, we see that we may have a slope of zero, and consequently a horizontal direction of our graph, at the top where the curve has stopped mounting and has begun to descend as surely as at the bottom where it has stopped falling and has begun to ascend. When, therefore, $dy/dx = 0$, y is either a minimum or a maximum. How can we tell which?

In the sort of curves with which we have been dealing, the slope of the line itself changes for different places along the x axis. At some points it becomes steeper and at others less steep; at some points it is rising and at some it is descending. Evidently the change of slope is itself a function of x; i.e., the rapidity of change in the slope is predetermined by the place along the x axis with which we are concerned. We might, therefore, differentiate the expression for the slope itself and get a value for the rapidity and direction with which the slope itself is changing for various values of x. If at the point in which we are interested (because, perhaps, at that point the y is either a maximum or a minimum), the second derivative has the negative sign, that means that, if we proceeded toward the higher values of x, our slope would bend in the minus direction—downward. We would, therefore, have been at the top of our curve, and our y would have been at a maximum. If, however, the sign of the second derivative is positive, that means that, as we move from that point up the x scale, our curve must bend upward (which is the plus direction), and we learn thereby that what we had was a minimum value of y. Let us try this on the last example differentiated above. Our derivative was, you remember, $(8 - 2x)$, and at our critical point this was equal to zero, so that we had

$$\frac{dy}{dx} = 8 - 2x = 0$$

We may designate the second derivative by d_2y/dx^2. Taking this second derivative according to the same rules we use for a first derivative

$$\frac{d_2y}{dx^2} = \frac{d(8 - 2x)}{dx} = -2$$

Sure enough, the second derivative is negative. It is this fact that it is negative rather than that it is numerically equal to 2 that interests us at present, for our only concern now is to know whether the curve would bend upward or downward if we proceeded out from this point. Our finding from the second differentiation is consistent with our graph; y is a maximum when $x = 4$.

Let us now go back and see whether we were correct in supposing that our previous two examples involved minima rather than maxima. In our first example (the graphed one)

$$y = x^2 - 3x - 5; \frac{dy}{dx} = 2x - 3; \frac{d_2y}{dx^2} = 2$$

This second derivative has the plus sign, and we were, therefore, correct in calling the y a minimum at the point where the slope was zero.

In our second illustration, involving the correlation formula,

$$y = 1 - \frac{2r\Sigma z_1 z_2}{N} + r^2; \frac{dy}{dr} = \frac{-2\Sigma z_1 z_2}{N} + 2r; \frac{d_2y}{dx^2} = 2$$

Here, again, the second derivative is positive in sign, and, consequently, we have a minimum for y.

Let us take yet one more exercise in this interesting topic of maxima and minima. A gardener wishes to enclose a tract of land with a high deer fence, and he wishes to know in what proportions he should lay out a rectangular plot so as to get the maximum amount of space enclosed with a given amount of fence. If we let k equal half of the given perimeter of his proposed tract, his diagram will look like Fig. 6. Let y be the area. Since the area of a rectangle is the product of its length by its width,

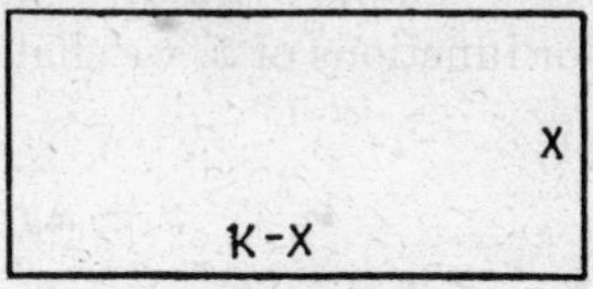

$$y = x(k - x) = kx - x^2$$

FIG. 6.

Differentiating this so as to ascertain for what length of x the area y will be a maximum and solving for x,

$$\frac{dy}{dx} = k - 2x = 0; \quad -2x = -k; \quad x = \frac{1}{2}k$$

In order to make sure we have a maximum and not a minimum, we shall take a second derivative.

$$\frac{d_2 y}{dx^2} = \frac{d(k - 2x)}{dx} = -2$$

The second derivative is negative, and, therefore, what we have is a maximum value for the area. So the field will be laid out most economically if the length is half the sum of the length and the width; *i.e.*, if the length equals the width and hence the tract is laid out square.

We shall later learn that there are circumstances under which we need to take a third derivative. It is, in fact, possible to differentiate as many times in succession as we please and as our purpose requires.

After this excursion into maxima and minima, from which we hope the reader will have derived a more complete comprehension of the meaning and possible applications of the process of differentiation, we shall take up again the technique of differentiating different algebraic forms. So far we have had only the simplest ones. We have to learn how to differentiate a product, a fraction, a power, a logarithm, etc.

THE DERIVATIVE OF A PRODUCT

We have already learned how to handle the differentiation of a function of x that involves a polynomial. From now on we shall let a single letter (say u or v) represent the function of x no matter how complex that function may be; for we know that, if we are called upon to differentiate u or v in any connection, we shall be able to differentiate the complex function of x that these simple symbols represent. Using u and v, then, to stand for functions of x, we shall inquire how to differentiate a product.

(1)
$$y = uv$$
$$y + \Delta y = (u + \Delta u)(v + \Delta v)$$

Expanding,

$$y + \Delta y = uv + u\,\Delta v + v\,\Delta u + \Delta u\,\Delta v$$

Subtracting our original equation,

(2)
$$\Delta y = u\,\Delta v + v\,\Delta u + \Delta u\,\Delta v$$

Dividing by Δx,

(3)
$$\frac{\Delta y}{\Delta x} = \frac{u\,\Delta v}{\Delta x} + \frac{v\,\Delta u}{\Delta x} + \Delta u\,\frac{\Delta v}{\Delta x}$$

(4) $\dfrac{dy}{dx} = u\dfrac{dv}{dx} + v\dfrac{du}{dx}$ $\qquad$ (Derivative of a product) (4)

The reader must have in mind in the transition from step (3) to step (4), and must continue to hold in mind in this transition in all the following developments, that we make the transition by letting Δx approach zero as its limit whereby the Δ's in the numerator will be dragged down with the Δx; and, as the Δx approaches its limit, we replace $\Delta y/\Delta x$ by dy/dx, or whatever other symbols happen to represent our functions in the particular problem. He must keep in mind, too, that, when a Δ is approaching zero as a limit and is not divided by another Δ which is also approaching zero as a limit, it drops out of the equation at the limit because its value is zero and it carries out with it all other factors by which it is multiplied.

Thus the derivative of a product turns out to be the first factor times the derivative of the second plus the second factor times the derivative of the first. The following is a more concrete example:

$$y = (ax^4)(bx^2). \quad \frac{dy}{dx} = \frac{d(ax^4)}{dx}(bx^2) + \frac{d(bx^2)}{dx}(ax^4)$$
$$= (4ax^3 \cdot bx^2) + (2bx \cdot ax^4) = 4abx^5 + 2abx^5 = 6abx^5$$

That is exactly what we would have obtained if, at the beginning, we had multiplied our two factors together and had differentiated the product, as the reader may wish to verify. In this case that would have been just as simple. But, of course, not all cases would permit such ready combination of the original factors.

THE DERIVATIVE OF A QUOTIENT (FRACTION)

Taking again u and v as functions of x, let $y = u/v$.

(1)
$$y + \Delta y = \frac{u + \Delta u}{v + \Delta v}$$

Subtracting from this the original equation,

(2)
$$\Delta y = \frac{u + \Delta u}{v + \Delta v} - \frac{u}{v}$$

Raising both fractions to a common denominator so that we may subtract,

$$\Delta y = \frac{v(u + \Delta u)}{v(v + \Delta v)} - \frac{u(v + \Delta v)}{v(v + \Delta v)} = \frac{uv + v\,\Delta u - uv - u\,\Delta v}{v^2 + v\,\Delta v}$$
$$\Delta y = \frac{v\,\Delta u - u\,\Delta v}{v^2 + v\,\Delta v}$$

(3) Dividing by Δx,

$$\frac{\Delta y}{\Delta x} = \frac{v(\Delta u/\Delta x) - u(\Delta v/\Delta x)}{v^2 + v\,\Delta v}$$

Letting Δx approach zero as a limit,

$$\frac{dy}{dx} = \frac{v(du/dx) - u(dv/dx)}{v^2} \quad \text{(The derivative of a quotient)} \quad (5)$$

THE DERIVATIVE OF A FUNCTION OF A FUNCTION

It often happens that an expression is complicated in a fashion that makes it difficult to differentiate in the straightforward manner we have so far learned. We may then find it feasible to simplify our procedure by dividing the process into two or more steps. Let us write the function,

$$\frac{\Delta y}{\Delta x} = \frac{\Delta y}{\Delta u} \cdot \frac{\Delta u}{\Delta x}$$

where y is a function of u and u is a function of x. Now let Δx approach zero as a limit. As Δx approaches zero as its limit, it will necessarily carry with it the Δ's of its functions. Hence

$$\frac{dy}{dx} = \frac{dy}{du} \cdot \frac{du}{dx}$$

That is, we may break up our expression into two factors, differentiate the first with respect to u and the u with respect to x, and take as our derivative the product of these two. Take, for example, the expression, $y = \sqrt{(x^3 - 2a)^3}$, which equals $(x^3 - 2a)^{\frac{3}{2}}$. We may let $(x^3 - 2a)$ equal u. Then $y = u^{\frac{3}{2}}$; $dy/du = \frac{3}{2}u^{\frac{1}{2}}$. Now differentiating the expression for which u stands, viz., $(x^3 - 2a)$, with respect to x, we have $du/dx = 3x^2$. Taking the product of these two derivatives, but substituting the value of the u for the u, we have

$$\frac{dy}{dx} = \frac{dy}{du} \cdot \frac{du}{dx} = \frac{3}{2}(x^3 - 2a)^{\frac{1}{2}} \cdot 3x^2 = \frac{9x^2}{2}\sqrt{x^3 - 2a}$$

Recourse to this dodge often makes comparatively easy differentiations that would otherwise be extremely difficult, and workers with calculus exercise great ingenuity in discovering ways in which to break up expressions into component factors that are more readily differentiated than the original one. Sometimes an expression is broken up into three or more factors, for evidently

$$\frac{dy}{dx} = \frac{dy}{du} \cdot \frac{du}{dv} \cdot \frac{dv}{dz} \cdot \frac{dz}{dx} \cdots \quad \text{(Derivative of a function}\atop\text{of a function)} \quad (6)$$

THE DERIVATIVE OF AN INVERSE FUNCTION

Another roundabout method that sometimes simplifies the process of differentiation is to shift temporarily from the necessity of differentiating with respect to x and to do the differentiating instead with respect to y, then to reach the differentiation with respect to x by a second step. By the same process as that used in the preceding section, it may be proved that

$$\frac{dy}{dx} = \frac{1}{dx/dy}. \quad \text{Hence } \frac{1}{dy/dx} = \frac{dx}{dy}$$

We may, therefore, differentiate with respect to y (as is indicated by the fact that the dy occurs in the denominator), then use the reciprocal of this derivative as the derivative of y with respect to x. Suppose, for example, we have the equation: $y^2 = 3x + 4$. We might transpose and solve for x as follows:

$$x = \frac{y^2 - 4}{3} = \frac{y^2}{3} - \frac{4}{3}$$

Differentiating now with respect to y,

$$\frac{dx}{dy} = \frac{2y}{3}$$

Since, as shown above,

$$\frac{dy}{dx} = \frac{1}{dx/dy}, \frac{dy}{dx} = \frac{1}{2y/3} = \frac{3}{2y}$$

Substituting in this last equation the value of y from the original equation, we have as our derivative:

$$\frac{dy}{dx} = \frac{3}{2\sqrt{3x + 4}}$$

INTRODUCING A NOTABLE CHARACTER—e

There is a remarkable quantity in mathematics to which we must give attention before we can proceed further. It is designated by the letter e and has as its value $\left(1 + \frac{1}{n}\right)^n$ as the n approaches infinity. Let us expand this value according to the binomial theorem and through this expansion determine the numerical value of e. The reader must remember that 1 raised to any power is still 1.

$$e = \left(1 + \frac{1}{n}\right)^n = 1 + n \cdot \frac{1}{n} + \frac{n(n-1)}{n^2 \cdot 1 \cdot 2} + \frac{n(n-1)(n-2)}{n^3 \cdot 1 \cdot 2 \cdot 3}$$
$$+ \frac{n(n-1)(n-2)(n-3)}{n^4 \cdot 1 \cdot 2 \cdot 3 \cdot 4} + \cdots$$

But as n approaches infinity the $(n-1)$, $(n-2)$, etc., will not differ appreciably from n, so that the factors containing n's will cancel out of each numerator and corresponding denominator. This will be particularly true near the beginning of the series, where the fractions have an appreciable size; and to the extent to which it is not true it will force more rapid convergence of the series, since the n factors in the numerator are smaller than the corresponding ones in the denominator. We shall then have

$$e = 1 + 1 + \frac{1}{1 \cdot 2} + \frac{1}{1 \cdot 2 \cdot 3} + \frac{1}{1 \cdot 2 \cdot 3 \cdot 4} + \frac{1}{1 \cdot 2 \cdot 3 \cdot 4 \cdot 5} + \cdots$$

This series rapidly converges and, while incommensurable with 1, has as its correct value to six decimal places 2.718281. To two decimal places e may be taken as 2.72.

If we develop, and then differentiate, the value of e^x, we shall begin to see wherein lies the remarkable property of e.

$$e^x = \left(1 + \frac{1}{n}\right)^{nx} = 1 + \frac{nx}{n} + \frac{nx(nx-1)}{n^2 \cdot 1 \cdot 2}$$
$$+ \frac{nx(nx-1)(nx-2)}{n^3 \cdot 1 \cdot 2 \cdot 3} + \cdots$$

Since the n's cancel out for the same reason as given above, this becomes, as n approaches infinity,

$$e^x = 1 + x + \frac{x^2}{1 \cdot 2} + \frac{x^3}{1 \cdot 2 \cdot 3} + \frac{x^4}{1 \cdot 2 \cdot 3 \cdot 4} + \cdots$$

Let us now differentiate this with respect to x, indicating the differentiation on the left and performing it on the right.

$$\frac{d(e^x)}{dx} = 1 + \frac{2x}{1 \cdot 2} + \frac{3x^2}{1 \cdot 2 \cdot 3} + \frac{4x^3}{1 \cdot 2 \cdot 3 \cdot 4} + \cdots$$
$$= 1 + x + \frac{x^2}{1 \cdot 2} + \frac{x^3}{1 \cdot 2 \cdot 3} + \cdots$$

But that is just what we had before. If we should continue to take successive derivatives we would always get the same thing we had to start with. e^x has, therefore, the remarkable property of giving a derivative exactly equal to the variable itself. This is a property of immense importance in higher mathematics.

THE DERIVATIVE OF A LOGARITHM

We are now in position to develop a formula for the derivative of a logarithm. Since logarithms are treated in practically all texts in algebra, except some of those intended for a single first-year course, we shall assume here that the reader is already familiar with them or that he will take occasion at once to go to a textbook in algebra to learn about them. A logarithm is a power to which a certain number, called the *base*, must be raised in order to give another number in which we are interested. Thus the power to which 10 must be raised in order to give 100 is 2; hence 2 is the logarithm of 100 to the base 10. The power to which 10 must be raised to give 247 is 2.3927; hence that is the logarithm of 247 to the base 10. But in calculus we seldom use the base 10; we use *e* instead, because of the remarkable properties we said above that it possesses. However, logarithms to the base *e* obey in every respect precisely the same laws as those with which the reader is, presumably, already familiar with the base 10.

Now for the derivative of a logarithm. Where v is any function of x, let $y = \log_e v$. We shall carry this through the four fundamental steps through which we carried earlier processes of differentiation.

$$(1) \qquad y + \Delta y = \log_e (v + \Delta v)$$

Subtracting original equation,

$$(2) \qquad \Delta y = \log_e (v + \Delta v) - \log_e v$$

It is one of the principles of logarithms that the log of one quantity minus the log of a second equals the log of the first-quantity-divided-by-the-second. Hence (2) becomes

$$\Delta y = \log_e \frac{(v + \Delta v)}{v}$$

Dividing by Δv,

$$\frac{\Delta y}{\Delta v} = \frac{1}{\Delta v} \left(\log_e \frac{v + \Delta v}{v} \right) = \frac{1}{\Delta v} \log_e \left(1 + \frac{\Delta v}{v} \right)$$

We may multiply and divide the right-hand member by v without changing its value. Hence

$$\frac{\Delta y}{\Delta v} = \frac{1}{v} \cdot \frac{v}{\Delta v} \log_e \left(1 + \frac{\Delta v}{v} \right)$$

But anything of the form $b \cdot \log u$ may, according to the laws of logarithms, be written $\log u^b$. Hence we may write

$$(3) \qquad \frac{\Delta y}{\Delta v} = \frac{1}{v} \log_e \left(1 + \frac{\Delta v}{v} \right)^{\frac{v}{\Delta v}}$$

The quantity in parentheses is of the form $\left(1 + \dfrac{1}{n}\right)^n.$ Now that is a familiar expression. We met it in our preceding section. Where the n is supposed to increase to infinity, it is precisely our old friend e. If we let Δv approach zero as its limit, the exponent $v/\Delta v$ will approach infinity, as it should to make our expression in parentheses equal e. Also, as Δv approaches zero as its limit, $\Delta_v/\Delta v$ will become dy/dv, and we shall have our derivative

$$\frac{dy}{dv} = \frac{1}{v} \log_e e$$

But any log of its own base is 1. Hence $\log_e e = 1$ and we have

$$\frac{dy}{dv} = \frac{1}{v}$$

But $dy/dx = dy/dv \cdot dv/dx$. Hence

$$\frac{dy}{dx} = \frac{1}{v} \cdot \frac{dv}{dx} = \frac{dv/dx}{v}$$

Remember that we started with the equation $y = \log_e v$. Putting this value for the y in our differential equation, we have:

$$\frac{d(\log_e v)}{dx} = \frac{dv/dx}{v} \qquad \text{(Derivative of a logarithm)} \quad (7)$$

The derivative of a logarithm to the base e of any function of x is, therefore, the derivative of that function divided by the function itself. Take the following concrete example:

$$y = x^2 + 4x - 8.$$
$$\frac{d(\log y)}{dx} = \frac{d(x^2 + 4x - 8)}{dx} \cdot \frac{1}{x^2 + 4x - 8} = \frac{2x + 4}{x^2 + 4x - 8}$$

THE DERIVATIVE OF A POWER FORM

In this case we have shifted our x function to a place where it would seem to be very difficult to get at—to the exponent. Let a be any constant and u any function of x to which a is raised as a power, and let b be any coefficient of the a^u; *i.e.*, let $y = ba^u$. Taking logarithms to the base e of each side of this equation (hereafter it is to be understood that our logarithms are always taken to the base e without our writing the e as a subscript), we have

$$\log y = \log (a^u) + \log b = u \log a + \log b$$

Transposing and solving for u,

$$u = \frac{\log y}{\log a} - \frac{\log b}{\log a} = \log y \frac{1}{\log a} - \frac{\log b}{\log a}$$

We shall now differentiate with respect to y. Since a is a constant, $1/\log a$ is a constant and will reappear as such in the derivative. Likewise $\log b$ is a constant, and therefore $\log a/\log b$ is a constant. But, since this constant is independent of y, its derivative is zero, so that it will disappear from the derivative of the whole expression. Remember that, as shown in our last section above, the derivative of the log of a quantity is the derivative of the quantity divided by the quantity, and notice that $dy/dy = 1$.

$$\frac{du}{dy} = \frac{d\left(\log y \dfrac{1}{\log a}\right)}{dy} - \frac{d(\log b/\log a)}{dy} = \frac{dy}{dy} \cdot \frac{1}{y} \cdot \frac{1}{\log a}$$

$$= \frac{1}{y} \cdot \frac{1}{\log a}$$

Under our topic, Derivative of an Inverse Function, we showed that

$$\frac{dy}{du} = \frac{1}{du/dy}$$

Therefore

$$\frac{dy}{du} = \frac{1}{(1/y) \cdot (1/\log a)} = y \cdot \log a$$

But our original equation was $y = ba^u$. Replacing the y above with this value from the original equation, we have

$$\frac{dy}{du} = ba^u \cdot \log a; \frac{dy}{dx} = \frac{dy}{du} \cdot \frac{du}{dx}$$

$$\frac{dy}{dx} = ba^u \cdot \log a \frac{du}{dx} \qquad \text{(Derivative of a power form)} \quad (8)$$

Therefore the derivative of a constant raised to a power which is a function of x is the constant raised to the original power times the log of the constant times the derivative of the x function that constitutes the power. If additional constants appear as coefficients of the one involving the x function in its exponent but not themselves raised to a power involving x, these coefficients recur unchanged in the derivative.

$$y = 20^{(x^3-2x^2+8)}; \frac{dy}{dx} = 20^{(x^3-2x^2+8)} \cdot (2.9957)(3x^2 - 4x)$$

The 2.9957 is the log of 20 and the $(3x^2 - 4x)$ is the derivative of the original exponent. The derivative is a general expression for the slope of the curve $y = 20^{(x^3-2x^2+8)}$ for any value of x in which we may chance to be interested. Suppose we wish to find the slope of the curve where $x = 1\frac{1}{3}$. By substituting in the above differential expression, we shall find that dy/dx is precisely zero where x equals $1\frac{1}{3}$. That is, the line is precisely parallel to the x axis where $x = 1\frac{1}{3}$.

We have an especially simple case in this formula where the constant is e. This occurs so frequently that it will pay us to derive a general rule involving it. We need only put e in place of a in the generalized case treated above.

$$\frac{d(e^u)}{dx} = e^u \log e \frac{du}{dx}$$

But since we are working with logarithms to the base e, log e equals 1, since any log of its own base is 1. Therefore

$$\frac{d(e^u)}{dx} = e^u \cdot \frac{du}{dx} \qquad \text{(Derivative of the power form } e^u) \quad (9)$$

If the function u should be simply x, the derivative would take a still simpler form, as follows:

$$\frac{d(e^x)}{dx} = e^x \frac{dx}{dx} = e^x \cdot 1 = e^x$$

Thus we come back again to the queer and important fact that we discovered when we first met this quantity e, a few pages back, *viz.*, that, when we differentiate e^x with respect to x, we get as our derivative precisely the same thing we had before differentiating.

MORE PRACTICE IN APPLICATIONS

After we had covered our first round of the simplest forms of differentiation, we paused to get some practice and to apply our techniques, so far, to finding maxima and minima. Now that we are through a second major cycle, let us again pause to make some applications. This time we shall take a fairly complicated function with which to work, but one that plays an extremely important part in social and educational statistics. The reader will need to watch his step in order to follow the process. But no new principles are involved beyond those treated in the preceding few sections. Indeed it is characteristic of calculus that its principles are simple but that its challenge consists in finding ingenious methods of analyzing the functions in question so as to put them into forms that are familiar; and in following out algebraic processes that sometimes become a little complicated. The function on which we shall practice here is the equation for the curve of a normal distribution. We shall later learn that this important statistical formula is

$$y = \frac{N}{\sigma\sqrt{2\pi}} e^{-\frac{x^2}{2\sigma^2}}$$

where N is the number of cases in the distribution, π is 3.1416, σ is a constant for a given distribution with which the reader is either already familiar or soon will be, y measures the height of the vertical ordinate at successive values of x, and x measures along the horizontal axis in terms of deviations from the mean of the whole distribution as origin. The meanings mentioned for these symbols are, of course, the ones customarily attached to them by mathematicians, and we are defining them here merely for the benefit of the lay reader.

An inspection of our equation will show that it is of the form $y = be^u$, for which form the derivative was given in our last preceding section. The $N/(\sigma\sqrt{2\pi})$ is the constant that corresponds to b and the $-x^2/2\sigma^2$ is the u. In order to save complications in our notation we shall carry along b for the complex value for which it stands. We shall rewrite the equation and then proceed with its differentiation.

$$y = be^{-\frac{x^2}{2\sigma^2}}$$

$$\frac{dy}{dx} = be^{-\frac{x^2}{2\sigma^2}} \cdot \frac{d(-x^2/2\sigma^2)}{dx} = (be^{-\frac{x^2}{2\sigma^2}})\left(-\frac{2x}{2\sigma^2}\right)$$

whence

$$\frac{dy}{dx} = -\frac{bx}{\sigma^2} e^{-\frac{x^2}{2\sigma^2}} = \frac{-bx}{\sigma^2 e^{+\frac{x^2}{2\sigma^2}}} \quad \text{(First derivative of the normal curve function)} \quad (10)$$

In this expression farthest to the right the e with its negative exponent could be transferred to the denominator by making its exponent positive, on the general principle that $a^{-b} = 1/a^b$.

Figure 7 shows the normal curve. The reader should give himself some practice in interpretation by testing the significance of the above derivative with reference to it. Remember that the x distances are measured from the mean (center) of the distribution as origin, plus to the right and minus to the left. According to the derivative, the slope should be plus (*i.e.*, up) on the left side of the curve where x is minus, for here we have minus times minus values of x which should give plus. Does the behavior of the actual curve conform to that deduction from the derivative? On the right side of the curve the slope should be

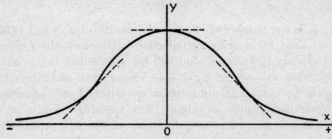

Fig. 7.—Graph of a normal distribution.

negative (downward), for here we have minus times plus values of x. Does inspection of the curve bear that out? If we substitute $x = 0$, we should have $dy/dx = 0$, for obviously the curve is horizontal (*i.e.*, has a slope of zero) at the middle of the distribution. Try substituting zero for x in the derivative, and see whether dy/dx turns out to be zero. Conversely, we should be able to make up our minds that we wish to find the place where the slope should be zero and to find it by setting the derivative equal to zero and solving for x. Let us try.

$$\frac{dy}{dx} = \frac{-bx}{\sigma^2 e^{\frac{x^2}{2\sigma^2}}} = 0$$

Clearing of fractions, then dividing through by $-b$,

$$-bx = 0; \text{ therefore } x = 0$$

Thus we deduce from the derivative that the curve should be parallel to the x axis at the middle of the distribution, where $x = 0$.

We might have divided our derivative equation by $-bx$ instead of multiplying through by the $\sigma^2 e^{\frac{x^2}{2\sigma^2}}$. We would then have:

$$\frac{-bx}{\sigma^2 e^{\frac{x^2}{2\sigma^2}}} = 0; \quad \frac{1}{\sigma^2 e^{\frac{x^2}{2\sigma^2}}} = 0$$

taking reciprocals,

$$\sigma^2 e^{\frac{x^2}{2\sigma^2}} = \frac{1}{0} = \infty$$

Dividing through by σ^2,

$$e^{\frac{x^2}{2\sigma^2}} = \frac{\infty}{\sigma^2} = \infty \, ; \, \log \, (e^{\frac{x^2}{2\sigma^2}}) = \log \infty = \infty \, ; \, \frac{x^2}{2\sigma^2} \, (\log e) = \infty$$

Since $\log e = 1$, $x^2/2\sigma^2 = \infty$;

$$x^2 = \infty \cdot 2\sigma^2 = \infty \, ; \, x = \sqrt{\infty} = \pm \infty$$

Thus the curve should become horizontal again at plus or minus infinity, as well as where x equals zero. Does inspection of the curve make that plausible?

If we take a second derivative, we shall have an expression for the rapidity with which the slope of the curve itself is changing with successive values of x. See whether you can verify the following as the derivative. For convenience we shall repeat the first derivative, then proceed to take from it a second derivative. The reader must remember that we have the following two principles involved: we have the product of two variables and we have the form e^u. If necessary he should turn back to the discussion of the differentiation of these two forms.

$$\frac{dy}{dx} = \frac{-bx}{\sigma^2} e^{-\frac{x^2}{2\sigma^2}}.$$

$$\frac{d_2 y}{dx^2} = \left(\frac{-b}{\sigma^2}\right) (e^{-\frac{x^2}{2\sigma^2}}) + \left(\frac{-bx}{\sigma^2}\right) (e^{-\frac{x^2}{2\sigma^2}}) \left(\frac{-x}{\sigma^2}\right)$$

$$= \frac{-b}{\sigma^2} e^{-\frac{x^2}{2\sigma^2}} + \frac{bx^2}{\sigma^4} e^{-\frac{x^2}{2\sigma^2}} = \frac{-b\sigma^2}{\sigma^4} e^{-\frac{x^2}{2\sigma^2}} + \frac{bx^2}{\sigma^4} e^{-\frac{x^2}{2\sigma^2}}$$

$$= \frac{b(x^2 - \sigma^2)}{\sigma^4} e^{-\frac{x^2}{2\sigma^2}}$$

$$= \frac{N}{\sqrt{2\pi}} \frac{(x^2 - \sigma^2)}{\sigma^5} e^{-\frac{x^2}{2\sigma^2}} \quad \text{(Second derivative of the normal function)} \quad (11)$$

By substituting in this expression different values of x, we could find the steepness of the slope for any value of x we choose. If we set the second derivative equal to zero, we shall find the value of x at which the change of x is a minimum. Let us try.

$$\frac{b(x^2 - \sigma^2)}{\sigma^4} e^{-\frac{x^2}{2\sigma^2}} = 0$$

Dividing through by $be^{-\frac{x^2}{2\sigma^2}}/\sigma^4$,

$$x^2 - \sigma^2 = 0; \; x^2 = \sigma^2; \; x = \pm\sigma$$

So the point at which the curve is nearest a straight line is exactly one σ each direction from the mean. That is the point where the curve stops bending inward and begins bending outward. Remembering that the whole distance from the mean to the place we have cut off the curve is about 2.5σ's, does our finding look plausible? Try dividing through by the coefficient of e, and see whether you can find another point at which the change of slope is a minimum.

If the reader has the necessary hardihood, he might try, on his own, to take a third derivative. He should find it to be

$$\frac{d_3y}{dx^3} = \frac{Nx(3\sigma^2 - x^2)}{\sigma^7\sqrt{2\pi}} e^{-\frac{x^2}{2\sigma^2}} \qquad \text{(Third derivative of the normal function)} \qquad (12)$$

This is an expression for the rapidity with which the change of slope is itself changing for various values of x. If the reader will set this derivative equal to zero and solve for x, he can find that point in the curve where it is bending most rapidly—where the tail begins rapidly to thin. If he wishes to verify the fact that at this point the speed of the bending is a maximum and not a minimum, he may take a fourth derivative and assure himself that at this point the value of the fourth derivative is negative in sign.

THE DERIVATIVE OF A SINE

In the applications of calculus to statistics as presented in this volume we make no use of differentiation of trigonometric functions. Nevertheless, because this plays so large a part in the full treatment of the calculus, we shall carry the reader through one development—"just for fun." If he does not care to follow for the sake of getting a glimpse into this part of the calculus, he may skip this section.   We shall find the derivative of the sine of an angle of value x.   We go through our customary four steps.

$$y = \sin x; \qquad (1)\ y + \Delta y = \sin (x + \Delta x)$$

Subtracting the original equation but merely indicating the subtraction on the right,

(2) $$\Delta y = \sin (x + \Delta x) - \sin x$$

In trigonometry the formula is established that

$$\sin A - \sin B = 2 \cos \tfrac{1}{2}(A + B) \sin \tfrac{1}{2}(A - B)$$

The A may stand for our $(x + \Delta x)$ and the B for our x.   Applying this theorem, we have

$$\Delta y = 2 \cos \tfrac{1}{2}(x + \Delta x + x) \sin \tfrac{1}{2}(x + \Delta x - x)$$
$$\Delta y = 2 \cos \left(x + \frac{\Delta x}{2} \right) \sin \frac{\Delta x}{2}$$

Dividing both members by Δx and rearranging the position of the 2 in a manner that will not change its effect upon the value, we have

(3) $$\frac{\Delta y}{\Delta x} = \cos \left(x + \frac{\Delta x}{2} \right) \left(\frac{\sin \Delta x/2}{\Delta x/2} \right)$$

We shall now let Δx approach zero as its limit.   As Δx approaches zero, the first factor on the right of the equation approaches cos x, for the $\Delta x/2$ approaches zero and drops out. The second factor in parentheses expresses the relation of the sine of an angle to the angle itself.   But, if the reader will visualize the relation of an angle to the sine of the angle, he will see that, as the angle becomes smaller, its sine becomes smaller. It can be proved that the ratio of an angle (measured in radians) to its sine approaches 1 as a limit as the angle approaches zero as a limit.   As the limit is reached, therefore, the whole of the quantity in the second parenthesis would become 1 and we would have

$$\frac{dy}{dx} = \cos x \cdot 1 = \cos x \quad \text{(Derivative of a sine of an angle)} \quad (13)$$

Thus the derivative of the sine of an angle is the cosine of that angle. Differentiation of the other trigonometric functions proceeds in a similar spirit.

PARTIAL DIFFERENTIATION

It frequently happens that a function contains two or more variables that are independent of one another; $y = f(x, z, w)$, so that the total behavior of y is dependent upon the aggregated effects of all the three factors upon which it depends. Since these factors are independent of one another, we may find the differential relation of y to each term in succession by differentiating with respect to it, while treating the others as constants. Thus in the case of $y = f(x, z, w)$, we may differentiate first with respect to x with z and w regarded as constants, then with respect to z holding x and w constant, and finally with respect to w holding x and z constant. The total derivative would then be the sum of these partial ones. This process is called *partial differentiation*. Its several processes are identical in procedure with those of simple differentiation. However, we employ a different symbolism. Several different symbols are used, and out of them we shall choose those of the type $D_x f$, the x standing for the variable with respect to which we are differentiating. Let us take an example.

$$y = x^2 + 2z^3 - 3x + z - 6$$

Differentiating first with respect to x while holding z constant,

$$D_x f = 2x - 3$$

Next differentiating with respect to z while holding x constant,

$$D_z f = 6z^2 + 1$$

We shall apply this process of partial differentiation to a practical problem. A farmer wishes to make a zinc-lined tank to hold 62.5 cu. ft. of water. In what dimensions shall he make it so the amount of zinc required shall be as little as possible? That is, with what dimensions will the sum of the areas of the bottom and the sides be a minimum?

Let x equal the length of the tank and y its width. Then the area of the bottom will be xy. The volume is the area of the bottom multiplied by the depth, since we are taking the tank to be a rectangular parallelepiped. That is, if d is the depth,

$$62.5 = dxy, \text{ or } d = \frac{62.5}{xy}$$

The total surface (S) is the sum of the bottom surface plus that of the two sides plus that of the two ends. Therefore,

$$S = xy + 2x\frac{62.5}{xy} + 2y\frac{62.5}{xy}$$

$$S = xy + \frac{125}{y} + \frac{125}{x}$$

For convenience in differentiating this may be written,

$$S = xy + 125y^{-1} + 125x^{-1}$$

Now the surface is a function of both the length and the width, and these two are independent of each other. We shall, therefore, resort to partial differentiation, first holding x constant while we differentiate with respect to y, then holding y constant while we differentiate with respect to x.

$$D_y f = x + (-1)(125y^{-2}) = x - \frac{125}{y^2}$$

$$D_x f = y + (-1)(125x^{-2}) = y - \frac{125}{x^2}$$

The S is to be a minimum by reason of the effect both of the length and of the width. Therefore each of the two partial derivatives must be equal to zero. Making them so and solving the equations we get, $x - 125/y^2 = 0$. Clearing of fractions, and transposing, $xy^2 = 125$. Similarly $y - 125/x^2 = 0$, so that $x^2y = 125$. Since each is equal to 125, $x^2y = xy^2$. Dividing through by xy, we have $x = y$. Substituting in $x^2y = 125$, we have $x^3 = 125$, $x = 5$. Similarly $y^3 = 125$, so that $y = 5$. Thus the surface of the tank is at a minimum for the volume in question when the tank is 5 ft. long, 5 ft. wide, and $2\frac{1}{2}$ ft. deep.

INTEGRATION

So far we have dealt with the process of differentiation, which involves determining the relation of infinitesimal increments of one variable to infinitesimal increments of another. The second part of calculus, as customarily treated, deals with *integration*. This is the reverse of differentiation; it involves having in hand a derivative and wishing to get back from it to the original function. At first sight it would seem that this should be easy; we would need only to retrace the steps that would have given us our quantity in hand as a derivative. That is precisely true. All we need to do in the process of integration is to recall what type of function gives us, when we differentiate it, a derivative of the type exemplified by the one we have in hand, then put down the original function as our needed integral. Only, it sometimes requires great ingenuity to recognize our quantity as a type of derivative with which we have dealt. Great ingenuity is exercised by mathematicians to put quantities, by algebraic manipulation, into forms that are familiar as derivatives.

The symbol of integration is $\int$. You customarily see it in such form as this: $\int f(x)dx$. This $\int$ is really only an old form of the letter s, and the indicated integration may be thought of as summing together the infinitesimal increments represented by dx the number of times indicated by the remainder of the expression, in this case $f(x)$ times, whatever that $f(x)$ may stand for. Let us take first our simplest cases. If we differentiate $y = x^4$, we get $dy/dx = 4x^3$. If, therefore, we are given the expression $\int 4x^3 dx$ and are told to integrate it, we, understanding that that command involves the order to get back the function which if differentiated would give it, might guess that

$$\int 4x^3 dx = x^4.$$

We could have obtained this by raising the exponent of the x^3 by 1, making a fraction out of 1 over this increased exponent, and multiplying the coefficient of the quantity to be integrated by this fraction. Thus

$$\int 4x^3 dx = \frac{1}{3+1} \, 4x^{(3+1)} = x^4$$

That, you see, is exactly the reverse of what we do when we differentiate an expression of this type. For when we differentiate, we *diminish* the exponent by 1 instead of increasing it, and we multiply by the original exponent instead of dividing by it. So integration is the reverse of differentiation. Let us take the more general case, and, treating it for the present just as we did above, see what is involved in going from the function to the derivative and then back again to the function.

$$y = ax^n; \frac{dy}{dx} = anx^{n-1}$$

$$\int dy = \int (anx^{n-1})dx = \frac{an}{(n-1)+1} x^{n-1+1} = ax^n$$

Our rule, then, for integrating a function of the form ax^n seems to be to increase the exponent of the x by 1, raising it to $(n+1)$, and to multiply the coefficient of the x by $1/(n+1)$.

But let us remind ourselves of the behavior of an independent constant. Differentiate $y = ax^n + b$: $dy/dx = anx^{n-1}$. Integrating this by the above rule we get

$$\int dy = \int (anx^{n-1})dx = \frac{an}{(n-1)+1} x^{n-1+1} = ax^n$$

The b which belonged to the original function has been lost. That will not do. As a matter of fact, when we integrate, we can never know whether or not there should be in our integral an independent constant. So we take no chances; we add a constant, calling it C. If, then, the C turns out to be of zero value, its inclusion has at least made us safe. This C is called the *constant of integration* and should always be added when integrating. So our full integral of the above function would be

$$\int dy = \int (anx^{n-1})dx = ax^n + C$$

Recall, now, how we differentiated $y = ax^n + bx^p + cx^q + d$:

$$\frac{dy}{dx} = nax^{n-1} + pbx^{p-1} + qcx^{q-1}$$

Going back from this derivative to the original function we would have

$$\int dy = \frac{na}{n-1+1} x^n + \frac{pb}{p-1+1} x^p + \frac{qc}{q-1+1} x^q + C$$

But each of these parts is precisely the integral of the corresponding part of the function being integrated, so that we have

$$\int dy = \int nax^{n-1}dx + \int pbx^{p-1}dx + \int qcx^{q-1}dx + C$$

In other words, the integral of the sum of any number of functions of x is the sum of the integrals of those functions.

We shall have now a few simple exercises in integration, so far as we have yet carried our principles. We shall complete some of them and leave others for the reader to complete. Note that a dx accompanies each, which indicates the variable with respect to which we are to integrate.

$\int 9x^2 dx = 3x^3 + C$

$\int 7x\, dx = \tfrac{7}{2}x^2 + C$

$\int (3x^2 - 3)dx = x^3 - 3x + C$

$\int (8x^4 + 6x^3 - 9x^2)dx = \tfrac{8}{5}x^5 + \tfrac{6}{4}x^4 - 3x^3 + C$

$\int 8x^3 dx =$

$\int (6x^5 - 4x)dx =$

$\int (x^3 + 4x + 3x^{-2})dx =$

STANDARD INTEGRAL FORMS

It is unnecessary for us to take up for detailed discussion each of the types of functions as we did under differentiation. It will be enough to place in a list, below, a few derivatives on the left and their integrals on the right. The reader will recognize that, if the differentiation of a certain type of function yields a certain type of derivative, then, by reason of the meaning of an integral, the integration of the type represented by the derivative will yield the integral function. Mathematical workers depend heavily upon such lists of standard integrals, referring to them to find the type involved in their problem and from this writing out the integral. If nothing has ever been differentiated that yields a particular type of derivative, then it is impossible to integrate that type of function—of which, however, there are very few in applied mathematics. Full texts in calculus, as well as some books of mathematical tables, give extensive lists of standard integral forms, while we give below only a very few.

$$\int dx = x + C$$

$$\int x^n dx = \frac{x^{n+1}}{n+1} + C$$

$$\int a^u du = \frac{a^u}{\log a} + C$$

$$\int e^x dx = e^x + C$$

$$\int e^{au} du = \frac{1}{a} e^{au} + C$$

$$\int \log x \, dx = x \cdot \log x - x + C$$

$$\int \frac{x \, dx}{\sqrt{a^2 \pm x^2}} = \pm \sqrt{a^2 \pm x^2} + C$$

$$\int \sin x \, dx = -\cos x + C$$

$$\int \cos x \, dx = \sin x + C$$

$$\int \tan x \, dx = -\log \cos x + C$$

$$\int \cot x \, dx = \log \sin x + C$$

$$\int \frac{dx}{\sin x \cos x} = \log \tan x + C$$

$$\int \frac{1}{x} dx = \log x + C$$

$$\int \frac{dx}{a + bx} = \frac{1}{b} \log (a + bx) + C$$

APPLICATIONS OF INTEGRATION

Area under a Curve.—There are a number of applications of the integral calculus to two of which we shall give particular attention at this time. The first of these is finding the area under a smooth curve of which the equation is known.

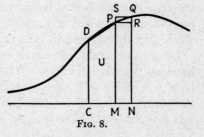

Let u be the area bounded by the curve of which the equation is $y = ax^v$, by the x axis, the fixed ordinate DC, and the variable ordinate MP.

FIG. 8.

Evidently as the distance CM varies the area $CMPD$ will vary. That is, as x takes on an increment, the area u will take on an increment; so that u is a function of x. Inspection of the diagram will show that

$$\text{Area } MNRP < \text{area } MNQP < \text{area } MNQS$$

But area $MNRP$ is equal to MN times MP, and area $MNQS$ is equal to MN times NQ. The MN is a variable distance to be added to CM which we may call Δx, and the area $MNQP$ is a variable area to be added to u which we may call Δu. Making these substitutions we have

$$MP \cdot \Delta x < \Delta u < NQ \cdot \Delta x$$

Dividing through by Δx we have

$$MP < \frac{\Delta u}{\Delta x} < NQ$$

If now we let Δx approach zero as a limit, $\Delta u/\Delta x$ will become du/dx, MP will approach NQ as a limit, and this limit will be y, the vertical ordinate of the curve at the point under consideration. Thus in the limit, $du/dx = y$.

But $\int du = u$. Therefore $\int y\, dx = \int ax^v dx = u$.
This shows that we can get areas under a curve by integrating the equation of the curve.

But, since x has successively different values, we must always find the integral *up to a certain value* of x. When we substitute a value for the x, we have the area under the curve from the origin (zero) up to that point. If we desire to find the area between limits neither of which is zero, we shall need to find the area up to the higher limit, then to the lower limit, and to take as our required area the former minus the latter. This we do whether the two points between which we desire to integrate lie on the same side of zero or on opposite sides; the process of algebraic subtraction will take proper care of signs.

Let us use again our curve on page 13 and suppose we can have no negative y values. The limits of our curve will then be $x = 0$ and $x = 8$, and we want to find the total area under the curve between those two limits. Our formula for the curve was $y = 8x - x^2$. The integral of this is

$$\int y\, dx = \int (8x - x^2)dx = 4x^2 - \tfrac{1}{3}x^3 + C$$

Substituting for x its upper limit value $x = 8$, we get

$$4x^2 - \tfrac{1}{3}x^3 + C = 4 \cdot 64 - \tfrac{1}{3} \cdot 512 + C \doteq 256 - 170\tfrac{2}{3} + C$$
$$= 85\tfrac{1}{3} + C$$

We must now substitute for the lower limit, which is $x = 0$. But, when we substitute zero for x, we get for our integral merely C. Subtracting the upper value from the lower one, the C's cancel out so that our whole area is $85\frac{1}{3}$.

Suppose we wish to find the area of this curve up only to where $x = 3$. We substitute 3 for x in the integral and get

$$4 \cdot 3^2 - \tfrac{1}{3} \cdot 3^3 + C = 36 - 9 + C = 27 + C$$

When we substitute zero for x, we get merely C in our integral. taking the difference between the values at these two limits, we have $(27 + C) - C = 27$.

Suppose we wish to find the area of the curve between the points where $x = 5$ and where $x = 6$.

$$\int_{x=5}^{x=6} y\, dx = \int_{x=0}^{x=6} (8x - x^2)dx - \int_{x=0}^{x=5} (8x - x^2)dx$$
$$= (4 \cdot 6^2 - \tfrac{1}{3} \cdot 6^3 + C) - (4 \cdot 5^2 - \tfrac{1}{3} \cdot 5^3 + C) + C - C$$
$$= (72 + C) - (58\tfrac{1}{3} + C) = 13\tfrac{2}{3}$$

The C disappears in the process of subtraction. The C always disappears when integrating between limits because always there is involved subtraction with the C appearing in both minuend and subtrahend.

The Equation of a Curve.—The second application of integration is in finding the equation for a curve when the slope of the curve is known. Thus, in developing the formula for the curve of a normal distribution we first obtain an expression for the slope at any point, x. How shall we get from this information the equation for the curve itself? If we had the equation of the curve, we know that we would need to differentiate it in order to get an expression for its slope. Obviously, therefore, if we have the expression for its slope, we need to employ the converse operation of integration in order to get the equation for the curve.

There are other types of application of integration, such as finding the length of a curve or the area between curves, and many of the type that involves summing elements that approach zero in size but of which the number bears a reciprocal relation to the size. Such types as finding the length of a curve or the area between curves would deserve elaboration here except for the fact that for our present purpose we do not need to draw upon them. For the type that involves summing infinitesimals into a whole, we shall have considerable use, but the application follows so obviously from the basic meaning of integration as not to require discussion. We take occasion at a point of application in our chapter on Measurement of Variability to develop the important Taylor series, and consequently refrain from developing it here.

INTEGRATION BY PARTS

A device to which mathematical workers often resort when direct integration is difficult is integration by parts. You remember that, when we differentiated a product, we got the following:

$$\frac{d(uv)}{dx} = u \cdot \frac{dv}{dx} + v \cdot \frac{du}{dx}$$

By transposition we may write this

$$u \frac{dv}{dx} = \frac{d(uv)}{dx} - v \frac{du}{dx}$$

When integrated this becomes

$$\int u \, dv = \int d(uv) - \int v \, du$$

But $\int d(uv)$ is equal to uv. Therefore

$$\int u \, dv = uv - \int v \, du \qquad (14)$$

In order to show how we may employ this combination of parts where we cannot integrate directly, let us take the following example: $\int dy = \int x e^x dx$. We may take $u = x$ and $dv = e^x dx$. Then $du = dx$ and $\int dv = v = \int e^x dx$. But we know the integral of $e^x dx$; it is simply e^x. Substituting all of these values in our Eq. (14) above,

$$\int x e^x dx = x e^x - e^x = (x - 1)e^x + C$$

We may sometimes integrate by parts several times in succession or may employ the formula resulting from the product of three or more factors instead of two as illustrated in this example.

SUCCESSIVE INTEGRATION

Just as it is possible to differentiate a number of times in succession ("partial differentiation"), so it is possible to integrate

any number of times in succession, either with respect to the
same variable or with respect to different variables.   In the case
of those functions which are commonly encountered in practice,
we can integrate in any order we please where we are integrating
each time for a different variable, just as was the case with
differentiation.   The expression at which we have arrived at
the climax of any process of integration constitutes the point
of departure for· the next integration.   No new principles are
involved, although usually expressions become more complicated
with added steps in successive integration.

CHAPTER II

MEASUREMENT OF CENTRAL TENDENCIES

PREVIEW OF STATISTICS

The General Nature of Statistics.—The student should realize from the beginning that there is nothing magical or occult or especially difficult about statistics. The task of the statistical worker is merely to describe succinctly a set of measurements or "variables," or the relations between sets of variables. As long as we have only small numbers of cases with which to deal, we can get along very well by describing them one by one, or our comparisons pair by pair. We may say about a group of three boys, for example, that John weighs 112 lb., Sam 123, and Charles 135. We may say, further, that Charles weighs more than Sam in spite of the fact that the former is older. But if we have 1,000 boys to describe, or 100, or even 20, we cannot talk about them thus one by one; to do so would require too much time. We are obliged, therefore, to adopt some more compact method of description that will tell the truth succinctly, yet do justice to the group. So we describe the weight in terms of an average and an expression for variability, and the closeness of relation between weight and age in terms of a coefficient of correlation.

The Tasks of the Statistician.—In giving an adequate description of a mass of quantitative data, we shall need to do one or another, or several, of the following things:

1. Mention some representative number to indicate the general size of the variables—a mean, a median, a mode, or other index of "central tendency." The popular term for this is "average."

2. Indicate how widely the variables are spread—how much they differ from one another. As measures of such variability we have average deviation, range, percentiles, etc.

3. Show the shape of the distribution. The frequency polygon resulting from the distribution of variables may be rectangular, or bell-shaped, or skew. If bell-shaped, it may be

highly peaked up in the middle (leptokurtic), or rather flat (platykurtic), or moderately peaked (mesokurtic). Measurements taken in connection with time trends, or summated measurements, may fit parabolas, or sine curves, or other types of regular or irregular trend curves, and we may wish to measure the goodness with which these curves fit the data.

4. Show the relation of two or more sets of variables to each other. Where we wish to show the relation of the sets to each other as wholes, we may indicate the percentage of overlapping or the difference between the means or the comparative variabilities. Where we wish to show the degree of parallelism between the corresponding measurements in different distributions, we may resort to coefficients of correlation.

5. Indicate how dependable our generalizations are (our means, standard deviations, coefficients of correlation) by showing how much they must be expected to change with further sampling. This is the problem of reliability.

6. Translate the variables with which we are working into forms that have a standard meaning, just as people long ago came to translate measures of distance or of weight into a few standard forms such as foot, meter, pound, or gram.

The whole of applied statistics is comprehended under the above six types of functions. The student will do well to keep the details of his work in statistics in this perspective. In this chapter we shall discuss the first of these tasks—measuring central tendencies. This has to do with giving a picture of the general size of the scores (the variables). There are several measures of central tendency which we shall take up in turn: arithmetic mean, median, mode, geometric mean, and harmonic mean.

THE ARITHMETIC MEAN

Definition and Formula.—The mean is that point in a distribution of scores around which the moments[1] are equal. It is well pictured by a seesaw. The fulcrum of a seesaw must be so placed that the moments on one side exactly balance those on

---

[1] Here we are employing the term *moments* in the sense in which it is used in physics in connection with rotary momentum. The term is also used in a different and more technical sense in statistics to designate the power to which deviations are raised before averaging them.

the other.   The mean is popularly called the *average*, although in technical statistics the term average is employed for any measure of central tendency.

The reader has doubtless long thought of the mean as the sum of the scores divided by the number of scores.   That is correct, but its truth follows as a corollary from the more general concept of equalized moments stated above.   We shall first concretely illustrate this correspondence and then give a generalized proof for it.   Consider the series of numbers 17, 13, 8, 7, 4, 4, 3, 2, 1, 1. The sum of the scores is 60, the number of scores is 10, and the mean 6.   Four of the scores are above the mean and six of them below.   The moments above are given by the deviations of the four high scores from the mean and are

$$(17 - 6) + (13 - 6) + (8 - 6) + (7 - 6)$$
$$= 11 + 7 + 2 + 1 = 21.$$

The moments below are

$$(6 - 4) + (6 - 4) + (6 - 3) + (6 - 2) + (6 - 1) + (6 - 1)$$
$$= 2 + 2 + 3 + 4 + 5 + 5 = 21.$$

Thus the sum of the moments above the mean equals the sum of those below the mean.

Now for the generalized proof.   Let the scores above the mean be represented by $a, b, c, d, \ldots, k$ and those below by $p, q, r, \ldots, z$; let the mean be M, the number of scores above the mean s and the number of scores below the mean t, the whole number of scores, $s + t$, being N.   Then, since the moments around M are to be equal

$$(a - M) + (b - M) + (c - M) + \cdots + (k - M)$$
$$= (M - p) + (M - q) + \cdots + (M - z)$$

But the M occurs in the scores above the mean s times and in the scores below the mean t times.   We may separate out the recurrent M's and have the following equation:

$$(a + b + c + \cdots + k) - sM$$
$$= tM - (p + q + r + \cdots + z)$$

Transposing, and multiplying both sides of the resultant equation by -1,

$$(s + t)M = (a + b + c + \cdots + k)$$
$$+ (p + q + r + \cdots + z)$$

Dividing by $(s + t)$,

$$M = \frac{a + b + c + \cdots + k + p + q + r + \cdots + z}{s + t}$$

But the numerator of the fraction on the right side of the equation is the sum of all the scores, while the denominator is the whole number of scores, N. Therefore M, the mean point about which the moments above and below are equal, has also as its value the sum of the scores divided by the number of scores. We may, therefore, regard as equivalent definitions of the mean (1) the sum of the scores divided by the number of scores and (2) the point in the distribution around which the moments are equal. The reader will soon see that the latter is the more illuminating definition.

The Mean of Grouped Scores.—We may hold on to definition 1 a little longer so as to apply it to grouped scores. In the distribution of Table I several of the scores are of the same size. The frequencies of these similar scores are shown by tallies in column 2 and by Arabic figures in column 3. We could, of course, find the mean of the distribution by adding, one by one, all the 103 scores, regardless of the fact that there are duplicates, and dividing by the number of scores. But we have available multiplication as a foreshortened form of addition; it is far more economical to multiply score 9 by 23, for example, and add the

TABLE I.—SCORES IN HANDWRITING ON THE THORNDIKE SCALE

(1)	(2)	(3)	(4)
X (score)	f (frequency)	f	fX
14	11	2	28
13	1111	4	52
12	1111 1	6	72
11	1111 1111	10	110
10	1111 1111 1111 1111	20	200
9	1111 1111 1111 1111 111	23	207
8	1111 1111 1111 1111	19	152
7	1111 1111 111	13	91
6	1111	5	30
5	1	1	5
Totals........	....	103	947

$$M = \tfrac{947}{103} = 9.19$$

product to the other moments than it is to add in the nine separately 23 times. We, therefore, multiply each score by its frequency, as shown in column 4, then add these products. The sum of these moments will obviously be the same as that of the scores added separately, and this sum divided by N will give the mean. Thus the formula will be[1]

$$M = \frac{\Sigma f X}{N}$$ (Arithmetic mean) (15)

Mean of Scores Grouped by Intervals.—If our scores are many and are widely spread, we cannot conveniently group them by individual scores; we find it more convenient to group them by intervals with a range of more than one unit. In Table II the scores are grouped in intervals with a range of 5 and with frequencies shown by tallies and then by Arabic numbers. Interval 149.5–154.4, for example, contains all the scores that have values between 149.5 and 154.499 . . . , just short of 154.5 but not including 154.5. All these scores may be thought of as centering around the mid-point of the interval in which they fall, which is 152. Similarly the scores in each of the other intervals may be thought of as centering around the mid-points of the intervals as shown in column 4 of the table. We may, therefore, get the average of the distribution by multiplying each of these mid-values by the frequency of scores in the corresponding intervals and by dividing by N. Intervals may be of any convenient length, but we usually like to make them of such length as to give from 12 to 18 intervals for a distribution. A smaller number will, however, do little harm when central tendencies are being calculated. A favorite length of interval is five or ten score points if this gives a number of intervals anywhere near what is desired. The interval ought normally to begin with a multiple of its unit of length. Thus, if the interval is three score points in length the initial number of each interval should be a multiple of three. The way in which to find the mid-point is to add the initial numbers designating the two successive intervals and divide the sum by two.

---

[1] The symbol Σ means that we are to sum the variable following it (fx). Σ is the Greek capital sigma. Some writers in statistics, especially those who follow recent practice in England, use S instead of Σ as the summation sign.

TABLE II.—EDUCATIONAL AGES OF 109 PUPILS EXPRESSED IN MONTHS

(1) Educational age	(2) Frequency	(3) Frequency	(4) X (mid-point)	(5) fX
179.5–184.4	1	1	182	182
174.5–179.4	ЖЖ 111	8	177	1,416
169.5–174.4	ЖЖ 1	6	172	1,032
164.5–169.4	ЖЖ	5	167	835
159.5–164.4	1111	4	162	648
154.5–159.4	ЖЖ ЖЖ 111	13	157	2,041
149.5–154.4	ЖЖ ЖЖ ЖЖ 1	16	152	2,432
144.5–149.4	ЖЖ ЖЖ 111	13	147	1,911
139.5–144.4	ЖЖ ЖЖ ЖЖ ЖЖ 11	22	142	3,124
134.5–139.4	ЖЖ ЖЖ 11	12	137	1,644
129.5–134.4	ЖЖ 1	6	132	792
124.5–129.4	111	3	127	381
Totals........	....	109	...	16,438

$$M = \frac{16,438}{109} = 150.8$$

A Mean from a Guessed Mean.—Falling back now on definition 2, we recall that the moments above a true mean are exactly
equal to those below.   We might, therefore, find the true mean
by trying one point after another until we get one that gives
equal moments on both sides.   Of course, no one would do so
foolish a thing in practice.   Nevertheless, odd as it may sound,
statisticians almost always (unless they are working with a
calculating machine) approach the calculation of a mean by
guessing the mean and then correcting the guess by an arithmetical adjustment of such sort as to balance the plus and
minus moments.   It is ordinarily much the easiest way.   Suppose the true mean of a distribution is, as the calculator is later
to learn, M.   But not yet knowing this, he guesses the mean at
M_g.   Let the amount by which his guessed mean differs from the
true mean be represented by c.   Then, if x is the deviation of a
score in the distribution from the true mean and x' is its deviation
from the guessed mean,[1] $x = x' - c$.   Summing the devia-

[1] The term conventionally employed for a deviation from an assumed
mean is the Greek letter ξ.   But we are avoiding it because the novice finds
it unfamiliar and difficult to write.   Besides, the best statistical practice is

tions for all the scores,

$$\Sigma x = \Sigma x' - \Sigma c$$

But c is the same for each of the N scores, and Σx (the sum of the deviations around the true mean) is, by definition of a mean, equal to 0. Therefore,

$$\Sigma x' - Nc = 0$$

Transposing and dividing through the equation by $-N$,

$$c = \frac{\Sigma x'}{N}$$

The amount by which the assumed mean missed the true mean equals the algebraic sum of the deviations from the assumed mean divided by the whole number of scores. Thus we may guess a mean at any point we please, compute the deviations from this point summed and divided by N, and add this quotient to our assumed mean to get the true mean. Our formula is, then,

$$M = M_g + c = M_g + \frac{\Sigma x'}{N} \text{ (Mean from a guessed mean)} \quad (16)$$

Application of the Formula.—This procedure may be applied to grouped or to ungrouped data. Let us consider first ungrouped data. Suppose you are finding the mean of grades for your class as listed in your record book. You may look them over in a general way and decide upon a suitable one as a guessed mean. Then begin at the top of the column and add mentally (algebraically) the deviations of the scores from this assumed mean, divide the excess by the number of students, and add this quotient algebraically to the assumed mean. The result will be the true mean.

When scores are grouped, as in Tables II and III, the principle is equally applicable. Let us take the more complex case, Table III. We assume a mean anywhere we please, say at the mid-point of interval 145–149. We always set the assumed mean at the mid-point because we want to regard the measures in the several intervals as centered around the mid-points. We must

---

to reserve Greek letters for "true" values, and this use does not come in that class.

now take the deviations from this assumed mean and multiply them by their corresponding frequencies. Each measure in interval 150–154 deviates +5 from the assumed mean, each in 155–159, +10, etc. But let us not carry along these big numbers, 5, 10, etc.; let us work in terms of intervals. Everything centered about the mid-point of interval 145–149 deviates 0 interval from the assumed mean, everything about the mid-point of interval 150–154 deviates 1 interval from the assumed mean and in the other intervals by the number of steps indicated in column 3.

TABLE III.—EDUCATIONAL AGES OF 109 PUPILS EXPRESSED IN MONTHS

(1) Educational age	(2) f	(3) x'	(4) fx'
180–184	1	7	7
175–179	8	6	48
170–174	6	5	30
165–169	5	4	20
160–164	4	3	12
155–159	13	2	26
150–154	16	1	16
145–149	13	0	0
140–144	22	−1	−22
135–139	12	−2	−24
130–134	6	−3	−18
125–129	3	−4	−12
Totals............	109		+83

$$c = \tfrac{83}{109} = 0.76. \qquad 0.76 \times 5 = 3.8. \qquad M = 147 + 3.8 = 150.8$$

We compute our moments as in the earlier exercises of this chapter and algebraically sum them according to the formula. But when we have found our c, it is in intervals, since that is the unit with which we have been working. An interval is, in our particular problem, 5 scores wide; hence a c of 0.76 interval equals a c of 3.8 score points. Add this correction to our assumed mean, 147, and we have 150.8 as the true mean, which is the same as we got before. Our formula is, thus,

$$M = M_o + \frac{\Sigma fx'}{N}i$$

The f in the formula is merely a "symbol of operation"; the formula would mean exactly the same if it were not there.

The f merely indicates that we have foreshortened our additions by resorting to multiplication by frequencies wherever there were several scores of the same value.

The worker will find the guessed mean method a very convenient method. It is customarily called *the short method*. Not a bit of accuracy is lost by it; the mean will turn out to be precisely the same no matter where the guessed mean is taken. In fact the method of finding a mean by adding the scores and dividing by N may be regarded as a form of guessed-mean method, the assumed mean being at zero.

The Meaning of a Score; Discrete versus Continuous Series.— When we compute means we are confronted with a difficulty about the meaning of scores. What does 6 mean? Does it mean just 6 or anything from 6 to a trifle short of 7? Or does it mean from 5.5 to 6.5? When there are 6 boys in a crowd there are just 6 and no fraction. Similarly a gun has fired just 6 times, a student has finished just 6 problems, a player has hit the ball just 6 times. But if a boy is reported to be 6 years old, that may mean anything from 6 to a trifle short of 7, or it may mean approximately 6—anywhere between $5\frac{1}{2}$ and just short of $6\frac{1}{2}$. The same is true of 6 miles, 6 hr., 6 lb.—where the report is so crude as to mention only whole numbers. Some data must be measured in terms that necessarily involve only whole numbers; there cannot in the nature of the case be fractions. Such a series of measures is said to be *discrete*. Other data involve no real breaks; each degree passes by infinitesimal gradations into the next. Such series are said to be *continuous*.

Now a discrete number should afford us no difficulty when computing a mean, except that the mean itself must be regarded as merely symbolic. Each number is exactly what it purports on the surface to be—a 6 is 6.000 and nothing else. We may add these numbers as they stand, divide the sum by N, and have an unequivocal mean. But if the measured series is continuous and our reports are crudely put in whole numbers, then our numbers must all be taken as stretching through a whole unit. Indeed the same thing is true even when we give our measurements in terms that add some decimals; the last decimal covers a stretch through the unit of its order. Our confusion is made worse by lack of uniformity in indicating the direction in which this range spreads from the value named. In some cases the score named stands at the mid-point of the range designated by it—eight years old means nearer eight than any other whole number, somewhere between seven and a half and just short of eight and a half. At other times the score stands for the value just across the lower margin—eight years old means from just eight to barely short of nine. With the former meaning, a number of eights, such as one would find in a frequency table, would tend to average exactly eight; but in the latter meaning, the average for the group would tend to be eight and a half. Evidently our measures of central tendency of a distribution of scores will give us different results under the two interpretations.

Both Kelley and Holzinger recommend that, unless the evidence in the data clearly indicates otherwise, we take all numbers in the former sense—as standing at the mid-point of a range from a half unit below to a half unit above. Thus 8 would cover from 7.5 to just short of 8.5 and 163.796 would cover 163.7955 to just short of 163.7965. That, then, involves taking roughly given numbers at their face value. But it affects the limits of intervals in a frequency table and makes necessary a form of tabulation different from that customarily advised in most of the elementary textbooks on statistics. For an interval must start where the range covered by a number starts: a half unit below the designated number. For purposes of tabulation it is safest to indicate the limits of the intervals in a way that makes this clear, as illustrated at the left below. However, if only whole numbers are involved in the tabulation (or whole units in respect to the digit farthest to the right in the interval designation), no confusion can occur from the simpler tabulation illustrated at the right provided one uses the correct mid-point and remembers when computing a median that the interval begins a half unit below the value indicated by the initial number designating the interval.

(1) Correct Way to Designate the Limits of Intervals When Number at Mid-point	(2) A Simpler Form of Designation Usually Satisfactory
19.5–24.499	20–24
14.5–19.499	15–19
9.5–14.499	10–14
4.5– 9.499	5– 9
−0.5– 4.499	0– 4

If, however, the context clearly indicates that the number stands for a range at the lower margin of which it is placed, this meaning should be followed in the tabulation, the mid-point should be determined accordingly, and the interpolation (which we shall shortly find to be involved in the computation of a median) should take as the beginning of the interval the value of the initial number rather than a half unit below that value. This is the method to which the reader has probably already been introduced in the more elementary books on statistics. Its interval limits may be indicated by either of the two following methods:

(1) Correct Way to Designate the Limits of Intervals When Number at Lower Margin	(2) A Simpler Form of Designation Usually Satisfactory
20.–24.999	20–24
15.–19.999	15–19
10.–14.999	10–14
5.– 9.999	5– 9
0.– 4.999	0– 4

In this latter case the mid-point of the interval can most easily be found by taking half of the sum of the initial numbers of two successive intervals, and the same technique will hold for the arrangement on the left in the former case. But for the arrangement on the right in the former case we must obtain the mid-point by taking half the sum of the initial and final numbers designating the limits of an interval.

If this latter method (customary in most elementary texts) is used in finding a mean from a frequency distribution, the mean will not tally with that obtained by adding the individual scores and dividing by their number unless either the mean obtained from adding the ungrouped scores is increased by 0.5 or that obtained from the frequency table has been diminished by 0.5.

THE MEDIAN

Meaning.—The median is the mid-point in a distribution—the point above or below which lie an equal number of cases. Note that, while for a mean the *moments* above and below must be equal, for a median the *number of cases* above and below must be equal. These two conditions are not identical except in a perfectly symmetrical distribution, and sometimes the mean and the median of a distribution may differ from each other considerably.

Computing a Median.—For the computation of a median the scores must be arranged in regular ascending order according to size, or at least they must be thought of in such order. Our median lies halfway up through the series; *i.e.*, $\frac{1}{2}N$ units from the beginning of the series. Suppose we have the ungrouped scores 2, 4, 5, 5, 7, 8, 8, 9, 9, 9. The number of items is 10, so that we must use up 5 scores—go to the end of the fifth score—for the median. The end of the fifth score is the upper limit of score 7, the value of which is 7.5. It happens that the next score in the series, 8, begins at 7.5, as stated above, so that to locate the median at 7.5 puts just half the scores below and half above. But if there had been a gap (say the next score had been a 9), we would make a rough adjustment by placing the median at the mid-point between where score 7 leaves off and where score 9 begins; that is halfway between 7.5 and 8.5, which is 8.0. If the number of items is odd, the median will fall at the middle of the range of the digit and will have the value $k.0$, where k represents the mid-score. But medians in small samples are usually very rough statistics, and we cannot afford to be very finicky about such nice adjustments as have just been mentioned.

We may illustrate the computation of a median from grouped data by Table III. We accumulate our frequencies up through as many intervals as we can without exceeding $\frac{1}{2}N$. When we have reached the bottom of an interval that, if included, would more than exhaust $\frac{1}{2}N$, we interpolate within that interval to locate our point; *i.e.*, we place it such a proportional part of the distance through the interval as the cases yet remaining from $\frac{1}{2}N$ bear to the whole number of cases in the interval.

In Table III, $\frac{109}{2} = 54.5$ scores from the beginning.

$$3 + 6 + 12 + 22 = 43 \text{ scores,}$$

which carries us to the beginning of the interval 145–149. 54.5 − 43 = 11.5 score points yet to go. Since the total frequency in this interval is 13, we must go 11.5/13 of the distance through the interval to find the median. As we have interpreted the meaning of scores here, the lower margin of the interval lies at 144.5. Therefore,

$$\text{Mdn.} = 144.5 + \left(\frac{11.5}{13} \cdot 5\right) = 144.5 + 4.4 = 148.9$$

Mid-score versus Median.—If one is seeking the middle score of a series, the formula for finding it is

$$\text{Mid-score} = \frac{N + 1}{2}$$

Thus, if there are 13 scores in a series, the middle score is the seventh one, which would be found from the expression

$$(13 + 1)/2 = 7.$$

At first sight it would seem as if there are 6 scores above the seventh score and 6 below and that the seventh should, therefore, be the median. But there are six scores below *where the seventh score begins* and 6 above *where the seventh ends*. The mid-score is, thus, a saddleback that stretches through an appreciable interval. The median, on the other hand, is a point in the distribution that separates the upper 50 per cent of the scores from the lower 50 per cent. This point is halfway between the opening value of the seventh score and its closing value. What these end-values are, if strictly interpreted, should be determined according to the principles laid down in the paragraph above regarding continuous versus discrete series. However, in practice, since a median from ungrouped data is a very rough measure, we ordinarily treat our numbers as if they were discrete— as if the mid-point of score 7 were just 7. The statistical worker will seldom wish to deal with mid-scores in contrast with medians; hence he will have little use for the formula for mid-score given above.

THE MODE

Meaning.—The mode is the score that occurs with the greatest frequency. To use it as a measure of central tendency is to employ a standard analogous to the determination of group evaluations by means of a plurality vote. In crude statistical work we pick out the mode merely by inspection. In fact we seldom employ the mode in psychological and educational statistics in any more refined form than this rough inspectional one. But there are more precise methods for finding the mode if one's problem justifies paying the price of employing them.

One of these more precise methods is to "smooth" one's distribution by averaging the frequencies in adjacent intervals and continuing thus to average until the irregularities of the distribution have been sufficiently ironed out to make one interval stand out in frequency above the others, which interval will then contain the mode. Of course, if the distribution is bimodal, peaks will appear at two places, or more than two if the distribution is multimodal, and the smoothing process dare not go so far as to cover up legitimate multimodality. The most precise method of dealing with the mode involves, however, the use of higher mathematics. It requires determining the equation of the best fitting curve and calculating the value of the x variable in the equation for that curve when the y variable is at a maximum. In Fig. 9 the frequency polygon of a set of scores is indicated by a broken line and the best-fit curve by a solid line. The equation of this curve has been found to be, we shall say, $y = 8x - x^2$. Now, to find the mode, we must find the place along the x axis where the y will have the maximum

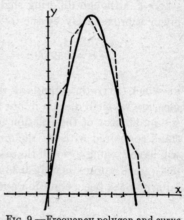

Fig. 9.—Frequency polygon and curve of best fit.

value. To do this, we differentiate[1] the equation and set the derivative equal to zero. Thus differentiating, we obtain $8 - 2x = 0$, or $x = 4$. The mode is, therefore, exactly at the point where $x = 4$.

Although the inspectional mode is the crudest of our measures of central tendency, the mathematical mode is the most easily determined with exact precision when once we have the equation for the curve of our distribution. Most empirical distributions will, of course, require best-fit curves with much more complex equations than the above hypothetical one, but we have been concerned merely to give the reader a glimpse as to how a mathematical mode is computed. The practical worker in our field of statistics will have little or no occasion to compute

[1] See preceding chapter on Calculus, pp. 10–15.

modes mathematically for empirical distributions. If one did have such necessity, he would probably wish to resort to a ready-made scheme that Karl Pearson has worked out, which would give good enough results for most purposes. By using the sort of procedure described above, he found that the mode of his "type III curve," which is representative of a wide variety of moderately skew curves, is given by the following formula:

$$\text{Mode} = \text{mean} - \frac{\text{mean} - \text{median}}{c}$$

where c, although differing slightly for different distributions, is given approximately by the following equation:

$$c = 0.3309 - \frac{0.0846(M - \text{Mdn.})^2}{\sigma^2 - 9(M - \text{Mdn.})^2}$$

in which σ is the standard deviation of the distribution—a measure we shall discuss in our next chapter. It is obvious that the numerator of the fraction in this last equation will be very small compared with the denominator; hence the whole fraction will have a value so small that it may be neglected. c will, therefore, equal approximately 0.33, which is about $\frac{1}{3}$. Substituting $\frac{1}{3}$ for c in the basic equation above, we have

$$\text{Mode} = M - 3(M - \text{Mdn.}) \qquad \begin{matrix}\text{(Mode computed from} \\ \text{the mean and the} \\ \text{median)}\end{matrix} \qquad (17)$$

Thus the mode of a distribution may be computed from a knowledge of the mean and the median.

Other Measures of Central Tendency

Geometric Mean.—Two other measures of central tendency are used occasionally, though little in our type of research, which we shall notice in passing. One of these is the geometric mean. It is used where the successive terms differ by a constant ratio instead of by an addend. It is the mean, therefore, of an exponential series. Growth in school population in the United States from 1900 to 1925 illustrates fairly well such a series; the numbers attending increased with a fairly constant acceleration, so that the trend line depicting the numbers curves continually upward, like that of money at compound interest. To find the geometric mean, we must take the Nth root of the product of our measures. Thus

$$\text{G.M.} = \sqrt[N]{x_1 \cdot x_2 \cdot x_3 \cdots x_N} \qquad \text{(Geometric mean)} \qquad (18)$$

But ordinarily the only feasible way in which to compute a geometric mean is by the aid of logarithms.

$$\log \text{G.M.} = \frac{1}{N} (\log x_1 + \log x_2 + \log x_3 + \cdots + \log x_N)$$

The geometric mean gives us the value a score would have midway through the series if it were actually located on the exponential curve determined by the average rate at which the scores are increasing. The mid-score is, thus, located on a uniformly inflected curve while the arithmetic mean is located on a straight line fitted to the measures, if the scores are arranged in successive order as to size. When the values are greater than unity and positive, the geometric mean is always smaller than the arithmetic mean, as a comparison of the straight and curved lines mentioned above would indicate; and no meaningful geometric mean can be computed if one of the scores is zero. To the extent to which the series of scores is irregular instead of exhibiting a systematic positive or negative acceleration, to that extent a geometric mean would lack pertinency and meaning.[1]

The Harmonic Mean.—The other measure of central tendency to come in for slight notice is the harmonic mean. It is the reciprocal of the mean of the reciprocals of the scores. Its formula, by definition, is

$$\text{H.M.} = \frac{1}{\dfrac{1}{N}\left(\dfrac{1}{x_1} + \dfrac{1}{x_2} + \dfrac{1}{x_3} + \cdots + \dfrac{1}{x_n}\right)} = \frac{1}{\dfrac{1}{N}\sum \dfrac{1}{x}}$$

$$= \frac{N}{\sum \dfrac{1}{x}} \qquad \text{(Harmonic mean)} \qquad (19)$$

This formula is properly employed where the data are given in a form that bears a reciprocal relation to a more significant

---

[1] A good elementary discussion of both the geometric mean and the harmonic mean, with many illustrations, can be found in J. E. Wert, *Educational Statistics*, McGraw-Hill Book Company, Inc., 1938, pp. 63–80.

and meaningful measure. Suppose, for example, data are given in terms of the number of problems pupils solved in an hour, while the number of minutes required per problem is believed to be the more straightforward measure. The harmonic mean would then be the one to use. The reader will find a good discussion of the conditions under which to use the harmonic mean in an article by Ferger.[1]

VALIDITY OF THE ASSUMPTIONS IN COMPUTING MEANS AND MEDIANS FROM GROUPED DATA

In computing a median from grouped data one assumes that the measures in the interval in which the median lies are equally distributed through the interval; hence the point may be located by interpolation. In computing a mean, one assumes that the measures in each interval are centered about the mid-point of the interval. These assumptions are seldom fulfilled in practice. If the reader will observe the curve of the normal distribution in Fig. 10 below, he will notice that the frequencies in the several

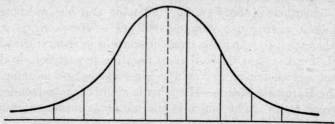

Fig. 10.—Normal distribution and "trapezoidal" intervals.

intervals make figures that are approximately trapezoids (except the middle one, which makes a double trapezoid). In order to fulfill the assumptions these figures would need to be rectangles, or other symmetrical figures. The mean of a trapezoid is not located at its mid-point but somewhere near the longer side. Hence, when the point around which the scores of an interval center is taken to be the mid-point of the interval, it is taken as farther away than it really is, and the moments are, in consequence, all too large. But in a perfectly symmetrical distribution this distortion corrects itself. For the curve behaves identically on the two sides, so that an excess of plus moments

[1] FERGER, WIRTH F., *J. Amer. Statistical Assoc.*, Vol. 26, pp. 36–40 (March, 1931).

on the one side is exactly neutralized by an excess of minus moments on the other side.   It is also obvious that the median is not displaced in a symmetrical distribution on account of the "trapezoidal" shape of the interval, because at the critical position the curve is practically flat and the positive slope of the lower half of the mid-interval is precisely balanced by the negative slope of the upper half.   But to the extent to which the distribution loses its symmetry, as all empirical distributions do, to that extent the assumptions about the distribution of scores within an interval lose validity.   But the error from this cause is likely to be small.

Another condition somewhat invalidating the assumptions is lack of uniformity of distribution within the intervals, due either to small sampling or to some selective factor.   If the number of cases in an interval is small, it is unlikely that they will make either a regular rectangle or a regular "trapezoid"; their mean will be erratic and seldom exactly coincide with the theoretical mean of the interval.   Hence means calculated from grouped data are likely to differ somewhat from those calculated from the raw scores and also to vary somewhat as intervals are changed in length or in placement, and the more so to the extent to which the number of cases is small.   In consequence the data should never be grouped into intervals involving a wider range than one unit, unless there are at least 40 cases.

Even if the number of cases is large, there is the possibility of irregular distributions within the intervals by reason of a selective factor favoring certain scores.   Thus percentage grades are likely to show local modes at 70, 75, 80, 85, etc.   The remedy in such case is to select the limits of the intervals in such manner that these modes come at the mid-points.   But, of course, that principle could not legitimately be followed at the expense of keeping the intervals of uniform width.

Exercises

Table IV contains data suitable for practice by any students for whom the computation of the various measures of central tendency has not yet been sufficiently automatized.   This table will be drawn upon also for exercises in connection with later chapters.   It is, therefore, advised that the student preserve the distributions set up in the exercises of this chapter (and the statistics derived from them) for use on those later occasions, so as to forestall the necessity of making them again.

TABLE IV.—Scores Made in Five Divisions of the Carnegie Foundation Test for College Students, Together with Intelligence Test Scores and Grade-point Averages at End of College Career

(Girls are labeled *G* and boys *B*)

Pupil	Literature	English total	Mathematics	Science	History and social studies	General intelligence	Final grade-point average
B	47	105	46	49	38	56	1.19
B	51	103	55	58	82	78	1.11
B	43	155	27	80	45	53	1.21
G	42	154	97	52	20	92	1.83
G	84	224	46	72	54	111	1.45
G	80	254	56	100	97	126	2.27
G	78	223	30	97	55	114	1.75
G	43	149	34	78	23	71	1.56
G	53	116	115	61	50	74	1.71
G	60	148	51	94	36	87	1.72
B	79	172	19	106	69	83	1.33
B	46	155	127	78	68	95	2.30
G	30	126	75	95	56	73	1.81
G	93	259	84	82	78	118	1.71
B	101	247	65	104	111	114	2.17
G	50	163	21	89	35	74	1.02
G	84	200	69	75	35	109	1.01
G	55	170	58	58	47	97	1.71
G	72	239	45	85	10	98	1.86
G	61	235	61	64	85	134	2.07
G	100	300	43	90	123	139	2.04
G	53	153	52	91	55	78	1.64
B	67	206	112	118	41	113	2.05
B	112	279	43	93	137	102	1.80
G	55	178	21	74	32	96	1.61
G	59	184	46	91	54	103	1.79
G	83	205	54	118	60	96	1.15
G	63	181	41	71	10	95	1.42
B	79	253	62	129	55	116	1.33
G	84	268	51	87	132	102	2.21

TABLE IV.—SCORES MADE IN FIVE DIVISIONS OF THE CARNEGIE FOUN-
DATION TEST FOR COLLEGE STUDENTS, TOGETHER WITH INTELLIGENCE
TEST SCORES AND GRADE-POINT AVERAGES AT END OF COLLEGE
CAREER.—(Continued)
(Girls are labeled G and boys B)

Pupil	Literature	English total	Mathematics	Science	History and social studies	General intelligence	Final gradepoint average
G	42	142	48	83	30	72	1.52
B	51	187	30	39	42	98	1.21
G	76	209	125	87	54	103	1.60
G	89	272	48	107	72	134	1.89
B	95	244	92	141	239	142	2.03
B	56	137	47	85	11	75	1.21
G	90	226	67	114	58	82	1.96
G	81	221	55	125	72	110	1.45
G	64	177	57	108	38	102	1.75
G	84	197	43	94	44	93	1.76
B	114	256	70	106	166	100	1.37
G	94	273	54	128	105	123	1.74
G	68	213	67	77	0	112	1.29
B	75	233	33	98	110	90	1.24
G	91	293	70	98	84	140	2.61
B	63	168	48	87	70	90	1.04
G	68	205	66	59	74	99	1.58
B	52	124	67	122	77	79	1.25
G	74	153	44	91	40	115	1.95
G	34	128	16	63	38	87	1.01
B	68	273	55	111	79	83	2.25
B	56	213	155	138	44	131	1.77
G	32	171	55	51	36	78	1.18
G	64	166	67	81	52	94	1.45
G	20	72	70	107	40	80	1.12
G	87	258	152	107	60	110	2.06
G	41	195	25	54	63	73	1.76
B	67	227	30	78	68	116	1.44
G	66	193	79	99	47	90	1.69
B	66	156	89	111	73	70	1.08

TABLE IV.—Scores Made in Five Divisions of the Carnegie Foundation Test for College Students, Together with Intelligence Test Scores and Grade-point Averages at End of College Career.—(*Continued*)
(Girls are labeled *G* and boys *B*)

Pupil	Literature	English total	Mathematics	Science	History and social studies	General intelligence	Final grade-point average
G	78	187	42	87	61	88	1.31
G	55	169	32	93	54	73	1.93
G	116	313	29	87	114	144	2.14
G	65	252	30	39	69	125	1.49
G	67	162	37	61	69	100	.92
G	107	224	25	90	87	136	1.40
B	57	168	98	98	95	79	.81
B	88	213	56	72	153	107	1.77
B	45	101	37	74	42	46	1.46
G	81	209	41	103	74	97	1.93
G	75	185	32	90	32	94	1.39
B	78	245	92	171	90	111	2.64
G	51	155	113	77	41	81	1.49
B	88	248	61	135	81	90	2.02
G	65	163	56	99	112	68	1.33
G	87	252	51	101	101	118	2.11
G	71	195	50	57	70	113	1.62
G	64	126	65	72	40	49	1.54
G	69	228	40	113	76	117	2.20
G	55	200	95	97	55	112	2.84
G	74	197	30	45	79	103	1.18
G	68	189	83	116	60	109	1.47
B	63	192	19	117	55	106	1.48
G	88	271	116	94	91	156	2.06
G	27	98	19	37	36	79	1.06
B	74	190	54	96	100	76	1.07
B	51	172	50	71	58	73	1.76
G	58	157	33	66	74	99	1.62
G	51	127	29	58	46	93	1.03
G	20	104	25	35	28	77	1.03

TABLE IV.—SCORES MADE IN FIVE DIVISIONS OF THE CARNEGIE FOUN-
DATION TEST FOR COLLEGE STUDENTS, TOGETHER WITH INTELLIGENCE
TEST SCORES AND GRADE-POINT AVERAGES AT END OF COLLEGE
CAREER.—(*Continued*)
(Girls are labeled *G* and boys *B*)

Pupil	Liter-ature	English total	Mathe-matics	Science	History and social studies	General intelli-gence	Final grade-point average
B	38	165	48	138	126	85	2.47
G	61	212	46	141	68	101	1.79
B	93	275	52	191	134	148	1.68
B	55	156	48	76	93	102	1.59
G	82	258	72	107	115	126	2.20
G	69	188	36	120	79	86	1.89
B	84	185	10	68	63	82	1.44
B	54	153	121	111	81	102	1.23
G	95	219	38	109	24	77	1.45
B	49	184	39	118	58	68	1.46
G	35	122	48	97	137	73	2.00
B	28	127	15	80	59	110	1.13
G	14	141	40	51	11	99	1.22
G	63	173	47	112	59	78	1.88
B	97	236	79	138	186	131	2.10
G	77	197	52	88	62	125	1.88
G	94	273	54	128	105	123	1.74
G	68	213	67	77	4	112	1.29
G	34	128	16	63	38	87	1.01
B	56	213	142	138	44	131	1.77
G	64	166	67	81	52	94	1.45
G	87	258	152	107	60	110	2.06
B	67	227	30	78	68	116	1.44

1. From Table IV compute the means of one or more of the columns by the adding-machine method; *i.e.*, by summing the individual scores and dividing by the number of scores.

2. Confirm this mean by assuming a mean and then correcting for excess moments, taking the scores severally.

3. Group the scores of one or more of the columns into frequency distributions, and compute the means. Try intervals of various lengths, and compare the mean in each case with that of Exercises 1 and 2.

4. Compute medians from the distributions of Exercise **3.** Compare means and medians. Try to account for any differences observed.

5. Determine the mode for the distributions of Exercise **3.** Compare means, medians, and modes. How does Pearson's formula for computing the mode from the mean and the median hold out in these trials?

6. The following table gives the number of pupils attending public high schools in the United States by 5-year periods from 1880 to 1925 and the ratio of the number at each period to the number at the preceding period. What is the most appropriate measure of central tendency to take for these data? Compute it.

TABLE V.—NUMBER OF PUPILS ATTENDING PUBLIC HIGH SCHOOLS IN THE UNITED STATES FROM 1880 TO 1925

Year	No. of pupils	Ratio of each period to previous period
1880	110,227	
1885	160,137	1.453
1890	202,963	1.267
1895	350,099	1.725
1900	519,251	1.483
1905	679,702	1.309
1910	915,061	1.346
1915	1,328,984	1.452
1920	1,857,155	1.397
1925	3,065,009	1.650

References for Further Study

FERGER, WIRTH F., "On the Use of the Harmonic Mean," *J. Amer. Statistical Assoc.*, Vol. 26, pp. 36–40 (March, 1931).

PEARSON, KARL: "Skew Variation in Homogeneous Material," *Trans. Roy. Soc. (London)*, Series *A*, Vol. 186, pp. 343*ff.*; and Vol. 197, pp. 443–459. (The formula for mode in terms of mean and median.)

CHAPTER III

MEASUREMENT OF VARIABILITY

Our preceding chapter dealt with formulas for finding some representative number with which to describe the *general size* of the scores of a distribution. In this chapter we shall take up formulas for expressing the *degree of scatter* in the scores—the extent to which they are grouped closely about the central tendency or spread widely from it. Just as was the case in dealing with central tendencies, we may have two types of measures for variability—measures in terms of moments and measures in terms of the location of points. The former include average deviation and standard deviation; the latter include such measures as range, percentiles, quartile range, and many other interpoint ranges. We shall treat first the measures of variability in terms of moments.

AVERAGE DEVIATION

The method of measuring variability likely to be most familiar to a layman, or to seem most reasonable to him when mentioned, is average deviation. This involves merely subtracting each score from the mean and finding the average (mean) of the deviations thus obtained, algebraic sign being disregarded. The formula is, if x represents the deviation of a score from the mean and the enclosing lines indicate that these deviations are to be taken without regard to algebraic sign,

$$\text{A.D.} = \frac{\Sigma|x|}{N} \tag{20}$$

If the data are grouped into a frequency distribution, the x's will merely be multiplied by their respective frequencies before being added. If the deviations are taken in intervals rather than in scores (the former is the proper way), the A.D. will be in intervals but can easily be changed to scores by multiplying by the width of the interval. The whole formula will, then, be

$$\text{A.D.} = \frac{\Sigma f|x|}{N} \cdot i \qquad \text{(Average deviation from the mean)} \qquad (20a)$$

This simple formula answers very well if the number of items is small or if the mean happens to be a convenient whole number. But if the mean contains decimals, the number of digits involved in each subtraction process, and in the summation processes, is likely to be inconveniently large. It is then most convenient to take the deviations from some assumed mean that is a whole number and to make a correction to atone for the error that would otherwise be introduced. Let c be the distance from the assumed mean to the true mean. Then, if x is the deviation from the true mean and x' the deviation from the assumed mean in the case of any score, the x for each score above the true mean will be $|x'| - c$, and that for each score below the true mean will be $|x'| + c$. Let us use the subscript l to refer to scores below the true mean and g to refer to those above the true mean. We shall then have the following:

$$\Sigma|x_g| = \Sigma|x_g'| - f_g c, \text{ and } \Sigma|x_l| = \Sigma|x_l'| + f_l c$$

Adding,

$$\Sigma|x_g| + \Sigma|x_l| = \Sigma|x| = \Sigma|x'| + (f_l - f_g)c$$

Dividing by N,

$$\text{A.D.} = \frac{\Sigma|x|}{N} = \frac{\Sigma|x'| + (f_l - f_g)c}{N} \qquad (21)$$

As in finding a mean from a guessed average, the $c = \Sigma x'/N$, i.e., the sum of the deviations about the assumed mean divided by the number of cases. Normal account must be taken of the algebraic sign of the c.

If the data are grouped in a frequency distribution, deviations should be taken in terms of intervals rather than in scores, each x' should be multiplied by the proper frequency when adding, and the whole fraction must be multiplied by the length of the interval to get back to scores. Thus the formula becomes

$$\text{A.D.} = \frac{\Sigma f|x'| + (f_l - f_g)c}{N} i \qquad \text{(Average deviation when deviations are taken from an assumed mean)} \qquad (22)$$

Each score that is greater than the true mean by no matter how little counts among the f_o's, and each that is less counts among f_l's. In a frequency distribution all the scores of a given interval count among the f_o's or the f_l's, according to whether the mid-point of the interval is above or below the true mean by no matter how little. Why this is true an examination of our formula will disclose.

It is important to note that the above formulas can be used only when the assumed mean differs from the true mean by less than one unit (or less than one interval). This is because otherwise there would be between the assumed mean and the true mean some deviations that do not use up the whole of the c. If the guessed mean with which one has started turns out to differ from the true mean by more than this, one must start again with a mean that fulfills this requirement, unless he wishes to make a somewhat complicated adjustment for the omitted c units.

Assumed Mean at Zero.—One can escape the limitation stated in the preceding paragraph by assuming the mean at zero, in which case all deviations become merely the scores themselves. The resultant formula is then of general application besides having some other advantages, particularly if one is working with a calculating machine. Let X represent any score and M represent the mean. Then each deviation above the mean will equal $X - M$, and each deviation below the mean will equal $M - X$. Our summed deviations will then be

$$\Sigma|x_o| = \Sigma X_o - f_o M, \text{ and } \Sigma|x_l| = f_l M - \Sigma X_l$$

Adding,

$$\Sigma|x| = (\Sigma X_o - \Sigma X_l) + (f_l - f_o)M$$

Dividing through by N and then making a rearrangement,

$$
\begin{aligned}
\text{A.D.} &= \frac{(\Sigma X_o - \Sigma X_l) + (f_l - f_o)M}{N} \\
&= \frac{(\Sigma X - 2\Sigma X_l) + (f_l - f_o)M}{N}
\end{aligned}
\qquad
\begin{matrix} \text{(Average devi-} \\ \text{ation in terms} \\ \text{of raw scores)} \end{matrix}
\quad (23)
$$

By formula (23) the computation of A.D. with an adding machine is very easy—perhaps the easiest of all the variability measures. Without even taking the trouble to arrange the scores in order of magnitude, one merely sums them on the machine to get ΣX and N and thence $\Sigma X/N = M$. Then he goes through the set of scores a second time, running in all the scores which are less than M to get ΣX_l and f_l. Scores which exactly equal the mean, if any, may either be counted among the X_l or among the X_g.

If we are dealing with a frequency distribution rather than with scores, we may work with the actual mid-point values, in which case the formula holds just as above (frequencies in the intervals being, of course, taken account of). Or we may work in terms of intervals instead of score values, then multiply by the length of the interval at the end of the process so as to get back to score values. For this purpose we may number our intervals in any way we please. But in this latter case we must replace the M of the formula by C, which as usual equals $\Sigma fX/N$. Our formula will then be written

$$\text{A.D.} = \frac{(\Sigma fX_g - \Sigma fX_l) + (f_l - f_g)C}{N} i$$

$$= \frac{(\Sigma fX - 2\Sigma fX_l) + (f_l - f_g)C}{N} i \qquad \begin{array}{l}\text{(Average de-}\\ \text{v i a t i o n in}\\ \text{a frequency}\\ \text{table)}\end{array} \quad (23a)$$

But since the M in the case of single scores would also be found by the formula $\Sigma X/N$, just as is our C, this last formula in either of its shapes is of general application. For if the data are individual scores, the f in each summation is 1, and the i is 1, so that they may be ignored as factors in actual operative processes. This is a particularly useful formula when working with a calculating machine. One needs only sum the whole series, divide the sum by N, then go back and sum again the items that have values less than the $\Sigma fX/N$ in order to get the $2\Sigma fX_l$, the f_l, and the f_g demanded in the formula.

Average Deviation from a Median.—An average deviation can be taken from a median, or from any of the other central tendencies, by precisely the same techniques as from the mean. Usually, however, point measures of variability rather than moment measures will be employed in connection with a median. But it is worth noting that the average deviation is a minimum when taken from the median rather than from the mean or from any other point.

We shall illustrate four procedures in finding the average deviation from a frequency distribution. Three of them are

variations based on formula $(23a)$; 1 is in terms of the actual
values of the mid-points of the intervals, as shown in the column
headed X; 2 is in terms of intervals with the numbering beginning
at 0; while 3 is in terms of intervals with the numbering beginning
at 1.   4 is based on formula (22).   It will be seen that all four
procedures give precisely the same result.

TABLE VI.—ILLUSTRATION OF THE COMPUTATION OF AVERAGE DEVIATION

Score	Mid-value X	f	fX	x' from 0	fx'	x' from 1	fx'	$\|x'\|$ from near mean	$f\|x'\|$
20–24	22	3	66	4	12	5	15	2	6
15–19	17	8	136	3	24	4	32	1	8
10–14	12	20	240	2	40	3	60	0	0
5– 9	7	12	84	1	12	2	24	1	12
0– 4	2	10	20	0	0	1	10	2	20
Totals...	..	53	546	..	88	..	141	..	46

Mean = 10.3.   Mean in intervals = 2.06

$$1.\ \text{A.D.} = \frac{546 - 2 \cdot 104 + (22 - 31)10.3}{53} = \frac{245.3}{53} = 4.63$$

$$2.\ \text{A.D.} = \frac{88 - 2 \cdot 12 + (22 - 31)\frac{88}{53}}{53} \cdot 5 = \frac{49.06}{53} \cdot 5 = 4.63$$

$$3.\ \text{A.D.} = \frac{141 - 2 \cdot 34 + (22 - 31)\frac{141}{53}}{53} \cdot 5 = \frac{49.06}{53} \cdot 5 = 4.63$$

$$4.\ \text{A.D.} = \frac{46 + (22 - 31)(-\frac{18}{53})}{53} \cdot 5 = \frac{49.06}{53} \cdot 5 = 4.63$$

STANDARD DEVIATION

Definition.—The standard deviation differs from the average
deviation only in the fact that the deviations are squared before
they are summed; then the square root of the mean of these is
taken.   The symbol conventionally used for standard deviation
is σ, the Greek letter sigma corresponding to our lower case s
—a practice upon which we shall comment in a footnote shortly.
By definition, the formula for the standard deviation of an array
of scores from the actual mean is

$$\sigma = \sqrt{\frac{\Sigma x^2}{N}}$$

Sigma from an Assumed Mean.—It is seldom convenient to take the deviations from the actual mean, since such deviations usually involve decimals which are cumbersome to handle when squared. It is much more convenient to work from some assumed mean that will involve only whole numbers. Let c be the amount by which the assumed mean differs from the actual mean. Then, if x represents the deviation from the correct mean and x' the deviation from the assumed mean, for one score,

$$x = x' - c, \text{ or } x' = x + c$$

Squaring this deviation for one item,

$$x'^2 = x^2 + 2xc + c^2$$

When we sum for the whole set of scores, the c^2 will enter as many times as there are items, thus becoming Nc^2; and the various x's, since they are different, will need to be represented by Σx^2. Summing we get

$$\Sigma x'^2 = \Sigma x^2 + 2c\Sigma x + Nc^2$$

But Σx (in the middle term) equals 0, since it is the sum of the deviations about the actual mean and such sum always equals zero. The whole middle term will, therefore, become zero and drop out. We shall then have

$$\Sigma x'^2 = \Sigma x^2 + Nc^2$$

Transposing,

$$\Sigma x^2 = \Sigma x'^2 - Nc^2$$

Dividing through by N and substituting σ_x^2 for $\Sigma x^2/N$,

$$\frac{\Sigma x^2}{N} = \frac{\Sigma x'^2}{N} - c^2; \sigma_x^2 = \frac{\Sigma x'^2}{N} - c^2$$

$$\sigma_x = \sqrt{\frac{\Sigma x'^2}{N} - c^2} \qquad \text{(Standard deviation from an assumed mean)} \qquad (24)$$

It will be observed that this formula holds absolutely, not merely approximately. One need have no hesitation in applying it to a distribution of any shape or in taking his assumed mean any place he pleases. The result will be precisely the same whether working from the actual mean or from any assumed mean.

Zero as the Assumed Mean.—If the assumed mean is taken somewhere near the true mean, the numbers will be smaller and the arithmetical work consequently less laborious if done by hand. But there will be both positive and negative signs with which to worry, which are somewhat annoying in any case and particularly so if one is working with a calculating machine. It is often most convenient, especially when working with a machine, to place the assumed mean at zero. Then all deviations will be positive. Moreover, the deviations will be precisely the same as the scores, since each score differs from zero by its whole self. And c will be the mean of the scores in an ungrouped series, or in any case $\Sigma fX/N$. The formula then becomes, where X represents any score,

$$\sigma_x = \sqrt{\frac{\Sigma X^2}{N} - \left(\frac{\Sigma X}{N}\right)^2} = \sqrt{\frac{N\Sigma X^2 - (\Sigma X)^2}{N^2}}$$

$$= \frac{1}{N}\sqrt{N\Sigma X^2 - (\Sigma X)^2} \quad \substack{\text{(Standard deviation in} \\ \text{terms of raw scores)}} \quad (24a)$$

The Population Variability.—The measure of variability discussed above is the standard deviation of the sample of scores one has in hand. If the size of the sample could be increased by the addition of further typical scores, the standard deviation would be slightly increased. As the sample approached the whole population in size (the "population" being a theoretically infinite number of individuals of the kind sampled in the distribution we have in hand), the standard deviation would approach the limit[1] as follows:

$$\tilde{\sigma} = \sigma\sqrt{\frac{N}{N-1}}$$

[1] The conventional symbol for an estimate of the population variance from a sample is s^2, as we have used it. However, best statistical usage reserves the Greek letters for "true" values, so that σ^2 should be used to designate the theoretical population variance rather than the computed variance of the sample. But American practice is so far committed to the use of σ as we have employed it in the early paragraphs of this chapter that we feel it would not be feasible to change at this stage. We shall, therefore, continue to use σ^2 for the computed sample variance and, following the Pearson School, employ the tilde over σ^2, $\tilde{\sigma}^2$, to indicate a theoretical population variance. We follow R. A. Fisher in using s^2 for an estimate of the population variance. Some other authors use s'^2 for the population value and s^2 for the sample value.

It is something of a nuisance to indicate square root each time we wish to talk about variability. So the term *variance* is used for the standard deviation squared. In this terminology the estimate of the population variance is the sample variance multiplied by $N/(N-1)$. Since $\sigma^2 = \Sigma x^2/N$ and $s^2 = \sigma^2(N/N-1)$, evidently

$$s_x^2 = \frac{\Sigma x^2}{N-1} \qquad \text{(Population variance estimated from a sample)} \qquad (25)$$

The proof sometimes given for the above formula for the estimate of the population variance is very complicated, involving the geometry of hyperspace. But a valid proof is really very simple.

Let x be a deviation from a sample mean and x_t a corresponding deviation from the mean of the whole population (which is the mean of all sample means). Then c, as we have used it above, is, for each sample, the mean of that sample. Therefore

$$\Sigma x^2 = \Sigma x_t^2 - N M_i^2$$
$$\Sigma x_t^2 = \Sigma x^2 + N M_i^2$$

Sum for all samples, call them S in number, and divide by SN where N is the number in each sample. Also consider the σ's of the samples sufficiently alike to be treated as an average (the straight bar over a symbol denotes it an average and the symbols above and below Σ denote the limits between which sums are taken).

$$\frac{\sum\limits_{1}^{SN} x_t^2}{SN} = \frac{\sum\limits_{1}^{S}\sum\limits_{1}^{N} x^2}{SN} + \frac{N\sum\limits_{1}^{S} M_i^2}{SN}$$

$$\tilde{\sigma}_x^2 = \overline{\sigma_x^2} + \sigma_m^2$$

On page 132 formula (64), we show that $\sigma_m^2 = \tilde{\sigma}_x^2/N$. Making this substitution and performing some simple algebraic operations,

$$\tilde{\sigma}_x^2 = \overline{\sigma_x^2} + \frac{\tilde{\sigma}_x^2}{N}; \quad N\tilde{\sigma}_x^2 = N\overline{\sigma_x^2} + \tilde{\sigma}_x^2$$

$$N\tilde{\sigma}_x^2 - \tilde{\sigma}_x^2 = N\overline{\sigma_x^2}; \quad \tilde{\sigma}_x^2 = \overline{\sigma_x^2}\frac{N}{N-1}$$

So if we were estimating the population variance from our scores, we would merely divide by $(N-1)$ instead of by N. If the scores in terms of which we were working were deviations from any other point than the actual sample mean, the proper adjustments could easily be made; for deviations from some other point than the actual sample mean we would have

$$s_x^2 = \frac{N\Sigma x'^2 - (\Sigma x')^2}{N(N-1)} \quad \begin{array}{l}\text{(Estimate of the population variance} \\ \text{when deviations in the sample are} \\ \text{taken from an assumed mean)}\end{array} \quad (26)$$

It is chiefly in connection with formulas for standard errors, a phase of theoretical statistics which we consider later, that we need estimates of the population variance rather than the sample variance. In trying to give a sense of the scatter of an empirical distribution for descriptive purposes, it is the variance of the sample rather than an estimate of the population variance that is customarily employed. But if, in order to make the statistics more strictly comparable when the samples are very small and of unequal sizes, one wishes to express the variability in terms of the population estimate rather than in terms of the sample, one should be careful to call his statistic an estimate of the population variability and to use the letter s to designate it.

Sigma from Grouped Data.—When scores are grouped into a frequency distribution, they are all considered to be centered about the mid-point of the interval in which they occur. We consider all the scores in the interval 10–19, for example, to be represented by a value of 14.5; all from 20 to 29 by 24.5; etc. Hence, instead of adding these values one by one (after squaring them), we resort to multiplication which is merely an abbreviated form of addition. Our formula then becomes the following, or any of its algebraic equivalents as indicated above:

$$\sigma_x = \sqrt{\frac{\Sigma f X^2}{N} - \left(\frac{\Sigma f X}{N}\right)^2} \qquad (27)$$

Nor do we bother to take these deviation values in score terms, since that would involve unnecessarily large numbers; we take the deviations, instead, in intervals, starting from the lowest interval, which we call *zero*. We can get back to score form by merely multiplying by the width of the interval. We do not lose a single iota of accuracy by this short-cut method. If we take our deviation in intervals, our whole formula then becomes

$$\sigma_x = \left[\sqrt{\frac{\Sigma f X^2}{N} - \left(\frac{\Sigma f X}{N}\right)^2}\right] i \qquad \begin{array}{l}\text{(General formula for} \\ \text{standard deviation)}\end{array} \quad (28)$$

For many purposes, especially if one is working with a calculating machine, the most convenient algebraic form in which to put this formula is the following:

$$\sigma_x = \frac{i}{N} \sqrt{N\Sigma fX^2 - (\Sigma fX)^2} \qquad (28a)$$

This formula is really general in application. The X may be a deviation from any mean as well as from zero. The f and the i are always implied in a formula whether expressed or not; they are merely "symbols of operation." However, if one is working with single scores instead of frequency distributions, the f and the i are each 1.

Correcting for Grouping.—When one groups data into a frequency distribution for the calculation of a standard deviation he loses something in accuracy. For he treats his items as if they

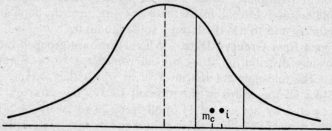

Fig. 11.—Mean of an interval of a normal distribution versus the mid-point.

were all at the mid-point whereas they are really scattered through the interval. When the deviation values are squared, those that lie beyond the mid-point should add relatively more to the moments than those that lie on the hither side. The matter is further complicated by the fact that the intervals normally make figures somewhat trapezoidal in shape. An examination of Fig. 11 will show that m_c, the mean of the scores in the interval around which the moments center, does not coincide with i, the mid-point of the class. When any kind of moments, whether squared or not, are taken from the mean of the distribution to i instead of to m_c, the moments are too great. And the same would be true of the aggregate of the moments and of their mean, whether squared before adding or not. Hence both the standard deviation and the average deviation taken from grouped data with an interval range of more than one unit are somewhat greater than the true ones. The same would be found to be true of all the interpoint variability measures to be discussed in our next section; all are somewhat too large when taken from grouped data. Sheppard has shown that, in a normal distribution, the correction to be made to the crude σ^2 is $-\frac{1}{12}$ when both the σ^2 and the $\frac{1}{12}$ are in i^2 units. Since all terms under the radical in the standard deviation formula when working with intervals as units (except, of course, the N) are in i^2 units, we may write our corrected formula

$$_c\sigma = \left(\sqrt{\sigma^2 - \frac{1}{12}} \right) i = \left[\sqrt{\frac{\Sigma x'^2}{N} - \left(\frac{\Sigma x'}{N} \right)^2 - \frac{1}{12}} \right] i$$

$$= \frac{i}{N} \sqrt{N \Sigma x'^2 - (\Sigma x')^2 - \frac{N^2}{12}} \qquad \text{(Standard deviation with Sheppard's correction)} \qquad (29)$$

In a technical note closing this chapter we give the proof of Sheppard's correction. Although the reader who has mastered the calculus of our last chapter will be able to follow the development if he watches his step, it is unfortunately about the most difficult of the proofs we undertake to give in this book.

Average deviation and the point measures of variability might also be corrected for broad categories. However, the corrections would be small, and, since we seldom employ these measures of variability in refined statistical work, the correction is scarcely worthwhile. Indeed this whole topic is introduced here not so much to urge making the correction as to warn against the calculation of variability measures from few intervals without recognizing that the results may involve appreciable error. A little experimenting will show that the correction of 0.08333 in the standard deviation formula will make very little difference if the number of intervals is 15 or 18 but will make considerable difference if the number is small. But note that the particular correction, $\frac{1}{12}$, applies only to standard deviation.

Table VII illustrates the computation of the standard deviation for the same data employed in the computation of average deviation in Table VI. In the illustration we take deviations from an assumed mean (at mid-point of interval 10–14) near the true mean, but all the processes would be completely similar if we were working from an assumed mean at the mid-point of the lowest interval or at any other place.

TABLE VII.—ILLUSTRATION OF THE COMPUTATION OF STANDARD DEVIATION

Score	Deviation x	Frequency f	fx	fx^2
20–24	2	3	6	12
15–19	1	8	8	8
10–14	0	20	0	0
5– 9	−1	12	−12	12
0– 4	−2	10	−20	40
Totals (Σ)...	...	53	−18	72

$$\sigma = \left(\sqrt{\frac{N\Sigma fx'^2 - \overline{\Sigma fx'}^2}{N^2}}\right) i = \left(\sqrt{\frac{3,816 - 324}{2,809}}\right)(5) = (1.12)(5) = 5.6$$

$$_c\sigma = \left(\sqrt{\frac{N\Sigma fx'^2 - \overline{\Sigma fx'}^2}{N^2}} - \frac{1}{12}\right) i = (\sqrt{1.2431 - 0.0833})(5) = 5.4$$

We have used $_c\sigma$ for the standard deviation with Sheppard's correction and σ for the standard deviation from coarse grouping. It will be observed that applying the correction here makes an appreciable difference because the number of intervals is rather small. The distribution departs considerably from normality, so that the assumptions involved in Sheppard's correction formula are not strictly fulfilled. But the error from that cause is small.

It is recommended that, for practice, the student compute the σ from various other assumed means.

POINT MEASURES OF VARIABILITY

So far we have discussed two measures of variability that are put in terms of moments. Another method of measuring scatter is in terms of the distance between points in the distribution. This takes many forms. The process involves, however, no particular difficulties, so that we may pass over its discussion very hastily. The technique of locating any of the required points within the distribution is precisely the same as the technique of locating a median, discussed in our preceding chapter. The principal interpoint measures of variability are the following:

1. *The Range.*—This is the distance from the lowest score to the highest. It may be stated in terms of the difference between

the lowest and the highest score. Or one may say, and with a richer meaning than the former, that the scores ranged from — to —.

2. *The Median Deviation.*—This involves subtracting each score from the mean or from the median, arranging the deviations in order of size regardless of algebraic sign, and finding the midpoint of the series. If the median deviation is to be taken from the median rather than from the mean, a less laborious method is available. But this measure of variability has little to recommend it, and it is seldom used.

3. *The Quartile Deviation, Called Q.*—This is the most widely used of the point measures of variability. It is the distance from a point one-quarter through the distribution (Q_1) to the point halfway through (Mdn. or Q_2). Ordinarily it is taken as half the distance between the first and the third quarter points and is called the *semi-interquartile range.* This method of computation has the effect of taking the average of the quartile ranges both above and below the median. The formula is

$$Q = \frac{Q_3 - Q_1}{2} \qquad \text{(Semi-interquartile range)} \quad (30)$$

4. *The Inter-quartile Range, or the Range of the Middle 50 per Cent.*—This is $Q_3 - Q_1$. It may be stated as the difference between the two quarter points, but it is much more informative to give the scores at the limits; *i.e.*, the middle 50 per cent ranged from — to —.

5. *P.E. is the same as Q* except that it has become customary to restrict its application to the quartile range of a theoretical (consequently perfectly normal) distribution. The term should not be employed in describing the variability of empirical distributions.

6. *Range from the 10th to the 90th Percentiles, Called D.*—This is a highly reliable measure of variability that deserves more use than it has so far had.

7. *The ten decile points,* located at the end of the distribution and at nine places within it so as to divide the distribution into ten equal parts. While this is not a measure of variability in the direct sense in which the others are (since no distances between

points are indicated) the location of the decile points does give an excellent account of the scatter of the distribution. Quintiles serve the same general purpose though not so completely.

8. *Percentiles.*—These divide the distribution into a hundred parts just as the decile points divide it into tenths. They might be located one by one by the same techniques as those employed in finding quarter points or decile points, but it is ordinarily sufficient to get them by interpolation from a smaller number of locations, either arithmetically or graphically. One method is to locate the decile points in score values, each determined in a

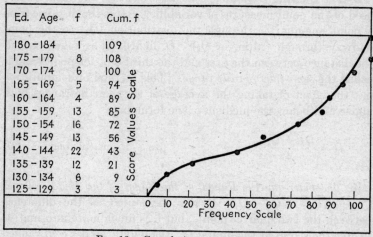

Ed. Age	f	Cum. f
180 – 184	1	109
175 – 179	8	108
170 – 174	6	100
165 – 169	5	94
160 – 164	4	89
155 – 159	13	85
150 – 154	16	72
145 – 149	13	56
140 – 144	22	43
135 – 139	12	21
130 – 134	6	9
125 – 129	3	3

Fig. 12.—Cumulative percentile curve.

manner analogous to that illustrated for the median, then interpolate roughly for the intermediate percentile points on the assumption of rectangular distributions within each of the nine interdecile ranges. Another method, and a better one, is to locate the percentile value of the top of each of the successive intervals by ascertaining how many hundredths of the whole distance through the distribution are covered by the frequency to the top of the interval in question, then to interpolate within each interval to allot roughly the intervening percentile values to the scores within the interval. For graphical determination the best way is to locate, on squared paper or on specially ruled paper (like the Otis Universal Percentile Graph), the score values at the tops of the successive intervals on the *y* axis and draw through these points by hand a smooth curve. To determine the score value of any desired percentile, P_a, find or erect an ordinate $P_a/100$ of the distance along the x axis from the location of the beginning of the frequencies to that where they end, and read the required value from the point along the y axis at which this ordinate cuts the curve. This is illustrated by the graph on page 76, utilizing the data of Table II, page 45.

As nearly as we can estimate from our setup, the 25th percentile has a score value of about 139; the 50th, about 141; and the 75th, about 159. We could make a much more accurate estimate if the chart were large and there were accurately ruled guide lines.[1]

SIZE OF SCORES AND VARIABILITY MEASURES

Effect of Multiplying or Dividing All Scores of a Distribution by a Constant.—If all scores of a distribution take the form ax, where a is a constant and x a variable, the standard deviation of the distribution becomes

$$\sigma_{ax} = \sqrt{\frac{\Sigma(ax')^2}{N} - \left[\frac{\Sigma(ax')}{N}\right]^2} = \sqrt{\frac{a^2\Sigma x'^2}{N} - \frac{a^2(\Sigma x')^2}{N^2}}$$

$$= a\sqrt{\frac{\Sigma x'^2}{N} - \left(\frac{\Sigma x'}{N}\right)^2} = a\sigma_x \qquad (31)$$

Thus, if all scores in a distribution are multiplied by a constant a, the standard deviation of the distribution also becomes a times as great. Obviously the same proof would hold if a were a fraction c/b. Therefore $\sigma_{\frac{c x}{b}} = (c/b)\sigma_x$. This same law could easily be shown to hold for average deviation and for all the point measures of variability.

Effect upon σ of Adding a Constant to All Scores in a Distribution.—It will next be shown that any constant may be added to all the scores of a distribution, or subtracted from the scores, without affecting the standard deviation.

[1] A. S. Otis has devised a new percentile chart on which the frequencies in a normal distribution can be plotted on a straight line instead of the inverted S of the usual percentile curve. This is accomplished by spacing the abscissa lines in inverse proportion to the frequencies in a normal distribution. The chart is published by the World Book Company.

$$\sigma_{x+a} = \sqrt{\frac{\Sigma(x'+a)^2}{N} - \frac{\overline{\Sigma(x'+a)}^2}{N^2}}$$

$$= \sqrt{\frac{\Sigma x'^2 + 2a\Sigma x' + \Sigma a^2}{N} - \frac{\overline{\Sigma x'^2} + 2\Sigma x' \cdot \Sigma a + \overline{\Sigma a}^2}{N^2}}$$

$$= \sqrt{\frac{\Sigma x'^2 + 2a\Sigma x' + Na^2}{N} - \frac{\overline{\Sigma x'^2} + 2Na\Sigma x' + N^2 a^2}{N^2}}$$

$$= \sqrt{\frac{N\Sigma x'^2 + 2Na\Sigma x' + N^2 a^2}{N^2} - \frac{\overline{\Sigma x'^2} + 2Na\Sigma x' + N^2 a^2}{N^2}}$$

$$= \sqrt{\frac{N\Sigma x'^2 - \overline{\Sigma x'^2}}{N^2}} = \sigma_x \quad (32)$$

The reader can easily verify the fact that, if we had used $(x' - a)$ instead of $(x' + a)$, we would have emerged with the same result. It is thus proved that adding a constant to each score in a distribution, or subtracting a constant from each score, does not affect the standard deviation; it only moves the whole distribution up or down. The same law can easily be shown to hold for all the other measures of variability.

MAKING VARIABILITY MEASURES COMPARABLE FOR DIFFERENT DISTRIBUTIONS

It follows from our demonstration that $\sigma_{ax} = a\sigma_x$ that the standard deviation of a distribution, as well as all the other measures of variability, is greatly affected by the order of size of its scores. A standard deviation of, say, 8 in one distribution does not necessarily mean greater relative scatter than a σ of 0.02 in another distribution, for the scores in the former may all be of an order 400 times as large as in the latter. In order to make variability measures comparable, Pearson has proposed a measure, called *coefficient of variation*, that puts variability in terms of the mean of the distribution, since the mean responds directly to the general order of size of the scores. The formula is

$$V = \frac{100\sigma}{M} \qquad \text{(Coefficient of variation)} \quad (33)$$

In spite of the fact that this measure has received considerable attention from statistical workers, the authors have doubts of its value. For the mean may be distorted by a padding of all the scores.   Consider the series of scores: 0, 3, 8, 12, 15, 20, 25, 29; and the series 20, 23, 28, 32, 35, 40, 45, 49.   The mean of the first array is 14 and that of the second array is 34.   The coefficient of variation of the first is 68 while that of the latter is only 28. Nevertheless the variabilities of the two distributions are precisely the same, the distortion in coefficients of variation being due solely to the padding of the scores in one of the arrays.   As a matter of fact, if the zero point in any distribution is located where the scores begin to diverge, as it should properly be, and if the distribution is normal, the mean will always tend to have a value of about 3 sigmas, so that all coefficients of variation would tend to be around 33.   Thus they would lose all value for comparative purposes.   They differ from 33, and hence seem to have a value, chiefly because of some abnormality in the placement of the zero point and only to small degree because of flatness in the distribution.   Thus the coefficient of variation tells us much more about the extent to which the scores are padded by a dislocation of the zero point than it does about comparable variabilities.   A much more promising standard measure of the shape of a distribution, comparable for all distributions, would be the measure of kurtosis called β_2, for which the formula is

$$\beta_2 = \frac{\Sigma x^4}{N\sigma^4} \qquad \text{(β_2, a measure of the kurtosis, \textit{i.e.}, the flatness, of a distribution)} \qquad (34)$$

But this measure has the disadvantage that it involves computing fourth powers of our scores, whereas for standard deviations we need only second powers.

MEASURES OF SYMMETRY IN DISTRIBUTIONS

If a distribution is symmetrical, its mode, median, and mean will all lie at the same point.   If it is skew positively (*i.e.*, has a larger tail stretching out toward the high scores than toward the low ones), its mean will be larger than its median and its mode will tend to lie below these two.   If it is negatively skew, the reverse will be the case.   Several measures of skewness have been proposed, but perhaps the following one is best:

$$\text{Skewness} = \frac{\text{mean} - \text{mode}}{\sigma} = \frac{M - [M - 3(M - \text{Mdn.})]}{\sigma} = \frac{3(M - \text{Mdn.})}{\sigma} \qquad (35)$$

The value substituted for mode in the formula is that shown for it on page 54.

Another measure of skewness, in terms of higher moments, is

$$\beta_1 = \frac{(\Sigma x^3)^2}{N^2 \sigma^6}$$
(β_1, a measure of skewness in terms of higher moments) (36)

For symmetrical distributions, including normal distributions, β_1 is zero. For a normal distribution β_2, mentioned above, is 3. We shall later give proof of this.

COMPARABLE SCORES

Scores from different types of data are likely to differ from one another very widely in general order of size and variability. Before they can be conveniently compared with one another and certainly before they can be legitimately averaged, it is desirable to put all of them in terms of similar units. One way of doing this is to take all of them as deviations from the means of their respective distributions divided by the standard deviation of the distribution. Thus, if X is a score and M_x the mean of the distribution to which X belongs, our deviation is $X - M_x$, and our standard score is

$$z_x = \frac{X - M_x}{\sigma_x} = \frac{x}{\sigma_x}$$
("Standard score" also called a z score) (37)

All z scores are comparable since they all tend to range from about -3 to $+3$, have a mean at zero, and a standard deviation of 1. That the mean is zero follows from the fact that, in any distribution, the deviations above the mean and those below the mean sum to zero. That the standard deviation of a full set of z scores is 1 may easily be shown as follows:

$$\sigma_{z_x} = \sqrt{\frac{\Sigma \frac{x^2}{\sigma_x^2}}{N}} = \sqrt{\frac{\Sigma x^2}{N \sigma_x^2}} = \sqrt{\frac{\sigma_x^2}{\sigma_x^2}} = \sqrt{1} = 1$$

We shall later find that z scores have the further advantage that the mean of the products of paired ones gives directly the coefficient of correlation between the two arrays.

COMBINING SIGMAS FROM DIFFERENT SAMPLES

Sometimes it is necessary to combine the standard deviations from a number of different samples, and the worker either does not have available the original scores or wishes to avoid the labor of an additional computation from the consolidated samples. It will not do simply to average the σ's. But, if the means of the samples are known as well as the σ's, the standard deviation for the consolidated set of samples can be correctly determined as follows:

If x' denotes the deviation of a score from a sample mean and x its deviation from the weighted mean of all the samples,

$$\Sigma x_1'^2 = N_1\sigma_1^2; \ \Sigma x_1^2 = N_1\sigma_1^2 + N_1 m_1^2$$
$$\Sigma x_2'^2 = N_2\sigma_2^2; \ \Sigma x_2^2 = N_2\sigma_2^2 + N_2 m_2^2$$
$$\cdots\cdots\cdots\cdots\cdots\cdots\cdots$$
$$\Sigma\Sigma x^2 = N_1\sigma_1^2 + N_2\sigma_2^2 + N_3\sigma_3^2 + \cdots + N_s\sigma_s^2 + N_1 m_1^2$$
$$+ N_2 m_2^2 + \cdots + N_s m_s^2$$

$$\sigma = \sqrt{\dfrac{N_1\sigma_1^2 + N_2\sigma_2^2 + N_3\sigma_3^2 + \cdots + N_s\sigma_s^2 + N_1 m_1^2 + N_2 m_2^2 + \cdots + N_s m_s^2}{N_1 + N_2 + N_3 + \cdots + N_s}}$$

(Formula for combining σ's from different samples) (38)

where m_j is the difference between the jth sample mean (j being any sample) and the weighted mean of all the means.

RELATIONS BETWEEN THE VARIABILITY MEASURES

When we come to the chapter on the normal curve, we shall find reasons for the following relations among measures of variability. They hold strictly only for perfectly normal distributions but will be found to represent the relations pretty closely in most of the distributions met in practice.

$$Q = 0.6745\sigma \qquad \sigma = 1.2532 \text{ A.D.}$$
$$\text{A.D.} = 0.7979\sigma \qquad \sigma = 1.4825Q$$
$$D = 2.5631\sigma \qquad \text{A.D.} = 1.1830Q$$

In the chapter on Reliability (page 151) we shall find that the standard deviation is the most "reliable" of the variability measures; its standard error is least of all in terms of its own magnitude. After this comes A.D., then D, then Q. This, and certain other mathematical properties, are given as reasons why the standard deviation is to be preferred to all other measures of variability in refined statistical work.

But, in spite of these advantages in theoretical statistics, the standard deviation is not a very apt statistic to use in describing variability for lay readers; it is "Greek" to them. Aside from the range, the variability measure likely to carry the most concrete meaning to laymen is the range of the middle 50 per cent. Of the moment values, it is the average deviation rather than the standard deviation which will seem most sensible and meaningful to such readers. As far as reliability is concerned, the superiority of the standard deviation over the average deviation is so slight as to leave the average deviation a useful statistic to employ in describing an empirical distribution, especially when addressing a lay audience.

AN INDEX OF INSTITUTIONALIZATION

Professor Floyd H. Allport and his associates have studied the conformist behavior of individuals under the pressure of the mores, or other sanctions, and have found that a j shaped curve frequently describes it. When coming upon a stop sign, for example, most automobile drivers may come to a full stop. But some may merely slow up to a near stop, a smaller proportion slow up less, and a small proportion may go ahead without any slackening of speed. If units of degrees of slowing are placed on an X axis and frequencies on a Y axis, the distribution of these frequencies will be shaped like a j, or like a reversed j. The statistics of j shaped curves have not been very fully worked. Such statistics as means and standard deviations are, of course, formally applicable to this type of distribution as well as to other types, but they do not seem to give a very apt description of the situation here involved. We are suggesting as a useful statistic for this purpose β_2', which has the conventional meaning of β_2 except that the moments are to be taken as deviations from the *norm* rather than from the mean. Let us approach this through an example.

Frederiksen, Frank, and Freeman[1] noted the behavior of motorists at a sharp turn on a multiple-lane highway, where safety demanded that cars should remain in their own lanes. They recorded the number of cars which

0. Conformed to the standard by staying completely in line.

[1] FREDERIKSEN, N., G. FRANK, and H. FREEMAN, "A Study of Conformity to a Traffic Regulation," *J. Abn. and Soc. Psychol.*, Vol. 34, p. 120 (1939).

1. Crossed the white line less than half a car width.
2. Crossed the white line more than half a car width but did not cut lanes.
3. Cut lanes.

The percentages in each of these cases are given below for cars driven by private chauffeurs, and beneath the line of frequencies per hundred are the calculations required for β_2'.

UNITS OF DIVERGENCE FROM THE NORM

x	0	1	2	3	Sum
f	85.3	12.1	1.7	0.8	100
x^2	0	1	4	9	—
fx^2	0	12.1	6.8	7.2	26.1
fx^4	0	12.1	27.2	64.8	104.1

$$\beta_2' = \frac{\mu_4}{\mu_2{}^2} = \frac{\Sigma x^4/N}{(\Sigma x^2/N)^2} = \frac{N\Sigma x^4}{(\Sigma x^2)^2} = \frac{(100)(104.1)}{(26.1)^2} = 15.3$$

For taxi drivers the percentages in the four classes were

0	1	2	3
80.4	14.3	3.1	2.1

$\beta_2' = 11.8$

The β_2' gives a measure of conformity which increases in size as the extent of institutionalization or socialization increases. It will be noted that private chauffeurs are more susceptible to the pressures upon them—their behavior is more institutionalized—than are the taxi drivers. This index of institutionalization would be 1 for complete nonconformity. For a chance allocation of frequencies into a rectangular distribution (with the norm taken as the first class), it would be 2 for four classes and nearly 2 for other numbers of classes, the formula for its exact value being

$$\frac{6(3n^2 - 3n - 1)}{5(2n^2 - 3n + 1)}$$

where n is the number of classes along the x axis. For a normal distribution (with the norm at the mode) it would be 3. As the extent of conformity increases so as to make a more and more narrow stemmed j, the index of institutionalization increases and approaches infinity as the conformity approaches completeness.

This procedure assumes equal spacing of the units of extent of conformity along the x axis. But we can see no alternative to this. It would be possible to take the moments for β_2 from the mean, as is the custom, but we believe taking them from the norm gives for this purpose a much more meaningful and useful index. If the investigator's purpose is not to measure the degree of institutionalization but instead, or in addition, to express the slope of the curve in terms of an equation, he has available the possibility of fitting to his data one of several types of curves, including the curve of decay which we discuss in Chap. XV.

PROOF OF SHEPPARD'S CORRECTION FORMULA

The reader is warned that the following discussion is highly technical. The student of relatively elementary statistics should skip it.

As a preliminary to the development of Sheppard's correction formula we shall need to develop Taylor's formula ("Taylor's series") because it is involved in the Sheppard development and was not included in our chapter on calculus.

Let S be the sum of a power series in terms of $(x - a)$, where x is a variable and a is a constant. Then the sum series must be a function of x, and, if we may assume that the series converges, we may write as follows:

$$(A) \quad S = f(x) = b_0 + b_1(x - a) + b_2(x - a)^2$$
$$+ b_3(x - a)^3 + \cdots$$

where the coefficients b_0, b_1, b_2, etc., remain to be determined. It is our purpose now to get values for these coefficients.

If we substitute in Eq. (A) $x = a$, we get $b_0 = f(a)$, for all the other terms become zero and drop out. That is, the first term on the right equals the value of the function on the left when x is evaluated at a. Take now the first derivative of $f(x)$ and get

$$f'(x) = b_1 + 2b_2(x - a) + 3b_3(x - a)^2 + 4b_4(x - a)^3 + \cdots$$

Substituting again $x = a$, we get $b_1 = f'(a)$. That is, the coefficient of the second term is the first derivative of the function $f(x)$ when that derivative is evaluated at $x = a$. Take now a second derivative

$$f''(x) = 1 \cdot 2b_2 + 1 \cdot 2 \cdot 3b_3(x - a) + 3 \cdot 4b_4(x - a)^2 + \cdots$$

Letting $x = a$, we get from the above

$$1 \cdot 2b_2 = f''(a); \; b_2 = \frac{f''(a)}{1 \cdot 2}$$

The third derivative is

$$f'''(x) = 1 \cdot 2 \cdot 3b_3 + 1 \cdot 2 \cdot 3 \cdot 4b_4(x - a) + \cdots$$

When this is evaluated at $x = a$ it gives

$$1 \cdot 2 \cdot 3b_3 = f'''(a); \; b_3 = \frac{f'''(a)}{1 \cdot 2 \cdot 3}$$

If we continue this process, we shall obviously get the following, when $f^n(a)$ stands for the nth derivative of the function $f(x)$ when the derivative is evaluated at $x = a$, and $\lfloor n$ stands for factorial n, *i.e.*, the product of all the integers from 1 to n inclusive:

$$(B) \quad S = f(a) + \frac{f'(a)}{\lfloor 1} (x - a) + \frac{f''(a)}{\lfloor 2} (x - a)^2$$

$$+ \frac{f'''(a)}{\lfloor 3} (x - a)^3 + \cdots + \cdots + \frac{f^n(a)}{\lfloor n} (x - a)^n + \cdots.$$

That is, if $f(x)$ is developable into a power series in $(x - a)$, the coefficients of the successive powers of $(x - a)$ must necessarily be the successive derivatives of $f(x)$ when these derivatives are evaluated at $x = a$, divided by the factorial of the power of $(x - a)$ in the respective terms.

That is Taylor's series. We can now put it in a form more useful for our immediate purpose by replacing a by x_i and then letting $x = a + h = x_i + h$, where $(x_i + h)$ varies over a subset of x values within which subset x_i is constant and h is a variable increment. Making in (B) these substitutions,

$$(C) \quad S = f(x_i + h) = f(x_i) + \frac{f'(x_i)}{\lfloor 1} h + \frac{f''(x_i)}{\lfloor 2} h^2 + \frac{f'''(x_i)}{\lfloor 3} h^3$$

$$+ \cdots + \frac{f^n(x_i)}{\lfloor n} h^n + \cdots$$

This second form of Taylor's series enables us, when more convenient, to shift from the development of a power series in terms of one variable to its development in terms of another variable.

We are now ready to take up the development of Sheppard's formula for the correction of a standard deviation for broad categories. In the discussion we shall need to anticipate some facts and symbolism about the normal curve which we treat in full in a later chapter.

The standard deviation is the square root of the sum of the squares of the individual scores (in deviation form) divided by the number of cases. But an integral is a sum, and in this development we shall freely replace the conventional summation sign by the symbol of integration. Remember that the scores are laid off as to size on the x axis and that the height of the curve, denoted by y, expresses the frequencies. Basically a standard deviation is determined from scores, but in practice it is often convenient to group scores into intervals and to treat these intervals as scores themselves. As pointed out on page 72, this grouping makes a difference, and it is the purpose of the present development to derive a formula for inferring the correct standard deviation, which would be obtained by working from individual scores, from the one obtained by working from intervals as units.

The height of any ordinate of the normal curve is dependent upon its place along the x axis; *i.e.*, the y is a function of x and may be written as $f(x)$. Since the standard deviation must sum the squares of all scores in the distribution from $-\infty$ to $+\infty$, we may write it,

$$(D) \qquad\qquad N\sigma_x^2 = \int_{-\infty}^{+\infty} x^2 f(x) dx$$

But when we work with grouped data, we do not consider the x placement of every individual score but take all within an interval as having the value of the mid-point of the interval. Let us call such mid-point x_i. The frequency corresponding to any x_i value will then, of course, be the population within the particular interval. If, for the sake of distinction from the corrected σ, we place a bar under the σ to indicate that it is the standard deviation computed from mid-points of intervals our formula will stand as follows:

$$(E) \qquad N\sigma_x^2 = \sum_{-\infty}^{+\infty} x_i^2 \int_{x_i-\frac{1}{2}h}^{x_i+\frac{1}{2}h} f(x)dx$$

where h is the length of the interval.

Let us now make the substitution $x = x_i + u$. Then since x_i is a constant for any interval, $dx = du$. Our limits of integration will now be $-\frac{1}{2}h$ and $+\frac{1}{2}h$, and we may write

$$(F) \qquad N\sigma_x^2 = \sum_{-\infty}^{+\infty} x_i^2 \int_{-\frac{1}{2}h}^{+\frac{1}{2}h} f(x_i + u)du$$

We shall now utilize Taylor's formula, (C) developed above, to expand $f(x_i + u)$ in powers of u, replacing $f(x_i + u)$ in (F) by this value. Then

$$(G) \quad N\sigma_x^2 = \sum_{-\infty}^{+\infty} x_i^2 \int_{-\frac{1}{2}h}^{+\frac{1}{2}h} \left[f(x_i) + \frac{f'(x_i)}{\underline{1}} u + \frac{f''(x_i)}{\underline{2}} u^2 \right. \\ \left. + \frac{f'''(x_i)}{\underline{3}} u^3 + \cdots \right] du$$

Indicating the integration term by term and taking the summation with each term, (G) may be written

$$(H) \quad N\sigma_x^2 = \sum_{-\infty}^{+\infty} x_i^2 \int_{-\frac{1}{2}h}^{+\frac{1}{2}h} f(x_i)du + \sum_{-\infty}^{+\infty} x_i^2 \int_{-\frac{1}{2}h}^{+\frac{1}{2}h} \frac{f'(x_i)}{\underline{1}} u\, du$$

$$+ \sum_{-\infty}^{+\infty} x_i^2 \int_{-\frac{1}{2}h}^{+\frac{1}{2}h} \frac{f''(x_i)}{\underline{2}} u^2 du + \sum_{-\infty}^{+\infty} x_i^2 \int_{-\frac{1}{2}h}^{+\frac{1}{2}h} \frac{f'''(x_i)}{\underline{3}} u^3 du + \cdots$$

Integrating as indicated in (H), we get

$$(I) \quad N\sigma_x^2 = \sum_{-\infty}^{+\infty} x_i^2 \left[f(x_i)u \right]_{-\frac{1}{2}h}^{+\frac{1}{2}h} + \sum_{-\infty}^{+\infty} x_i^2 \left[\frac{f'(x_i)u^2}{2\underline{1}} \right]_{-\frac{1}{2}h}^{+\frac{1}{2}h}$$

$$+ \sum_{-\infty}^{+\infty} x_i^2 \left[\frac{f''(x_i)u^3}{3\underline{2}} \right]_{-\frac{1}{2}h}^{+\frac{1}{2}h} + \sum_{-\infty}^{+\infty} x_i^2 \left[\frac{f'''(x_i)u^4}{4\underline{3}} \right]_{-\frac{1}{2}h}^{+\frac{1}{2}h} + \cdots$$

We must now evaluate expression (I) between the limits specified; $i.e.$, we must substitute in each term $-\frac{1}{2}h$ and $+\frac{1}{2}h$ and take the difference between the values at these two limits. When we do so, each term containing an even power of u will drop out, since the upper and the lower limits will yield the same numerical value and will have the same sign. We are thus left with the following:

$$(J) \quad N\underline{\sigma}_x^2 = h \sum_{-\infty}^{+\infty} x_i^2 f(x_i) + h^3 \sum_{-\infty}^{+\infty} x_i^2 \frac{f''(x_i)}{2^2 \lfloor 3}$$

$$+ h^5 \sum_{-\infty}^{+\infty} x_i^2 \frac{f''''(x_i)}{2^4 \lfloor 5} + \cdots$$

The values of the summation terms may be found by the Euler-Maclaurin sum formula. This formula puts the expression of a sum in terms of an integral and certain further terms which themselves involve derivatives. Since in our special case we are dealing with the normal curve function and since all the terms of the Euler-Maclaurin sum formula for this case, except the first, involve derivatives of the normal function which are to be evaluated at the limits $-\infty$ and $+\infty$, where they equal zero, all the terms except the first in each summation drop out. The Euler-Maclaurin formula also involves $1/h$ as a coefficient of each integral when the sum is equated to it. Hence, applying the Euler-Maclaurin formula to (J), we are left with

$$(K) \quad N\underline{\sigma}_x^2 = \int_{-\infty}^{+\infty} x^2 f(x) dx + h^2 \int_{-\infty}^{+\infty} x^2 \frac{f''(x)}{2^2 \lfloor 3} \, dx$$

$$+ h^4 \int_{-\infty}^{+\infty} x^2 \frac{f''''(x)}{2^4 \lfloor 5} \, dx + \cdots$$

Let us now consider in succession the terms on the right. Remember that $f(x)$ is y, the frequency; and notice that x has replaced x_i. From (D) we have that the first term is $N\sigma_x^2$.

The second term requires multiplying x^2 by the second derivative of the normal curve, integrating, and multiplying by $h^2/2^2 \lfloor 3$ which equals $h^2/24$. On page 27 we showed that the second derivative of the normal curve function is $\dfrac{x^2 - \sigma^2}{\sigma^4} f(x)$. Substituting this value for $f''(x)$ in the second term and $N\sigma_x^2$ for the first term and neglecting the remaining terms, which when evaluated are found to have values so small that they may be considered trivial compared with the value of the first two, we may write

$$N\underline{\sigma}_x^2 = N\sigma_x^2 + \frac{h^2}{24} \int_{-\infty}^{+\infty} x^2 \left(\frac{x^2 - \sigma^2}{\sigma^4}\right) f(x)dx$$

Separating the second term into two integrals,

$$N\underline{\sigma}_x^2 = N\sigma_x^2 + \frac{h^2}{24} \int_{-\infty}^{+\infty} \frac{x^4 f(x)}{\sigma^4} \, dx - \frac{h^2}{24} \int_{-\infty}^{+\infty} \frac{x^2 f(x)}{\sigma^2} \, dx$$

In the normal curve chapter we learn that the quantity

$$\int_{-\infty}^{+\infty} \frac{x^4 f(x)}{N\sigma^4},$$

which is called β_2, equals 3 for a normal distribution. The second-term integral has, therefore, the value $3N$. As we have seen before, the value of the integral in the numerator of the third term is $N\sigma^2$. Making these substitutions, we have

$$N\underline{\sigma}_x^2 = N\sigma_x^2 + \frac{3Nh^2}{24} - \frac{Nh^2}{24}$$

Canceling the N appearing in each term and combining the last two terms, we are left with

$$\underline{\sigma}_x^2 = \sigma_x^2 + \frac{h^2}{12}$$

Transposing and indicating the square root, we get the formula

$$\sigma_x^2 = \sqrt{\underline{\sigma}_x^2 - \frac{h^2}{12}}$$

The reader must be cautioned that the $\underline{\sigma}_x^2$ under the radical has been developed in terms of *score* values. In practice it will, in a frequency distribution, have been calculated in terms of intervals. By applying formula (31), we can put this in terms of intervals. Calling σ_u^2 the variance calculated in intervals as units,

$$\sigma_x = \sqrt{h^2\sigma_u^2 - \frac{h^2}{12}} = h\sqrt{\sigma_u^2 - \frac{1}{12}} \qquad \begin{array}{l}\text{(Standard deviation} \\ \text{with Sheppard's} \qquad \text{(39)} \\ \text{correction)}\end{array}$$

90 STATISTICAL PROCEDURES

Exercises

1. Using the distributions set up in the exercises from Table IV in Chap. II, compute variability measures to as great extent as may be needed to bring you to the necessary masteries.

   a. Standard deviations.

   b. Average deviations.

   c. Percentiles.

   d. Decile points.

   e. Quartile points.

   f. Interdecile ranges.

   g. Interquartile ranges.

   h. Semi-interquartile ranges.

2. Compute one or more standard deviations from distributions grouped into broad categories (three to six intervals) and apply Sheppard's correction. If you have employed the same data from Table IV from which you computed σ's in Exercise 1, compare the σ obtained from broad groupings with that obtained from individual scores or from groupings in narrow ranges.

3. Compute measures of skewness for the distributions with which you have worked.

4. Turn a sample of scores from one of the distributions into "standard scores." How nearly does the mean of the standard scores of this sample come to zero? Why the discrepancy?

5. For a sample of about 40 scores from one of the distributions compute β_2.

6. For this same sample compute β_1.

References for Further Study

DICKEY, J. W.: "On the Reliability of a Standard Score," *J. Educ. Psychol.*, Vol. 21, pp. 547–549.

HORST, PAUL: "Obtaining Comparable Scores from Distributions of Different Shapes," *J. Amer. Statistical Assoc.*, Vol. 26, pp. 453–460.

SHEPPARD, W. F.: "The Calculation of the Moments of a Frequency Distribution," *Biometrika*, Vol. 5, pp. 452–453. (On the same topic see also Pearson in *Biometrika*, Vol. 3, pp. 308–309.)

REITZ, H. L.: *Handbook of Mathematical Statistics*, 1924, p. 30. (An additional correction in A.D. for the interval containing the mean.)

CHAPTER IV

THE BASIC FORMULAS OF RECTILINEAR CORRELATION

Correlation relates to the extent to which two series vary concomitantly. We can compute a coefficient of correlation when, and only when, scores in two related series are *paired*. Thus we can determine the coefficient of correlation between history scores and geography scores if each of a set of students has a score in history and a score in geography. We can correlate the scores of a set of boys with those of a set of girls if both sexes have taken the same test and our concern is to see how closely the two sexes parallel each other in the proportion knowing the several items of the test, for here each item has a pair of scores. But, apart from the binding of the two series by paired scores, it is not possible to apply correlation methods in the technical sense.

It is important that a student should understand the nature of correlation, not merely work with its formulas as magic. The principle back of correlation is really very simple. Suppose a student makes the score of 9 points above the mean score for his group on a history test and also 9 points above the mean on a geography test. We shall lay this off on Fig. 13 by going 9 units to the right from the intersection of the two central axes for the geography score and then 9 units upward to represent the history score. Point A, therefore, represents the location of this student with respect to both his scores. Suppose student B makes 12 above the mean in history and also 12 above the mean in geography; C makes 14 below the mean in history and 14 below in geography; D makes 8 below in each; and E makes 15 above in each. It is easy to draw a straight line through all of these points; and this line will pass through the intersection of the XX and the YY axes, which point is technically termed the *origin*. At point A on this line the perpendicular distances to the XX axis and to the YY axis are equal. That is, $AS = SO$, whence $AS/SO = 1$. A corresponding thing is true if we take other points on the line: B, C, D, E, or any other. The value repre-

91

sented by the **ratio** between these two legs of the right triangle, also, is called the *slope* of the line which constitutes the hypotenuse, for which value we shall employ the letter b. In our problem, b is evidently 1. Each y value is, therefore, equal to 1 times the corresponding x value, and the relation is one of perfect agreement.

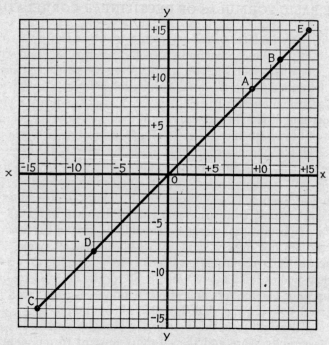

Fig. 13.—Perfect correlation.

But let us next post, in Fig. 14, dots representing the scores in Table VIII, page 93. These dots have a tendency to fall along a straight line, but we would have a difficult time to draw a single line through all of them and certainly no *straight* line could be made to pass through them all. But we can draw a straight line that passes through the group of them and that represents the general trend of the group of points as nearly as possible. This line will have a slope which will indicate the general tendency of the scores in the one series to be greater or less when those of the other are greater or less. We shall call the slope of this line b, as before.

But how find the value of this b?   The answer to that question constitutes the essence of a correlation formula.   One can make

TABLE VIII.—ILLUSTRATION OF COMPUTATION OF CORRELATION BY INDIVIDUAL PAIRS

Data, scores on the Abbott-Trabue Test of Appreciation of Poetry by the same pupils at interval of 5 months, slightly doctored

Individual	First score, X	Second score, Y	Deviation of X from mean, x	Deviation of Y from mean, y	x^2	y^2	xy
A	4	4	−1	−1	1	1	1
B	7	6	2	1	4	1	2
C	7	7	2	2	4	4	4
D	8	7	3	2	9	4	6
E	6	5	1	0	1	0	0
F	7	5	2	0	4	0	0
G	2	5	−3	0	9	0	0
H	8	7	3	2	9	4	6
I	7	8	2	3	4	9	6
J	6	6	1	1	1	1	1
K	3	4	−2	−1	4	1	2
L	3	2	−2	−3	4	9	6
M	5	3	0	−2	0	4	0
N	4	4	−1	−1	1	1	1
O	5	3	0	−2	0	4	0
P	3	9	−2	4	4	16	−8
Q	4	5	−1	0	1	0	0
R	4	3	−1	−2	1	4	2
S	3	1	−2	−4	4	16	8
T	6	6	1	1	1	1	1
U	9	8	4	3	16	9	12
V	2	5	−3	0	9	0	0
W	6	6	1	1	1	1	1
X	5	3	0	−2	0	4	0
Y	1	3	−4	−2	16	4	8
Σ					108	98	59

$$r = \frac{\Sigma xy}{\sqrt{\Sigma x^2 \cdot \Sigma y^2}} = \frac{59}{\sqrt{108 \cdot 98}} = 0.57$$

an empirical estimate of b by stretching a string and adjusting it until it seems most nearly to fit the measures.   The student is advised to try that method with the problem of Fig. 14.   Starting from any point whatever on his thread, he should count the number of units on the squared paper down (or up) to the *XX* axis, then the number along this axis back to the origin (where the axes intersect). The former divided by the latter is the slope of the line and approximately the coefficient of correlation.

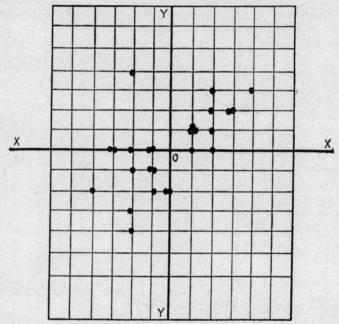

FIG. 14.—Positive but imperfect correlation.

The Pearson product-moment correlation formula is merely a more precise device for finding the slope of this line. It is based on a principle, generally accepted by mathematicians, that a line best fits its data *when the sum of the squares of the misses (errors) is a minimum*. The development of a formula for the slope of a line that fulfills this condition is very simple, but it involves a little calculus.

Let b be the slope of the line required (the straight line that best fits the trend of the paired measures); let x be a given score in the first series (in deviation form); let y be a corresponding score in the second series; and let $\bar{y}$ be the value this y score would need to have if it were to lie exactly on the regression line.

Then, by definition of b,

$$\bar{y} = bx$$

The "error" by which y misses $\bar{y}$ is $(y - \bar{y})$. The condition of best fit is that the sum of the squares of such errors for all the pairs of scores in the problem shall be a minimum. Hence $\Sigma(y - \bar{y})^2$ is to be a minimum. Substituting for $\bar{y}$ its equivalent bx, squaring, then placing the summation sign with each member, which is a legitimate way of summing such a quantity, we have

$$\Sigma(y - \bar{y})^2 = \Sigma(y - bx)^2 = (\Sigma y^2 - 2b\Sigma xy + b^2 \Sigma x^2)$$

is to be a minimum. Since we are to find a value for b that will make this quantity a minimum, we must differentiate the expression with respect to b and set the derivative equal to zero (see page 10 of this volume). Since the first term contains no b, it will disappear from the derivative. In each of the other two terms the elements other than b will be unaffected by the differentiation, but the b will have its exponent decreased by 1, and the coefficient of the term will be multiplied by what had been the exponent of the b. Thus differentiating, we get

$$-2\Sigma xy + 2b\Sigma x^2 = 0$$

Transposing, then dividing by the coefficient of b,

$$2b\Sigma x^2 = 2\Sigma xy; \; b_{yx} = \frac{\Sigma xy}{\Sigma x^2} \qquad \begin{array}{l}\text{(Formula for the slope of a} \\ \text{straight line fitting the} \\ \text{trend of paired measures} \\ \text{so as to minimize the } y \\ \text{residuals)}\end{array} \quad (40)$$

That is the formula for the slope of a line fitting paired measures so as to minimize the y residuals; it is called the *regression formula for y on x*. Frequently it is used in just that form, especially in business statistics. But we may put it in more familiar shape if we divide both sides of the equation $2b\Sigma x^2 = 2\Sigma xy$ by $2N$, N being the number of pairs of scores in the problem.

$$b \frac{\Sigma x^2}{N} = \frac{\Sigma xy}{N}$$

Now we have seen $\Sigma x^2 / N$ before; it is σ_x^2. Making this substitution,

$$b\sigma_x^2 = \frac{\Sigma xy}{N}; \; b = \frac{\Sigma xy}{N\sigma_x^2}$$

But still our formula for the slope of the line lacks a standard meaning, because x and y may be measured in different units, and the slope is greatly affected by the relative variabilities of the measures employed. We shall remedy this by choosing a new symbol, r, for the slope of the line when our measures have been taken as x/σ_x and y/σ_y, thus making the measures of equal variability. In this notation

$$\frac{\bar{y}}{\sigma_y} = r\frac{x}{\sigma_x}; \text{ therefore } \bar{y} = rx\frac{\sigma_y}{\sigma_x}$$

But in our former notation, $\bar{y} = bx$. Therefore

$$rx\frac{\sigma_y}{\sigma_x} = bx, \, r = b\frac{\sigma_x}{\sigma_y}, \text{ and } b = r\frac{\sigma_y}{\sigma_x}$$

Substituting the value of r thus derived,[1]

$$r = b\frac{\sigma_x}{\sigma_y} = \frac{\Sigma xy}{N\sigma_x^2} \cdot \frac{\sigma_x}{\sigma_y} = \frac{\Sigma xy}{N\sigma_x\sigma_y} \quad \begin{array}{l}\text{(Pearson product-moment}\\ \text{formula for coefficient of}\\ \text{correlation)}\end{array} \quad (41)$$

If we choose to do so, we may put this basic correlation formula in a little different shape by substituting for σ_x its value $\sqrt{\Sigma x^2/N}$ and for σ_y its value $\sqrt{\Sigma y^2/N}$ and have

$$r = \frac{\Sigma xy}{N\sqrt{(\Sigma x^2/N \cdot \Sigma y^2/N)}}$$

$$= \frac{\Sigma xy}{\sqrt{\Sigma x^2 \cdot \Sigma y^2}} \quad \begin{array}{l}\text{(Second form for the basic Pearson prod-}\\ \text{uct-moment correlation formula)}\end{array} \quad (41a)$$

This is the principal formula for r, the Pearson product-moment formula, whenever the measures are taken in the form of deviations from the means. It is, you see, merely the formula for the slope of the straight line best fitting the measures when the correlation chart has been laid off square—when the variabilities in the two directions have been equalized. This line is called the *regression line*. The student who knows a little trigonometry will see that r is the tangent of the angle that the regression line makes with the X axis under the special condition

---

[1] The standard deviations of the samples must be used in this and in subsequent formulas for correlation, not the population s. If population values are used in the denominator, they must also be used in the numerator, and the two corrections precisely cancel each other.

that the variabilities of the two sets of measures shall have been equalized. When we gather our data into columns, as is done in Table IX, the regression line becomes the straight line most nearly fitting the *means* of the columns as well as the straight line most nearly fitting the separate measures. For this reason it is sometimes called the *line of the means*. An r may be calculated either from the individual paired scores or from a correlation chart in which the scores have been grouped into intervals. The formula has precisely the same fundamental meaning and essentially the same form when using either arrangement. As the student goes on through statistics, he will have many occasions to marvel at the unexpected ways in which this correlation formula crops up and at the transformations through which it can be put. It is one of the most fascinating formulas of mathematical science.

An inspection of the formula will show that the new element involved in correlation is Σxy; the sigmas we have treated in an earlier chapter. Σxy involves multiplying each x by its paired y value and then summing these products algebraically (the multiplying being done, of course, pair by pair before the adding). The multiplying may be done pair by pair, or the xy products of a like value may be grouped into frequencies and each xy value multiplied by its frequency before addition. It is this latter thing that one is doing when he computes an r from a correlation chart. Sample solutions are shown on pages 93 and 100.

The formula for r that we developed above,

$$r = \frac{\Sigma xy}{N\sigma_x\sigma_y}$$

was based upon measures that are taken as deviations from the exact means of the series to which they belong. But it is seldom desirable to take deviations from the true mean in working a problem in correlation, since customarily we get decimals which are cumbersome to handle. We do better to work from some convenient assumed mean even though we may know the true mean, just as was the case also in computing standard deviations. The development of a correction formula that will allow us to use an assumed mean and yet get the correct r is very simple.

Let x be the deviation of a score from the true mean in the X series and y a corresponding deviation in the Y series. Let x'

and y' be, correspondingly, deviations from the assumed means. Let c_x be the amount by which the assumed mean in the X series differs from the true X mean and c_y be a corresponding value in the Y series. Then for any one pair,

$$x' = x + c_x, \text{ and } y' = y + c_y$$

The product of any one pair will be

$$x'y' = (x + c_x)(y + c_y) = xy + xc_y + yc_x + c_xc_y$$

Summing for all the pairs,

$$\Sigma x'y' = \Sigma xy + c_y\Sigma x + c_x\Sigma y + \Sigma c_xc_y$$

But, since x and y are the deviations from the true means, their respective sums equal zero. Hence the two middle terms become zero and drop out. Also Σc_xc_y becomes Nc_xc_y, because this term is taken once for each pair. Therefore

$$\Sigma x'y' = \Sigma xy + Nc_xc_y$$

Transposing,

$$\Sigma xy = \Sigma x'y' - Nc_xc_y$$

Substituting this value in the original Pearson formula above,

$$
\begin{aligned}
r &= \frac{\Sigma x'y' - Nc_xc_y}{N\sigma_x\sigma_y} \\
&= \frac{(\Sigma x'y'/N) - c_xc_y}{\sigma_x\sigma_y}
\end{aligned}
$$

(One form of the product-moment formula when measures are taken from assumed means) (42)

In dealing with the c's in the above formula, it must be remembered that the algebraic sign is to be considered. Sometimes the product of the two c's must be added arithmetically to the rest of the formula instead of subtracted—if one happens to be positive and the other negative.

We can, perhaps, simplify this formula further for ease of computation by noting that c_x, the amount our assumed mean in the X series missed the true mean, is always equal to $\Sigma x'/N$ and similarly c_y is equal to $\Sigma y'/N$. This is true no matter where the assumed mean is taken, as we have already learned in our chapter on central tendencies. It is true even when the assumed mean is taken at zero, in which case all the deviations will be precisely

the same as the corresponding scores and the c's will be exactly
the means of the respective series. We shall, therefore, have
perfectly general formulas if we substitute these values for the
c's. We may also substitute for our σ's equivalent values we
learned in our chapter on variabilities. Then

$$
\begin{aligned}
r &= \frac{\Sigma x'y' - Nc_xc_y}{N\sigma_x\sigma_y} \\
&= \frac{\Sigma x'y' - N(\Sigma x'/N) \cdot (\Sigma y'/N)}{N\sqrt{(\Sigma x'^2/N) - (\Sigma x'/N)^2}\ \sqrt{(\Sigma y'^2/N) - (\Sigma y'/N)^2}} \\
&= \frac{\Sigma x'y' - \dfrac{\Sigma x' \cdot \Sigma y'}{N}}{\sqrt{\Sigma x'^2 - \dfrac{(\Sigma x')^2}{N}}\ \sqrt{\Sigma y'^2 - \dfrac{(\Sigma y')^2}{N}}} \\
&= \frac{N\Sigma x'y' - \Sigma x' \Sigma y'}{\sqrt{[N\Sigma x'^2 - (\Sigma x')^2][N\Sigma y'^2 - (\Sigma y')^2]}}
\end{aligned}
$$

(Recommended general formula for product-moment correlation when measures   (43)
are taken from an assumed mean)

The x's and the y's may be taken from any mean the worker
pleases, and the resulting r will be not only approximately
but absolutely the same; or the scores may be taken exactly
as they stand, which amounts to taking them as deviations
from zero as an assumed mean. To take them thus as original
scores saves all subtractions and all necessity for watching
algebraic signs (unless the original scores themselves involve
differently signed numbers). But the numbers will be larger
than if we work from a mean near the true mean. When working
with a Monroe calculating machine, we always use this last
formula, taking the x''s and the y''s in terms of the original
scores, because the formula taken in this manner fits the calculating machine ideally and large numbers are no handicap in working
with a machine. But the worker who is operating with a pencil
may prefer smaller numbers, even if he must bother with plus
and minus signs, and hence will wish to work from an assumed
mean as close as feasible to the true one. But the formula is
precisely the same in either case. We recommend the last
formula given above and the basic formula (for measures taken
as deviations from the true means) as the only product-moment
correlation formulas worth the student's effort to remember.

TABLE IX.—SCORES ON ODD-NUMBERED AND EVEN-NUMBERED ITEMS OF A TEST IN EDUCATIONAL PSYCHOLOGY BY 106 COLLEGE STUDENTS
Arranged in a correlation table

Evens	Odds													f_y	Y	fY	fY^2
	10–14	15–19	20–24	25–29	30–34	35–39	40–44	45–49	50–54	55–59	60–64	65–69	70–74				
65–69													2	2	11	22	242
60–64											1			1	10	10	100
55–59										1	2	1		4	9	36	324
50–54									2	2				4	8	32	256
45–49					1		1	2	1	1				6	7	42	294
40–44			1	1			3	3	2	2				12	6	72	432
35–39				1	3	1	3	2	2	1				13	5	65	325
30–34				5	6	6	9		1					27	4	108	432
25–29	1	1	1	5	5	5	2	1						21	3	63	189
20–24	1		1	3	2	2								9	2	18	36
15–19	1	1	1	1		1								5	1	5	5
10–14			1		1									2	0	0	0
f_x	3	2	5	16	18	15	18	8	8	7	3	1	2	106		473	2,635
X	0	1	2	3	4	5	6	7	8	9	10	11	12				
fX	0	2	10	48	72	75	108	56	64	63	30	11	24				
fX^2	0	2	20	144	288	375	648	392	512	567	300	121	288				
ΣY_c	6	4	12	53	65	49	82	45	49	49	28	9	22			473	
ΣXY_c	0	4	24	159	260	245	492	315	392	441	280	99	264				

$$r = \frac{N \Sigma XY - \Sigma X \cdot \Sigma Y}{\sqrt{(N \Sigma X^2 - \overline{\Sigma X^2})(N \Sigma Y^2 - \overline{\Sigma Y^2})}}$$

$$= \frac{106 \cdot 2975 - 563 \cdot 473}{\sqrt{(106 \cdot 3657 - 563^2)(106 \cdot 2635 - 473^2)}} = 0.78$$

The product-moment formula for correlation holds exactly only for scores taken pair by pair; when an r is computed from a correlation chart, it loses somewhat in precision. However, if the number of cases is 40 or more and the number of categories for each of the arrays is reasonably large, the loss is sufficiently small to be negligible. But one should never compute an r from a correlation chart where the number of cases is less than 30 or 40 unless the range of scores in an interval is only one or two. The number of categories should be about 12 or more. If an r must be computed from a small number of categories, Sheppard's correction should be made in the standard deviations that constitute the denominator of the fraction (see page 89). We shall in a later chapter more fully discuss the problem of correcting r for a small number of categories.

THE SUMS AND THE DIFFERENCES FORMULAS FOR r

Sometimes it is very convenient to employ a formula for r that involves adding or subtracting the paired scores instead of multiplying them. We shall develop formulas for that purpose.

Let d be the difference between any two paired scores when the scores are expressed in terms of deviations from the means of their respective series.   Then

$$\sigma_d^2 = \frac{\Sigma(x-y)^2}{N} = \frac{\Sigma(x^2 - 2xy + y^2)}{N} = \frac{\Sigma x^2}{N} - \frac{2\Sigma xy}{N} + \frac{\Sigma y^2}{N}$$

Multiplying both numerator and denominator of the middle term by $\sigma_x \sigma_y$ and putting each of the other terms in the form of equivalent σ's,

$$\sigma_d^2 = \sigma_x^2 + \sigma_y^2 - \frac{2\Sigma xy}{N\sigma_x\sigma_y} \cdot \sigma_x\sigma_y$$

But the final term now contains the formula for r.   Substituting r for its equivalent, then transposing and solving for r, we have

$$\sigma_d^2 = \sigma_x^2 + \sigma_y^2 - 2r\sigma_x\sigma_y; \quad 2r\sigma_x\sigma_y = \sigma_x^2 + \sigma_y^2 - \sigma_d^2$$

$$r = \frac{\sigma_x^2 + \sigma_y^2 - \sigma_d^2}{2\sigma_x\sigma_y} \quad \begin{array}{l}\text{(Formula for } r \text{ in terms of the difference}\\ \text{between scores when in deviation} \quad (44)\\ \text{terms)}\end{array}$$

We arrived at this result by taking all our measures as deviations from the means of their respective series. But we can easily show that the same formula holds if we work with the difference between raw scores instead of the difference between deviation scores. σ_x^2 and σ_y^2 will be the same, of course, regardless of whether we computed them in terms of deviations or in terms of raw scores, provided we made the proper correction on account of taking zero as the assumed mean.   We need only show that, if d is the difference between paired scores when these scores are in deviation form and D is the difference between corresponding raw scores, then σ_d equals σ_D.

$$d = (x - y) = [(X - M_x) - (Y - M_y)]$$
$$= X - Y - (M_x - M_y) = D - (M_x - M_y)$$

σ_d will necessarily be the same as σ_D because in the latter case each item will merely have a constant $(M_x - M_y)$ subtracted from it to make it identical in value with its corresponding d, and the subtraction of the same value from each term of a series does not affect the standard deviation of that series (see page 77). We may, therefore, write our formula for r as follows:

$$r = \frac{\sigma_x^2 + \sigma_y^2 - \sigma_D^2}{2\sigma_x\sigma_y}$$

(Formula for r in terms of the differences between raw scores)

If the variabilities of the two arrays are equal, as would be approximately true of two forms of a test, this formula simplifies to the following:

$$r = \frac{1}{2}\left(\frac{\sigma^2}{\sigma^2} + \frac{\sigma^2}{\sigma^2} - \frac{\sigma_D^2}{\sigma^2}\right) = \frac{1}{2}\left(1 + 1 - \frac{\sigma_D^2}{\sigma^2}\right)$$

$$r = 1 - \frac{\sigma_D^2}{2\sigma^2}$$

(Formula for r in terms of differences, assuming equal variabilities in the two arrays) (45)

If, finally, the means are equal as well as the variabilities, we can simplify formula (45) a little further by considering the σ_D^2.

$$\sigma_D^2 = \frac{\Sigma D^2}{N} - \left(\frac{\Sigma D}{N}\right)^2$$

But

$$\Sigma D = \Sigma(X - Y) = (\Sigma X - \Sigma Y) = (NM_x - NM_y)$$
$$= N(M_x - M_y)$$

But, if the means are equal, the difference between M_x and M_y is zero and ΣD becomes zero. Therefore $(\Sigma D/N)^2$ becomes zero and σ_D^2 equals $\Sigma D^2/N$. Substituting this value in formula (45), we get

$$r = 1 - \frac{\Sigma D^2}{2N\sigma^2}$$

(Formula for r in terms of differences between paired scores, assuming equality of variabilities and of means in the two arrays) (46)

This formula can be applied in certain practical situations, particularly in the correlation between two forms of the same test or two halves of the same test, but always with a certain risk that the assumption of equality of means may not hold. However, it is especially useful to us just now because it is the basis for the development of the important Spearman ranks correlation formula which we shall treat presently.

The reader will be easily able to verify the fact that, if we had taken $X + Y = S$, we would have arrived by a similar procedure at a formula for r in terms of the sums of paired scores as follows:

$$r = \frac{\sigma_S^2 - \sigma_x^2 - \sigma_y^2}{2\sigma_x\sigma_y} \qquad \text{(Fomula for } r \text{ in terms of sums of paired scores)} \qquad (47)$$

and if the variabilities may be assumed equal,

$$r = \frac{\sigma_S^2}{2\sigma^2} - 1 \qquad \text{(Formula for } r \text{ in terms of sums of paired scores, assuming equal variabilities in the two arrays)} \qquad (48)$$

Occasionally we may have standing on our records an average between the paired scores instead of the sum of the scores, and we may wish to employ these data to get a coefficient of correlation between the two arrays from which the averages were taken. This would be the case, for example, where a teacher had entered in her book a mid-term grade, an end-term grade, and a final grade that was the average of the two and wished later to learn what had been the correlation between the grades for the two halves of the term. Since all measures are half as great as when couched in sums instead of averages, the variance will be one-fourth as large as that of the sums. σ_S^2 equals, therefore, $4\sigma_{av}^2$, and

$$r = \frac{4\sigma_{av}^2 - \sigma_x^2 - \sigma_y^2}{2\sigma_x\sigma_y} \qquad \text{(Formula for } r \text{ in terms of the averages between paired scores)} \qquad (49)$$

THE SPEARMAN RANKS FORMULA FOR CORRELATION

We shall next develop a formula for computing a coefficient of correlation between two series when put in terms of the rank order of the items instead of raw scores. Thus we may know about a set of pupils only the order in which they rank in history and the order in which they rank in geography, and yet we may wish to compute a coefficient of correlation between standings in these two subjects. Or, even if we know the actual scores, we may prefer to translate these scores into rank orders and then compute the correlation coefficient from the ranks, on the ground that the mathematics involved is somewhat simpler. The formula that we shall treat for this purpose was first developed by Spearman, the method is called the *Spearman ranks method*, and the symbol for the coefficient of correlation thus derived is designated by the Greek letter ρ (rho).

Our starting point in the development of Spearman's formula is our formula (46) above; for in the case of two sets of continuous ranks with the same number of individuals in each set it is clear that the means of the two arrays would be equal and so would the variabilities. However, our scores have now become ranks, so that D is now the difference between the ranks of an individual item in the two series. We might, with any given problem, apply in the customary way this formula just as it stands. But in the special case of ranks we can put it in a much more convenient form by getting a simpler equivalent for the σ^2 of the denominator.

This σ^2 is the square of the standard deviation of a set of n continuous ranks.

$$\sigma_{rk_n}^2 = \frac{(1^2 + 2^2 + 3^2 + 4^2 + \cdots + n^2)}{n} - \left(\frac{1 + 2 + 3 + 4 + \cdots + n}{n}\right)^2$$

For the sake of an abbreviated notation we may use Σn^2 to represent the sum of the squares of all numbers to n,

$$(1^2 + 2^2 + 3^2 + \cdots + n^2),$$

and Σn for the sum of the numbers 1 to n. Our formula for the standard deviation of n continuous ranks will then stand as

$$\sigma_{rk_n}^2 = \frac{\Sigma n^2}{n} - \left(\frac{\Sigma n}{n}\right)^2$$

Our hardest job will be to get a value for Σn^2. We shall attack that first. Let us write down the following identity:

$$(n + 1)^3 - n^3 = (n^3 + 3n^2 + 3n + 1) - n^3$$

or

$$(n + 1)^3 - n^3 = 3n^2 + 3n + 1$$

This statement is true for all values of n, since it is an identity by selection. Therefore, we may replace n by $(n - 1)$ and still retain an identity. That is, we shall have

$$[(n - 1) + 1]^3 - (n - 1)^3 = 3(n - 1)^2 + 3(n - 1) + 1$$

or

$$n^3 - (n - 1)^3 = 3(n - 1)^2 + 3(n - 1) + 1$$

If again we replace n in this expression by $(n - 1)$, we shall obtain the identity

$$(n - 1)^3 - [(n - 1) - 1]^3 = 3[(n - 1) - 1]^2 + 3[(n - 1) - 1] + 1$$

or

$$(n - 1)^3 - (n - 2)^3 = 3(n - 2)^2 + 3(n - 2) + 1$$

etc. In general, then, we shall have a set of statements which are identically true. These statements may be written as follows:

$$(n + 1)^3 - n^3 = 3n^2 + 3n + 1$$
$$n^3 - (n - 1)^3 = 3(n - 1)^2 + 3(n - 1) + 1$$
$$(n - 1)^3 - (n - 2)^3 = 3(n - 2)^2 + 3(n - 2) + 1$$
$$(n - 2)^3 - (n - 3)^3 = 3(n - 3)^2 + 3(n - 3) + 1$$
$$(n - 3)^3 - (n - 4)^3 = 3(n - 4)^2 + 3(n - 4) + 1$$

. . . .

$$[n - (n - 2)]^3 - [n - (n - 1)]^3 = 3[n - (n - 1)]^2 + 3[n - (n - 1)] + 1$$

or

$$2^3 - 1^3 = 3 \cdot 1^2 + 3 \cdot 1 + 1$$

Now if we add these identities we shall, of course, obtain as the sum another identity. Making the addition, we notice that certain terms cancel each other. On the left side of the equation we shall have uncanceled only the first and the last terms. On the right none will cancel. But in the first term the quantity in parentheses starts at n and decreases by 1 down to 1, so that, when we add the first terms for all the equations, we shall have $3\Sigma n^2$. For the same reason we shall have for the second term on the left $3\Sigma n$. There is in the third term a 1 for each of the n equations, so that the sum of these will be n. The summing will, therefore, give us the equation,

$$(n + 1)^3 - 1^3 = 3\Sigma n^2 + 3\Sigma n + n$$

or

$$n^3 + 3n^2 + 3n = 3\Sigma n^2 + 3\Sigma n + n$$

Σn equals, of course, half the sum of the first and the last term multiplied by the number of terms, $i.e.$,

$$\Sigma n = \frac{n(n+1)}{2}$$

Substituting this value, transposing so that we may have on the left side of the equation the Σn^2 (for which we are seeking a value) and all other terms on the right, clearing of fractions by multiplying through the equation by 2, and then factoring, we have the following:

$$n^3 + 3n^2 + 3n = 3\Sigma n^2 + 3\Sigma n + n$$

$$3\Sigma n^2 = n^3 + 3n^2 + 3n - 3n\frac{(n+1)}{2} - n$$

$$6\Sigma n^2 = 2n^3 + 6n^2 + 6n - 3n(n+1) - 2n$$

$$6\Sigma n^2 = 2n^3 + 6n^2 + 6n - 3n^2 - 3n - 2n$$

$$6\Sigma n^2 = 2n^3 + 3n^2 + n$$

$$6\Sigma n^2 = n(2n^2 + 3n + 1)$$

$$6\Sigma n^2 = n(2n + 1)(n + 1)$$

$$\Sigma n^2 = \frac{n(2n + 1)(n + 1)}{6}$$

Repeating, now, our formula for the variance of a set of ranks, substituting in it the values of Σn^2 and of Σn which we found in the above process of reasoning, and simplifying algebraically, we have

$$\sigma_{rk_n}^2 = \frac{\Sigma n^2}{n} - \left(\frac{\Sigma n}{n}\right)^2 = \frac{n(2n+1)(n+1)}{6n} - \frac{n^2(n+1)^2}{4n^2}$$

$$= \frac{(2n^2 + 3n + 1)}{6} - \frac{(n^2 + 2n + 1)}{4}$$

$$= \frac{4n^2 + 6n + 2 - 3n^2 - 6n - 3}{12}$$

$$\sigma_{rk_n}^2 = \frac{n^2 - 1}{12} \qquad \text{(Formula for the standard deviation squared of a set of } n \text{ ranks)} \qquad (50)$$

We are now near the end of our development. We shall repeat formula (46), from which we started, but shall substitute ρ for r in recognition of the fact that we are dealing with ranks instead of raw scores, and then simplify our formula algebraically.

$$\rho = 1 - \frac{\Sigma D^2}{2N\sigma_{rk_N}^2} = 1 - \frac{\Sigma D^2}{\dfrac{2N(N^2-1)}{12}} = 1 - \frac{\Sigma D^2}{\dfrac{N(N^2-1)}{6}}$$

$$= 1 - \frac{6\Sigma D^2}{N(N^2-1)} \qquad \text{(Correlation formula from ranks)} \qquad (51)$$

From this formula, it may be remarked parenthetically, we may easily derive a general formula for the standard deviation of any rectangular distribution. If we regard the length of the rectangle as divided into n equal intervals, the length of the rectangle will be the sum of these n divisions. If a is the frequency in each interval (in a rectangular distribution the frequency must be the same in each interval), the standard deviation will be, when squared,

$$\sigma_{\text{rec}}^2 = \frac{\Sigma an^2}{an} - \left(\frac{\Sigma an}{an}\right)^2 = \frac{a\Sigma n^2}{an} - \frac{a^2\overline{\Sigma n}^2}{a^2 n^2} = \frac{\Sigma n^2}{n} - \left(\frac{\Sigma n}{n}\right)^2$$

which is just what we had to begin with in the above development. The standard deviation of the rectangular distribution will, therefore, be $\sqrt{(n^2 - 1)/12}$. Now, if we let the number of subdivisions increase indefinitely (by allowing our intervals to become indefinitely small), so that we eliminate the inaccuracy resulting from grouping the contents about the mid-points of intervals instead of taking the items in their proper places, the 1 will become negligible in comparison with the n^2. Consequently, if we replace n^2 by s^2 as the limit is approached, $(n^2 - 1)$ will approach s^2, and we shall have

$$\sigma_{\text{rec}} = \sqrt{\frac{s^2}{12}} = s\sqrt{\frac{1}{12}} \qquad \text{(Formula for the standard deviation of any rectangular distribution)} \qquad (52)$$

Thus the standard deviation is $\sqrt{\frac{1}{12}}$ times the length of the rectangle.

Returning to our principal development, it will be observed that the formula for ρ is merely a transformation of the formula for r. The ρ is therefore substantially equivalent to r. The two would be identical if it were not for the fact that something is lost in accuracy when translating scores into ranks, because ranks are equally spaced while scores seldom are. Pearson has given a formula for translating ρ into r. It is as follows:

$$r = 2 \sin\left(\frac{\pi}{6}\right) \rho \qquad \text{(Formula for translating } \rho \text{ to } r) \qquad (53)$$

The π here is in radian units for measuring an angle and is equivalent to 180°. This 180° divided by 6 always gives 30°, so that one needs each time to multiply 30° by his obtained ρ, to look up in a set of trigonometric tables the sine of the resultant angle, then to take r as twice this sine. Suppose ρ turns out to be 0.10. This 0.10 times 30° equals 3°. Looking up in a table of trigonometric functions the sine of 3°, we find it to be 0.05234. This multiplied by the 2 called for in our formula gives the value of r to the nearest third decimal place 0.105. Suppose ρ is 0.50. Thirty degrees multiplied by 0.50 gives 15°. The sine of 15° is 0.25882, and twice this is 0.518, which is the equivalent value of r. If ρ is 0.97, this times the 30° gives 29.1, which equals 29° and 6'. The sine of this angle is 0.48634, and, consequently, r is 0.973.

In many texts in statistics, tables are printed giving the equivalents in r for each value of ρ. But Pearson's correction formula is based upon the assumption of a large normal distribution in each of the correlated series in which the scores corresponding to the ranks are found. The distributions from which the ranks for the computation of ρ are nearly always taken are very small and rarely if ever completely normal. Pearson's correction would seem then, to be inapplicable in the practical situations in which we employ ρ; although on the average from many applications we would be nearer the truth with the application than without it, in any particular case we could not be at all sure that we were nearer the truth after we had applied it than before. Besides, the correction is never greater than 0.018, and that is practically always well within the probable error of the correlation coefficient. ρ is often considerably in error as compared with r, due to loss in accuracy in the translation of scores into ranks, but this is a loss that can never be regained by this correction formula or by any other. We advise, therefore, making little or nothing of the difference between ρ and r and only employing the symbol ρ to indicate that the correlation was computed by the cruder ranks method.

The ranks method may be employed where the number of cases is small, since with a small number of cases any coefficient of correlation shows only roughly the degree of actual relation between the areas sampled and the crude ranks method serves the purpose sufficiently well. But, whenever the number of pairs goes beyond about 30, the labor of translating scores into ranks is greater than the saving from the simpler mathematical processes involved in the ranks formula. For that reason the Spearman ranks formula is not advised except perhaps where

N is less than 30, unless the original data are ranks instead of scores. But this is only a matter of convenience. There is no truth in the idea that the Pearson product-moment formula is less applicable to a small number of cases than the Spearman; the two formulas are merely different algebraic forms of the same thing, so that, wherever the one is applicable, the other is also applicable.

There is another correlation method based on ranks that is usually treated in books on statistics which we shall mention here merely to dismiss. It is called the *foot-rule method* and the coefficient derived by it is represented by the symbol R. It is not equivalent to the Pearson product-moment r but requires tables for translation. It seems to have no merits to recommend it, not even the ease of computation that some persons claim. We do not recommend that research workers learn it.

ASSUMPTIONS ABOUT THE SHAPE OF THE DISTRIBUTIONS IN THE r FORMULA

If the reader will recall our calculus development of the Pearson product-moment formula for r, he will notice that no assumptions whatever were involved regarding the shape of the distributions in the correlated series. The formula is general; it holds for distributions of any shape. r's may be computed between two series of percentiles, in spite of the fact that these make a rectangular distribution. If the regular product-moment formula were applied to two sets of correlated ranks, the resulting r would be identical with that gotten by the Spearman method. The regular product-moment formula may be applied where one array is given in scores and the other in percentiles or in ranks. Kelley recommends[1] that, where one set of scores is known only in terms or ranks and the other in actual scores, a regular Pearson r be computed between the two series as they stand rather than lose further accuracy by translating the known scores into ranks. The Pearson correction formula, where ρ' has been calculated between a set of scores and a set of ranks, is

$$r = \sqrt{\frac{\pi}{3}}\,\rho' \qquad r = 1.0233\rho' \tag{54}$$

[1] KELLEY, T. L., *Statistical Method*, The Macmillan Company, 1923, p. 194.

But the correction here, too, is so small that it is scarcely worth making unless the N is large.

PREDICTING IN TERMS OF THE REGRESSION EQUATION

Of what use is a coefficient of correlation when computed? There are two uses it may serve: (1) to enable us to infer the score of an individual in a second array from our knowledge of his standing in a first array with which this second one is correlated by a known amount; and (2) to express the degree of interrelation, of concomitance, of community, between two systems of variables. We shall first consider the former of these applications.

At the opening of this chapter we saw that, if two series of paired scores are related, the scores in the one series may be treated as a function of those in the other. Also, if the relation is the simple rectilinear one with which we are dealing in this chapter, any y score will be a certain multiple of the corresponding x score, provided each is measured from the mean. This multiplier we called b, and for it we found a general formula $b = \dfrac{\Sigma xy}{\Sigma x^2}$. This b is, as we said, the slope of the line that best fits the trend of the paired measures. It is called the *regression coefficient*. If it is the slope that the straight line makes with the x axis when it passes through the successive x values in such manner as best to fit the corresponding y measures, we call it the coefficient of the regression of y upon x and designate it by b_{yx}. If it is the slope that the line makes with respect to the y axis when it passes through the successive y values in such manner as best to fit the corresponding x measures, we call it the coefficient of regression of x on y and designate it by b_{xy}.

Our development at the opening of the chapter showed that, when our terms are taken as deviations from the means of their respective arrays,

$$b_{yx} = \frac{\Sigma xy}{\Sigma x^2} = \frac{\Sigma xy}{N\sigma_x^2} = \frac{\Sigma xy}{N\sigma_x^2} \cdot \frac{\sigma_x \sigma_y}{\sigma_x \sigma_y} = \frac{\Sigma xy}{N\sigma_x \sigma_y} \cdot \frac{\sigma_y}{\sigma_x}$$

But the first part of this last term contains the formula for r. Substituting r for this value, we have for our regression coefficient of y upon x,

$$b_{yx} = r\frac{\sigma_y}{\sigma_x} \qquad \text{(Regression coefficient, } y \text{ on } x\text{)} \quad (55)$$

If in our calculus development we interchange y and x, so that we compute $\bar{x}$ in terms of y, we get,

$$b_{xy} = \frac{\Sigma xy}{\Sigma y^2} = r\frac{\sigma_x}{\sigma_y} \qquad \text{(Regression coefficient, x on y)} \quad (55a)$$

We may now revert to our original equation for a straight line $\bar{y} = b_{yx}x$ and substitute it in the value that we have just obtained for b_{yx}.

$$\bar{y}_i = r\frac{\sigma_y}{\sigma_x} \cdot x_i \text{ and similarly } \bar{x}_i = r\frac{\sigma_x}{\sigma_y} \cdot y_i \quad \begin{array}{c}\text{(Regression equa-}\\ \text{tion in devia-}\\ \text{tion form)}\end{array} \quad (56)$$

These are the regression equations in deviation form. From the former we can predict the most probable y score for an individual from a knowledge of his x score, and from the latter we can predict his most probable x score from a knowledge of his y score. Suppose, for example, we know that the correlation between intelligence test scores earned at entrance to college and "point averages" attained in college is .40 and that a certain boy makes a score of 18 below the mean in the intelligence test. The σ of the intelligence test scores is, we shall say, 30 while that of the "point averages" is 0.60. What point-average attainment may be expected of him? The anticipated point average is the y; the other elements in the equation we know.

$$\bar{y}_i = .40\frac{.60}{30}(-18) = -0.144$$

The boy would, therefore, have indicated as his most probable score 0.144 below the mean.

So far we have been dealing with the regression equation in deviation form. If we prefer, as normally we would, to handle it in terms of raw scores, we need only put for x_i its equivalent $(X_i - M_x)$ and for $\bar{y}_i$ its equivalent $(\bar{Y}_i - M_y)$, where the M's are the means. Our regression equation will then be

$$(\bar{Y}_i - M_y) = r\frac{\sigma_y}{\sigma_x}(X_i - M_x); \ \bar{Y}_i = r\frac{\sigma_y}{\sigma_x}(X_i - M_x) + M_y$$

$$\bar{Y}_i = r\frac{\sigma_y}{\sigma_x}X_i + \left(M_y - r\frac{\sigma_y}{\sigma_x}M_x\right) \quad \begin{array}{c}\text{(The regression equation}\\ \text{in score form)}\end{array} \quad (57)$$

The one for X would be symmetrical with this one for Y.

Let us now illustrate the operation of this "score form" regression equation. Let us say the mean of our intelligence test scores is 100 and the σ is 30, the mean of the point averages is 1.40 and the σ is .60, while the correlation between the two series is .40. A certain boy makes a score of 82 in the intelligence test. What may he be expected to earn in point-average achievement?

$$\bar{Y}_i = .40\,\frac{.60}{30}\,82 + \left(1.40 - .40\,\frac{.60}{30}\,100\right)$$
$$\bar{Y}_i = .656 + 1.40 - .80 = 1.256$$

These data are intended to be for the same case as those of our illustration in the deviation form, and the result is the same in meaning as that we obtained there, as the reader can easily verify. The worker will likely be computing expectations for many individuals at one sitting. The value in parentheses will be the same for all cases and may be worked out once for all as far as a particular set of data is concerned. Likewise the $r(\sigma_y/\sigma_x)$ may be computed once for all the needed applications. The routine computations for individual cases will then be very easy.

Whenever we employ one measure as a criterion of probable standing in another, we are interested in the regression equation as a tool for making our predictions for individuals specific rather than general. We employ aptitude measures, particularly, in this manner: general intelligence tests, special prognosis tests, measures of social status, of character traits, etc. We have more or less vaguely in mind the element of prediction, too, when we are concerned with the reliability of a test, for what we have at stake is the question of how nearly individuals may be expected to make the same scores upon repetition of the test. In connection with prediction of scores the question comes up, then, as one of major importance for us: *How accurately* can we predict by the use of a regression equation? This extremely important problem we shall discuss next, and we shall develop a general formula for the standard error of such estimates.

STANDARD ERROR OF ESTIMATE

Whenever a score is predicted for a particular individual by means of the regression equation, it is predicted as lying on the regression line. But an inspection of Fig. 14 and Table IX will show that, in any problem where we do not have perfect correlation, by no means all of the actual y measures that correspond to a given x value lie on the regression line; they scatter considerably above and below this line. That phenomenon of scatter is, perhaps, most obvious when we examine a correlation chart where the data are grouped into intervals, as is the case in Table IX. As we go out along the X axis, we find a series of columns approximately normal in shape with their means at successively higher y values, and the regression line passing near the center of each column. The y value calculated to correspond with a given x value would lie at the point in the column where the regression line crosses. The fact that the column scatters from this point shows that many of the calculated $\bar{y}$'s miss the actual values to the extent of the scatter of the columns. We wish to get a measure of the extent of these errors in estimating a y score from a known x score by means of a coefficient of correlation. We shall, therefore, compute a standard deviation of these "misses." This is called the *standard error of estimate*, and its symbol is σ_{est}.

Let $\bar{y}$ be a predicted score and y the score that turns out in fact to be the one paired with x. Then $(y - \bar{y})$ will be the "error" in this particular case. Remembering that our x's and our y's are being taken as deviations from their respective means and that $(y - \bar{y})$ will be in deviation form if the relation is a rectilinear one, since $\bar{y}$ will then be the mean of the column in which it occurs, and remembering our value of $\bar{y}$ from the regression equation,

$$\sigma_{est_y}^2 = \frac{\Sigma(y - \bar{y})^2}{N} = \frac{\Sigma\left(y - r\frac{\sigma_y}{\sigma_x}x\right)^2}{N}$$

$$\sigma_{est_y}^2 = \frac{\Sigma y^2}{N} - 2r\frac{\sigma_y}{\sigma_x} \cdot \frac{\Sigma xy}{N} + r^2\frac{\sigma_y^2}{\sigma_x^2} \cdot \frac{\Sigma x^2}{N}$$

In this we have the equivalent of σ_y^2 and of σ_x^2. If we multiply both numerator and denominator of the middle term by σ_y, we shall have for the part of the term containing Σxy the formula for r. Therefore we have

$$\sigma_{est_y}^2 = \sigma_y^2 - 2r\sigma_y^2\frac{\Sigma xy}{N\sigma_x\sigma_y} + r^2\frac{\sigma_y^2}{\sigma_x^2} \cdot \sigma_x^2$$

$$\sigma_{est_y}^2 = \sigma_y^2 - 2r^2\sigma_y^2 + r^2\sigma_y^2; \ \sigma_{est}^2 = \sigma_y^2 - r^2\sigma_y^2 = \sigma_y^2(1 - r^2)$$

$$\sigma_{est_y} = \sigma_y\sqrt{1 - r_{xy}^2} \qquad \text{(Standard error of estimate)} \quad (58)$$

A *probable error* is 0.6745 times as great as a standard deviation (in a normal distribution, which we assume here). Therefore

$$\text{P.E.}_{\cdot\text{est}_y} = 0.6745\sigma_y\sqrt{1 - r_{xy}^2} \qquad \begin{matrix}\text{(Probable error of}\\ \text{estimate)}\end{matrix} \qquad (58a)$$

Let us now illustrate the application of this formula. We shall employ the same data as used previously in this section (page 111).

For the boy of our illustration a point average of 1.256 was predicted on the basis of his intelligence test score, where the r was taken to be .40 and the σ_y (standard deviation of the point averages) to be 0.60. How accurate is the prediction?

$$\sigma_{\text{est}} = 0.60\sqrt{1 - .40^2} = 0.60\sqrt{1 - .16} = 0.60\sqrt{.84} = 0.55$$
$$\text{P.E.}_{\cdot\text{est}} = 0.6745 \cdot 0.55 = 0.371$$

This last value means that the chances are 50 in 100 that a student's actual point average will not differ from his predicted one by more than 0.371 but that, conversely, they are also the other 50 in 100 that the score *will* be missed by more than that amount. The value of σ_{est} means that in approximately two-thirds of the cases we may expect to find our prediction in error by 0.55 or less, while in the other third our errors may be greater than that amount. In the case of our particular boy the chances are 1 to 1 that his point average will not be found to go above 1.627 or below 0.885, while they are 2 to 1 that it will not go above 1.806 or below 0.706.

That is really not very accurate predicting. It requires a very high coefficient of correlation to enable us to forecast the standing of individuals with reasonable accuracy. If we had no means of predicting a score at all, but merely drew for individuals scores at random, the $\bar{y}$ scores for any given x value would scatter purely by chance; *i.e.*, they would scatter for any x value to the same extent to which the scores of the whole test scatter. To the extent to which a correlation coefficient instead of chance guides us in predicting scores, to that extent the actual $\bar{y}$ scores for a given x value will have a smaller scatter, and with a perfect correlation coefficient as a guide they will all lie exactly on the regression line; there will be no scatter at all. Where the y scores are collected into columns, as they are in Table IX, this relation is very obvious. The length of any column shows the extent of error in the prediction, and its shortness as compared with the column of totals at the extreme right indicates the improvement we have made over chance by reason of the guidance afforded by the correlation coefficient. We may conveniently make a ratio out of the scatter of a column and the scatter of the whole distribution, and this ratio will show the proportion of chance still remaining in our prediction. We shall call this ratio k. Then

$$k = \frac{\sigma_y \sqrt{1 - r^2}}{\sigma_y} = \sqrt{1 - r^2}$$

This ratio $\sqrt{1 - r^2}$ Kelley has named the *coefficient of alienation*. It furnishes a very fruitful way of looking at a coefficient of correlation and of passing judgment as to how high a correlation must be in order to be satisfactory. The student should apply this test to coefficients of various sizes. He will find that, where r equals .10, there remains 99.5 per cent of guess in a prediction based on it; the prediction has been improved only one-half of 1 per cent over pure chance. Where r is .80, 60 per cent of chance still remains; we are only 40 per cent better off than if we drew predicted scores out of a hat. Even where r is .95, there remains 31 per cent of the element of chance in predicting placement of individuals. It is obvious that for the safe placement of individuals very high correlation coefficients are required—much higher than those called *high* by Rugg and others.

If we are concerned with the prediction of *averages* for a group rather than with scores for individuals, much lower correlations may serve our purpose. We shall later see that the standard error of a mean of a group of y scores predicted on the basis of a correlation is $\frac{\sigma_y}{\sqrt{N}} \sqrt{1 - r_{zy}^2}$. Thus the error of prediction of means of a class of 100 members would be only one-tenth as great as that involved in the prediction of standings of individuals.

The high residual scatter of y scores for a single x range, as shown by the coefficient of alienation, shows that we can place a subject only very roughly in a second measure from a knowledge of his score on a first measure, unless the coefficient of correlation between the two measures is very high. But a further consideration will show that we can have considerable assurance against

expectation of extreme shifts even when guided by relatively low
r's. Let us, therefore, ask what are the probabilities of reaching
certain critical positions in a second array when position in a
first array and the r between the arrays are known. Let us
return to the case of the hypothetical student of our above
discussion who made 82 on the intelligence test and ask what are
his chances of making honors in college, which requires a 2.5
average or better. He belongs to a subarray of students for
whom the predicted mean is 1.256. The standard deviation of
this subarray (column in the correlation chart) is the standard
error of estimate,

$$\sigma_c = \sigma_y \sqrt{1 - r^2} = 0.55$$

He aspires to reach a point average of 2.50, which is 1.244 points,
or 2.26 of the standard deviations of his subclass, above the mean
of his subclass. Will anybody in his subclass rise as high as that?
Yes, whatever percentage in a normal distribution lies 2.26σ's
above the mean. Reference to the table, page 486, shows that
0.0119 will do so. Thus he has about 12 chances in 1,000 to
make honors. But, conversely, there are in the subclass 0.9881,
or 98.81 per cent, who fall below that critical point; so that there
are about 988 chances in 1,000 that a student making his intelligence test score will not reach the honors level. The odds,
therefore, that he will not make it are 83 to 1 (obtained by
dividing the chances against by the chances for). Suppose,
next, we raise the question: What are the odds that he will make
the minimum for graduation, a point average of 1.00? This is
below the predicted mean for his subclass by 0.256 points, which
is 0.46σ. The probability that he will fall below this point is
0.3228 and the probability of being above it is 0.6772, so that
his chances of making the minimum grade of graduation are
roughly two to one.

We give, on pages 508 to 510 of the Appendix, a table showing
the chances in 1,000 of passing from each tenth in a criterion
array to each tenth in a predicted array for r's by .10's from
.05 to .95. Of course, for an r of 1.00 the prediction would
be perfect. The prediction is made from the mid-point of
each tenth in the criterion to just across the border in the dependent array. Thus, the chance of shifting from the 4th tenth in
the criterion to the 6th tenth in the dependent array means the

chances in 1,000 that a student who stands on the 45th percentile in the former array will be found above the 60th percentile in the latter array.

r IN TERMS OF COLUMN VARIANCE

The reader is asked to think again of Table IX, where the data of the correlation table are gathered into columns. These columns tend to have the same degree of scatter. Equal variability in the columns of a correlation table is called *homoscedasticity*, and the assumption of homoscedasticity is often made in the development of statistical formulas. If we assume it here, as we have been doing in this section, we can take the standard error of estimate to be the standard deviation of any one of these columns. We can then make some interesting algebraic transformations. Let us call the standard deviation of any column σ_c. Then

$$\sigma_c = \sigma_y \sqrt{1 - r^2}; \; \sigma_c^2 = \sigma_y^2(1 - r^2) = \sigma_y^2 - r^2\sigma_y^2$$

$$r^2\sigma_y^2 = \sigma_y^2 - \sigma_c^2; \; r^2 = \frac{\sigma_y^2}{\sigma_y^2} - \frac{\sigma_c^2}{\sigma_y^2} = 1 - \frac{\sigma_c^2}{\sigma_y^2}; \; r = \sqrt{1 - \frac{\sigma_c^2}{\sigma_y^2}};$$

$$r^2 = 1 - \frac{\sigma_c^2}{\sigma_y^2} \qquad \text{(Coefficient of determination)} \quad (59)$$

This makes obvious the relation between the scatter of the columns and the coefficient of correlation. Conceivably we might compute an r from this formula. However, the fact that σ_c is the standard deviation of the column *from the regression line* as origin rather than from the mean of the column makes the computation of an r in this manner impractical unless perfect rectilinearity of regression may be assumed. But we shall later see that another measure of correlation, η, makes use of just this procedure, except that there we compute σ_c from the means of the columns.

An equation involved in the above development puts us in position to prove that an r must always lie between $+1.00$ and and -1.00. You will find above the expression: $\sigma_c^2 = \sigma_y^2(1 - r^2)$. Now σ_c^2 (if it differs from zero) must be positive in sign, since any σ^2 is made up of squared measures which are always positive if the measures are real. For the same reason σ_y^2 on the right-hand side of the equation must be positive. Therefore the $(1 - r^2)$ must be positive (or zero), since otherwise the sign of the product on the right would have the minus sign and σ_c^2 would need to be a negative quantity. But $(1 - r^2)$ can be positive only if r does not go above $+1.00$ or below -1.00. Therefore r must lie between plus 1 and minus 1 inclusive.

We have now shown how a coefficient of correlation can be used in the prediction of scores in an array that is not yet in hand but with which the correlation of a criterion is known on the basis of past experience, and we have seen the limitations of accuracy of these predictions in terms of the standard error of estimate and of the coefficient of alienation. We have next to discuss the other use of an r, *viz.*, to express the degree of community between two sets of data.

DETERMINING AMOUNT OF COMMUNITY BY CORRELATION

In analyzing the "inductive methods" employed in scientific inquiry, John Stuart Mill listed as one of them *the method of concomitant variation*. When the height of the mercury column in a thermometer rises as the temperature becomes higher and falls as the temperature lowers, a causal relation between these two concomitantly varying phenomena is indicated. If certain electrical disturbances are found on the earth simultaneously with spots on the sun, not only occurring simultaneously with the latter or else with a fixed lag but also varying in intensity as the latter vary in intensity, a causal connection is likewise indicated. Correlation in statistics is similarly merely a mathematical method of making more specific this matter of concomitance of variation between two sets of variables. It is, therefore, one of our methods of attempting to establish "laws" and to get at causal relations where the problem of isolating single variables is difficult or impossible. For a "law" is merely a description of concomitance of behavior between two or more factors when the existence and the nature of that concomitance have been supposedly infallibly determined; and causality is merely another name for such concomitance where we believe we know the direction of influence. In the physical sciences it is often (though not always) possible to isolate the two independent factors, and thus to determine the relation between them in a manner that will not vary from sample to sample. But in social phenomena we must ordinarily be content to let some irrelevant elements drag along mixed up with either or both of the variables we are attempting to study, and these obscure the nature of the relation between our variates under study and cause the measurable kind and amount of concomitance to vary somewhat from sample to sample. The correlation technique is a very powerful device for analyzing such concomitance.

Since the measured concomitance between the variables will differ somewhat from sample to sample because of the presence of irrelevant elements which weight our scores, our first concern is to know whether there is in fact a real connection between our variables. When we study reliability in a subsequent chapter, we shall find that, even if there were in the total population a true correlation of zero, we would get r's differing from zero in samples, some positive and some negative, and that the standard deviation of this set of r's could be estimated from the formula

$$\sigma_r = \frac{1 - 0^2}{\sqrt{N - 1}} = \frac{1}{\sqrt{N - 1}}$$

Thus, if the sample contained 65 cases, the standard error would be .125. So an r as large as $+.125$ could be expected to occur merely by chance fluctuation from uncorrelated populations about one time in seven (1,587 in 10,000), and one of $-.125$ equally often; one of $+.25$, 228 times in 10,000; one of $+.375$, 13 times in 10,000; etc. So, if one has obtained from a sample of this size an r of $+.125$, or even of $+.25$, there is considerable risk in asserting positive correlation because the obtained r might have arisen merely by chance fluctuation. It is conventionally said that, in order to give assurance that there is a true correlation in the direction indicated by the sign of the one obtained in the sample, an obtained r should be at least three times as large as the standard error. We shall later show that this notion can be easily overworked. What we have is really different degrees of probability of an actual connection when the ratio of an obtained r to the standard error is certain amounts. If the sample is reasonably large and the ratio of the r to its standard error is 1, the odds are about 5 to 1 that there is a true r between the two sets of variables somewhat above zero in the same direction as that of the sample; if the ratio is 2, the odds are about 43 to 1; if 3, the odds are about 740 to 1; if 4, about

32,000 to 1; etc. Moreover, if several successive samplings give r's with the same sign, the probability that there is a true correlation with that sign is greatly increased. Even if the r's are prevailingly, though not exclusively, of one sign, an r with that sign is indicated with a reliability for the set that is likely to be considerably higher than the reliability indicated by the samples considered separately. We shall discuss and illustrate this point at length in a later chapter (pages 469 to 474).

Our first concern, then, in studying the community between two sets of variables is to have assurance that there is a real correlation between them; and this we determine, as we have shown, by finding whether the relation of an r to its σ is sufficiently high to guarantee this. Our second concern is to find some meaningful way in which to express the *amount* of this community. This we shall do by interpreting r in terms of the percentage of overlapping between the two measures.

A Coefficient of Correlation as Proportion of Overlapping.— Suppose that a set of c elemental factors contribute to both scores x and y, while there are additional elemental factors, a, that contribute to x but not to y, and b factors which contribute to y but not to x. We would then have $x = a + c$ and $y = b + c$. Factor c is correlated with both x and y; but the other elements are independent of each other and of c.

If we measure x and y as deviations from their respective means, the sums which equal these may be regarded as measured from their means and also the constituent addends from their respective means. Then

$$r = \frac{\Sigma xy}{N\sigma_x\sigma_y} = \frac{\Sigma(c + a)(c + b)}{N\sigma_{c+a}\sigma_{c+b}} = \frac{\Sigma c^2 + \Sigma cb + \Sigma ca + \Sigma ab}{N\sigma_{c+a}\sigma_{c+b}}$$

But since c and a, c and b, and a and b are independent of one another, and since each is in deviation form so that when summed alone each yields zero, the sum of the products in each of the last three terms of the numerator would approach zero, and these terms would drop out of the equation. We would have left

$$r = \frac{\Sigma c^2}{N\sigma_{c+a}\sigma_{c+b}} = \frac{\Sigma c^2/N}{\sigma_{c+a}\sigma_{c+b}} = \frac{\sigma_c^2}{\sigma_{c+a}\sigma_{c+b}}$$

It can easily be shown that, since the series a and c are uncorrelated, σ_{c+a} equals $\sqrt{\sigma_c^2 + \sigma_a^2}$, as follows:

$$\sigma_c^2 = \frac{\Sigma c^2}{N} \text{ and } \sigma_a^2 = \frac{\Sigma a^2}{N}; \text{ whence } \sigma_c^2 + \sigma_a^2 = \frac{\Sigma c^2 + \Sigma a^2}{N}$$

Since a and c are uncorrelated and are in the form of deviations from their respective means, $2\Sigma ac$ will equal zero. Hence we can insert that value in the numerator of our fraction without changing its value.

$$\sigma_c^2 + \sigma_a^2 = \frac{\Sigma c^2 + 2\Sigma ac + \Sigma a^2}{N} = \frac{\Sigma (c + a)^2}{N} = \sigma_{c+a}^2$$

Therefore $\sigma_{c+a} = \sqrt{\sigma_c^2 + \sigma_a^2}$; and similarly $\sigma_{c+b} = \sqrt{\sigma_c^2 + \sigma_b^2}$. Making this substitution in our equation above,

$$r = \frac{\sigma_c^2}{\sqrt{\sigma_c^2 + \sigma_a^2}\sqrt{\sigma_c^2 + \sigma_b^2}} \tag{60}$$

Let us now assume that σ_a^2 equals σ_b^2. That is to assume that there are as potent factors accompanying the x variable that contribute to the total variance but not to the correlation as there are accompanying the y variable. This is not a violent assumption, but, even if it does not hold strictly true, that fact would not appreciably vitiate the conclusion we are about to draw. Making this assumption, the two terms under the radical sign become alike, and their product gives us one of them with the radical sign removed. Making this adjustment and then availing ourselves of the converse of the showing made above about the relation of σ_{a+c}^2 to $\sigma_a^2 + \sigma_c^2$, we have

$$r = \frac{\sigma_c^2}{\sigma_c^2 + \sigma_a^2} = \frac{\sigma_c^2}{\sigma_{c+a}^2} \tag{60a}$$

Let us call σ_c^2 the variance due to the common factor and σ_{c+a}^2 the total variance. Our results, then, mean that the coefficient of correlation between two arrays is *that proportion of the total variance which is due to the common factor present in each test.*[1]

---

[1] Compare Kelley's development, *Interpretation of Educational Measurements*, pp. 193–195. In our development we took no cognizance of the possibility of imperfect measurements of x or y, which if present would vitiate some of our assumptions. Hence the finding holds strictly for r only when x and y are perfectly measured, *i.e.*, for the "true" r, the r "corrected" for "attenuation."

We may put this into more meaningful form if we make some fairly well-warranted assumptions about the nature of our a, b, and c factors. Let us suppose that the c factors in any one item (score) are elemental units equal to one another in potency and any one of them equally likely in a given item to be present or absent. Let us make similar assumptions about b and a. These assumptions square readily with the behavior of "determiners" in controlling traits and with the Mendelian laws of heredity. The number of c factors will then vary from item to item in such manner that they will make a normal distribution with the mode at half the maximum number. We shall learn in Chap. X that the standard deviation of a point binomial is $\sqrt{pqn}$. In this case both p and q are 0.50 and the n is the aggregate number of c factors in all the scores combined, which we shall call n_c. Therefore

$$\sigma_c = \sqrt{0.50 \cdot 0.50 n_c} = 0.50\sqrt{n_c}$$

and similarly $\sigma_a = 0.50\sqrt{n_a}$ and $\sigma_b = 0.50\sqrt{n_b}$. By utilizing the principle, developed above, that $\sigma_{a+c} = \sqrt{\sigma_a^2 + \sigma_c^2}$ we would have likewise $\sigma_{c+a} = 0.50\sqrt{n_c + n_a}$, and $\sigma_{c+b} = 0.50\sqrt{n_c + n_b}$. Substituting these values in our formula (60) for r obtained above,

$$r = \frac{0.25 n_c}{0.50\sqrt{n_c + n_a}\,0.50\sqrt{n_c + n_b}} = \frac{n_c}{\sqrt{(n_c + n_a)(n_c + n_b)}} \quad (61)$$

If now we assume that n_a equals n_b, which is similar to the assumption we made in our development above, our equation would become,

$$r = \frac{n_c}{n_c + n_a} \quad (62)$$

Put in words this means that, if there is as much of the measured factor x that is not y as there is of measured y that is not x, the coefficient of correlation between x and y expresses the percentage of overlapping between the two universes.

Suppose now that b equals zero; i.e., suppose that all of y is included within x but not all of x is included in y. We would then have

$$r = \frac{n_c}{\sqrt{(n_c + n_a)n_c}}; r^2 = \frac{n_c^2}{(n_c + n_a)n_c} = \frac{n_c}{n_c + n_a} \quad (63)$$

That is, if all of y is included in x but not all of x is included in y, the percentage of overlapping is equal to the square of the coefficient of correlation between x and y. We would have the former condition fulfilled if some factors in measured intelligence contributed toward attainment in scholarship while some others contributed toward leadership, toward social graces, etc., but not toward academic scholarship; if scholarship, conversely, were due in part to the intelligence factor that the tests can measure but also in part to the social status of the home, to health, and to accidents of morale; and if the collateral factors in intelligence were equal in number to the collateral ones in scholarship. The r would then be the percentage of overlapping between measured intelligence and measured scholarship. We would have the latter condition fulfilled if all of study hours contributed toward scholarship but scholarship were due not only to study but to some other factors in addition. Here the square of the coefficient of correlation between study hours and scholarship would give the percentage of overlapping.

Since the "true" r involved in our formulas is always a little greater than the r obtained from fallible measurements, while the square of the true r is likely to be a little less than the obtained one, and since the conditions obtaining in life are usually somewhere between those of our two assumptions, the coefficient of correlation may be regarded as fairly descriptive of the percentage of overlapping between the two universes correlated. The size of the correlation shows us the extent to which the factor x is adequate to account for the factor y—the percentage of the behavior of y that is attributable to x—or the reverse.

Exercises

1. From the data of Table X, page 124, determine the relation between size of school for defectives and the economy with which such school can be run, where economy is measured in terms of cost per pupil.

2. If you have used the Pearson product-moment formula in Exercise 1, turn the scores now into ranks and compute ρ. Compare it with r.

3. Compute the standard error of estimate for the r of Exercise 1, and concretely interpret its meaning.

4. Compute r's between one or more pairs of columns in Table IV, pages 58 to 61.

5. Recompute one or more of the r's of Exercise 4 using only five intervals in each array. Compare with the r's from the individual pairs of scores, or from 15 or more intervals. Make Sheppard's correction in the σ's of your

TABLE X.—PER CAPITA COSTS AND ENROLLMENT IN 45 PUBLIC RESIDENTIAL SCHOOLS FOR DEAF CHILDREN IN THE UNITED STATES[1]

Name of school	Enrollment	Per capita costs
Clarke School for the Deaf, Massachusetts	142	$1,147.10
Pennsylvania State Oral School for the Deaf	102	878.35
New Jersey School for the Deaf	360	847.70
Columbia Institution for the Deaf	207	823.67
North Dakota School for the Deaf	111	767.33
Mystic Oral School, Connecticut	122	754.49
New York Institution for the Deaf and Dumb	360	725.13
Pennsylvania Institution for the Deaf	536	695.21
Western Pennsylvania School for the Deaf	303	656.92
Iowa School for the Deaf	361	644.95
Rhode Island School for the Deaf	96	644.86
Northern New York Institution for Deaf-mutes	104	620.29
Beverly School for the Deaf, Massachusetts	81	619.96
Institution for the Improved Instruction of Deaf-Mutes, N. Y.	254	617.32
Central New York School for the Deaf	116	611.77
California School for the Deaf	267	603.06
Missouri School for the Deaf	307	590.59
Florida School for the Deaf and the Blind	239	585.77
Rochester School for the Deaf, New York	220	570.28
American School for the Deaf, Connecticut	223	560.54
Wisconsin School for the Deaf	220	539.52
Illinois School for the Deaf	596	521.29
Kansas State School for the Deaf	221	518.46
Maryland State School for the Deaf	175	514.61
St. Joseph's Institute for Deaf Mutes, New York	410	512.45
South Dakota School for the Deaf	111	511.74
Le Couteuix St. Mary's Institution, New York	226	470.37
Minnesota School for the Deaf	324	461.24
Nebraska School for the Deaf	204	450.98
Washington State School for the Deaf	152	441.49
Texas School for the Deaf	510	408.25
Louisiana State School for the Deaf	214	398.41
Indiana State School for the Deaf	443	380.00
Oklahoma School for the Deaf	393	382.72
Kentucky School for the Deaf	337	379.82
Michigan School for the Deaf	477	365.65
Oregon State School for the Deaf	120	360.22
Ohio State School for Deaf	524	357.87
Arkansas School for the Deaf	328	356.58
Maine School for the Deaf	122	354.62
Alabama Institute for the Deaf and Blind	334	334.07
Tennessee School for the Deaf	334	308.16
Georgia School for the Deaf	261	305.69
Mississippi School for the Deaf	259	299.23
North Carolina School for the Deaf	370	291.95

[1] After S. G. Crayton, *Bull., Univ. Ky. Bur. School Service*, Vol. 7, No. 1, pp. 122–123.

r formula as applied to the five-category problem, and then compare your r with the one from narrow categories (see page 397).

6. From a sample of 30 or 40 pairs, compute an r by the sums and by the differences methods and compare the convenience of these methods with that of the Pearson product-moment method.

References for Further Study

GIMBEL, E. J.: "Spurious Correlation and Its Significance to Physiology," *J. Amer. Statistical Assoc.*, Vol. 21, pp. 179–194.

HOLZINGER, KARL: "Formulas for the Correlation between Ratios," *J. Educ. Psychol.*, Vol. 14, pp. 344–347.

KELLEY, TRUMAN L.: *Interpretation of Educational Measurements*, World Book Company, 1927, pp. 193–196 (a different proof for percentage of overlapping as interpretation of coefficient of correlation).

NYGARD, P. H.: "Percentage Equivalents for the Coefficient of Correlation," *J. Educ. Psychol.*, Vol. 17, pp. 86–92.

RIETZ, H. L.: "On Functional Relations for Which the Coefficient of Correlation is Zero," *J. Amer. Statistical Assoc.*, Vol. 16, pp. 472–476.

SOPER, YOUNG, CAVE, and PEARSON: "On the Distribution of the Correlation Coefficient in Small Samples," *Biometrika*, Vol. 11, pp. 328–378.

SYMONDS, PERCIVAL: "Variations of the Product-moment Coefficient of Correlation," *J. Educ. Psychol.*, Vol. 17, pp. 458–469.

WALKER, HELEN M.: "Note on Correlation of Averages," *J. Educ. Psychol.*, Vol. 19, pp. 635–641.

WOOD, KARL D.: "Rapid Correlation by an Empirical Method," *J. Educ. Psychol.*, Vol. 19, pp. 643–651.

WORKING, HOLBROOK: "Use for Trigonometric Tables in Correlation," *J. Amer. Statistical Assoc.*, Vol. 17, pp. 265–269.

CHAPTER V
RELIABILITY OF STATISTICS
STANDARD ERROR OF A MEAN

Variability in Means.—When we take the mean of a group, we are customarily taking the mean of a sample out of a larger population. We may, for example, get questionnaire returns from 100 individuals declaring their several incomes and compute from these the. mean income for the group. This we would characteristically wish to take as evidence of the average income of the whole population from which we drew the sample. Similarly we might wish to get some evidence of the extent of general information possessed by the high-school pupils of our city and might content ourselves with administering a test of general information to several hundred of these, on the faith that what we learned about these hundreds would be fairly representative of the whole city. Even if we test all the individuals of a given set, our findings still constitute essentially a sampling, since to get a complete picture of the situation, we would need to retest the group for all sorts of possible changes of conditions.

As we draw other samples from our population, the obtained means are likely not to be precisely the same as the first one. From our second 100 respondents regarding income, and from the third, and the fourth, etc., our means would fluctuate somewhat. The same thing is true wherever we employ samples, even where we retest the same group. It may be of much importance to know how great shifts to expect in further samples, since such knowledge would permit us to know with how great confidence to accept the mean we have in hand. One way would be to draw very many samples and to compute their actual means in order to learn empirically how stable these means are. But ordinarily that is not feasible; it is too expensive in time and money. But fortunately statistical principles permit us to infer the extent of this fluctuation theoretically from data furnished by our single sample. Such theoretically inferred standard deviation of means from possible further samples is

126

called the *standard error* of the mean to distinguish it from a standard deviation that has been empirically computed. In this section we shall develop the formula for this measure of the reliability of a mean.

Development of the Formula for the Standard Error of a Mean. Let us conceive our measures as deviations from the mean of all the means of a great many random samples, say S samples. Then for the value of the deviation of the mean of any one sample from the mean of all the means we would have

$$M_1 = \frac{x_1 + x_2 + x_3 + \cdots + x_n}{n}$$

where the x's are the individual measures and n is the number of them in the set. Squaring for this mean,

$$M_1^2 = \frac{(x_1 + x_2 + x_3 + \cdots + x_n)^2}{n^2}$$

$$= \frac{x_1^2 + x_2^2 + x_3^2 + \cdots + 2x_1x_2 + 2x_1x_3 + \cdots + 2x_2x_3 + \cdots}{n^2}$$

We may write this

$$n^2 M_1^2 = \sum_1^n x_i^2 + 2 \sum_{i=1}^n \sum_{j=1}^n x_i x_j, \quad i \neq j,$$

where the symbolism in the cross-products term means that each item, as x_1, is combined with every other than itself in the sample and that each of the items, $x_1, x_2, \ldots, x_j, \ldots, x_n$, is similarly thus combined with the others, all of them summed together constituting the tail of the expression. We shall have similar expressions for M_2, M_3, etc., though with what we must take to be different x's. The standard-error-squared of the means is the sum of all the squared means divided by the number of means, which we have agreed shall be S. Summing all these sets of values together, we have the formula

$$n^2 \frac{\Sigma M^2}{S} = \left\{ \sum_1^S \sum_1^n x_i^2 + \sum_1^S \left[\sum_{i=1}^n \sum_{j=1}^n 2x_i x_j \right] \right\} \frac{1}{S}$$

where now the symbolism in the last term indicates that the cross products are kept segregated by samples in summing, but the values within the several samples are then summed for the whole set of S samples.

In the conventional proof, followed by Kelley, Jones, and others, it is claimed that the tail of this expression amounts substantially to zero, the following theorem being cited as proof:[1] *The sum of products of measures which are independent of each other and whose means are zero, equals zero.* But the proof is invalid because the theorem upon which it rests is inapplicable. For, on the one hand, the means of the measures within the several sets in which the products are obtained are not zero but M_1, M_2, M_3, etc.; and, on the other hand, the products are not inclusive of all, since those of the type $x_1 x_1$ are definitely withheld and included in the Σx^2's. We shall resort to a more round-about, but mathematically defensible, development to prove that the tail approaches zero as a value only under certain conditions. Meanwhile, noticing that $\Sigma M^2 / S$ is σ_M^2 and clearing of fractions, we shall write our formula more simply as follows:

$$(A) \qquad n^2 S \sigma_M^2 = \sum_1^S \sum_1^n x_i^2 + \sum_1^S \left[\sum_{i=1}^n \sum_{j=1}^n 2 x_i x_j \right]$$

We have said that S should represent many samples. In order to exhaust the situation and thus perfect our development, we shall make S all the possible different samples that can be drawn from a total population of N taken n at a time. These samples must always be different, but the slightest possible difference will do—merely the change of a single x in the whole set of n x's. Reference to the treatment of the mathematics of choice in a textbook in algebra will show that the number of combinations of N things taken n at a time (consequently the numerical value of S) is given by the formula

$$(B) \qquad \frac{N(N-1)(N-2)(N-3)(N-4) \cdots (N-n+1)}{n(n-1)(n-2)(n-3)(n-4) \cdots 1}$$

In the set of S samples there will be, as implied above, duplication of variates. How many duplications? Consider first the part of the expression containing $\Sigma \Sigma x^2$. All the x^2's will, of course, appear in the summation as a whole, but not every one will appear in each sample. It will, however, appear as often

[1] KELLEY, T. L., *Statistical Method*, p. 84.

as combinations can be made of the other x^{2}'s taken so as to leave room for it; *i.e.*, the number of times it will occur is the total possible number of combinations that can be made of $N - 1$ things taken $n - 1$ at a time. In all of our future manipulations in this chapter we shall use formula (B) as the basic formula. To learn how many combinations can be made of $N - 1$ things taken $n - 1$ at a time we need only substitute $N - 1$ for N and $n - 1$ for n. Doing this we shall have, as the frequency with which each of the x^{2}'s will occur,

$$\frac{(N - 1)(N - 2)(N - 3)(N - 4) \cdots (N - n + 1)}{(n - 1)(n - 2)(n - 3)(n - 4) \cdots 1}$$

Since each of the x^{2}'s will occur this same number of times, we may use it as a coefficient for the summation of all the x^{2}'s. Thus the first quantity in the right-hand member of our equation will have the value

$$\frac{(N - 1)(N - 2)(N - 3)(N - 4) \cdots (N - n + 1)}{(n - 1)(n - 2)(n - 3)(n - 4) \cdots 1} \sum_{1}^{N} x_i^2$$

where $\sum_{1}^{N} x_i^2$ is the sum of all the different x^{2}'s in the whole N population.

We shall next deal with the treble summation constituting the second part of the expression in Eq. (A). In order to be able to substitute a known value for it later, we need to ascertain how many times each combination of elements, $x_i x_j$, will recur in it. Within each sample there will be no duplication of paired terms, but successive samples will partly overlap and partly differ. So there will be duplications of a given paired element, just as in the case of the x^{2}'s, but perhaps a different number. Let us see how many.

Within each sample the number of different paired elements is the number of possible combinations of n things taken two at a time. If, in our basic formula (B), you will substitute 2 for n and n for N, you will find this number to be $n(n - 1)/2$. The number of samples has already been given in formula (B). Therefore, the total number of paired items in the whole of the tail for all the samples combined is the product of the number of samples and the number of items in each sample, *viz.*,

$$\frac{N(N-1)(N-2)(N-3)(N-4)\ \cdots\ (N-n+1)n(n-1)}{2n(n-1)(n-2)(n-3)\ \cdots\ 1}$$

But the whole number of different paired items is the number that can be made from the whole population of N taken two at a time. This, as appropriate substitution in formula (B) will show, is $N(N-1)/2$. Since all the possible variates occur and with equal frequencies, the number of times each will occur is the total number divided by the number of different ones. That is,

$$\frac{2N(N-1)(N-2)(N-3)\ \cdots\ (N-n+1)n(n-1)}{2N(N-1)n(n-1)(n-2)(n-3)\ \cdots\ 1}$$

Certain of these terms cancel out, leaving as the frequency of occurrence of each possible different pair,

$$(C) \qquad \frac{(N-2)(N-3)\ \cdots\ (N-n+1)}{(n-2)(n-3)\ \cdots\ 1}$$

Abandoning that line of development for the moment, we may write

$$(x_1 + x_2 + x_3 + \cdots + x_N)(x_1 + x_2 + x_3 + \cdots + x_N) = 0$$

for each quantity in parenthesis sums all of our N items, and they aggregate zero because the measures were taken as deviations from the mean of the whole set.   Multiplying out,

$$x_1^2 + x_2^2 + x_3^2 + \cdots + 2x_1x_2 + 2x_1x_3 + 2x_1x_4$$
$$+ \cdots + 2x_2x_3 + \cdots = 0$$

This we may write more briefly as $\sum_1^N x_i^2 + 2 \sum_{i=1}^N \sum_{j=1}^N x_i x_j = 0$.

Therefore, transposing, $2 \sum_{i=1}^N \sum_{j=1}^N x_i x_j = -\sum_1^N x_i^2$. This double summation involves *the value* for the sum of all possible products of different variates taken two at a time in a population of N in terms of $\sum_1^N x_i^2$. Formula (C) gave the number of times such systems of paired products recur in the treble summation of formula (A).   Therefore the *value* of the second part in formula (A) is the product of the $-\sum_1^N x_i^2$ and the coefficient indicated in formula (C). So, substituting in formula (A) the two coefficients thus determined, we have

$$Sn^2\sigma_M^2 = \frac{(N-1)(N-2)\,\cdots\,(N-n+1)}{(n-1)(n-2)\,\cdots\,1} \sum_1^N x_i^2$$
$$- \frac{(N-2)(N-3)\,\cdots\,(N-n+1)}{(n-2)(n-3)\,\cdots\,1} \sum_1^N x_i^2.$$

Let us examine this expression closely. If we multiply the first of the members on the right by N/n, we shall have the equivalent of S, for we shall have the formula for the number of combinations that can be formed of N things taken n at a time. Similarly we shall have S as the coefficient of the second term if we multiply by $\dfrac{N(N-1)}{n(n-1)}.$ We can do such multiplying if we indicate a compensating division or (which amounts to the same thing) a multiplication by the reciprocals of these terms. Making these adjustments, we have

$$Sn^2\sigma_M^2 = \frac{n}{N} S \sum_1^N x_i^2 - \frac{n(n-1)}{N(N-1)} S \sum_1^N x_i^2$$

Dividing through by nS and taking $\Sigma x^2/N$ out of the parentheses, we have

$$n\sigma_M^2 = \frac{\sum_1^N x_i^2}{N} \left(1 - \frac{n-1}{N-1} \right)$$

But N is the number of items out of which $\sum_1^N x_i^2$ is constituted, since this has been so carried as not to include the duplicates.

Therefore, $\dfrac{\sum_1^N x_i^2}{N}$ is the $\bar{\sigma}^2$ of the whole N population. Making this substitution and again dividing by n:

$$(D) \qquad\qquad \sigma_M^2 = \frac{\bar{\sigma}_x^2}{n} \left(1 - \frac{n-1}{N-1} \right)$$

Now let N increase infinitely. Then the value of the fraction in the parentheses will approach zero in value and, in the limit,

$$\sigma_M^2 = \frac{\tilde{\sigma}_x^2}{n}, \text{ and } \sigma_M = \frac{\tilde{\sigma}_x}{\sqrt{n}} \qquad \text{(Standard error of a mean)} \quad (64)$$

Notice that formula (64) has in its numerator $\tilde{\sigma}$, the standard deviation of the population. Of course, we could never know $\tilde{\sigma}$ and would need either to substitute for it s, an *estimate* of the population value, or merely σ, the standard deviation of the sample. On page 70 we showed that

$$\tilde{\sigma}_x = \bar{\sigma}_x \sqrt{\frac{n}{n-1}}$$

Making that substitution, we have

$$\sigma_M = \frac{\tilde{\sigma}_x}{\sqrt{n}} = \frac{\bar{\sigma}_x}{\sqrt{n}} \sqrt{\frac{n}{n-1}} = \frac{\bar{\sigma}_x}{\sqrt{n-1}} \quad \begin{array}{l}\text{(Standard error}\\\text{of a mean)}\end{array} \quad (64a)$$

This $(n-1)$ instead of n always belongs theoretically to a standard error of a mean. However, in educational statistics we customarily neglect the distinction because our n's are so large that the subtraction of a 1 does not make an appreciable difference. While it is not worth the student's trouble to make the correction in most statistical practice, he should remember that it always theoretically belongs in his formula and should employ it whenever, in sufficiently trustworthy measures, his n becomes small enough that the correction would make an appreciable difference.[1]

Effect of Restricted Selection.—We wish now to direct the attention of the reader to the $(n-1)/(N-1)$ of formula (D). For the formula to hold in the simple way in which we left it at the close of our last paragraph above, the N must be very large. That is not always the case. Suppose, for example, you were taking samples of 25 pupils each from a total set of 50 pupils. Here n would be half as large as N. Disregarding the 1 subtracted from each, on the ground that it makes little difference with numbers of reasonable size,

$$\sigma_M = \frac{\tilde{\sigma}_x}{\sqrt{n}} \sqrt{1 - \frac{25}{50}} = \frac{\tilde{\sigma}_x}{\sqrt{n}} \sqrt{1 - .50}$$

[1] We treat the reliability of small samples on pp. 171–176.

It is obvious that the limitation of the sampling here has a marked influence in decreasing the size of the standard error of the mean. In general, if we let p represent the percentage that the sample is of the whole population from which the samples are drawn;

$$(E) \qquad \sigma_M = \frac{\tilde{\sigma}_x}{\sqrt{n}} \sqrt{1-p}$$

Ordinarily the research worker will not have occasion to use this formula as here presented, but it is interesting and important as generalizing a principle we shall treat in our next paragraph.

Standard Error of a Mean in Correlated Series.—In our previous section we saw that restriction of the population from which samples are drawn operates to reduce the standard error of the mean, making it $\sqrt{1-p}$ times as great as it would be if the samples came from an unrestricted population. That is because the successive samples overlap one another to the extent to which they are crowded into a small total population. We have a special case of such restriction when the successive samples are matched with an initial one in a relation that involves correlation. We have seen (page 120) that correlation depends upon overlapping of the correlated samples, but not necessarily because of narrow boundaries of the total population from which samples are drawn. Restriction due to correlation would happen, for example, when a class was retested with the same test or with a different form of the same test. It would happen equally certainly if a number of groups matched with an initial group for ability (say, on intelligence scores) were tested with the same test. In both cases the successive samples would fluctuate less, and hence have a smaller standard error, than if they had not been matched with an array with which they were correlated. We shall undertake to develop a formula for the standard error of a mean under this condition of correlation.

Suppose we have a series of x scores and another series of y scores, the two sets being correlated. The x scores corresponding to y scores of a given size would scatter so that their standard deviation would be $\sigma_x\sqrt{1-r_{xy}^2}$ (see page 113). The x's and the y's may be any sort of units, including means. So the x means corresponding to y means of a given size would scatter in such way that the measures of their variability would be, if σ_{m_x} is the standard deviation of the means of a random selection of samples and $\sigma_{m_{x_i}}$ that of a column of means of samples belonging to a particular level of ability as measured by the matching test,

$$\sigma_{m_{x_i}} = \sigma_{m_x}\sqrt{1 - r^2_{m_x m_y}}$$

But we have already shown in this chapter that $\sigma_m = \dfrac{\tilde{\sigma}_x}{\sqrt{n}}$, and we shall shortly show (page 162) that $r_{m_x m_y} = r_{xy}$. Substituting these values, we have (since the i subscript has been employed merely to indicate any particular level of ability at which we are matching so that we may now drop it from our notation)

$$\sigma_M = \frac{\tilde{\sigma}_x}{\sqrt{n}} \sqrt{1 - r^2} \quad \begin{array}{l}\text{(Standard error of a mean in the case}\\ \text{of correlated samples matched on a}\\ \text{fallible criterion)}\end{array} \quad (65)$$

The r here is the coefficient of correlation between the matching element and the successive samples. In order to involve this principle, it is only necessary that the groups be matched for equality of *means*, since that will force correlation of individuals. However, the r could not be *computed* unless individuals were paired as well as means, though it might be known from previous experience with the measures.

We have treated the case where the matching is on a fallible criterion—the criterion measures having a certain unreliability which results in our accepting certain sample groups as matched with the others when, truly measured, they would not belong. We shall later see (page 207) that the scatter of correlated measures about the *true* scores with which they should be paired rather than about the fallible ones with which they appear to be paired is measured by $\sigma_x\sqrt{1 - r}$. The same is true when our correlated measures are means. Our formula, therefore, where the matching is on a "true" criterion, would be

$$\sigma_M = \frac{\tilde{\sigma}_x}{\sqrt{n}} \sqrt{1 - r} \quad \begin{array}{l}\text{(Standard error of a mean in the case}\\ \text{of correlated samples matched on an}\\ \text{infallible criterion)}\end{array} \quad (66)$$

We would have such matching on a true criterion where the same group was to be retested, for here the paired individuals are the same persons, consequently truly paired as to ability. The variability of the means to be expected if we should repeatedly retest the same group is, probably, what we usually have in mind when we think of the standard error of a mean; hence formula (66) is the one most often to be used. The r here is the reliability coefficient of the test. If we have in mind the variability to be expected in case we should sample successive groups of the same mental age or of the same social status, we should use formula (65). Here the r would be the coefficient of correlation between our test and mental age or social status, either as determined by calculation in this case or as known from previous experience with the measures. If we have in mind the fluctuation of the means of random samples from our population regardless of matching for equality in any factor, we should employ formula (64). One cannot speak with precision about the standard error of a mean unless he indicates whether he refers to a random sampling, to a sampling matched on a fallible criterion (as when one measures, say, the voluntary reading of pupils of the same average educational age), or to repeated testing of the same group (which involves matching on an infallible criterion). The use of the correct rather than an incorrect formula may make a vast difference. The standard deviation of the total score on the Stanford Achievement Test in the fourth grade is given by Kelley[1] as 10 points and the mean as 32.7. A reliability coefficient of .89 is claimed in the test manual for this grade. By the conventional formula (64a) the standard error of the mean would be for a group of 37 pupils, $10/\sqrt{36} = 1.7$. By the correct formula it would be

$$\frac{10}{\sqrt{36}} \sqrt{1 - .89} = 0.55.$$

This latter is just about a third of the former.

APPLICATIONS OF THE STANDARD-ERROR CONCEPT

Having developed our formula for determining the standard error of a mean, we wish now to see what is to be done with it in a particular research situation. One use is merely to give a *sense* of the variability of the mean in comparison with the absolute size of the mean, just as the size of a coefficient of cor-

[1] KELLEY, T. L., *Interpretation of Educational Measurements*, World Book Company, 1927, p. 198.

relation yields a sense of the closeness of relation between the correlated arrays. Therefore just to say that the mean is 47 and its standard error is 4 is to some extent meaningful. But we can make the interpretation much more meaningful if we make certain assumptions about the distribution of the means of samples and under these assumptions draw inferences regarding the probability that the true mean does not lie beyond certain limits.

It may be reasonably assumed that if a great many samples were drawn from a population and means of measurements of some kind were calculated from the samples, these means would make a normal distribution. Suppose we have given to 101 high-school pupils a general information test and have obtained a mean of 93 and a standard deviation of 20. The standard error of this mean [formula (64a)] would be $20/\sqrt{100}$, which equals 2. If we were to repeat the test with many other groups of high-school pupils, the means would fluctuate in such manner as is indicated in the accompanying bell-shaped curve. These means would gather around the true mean at the center of the distribution. What this true mean is we do not know. Most writers on elementary statistics assume that it is the obtained mean that lies at the center of the distribution. This is a wholly unwarranted assumption and an unnecessary one. We shall not fall

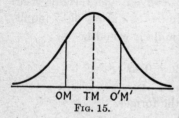

OM TM O'M'
Fig. 15.

into that blunder, although to do so would make our explanation simpler. Let us place our obtained mean off somewhere from the center of the distribution, say at OM. It is possible that the true mean may lie, say, as high as 95, which is one σ_M above 93. For, if the true mean were 95, we would still get a mean as low as 93 sometimes; in the whole distribution of samples, means of 93 or less would be obtained in all that proportion of the cases lying in the tail of the normal distribution below point OM. The ordinate OM lies 1σ away from the mean, and reference to our table of integrals of the normal curve in the Appendix will show that, when $x/\sigma_x = 1$, the percentage of cases between the mean and the ordinate is 34.13, and hence the percentage in the tail is $(50 - 34.13) = 15.87$. Hence we would be among

15.87 per cent of the cases if our sample mean lay at one standard error below the true mean. But, if this is so, something has happened to us that would happen only 15.87 times out of 100. The odds against that are about 5.3 to 1 (34.13 + 50 divided by 15.87). Hence we infer that the true mean probably does not lie as far above ours as we hypothetically assumed; the chances are only 15.87 in 100 that it does. In a similar manner we can test the probability of our having obtained the mean we did if the true mean lay as low as 91, which is one standard error below ours. The chances that we would have obtained our mean of 93, if the true mean is only 91, are again only 15.87 in 100, as the proportion above ordinate $O'M'$ indicates; hence the chances are 15.87 in 100 that the true mean does lie as low as 91. Putting these cases together, we may say that the chances are 15.87 in 100 that the true mean lies at 91 or below and also 15.87 in 100 that it lies at 95 or above; but that, conversely, the chances are 68.26 in 100 (about 2 to 1) that the true mean lies *between* 91 and 95. We may make similar hypotheses about our chances of having obtained the mean we did if it lies two σ_M's above or two below the true mean and may find that the chances are 95.44 in 100 that the true mean lies between plus and minus two standard errors of the obtained one, *viz.,* between 97 and 89. Or we can make our limits three or four standard errors, or fractional parts of these measures. Or we can make computations of the probability that the true mean does not lie beyond a standard errors above or beyond b standard errors below the obtained one. We can also make these interpretations in terms of P.E.'s instead of σ's, either by employing tables made up in terms of P.E. units or by remembering that P.E. equals 0.6745σ and working with tables in terms of σ accordingly. The interpretation in terms of P.E. is particularly simple because the chances are 50–50, or the odds one to one, that the true mean does not lie more than one P.E. above or below the obtained one. This same type of interpretation holds for all other measures of reliability.

Fiducial Limits

The above discussion of the limits between which the true mean or other statistic (called the *parameter* or the *population parameter*) may, with a given degree of confidence, be expected to fall was conducted in quite untechnical terms. In recent years this principle has been dealt with in a much more straightforward but highly technical manner by R. A. Fisher and others under the term *fiducial limits*. But, because of the desirability of covering the case of small samples as well as large samples, the standard of confidence is put in terms of *probability* of correctness rather than in terms of abscissa values, as we put it above. We shall later see that the proportion of the area of the distribution of t's (standard-error units) lying between certain t values is somewhat dependent upon the size of the samples, hence must be put in terms of both t and n; and this same thing is, consequently, true of the probability that the parameter lies between the values corresponding to these points. The selection of the fiducial (confidence) limits is, of course, arbitrary, but 95 per cent is customarily taken as an acceptable fiducial probability for satisfactory significance and 99 per cent for high significance. The former standard means that 95 per cent of the estimates of the parameter made from an infinite supply of samples lie between ordinates OM and $O'M'$ in our figure, page 136, while 5 per cent ($2\frac{1}{2}$ in each tail) lie outside. If the sample is large so that the distribution may be considered normal, an inspection of our table of the normal curve function on page 484 will show that the t corresponding to 0.025 in the tail is plus or minus 1.96. In the latter case, with 0.005 in the tail, the t is 2.5758. So in our example with a large population (100), a mean of 93, and a standard error of the mean of 2, the chances are 95 in 100 that the true mean lies between $93 \pm (2)(1.96)$, or between 89.08 and 96.92. Correspondingly, the chances are 99 in 100 that the true mean lies between $93 \pm (2)(2.5758)$, or between 87.85 and 98.15. If the sample had been small, say 12 individuals, we would go to Fisher's t table, page 173, enter it with $n = N - 1 = 11$, and find along that row in the column headed .05 the $t = 2.201$, and in the column headed 0.01 the $t = 3.106$. Then the corresponding fiducial limits for a fiducial probability of 95 per cent would be $93 \pm (2)(2.201) = 93 \pm 4.402$; and for a 99 per cent fiducial probability, $93 \pm (2)(3.106)$. Thus the "confidence belt" would extend between 88.598 and 97.402 in the former case and between 86.788 and 99.212 in the latter. We could claim that the true mean would be found somewhere within the former range with the chances 95 in 100 that our claim would be correct or that it would fall somewhere within the latter range with the chances 99 in 100 that the claim would be correct.

This interpretation has been applied to means. A corresponding interpretation is applicable to variability measures, to r's, to proportions, or to any other statistics where we can know the form of the distribution of the estimates of the parameter made from samples. It is also applicable to differences between statistics, or to sums of statistics.

It would be beyond the scope of this book to go into a technical treatment of this issue. The reader who is interested may pursue it in the monographic literature. He should begin with Fisher's initial article, "Inverse Probability," *Proceedings of the Cambridge Philosophical Society*, Vol. 26, pages 528 to 535 (1930), which he will not find very difficult. Another general expository article is by S. S. Wilks, "Fiducial Distributions in Fiducial Inference," *Annals of Mathematical Statistics*, Vol. 9, pages 272 to 280 (1938). For a technical discussion of the case of large samples see Wilks, "Shortest Average Confidence Intervals from Large Samples," *Annals of Mathematical Statistics*, Vol. 9, pages 166 to 175 (1938); and for a thorough discussion of the general case, see J. Neyman, "Outline of a Theory of Statistical Estimation Based on the Classical Theory of Probability," *Transactions of the Royal Society of London*, Philosophical, Series A, Vol. 236, pages 333 to 380 (1937).

THE STANDARD ERROR OF A STANDARD DEVIATION

We shall develop first a formula for the standard error of s^2, an estimate of the population variance, and then pass to the standard error of s and of σ. By definition of a standard deviation

$$\sigma^2 = \frac{\Sigma x^2}{n}$$

when the values are taken as deviations from the mean of the sample, the summation is through the sample and n is the number of individuals in the sample. If we conceive the x's as deviations from the mean of the whole population, we shall have s^2 if the summation runs through the sample,[1] or $\tilde{\sigma}^2$, the theoreti-

---

[1] Irwin proves that $\Sigma(x_r - m)^2/n'$ gives an unbiased estimate of the population variance, where x_r is a variable in sample r and m is the grand

cal standard deviation of the population, if the summation covers the whole population.

Remember that $\tilde{\sigma}^2$ is the mean of all the s^2's. Let the deviations of the several s^2's from this $\tilde{\sigma}^2$ be represented by d_1, d_2, d_3, etc. Then $d_1 = s_1^2 - \tilde{\sigma}^2$; and squaring, $d_1^2 = (s_1^2 - \tilde{\sigma}^2)^2$. But $s_1^2 = \Sigma x_1^2/n$, where the summation is over the sample. Substituting accordingly,

$$d_1^2 = \left(\frac{\Sigma x_1^2}{n} - \tilde{\sigma}^2\right)^2 = \left(\frac{\Sigma x_1^2 - n\tilde{\sigma}^2}{n}\right)^2$$

$$= \left[\frac{(x_a^2 - \tilde{\sigma}^2)}{n} + \frac{(x_b^2 - \tilde{\sigma}^2)}{n} + \frac{(x_c^2 - \tilde{\sigma}^2)}{n} + \cdots + \frac{(x_n^2 - \tilde{\sigma}^2)}{n}\right]^2$$

In order to carry along less cumbersome notation, we shall represent the quantities in parentheses by ω_a, ω_b, etc. Then

$$d_1^2 = \frac{(\omega_a + \omega_b + \omega_c + \cdots + \omega_n)^2}{n^2}$$

We shall have similar expressions for d_2, d_3, etc., involving each of the other samples of the whole set of S. If we sum for all these squared deviations and divide by S, we shall have

$$\frac{\Sigma d^2}{S} = \frac{\Sigma(\Sigma \omega^2 + 2\Sigma\Sigma\omega_i\omega_j)}{Sn^2}; \text{ or } Sn^2\sigma_{s^2}^2 = \Sigma(\Sigma\omega^2 + 2\Sigma\Sigma\omega_i\omega_j)$$

But this is precisely similar in form to Eq. (A) in our development of the formula for the standard error of a mean. It will simplify in precisely the same manner, so that we arrive at an equation parallel to Eq. (D),

$$\sigma_{s^2}^2 = \frac{\Sigma\Sigma\omega^2}{Nn}\left(1 - \frac{n-1}{N-1}\right)$$

where N is the whole population from which the samples are drawn. Substituting for ω the value for which we let it stand and for $(n-1)/(N-1)$ p in the same sense as used in our development of the formula for the sigma of a mean,

$$\sigma_{s^2}^2 = \frac{\Sigma\Sigma(x^2 - \tilde{\sigma}^2)^2}{Nn}(1-p) = \frac{1}{n}\left(\frac{\Sigma x^4}{N} - \frac{2\Sigma x^2\tilde{\sigma}^2}{N} + \frac{\Sigma\tilde{\sigma}^4}{N}\right)(1-p)$$

mean. That is, the sum of the squared deviations from the population mean divided by the number of items in the sample gives s^2. *J. Roy. Statistical Soc.*, Vol. 94, p. 286.

Multiplying numerator and denominator of the first quantity by $\bar{\sigma}^4$, remembering that $\Sigma x^2/N$ is $\bar{\sigma}^2$ (since the x^2's have been summed for the whole population with no duplicates) and that, in summing, $\bar{\sigma}^4$ was taken N times so that $\Sigma\bar{\sigma}^4$ would equal $N\bar{\sigma}^4$, we have

$$\sigma_{s^2}^2 = \frac{1}{n}\left(\frac{\Sigma x^4}{N\bar{\sigma}^4}\cdot\bar{\sigma}^4 - 2\bar{\sigma}^4 + \bar{\sigma}^4\right)(1 - p)$$

But $\Sigma x^4/N\bar{\sigma}^4$ is β_2. Therefore $\sigma_{s^2}^2 = (1/n)(\beta_2\bar{\sigma}^4 - \bar{\sigma}^4)(1 - p)$. In a normal distribution β_2 equals 3. We may safely assume normality here, since the distribution to which the β_2 refers is not that of one of the samples but that of the very large total population, N. Substituting 3 for β_2, we have

$$(F) \qquad \sigma_{s^2}^2 = \frac{1}{n}(3\bar{\sigma}^4 - \bar{\sigma}^4)(1 - p) = \frac{2\bar{\sigma}^4}{n}(1 - p)$$

The p is zero for random samples from an infinite universe. So,

$$\sigma_{s^2}^2 = \frac{2\bar{\sigma}^4}{n}; \sigma_{s^2} = \bar{\sigma}^2\sqrt{\frac{2}{n}} \qquad \text{(Standard error of estimates of the population variance)} \qquad (67)$$

Since, whatever the nature of the scores represented by x and whatever the multiplier represented by a, $\sigma_{ax} = a\sigma_x$ and $\sigma_{ax}^2 = a^2\sigma_x^2$ (see page 77) and since $\sigma^2 = \left(\dfrac{n-1}{n}\right)s^2$, and since $\bar{s} = \bar{\sigma}$,

$$\sigma_{\sigma^2}^2 = \left(\frac{n-1}{n}\right)^2\sigma_{s^2}^2 = \left(\frac{n-1}{n}\right)^2\cdot\frac{2\bar{\sigma}^4}{n} = \left(\frac{n-1}{n}\right)^2\cdot\frac{2\bar{\sigma}^4}{n}\left(\frac{n}{n-1}\right)^2$$

$$\sigma_{\sigma^2}^2 = \frac{2\bar{\sigma}^4}{n}; \sigma_{\sigma^2} = \bar{\sigma}^2\sqrt{\frac{2}{n}} \qquad \text{(Standard error of the sample variance)} \qquad (67a)$$

Note that $\bar{\sigma}$ means the average sample value, not the population value. Ordinarily we must substitute for it the σ of the sample we have in hand. For the $\bar{\sigma}$ of formula (67) we must substitute the s computed from the sample in hand by dividing the sum of squares by $(n - 1)$ instead of by n, as explained on page 70.

The above paragraphs gave us the standard errors of s^2 and of σ^2. We need also the standard errors of s and of σ. These do not come through quite so smoothly; in any simple form our formulas must be approximations.[1]

[1] T. Kondo presents (*Biometrika*, Vol. 22, pp. 36–64) a thorough study of the sampling variance of σ, with different assumptions and degrees of

Let us set up an identity, then put it through certain algebraic transformations. s_j shall represent the estimate of the population variability made from any one sample.

$$s_j^2 = \tilde{\sigma}^2 + s_j^2 - \tilde{\sigma}^2 = \tilde{\sigma}^2 \left(1 + \frac{s_j^2 - \tilde{\sigma}^2}{\tilde{\sigma}^2}\right)$$

$$s_j = \tilde{\sigma} \left(1 + \frac{s_j^2 - \tilde{\sigma}^2}{\sigma^2}\right)^{\frac{1}{2}}$$

Expanding the expression on the right by the binomial theorem,

$$s_j = \tilde{\sigma} \left[1 + \frac{1}{2}\left(\frac{s_j^2 - \tilde{\sigma}^2}{\tilde{\sigma}^2}\right) - \frac{1}{8}\left(\frac{s_j^2 - \tilde{\sigma}^2}{\tilde{\sigma}^2}\right)^2 \right.$$
$$\left. + \frac{1}{16}\left(\frac{s_j^2 - \tilde{\sigma}^2}{\tilde{\sigma}^2}\right)^3 - \cdots \right]$$

Since $(s_j^2 - \tilde{\sigma}^2)/\tilde{\sigma}^2$ has usually a value less than 1, the terms beyond the second will be small in value compared with the first two. We may, therefore, take, approximately,

$$s_j = \tilde{\sigma} \left[1 + \frac{1}{2}\left(\frac{s_j^2 - \tilde{\sigma}^2}{\tilde{\sigma}^2}\right)\right] = \tilde{\sigma} + \frac{1}{2\tilde{\sigma}}(s_j^2) - \frac{\tilde{\sigma}}{2}$$

This expression contains a multiple of s_j^2 and a constant addend. Since the s's are regarded as variates of which we are to estimate the standard deviation, we have a situation similar to $\sigma_{ax+b} = a\sigma_x$ and $\sigma_{ax+b}^2 = a^2\sigma_x^2$ (see page 77). Applying this principle,

$$\sigma_s^2 = \frac{1}{4\tilde{\sigma}^2}\sigma_{s^2}^2$$

Substituting for $\sigma_{s^2}^2$ the value given in formula (67),

$$\sigma_s^2 = \frac{1}{4\tilde{\sigma}^2}\cdot\frac{2\tilde{\sigma}^4}{n} = \frac{\tilde{\sigma}^2}{2n}; \; \sigma_s = \frac{\tilde{\sigma}}{\sqrt{2n}} \qquad \text{(Standard error of } s) \quad (67b)$$

Since $\sigma = s\sqrt{(n-1)/n}$, the standard error of σ will be that

---

approximation. The outcomes are complicated formulas which differ somewhat in the values they give according to the assumptions. Fisher and some others give formula (67) with $(N-1)$ instead of N as the denominator. But we cannot find any approximation in our derivation which if corrected would lead to this $(N-1)$. If that denominator is $(N-1)$, the numerator in our σ_σ formulas would be the population value instead of the average sample value.

multiple of the standard error of s, and $\sigma^2{}_\sigma$ will be the square of that multiple of σ^2_s. Therefore, for random samples,

$$\sigma^2{}_\sigma = \frac{n-1}{n} \cdot \frac{\bar{s}^2}{2n} = \frac{\bar{\sigma}^2}{2n}; \qquad \sigma_\sigma = \frac{\bar{\sigma}}{\sqrt{2n}}$$

Note that $\bar{s}$ is the average standard deviation from samples, not $\bar{\sigma}$.

It will be where we are comparing variabilities in small samples of unequal sizes that we shall need σ_s instead of σ_σ, because when samples are very small and unequal in size, or at least when one of them is small, the sample standard deviations are likely to give a false impression of the true relation, as explained on pages 69 to 71.

We have been considering the special case of random samples. In the more general case, involved in Eq. (F) above, the factor $(1 - p)$ is included. That belongs here as well. The p has here the same force as in our discussion on the standard error of the mean. It is the percentage our sample is of the whole population, hence also the percentage of overlapping from sample to sample. If the successive samples are correlated with an initial array with which they are matched, the p represents the coefficient of correlation between this array and each of the samples, so that we have the following formulas for the standard error of a standard deviation:

$$\sigma_\sigma = \frac{\bar{\sigma}}{\sqrt{2N}} \sqrt{1-r} \qquad \begin{array}{l}\text{(Standard error of a standard devia-}\\ \text{tion when samples are matched with}\\ \text{a true criterion, as where we take}\\ \text{repeated tests of the same group)}\end{array} \quad (68)$$

$$\sigma_\sigma = \frac{\bar{\sigma}}{\sqrt{2N}} \sqrt{1-r^2} \qquad \begin{array}{l}\text{(Standard error of a standard devia-}\\ \text{tion when samples are matched on}\\ \text{a fallible criterion, as where we}\\ \text{measure the moral judgment of}\\ \text{pupils of the same average educa-}\\ \text{tional age)}\end{array} \quad (68a)$$

$$\sigma_\sigma = \frac{\bar{\sigma}}{\sqrt{2N}} \qquad \begin{array}{l}\text{(Standard error of a standard deviation in case}\\ \text{of random samples from an unrestricted popu-}\\ \text{lation, where consequently no correlation is}\\ \text{present)}\end{array} \quad (68b)$$

STANDARD ERROR OF A FREQUENCY AND OF A PROPORTION

In our chapter on the normal curve it will be shown (page 298) that the standard deviation of a point binomial is $\sqrt{npq}$. In this formula, p is the probability of "success" in the case of any one "event," and q is the probability of "failure" while n is the number of "events" and therefore the exponent of the point binomial. To speak concretely, if n is the number of pennies tossed, p the probability of a "head" (of success) in each penny, and q the probability of a tail (of failure), then $(p + q)^n$ gives the distribution of successes and $\sqrt{npq}$ is the standard deviation of the distribution of the successes or of the failures. With ordinary pennies $p = q = \frac{1}{2}$, but with weighted coins p and q might have different values; but always $p + q$ would be 1.

Now it makes no difference to the nature of the distribution or to its standard deviation whether the n pennies are tossed at one throw or whether they are tossed one at a time and considered in sets of n each. It is this latter sort of case we would have if we entered one after another 100 homes as a sample to determine how many of them have telephones, if we measured as a sample 100 children to ascertain what proportion have intelligence quotients between 40 and 70, or if we investigated proportions in any sort of sample at all. If we think of ourselves as drawing such samples one after another, we have precisely the same sort of situation as if we toss a set of n coins repeatedly whether all at once or one at a time. Hence, if we know the probability of success in the case of particular individuals, we can foretell what standard deviation to expect if we were to continue drawing until we had a large distribution of samples; it would be $\sqrt{npq}$ where the n is the number constituting a set, which is the sort of application we are in the habit of calling *the population of our sample*. Thus to draw sample after sample is the same thing in principle as tossing a set of n coins many times in succession. In such application we seldom actually draw a large number of samples and compute the actual standard deviation but, instead, infer it from what we know of the properties of the distribution that generalizes the point binomial; hence we speak of the *standard error of sampling* rather than of the standard deviation of a binomial distribution.

But how can we know the p and the q? We assume them to be the ones indicated by the behavior of our sample in hand. That is, we take it that we have in hand the most probable combination of successes and failures and use this combination to define the p and the q; if 25 per cent of the homes in our sample have telephones and 75 per cent do not, we assume for purposes of our formula that $p = \frac{1}{4}$ and $q = \frac{3}{4}$. This assumption is a precarious one, since we may have happened upon a sample that involves a marked deviation from the modal one; but we can do no better than to accept it on faith as representative.

Success may be defined in any way that fits our purpose: having a telephone, brushing the teeth at least once a day, falling between score 45 and score 64 on a certain geography test, standing above score 90 on an intelligence test, or whatever else we please. We can, thus, very appropriately define *success* as coming within any category in a distribution and *failure* as lying outside such category; and hence the standard error of a frequency in any category is given by the formula

$$\sigma_f = \sqrt{Npq} \qquad \text{(Standard error of a frequency in any category in a binomial distribution)} \qquad (69)$$

Here N is the total population of the sample (including both the cases within and those without the category under consideration), p is the probability of being in the category as indicated by the proportion that is in it in the sample, and q equals $(1 - p)$.

If we divide the frequency by the total number, we shall, of course, have the proportion of individuals in the category. We have already shown (page 77) that $\sigma_{\frac{x}{a}} = \frac{1}{a}\sigma_x$. Applying this principle, but remembering that we must square our divisor when we place it under the radical sign, we have

$$\sigma_p = \sqrt{\frac{Npq}{N^2}} = \sqrt{\frac{pq}{N}} \qquad \text{(Standard error of a proportion)} \qquad (70)$$

THE STANDARD ERROR OF A PERCENTILE

Let P be the true point designating a percentile in which we are interested, *i.e.*, the point at which this percentile would be located in the average of a very large number of samples from a population. In a particular sample the obtained percentile might go up to P_2, which is a distance Δ_P above P, or

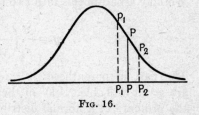

Fig. 16.

down to P_1, a distance of Δ_P below. If we take the figure PP_2P_2P to be for practical purposes a rectangle and denote its height by y, its area (f) would be $y\Delta_P$. We would have, therefore, $y\Delta_P = f$, or $\Delta_P = f/y$. Squaring, $\Delta_P^2 = (f^2/y^2)$. Summing for all the samples and dividing by the number of samples,

$$\frac{\Sigma\Delta_P^2}{S} = \frac{\Sigma f^2/S}{y^2}, \text{ or } \sigma_{P_p}^2 = \frac{\sigma_f^2}{y^2}$$

But σ_f^2 is the same as the σ^2 of the area of the tail of the distribution, p; for the tail is bounded by the line PP so that the positive and negative increments of the tail are identical with those that constitute f. We have just shown that the standard error of a frequency, and hence of the tail p and consequently of f, is

$$\sigma_f = \sqrt{Npq}, \text{ whence } \sigma_f^2 = Npq$$

where N is the total population of the sample, p is the proportion of cases in the category under consideration (here the one tail), and q is the proportion of cases outside the category (in this case the other tail).

Substituting this value in the equation above, we have

$$\sigma_{P_p}^2 = \frac{Npq}{y^2} \qquad \text{(One form of the standard error of a percentile)} \qquad (71)$$

This is the formula we need, but we desire a simpler value for the y^2. The y is the ordinate of a normal distribution at the position P. In our treatment of the normal curve we show that

$$y = \frac{N}{\sigma\sqrt{2\pi}}\, e^{-\frac{x^2}{2\sigma^2}}$$

We may separate this into two factors as follows:

$$y = \frac{N}{\sigma}\left(\frac{1}{\sqrt{2\pi}}\, e^{-\frac{x^2}{2\sigma^2}}\right)$$

The part in parentheses is z for which numerical equivalents are given in Table XLIV in the Appendix, since z is defined as the ordinate of a normal distribution in which $N = 1$. Therefore

$$y = \frac{Nz}{\sigma}, \text{ and } y^2 = \frac{N^2z^2}{\sigma^2}$$

Substituting this value of y^2 in formula (71), and simplifying the formula, we have

$$\sigma_{P_y}^2 = \frac{Npq}{N^2 z^2 / \sigma^2} = \frac{\sigma^2 Npq}{N^2 z^2} = \frac{\sigma^2 pq}{z^2 N}$$

wherefore

$$\sigma_{P_y} = \frac{\sigma}{z} \sqrt{\frac{pq}{N}}$$ (Standard error of a percentile in a normal distribution)   (72)

The resultant standard error of the percentile is in the same units as the σ; if the σ is put in terms of score points the standard error is in terms of score points.

As an example, take a distribution of 100 cases with a standard deviation of 12, and find the standard error of the 20th percentile. Looking in Table XLIII, we find that, when $p = .20, z = 0.2800$. Substituting the known values in our formula we have

$$\sigma_{P_{20}} = \frac{12}{0.280} \sqrt{\frac{(.80)(.20)}{100}} = \frac{12}{0.280} \sqrt{\frac{.16}{100}} = 1.71$$

Certain percentiles are employed so frequently that it will be worth while to determine here their standard errors. One of these is the median. The median is the 50th percentile. In order to determine its standard error we need only make both p and q equal .50, determine the z from our table at the point where $p = .50$ (which is 0.3989), and solve for σ_{Mdn}.

$$\sigma_{\text{Mdn}} = \frac{\sigma}{0.3989} \sqrt{\frac{(.50)(.50)}{N}} = 1.253 \frac{\sigma}{\sqrt{N}}$$

(Standard error of a median)   (73)

Since, when working with medians instead of means, we usually have point measures in hand rather than moment measures, this formula will customarily be more convenient when put in terms of probable error and of the quartile deviation of the distribution. In a normal distribution Q is 0.6745 times σ, and similarly P.E. is 0.6745 times the standard error. Therefore, multiplying both sides of our equation by 0.6745 and substituting the equivalent symbols, we have

$$\text{P.E.}_{\text{Mdn}} = \frac{1.253Q}{\sqrt{N}}$$ (Probable error of a median)   (73a)

The standard error of a quarter point is found by a similar procedure as follows:

$$\sigma_{Q_1} \text{ or } \sigma_{Q_3} = \frac{\sigma}{0.3178} \sqrt{\frac{(.75)(.25)}{N}} = \frac{1.3626\sigma}{\sqrt{N}} = \frac{2Q}{\sqrt{N}} \text{ (nearly)}$$

(Standard error of a quarter point)   (74)

Multiplying both sides of the equation by 0.6745, as above:

$$\text{P.E.}_{Q_1} \text{ or } \text{P.E.}_{Q_3} = \frac{1.3626Q}{\sqrt{N}}$$

(Probable error of a quarter point)   (74a)

By the same procedure

$$\text{P.E.}_{P_{10}} \text{ or } \text{P.E.}_{P_{90}} = \frac{1.709Q}{\sqrt{N}}$$

(Probable error of the first or ninth decile)   (74b)

THE STANDARD ERROR OF INTERPOINT RANGES

We often wish to state our variabilities in terms of the range between two points, as the interquartile range or the range between the first and the ninth decile points which Kelley has called D. We can compute a standard error for such ranges as follows, considering our statistics to be in the form of deviations from the means of the whole sets of these statistics. We shall let P_1 and P_2 represent the two percentile points between which we are considering the range.

$$\sigma^2_{P_2 - P_1} = \frac{\Sigma(P_2 - P_1)^2}{S} = \frac{\Sigma P_2^2}{S} + \frac{\Sigma P_1^2}{S} - \frac{2\Sigma P_2 P_1}{S}$$

If we recognize the first term as $\sigma^2_{P_2}$ and the second as σ^2_P and multiply the third by $(\sigma_{P_1}\sigma_{P_2})/(\sigma_{P_1}\sigma_{P_2})$, we shall have

$$\sigma^2_{P_2 - P_1} = \sigma^2_{P_2} + \sigma^2_{P_1} - 2\frac{\Sigma P_2 P_1}{S\sigma_{P_2}\sigma_{P_1}} \cdot \sigma_{P_2}\sigma_{P_1}$$

This last term contains an expression for $r_{P_2 P_1}$. When we substitute this we shall have

$$\sigma^2_{P_2 - P_1} = \sigma^2_{P_2} + \sigma^2_{P_1} - 2r_{P_2 P_1}\sigma_{P_2}\sigma_{P_1}$$

(General formula for the standard error of interpercentile ranges)   (75)

We encounter here the need for a formula for the r between percentiles. The following development of such formula follows in the main the development by Yule.

Let P_{p_1} and P_{p_2} be two percentile points, the former marking off a tail of p_1 in the distribution and the latter a tail of p_2. If we make here the same assumption that we did in connection with the development of a formula for the standard error of the percentile (see page 145), *viz.* that through the small distance through which the percentile fluctuates from sample to sample the curve may be considered substantially flat, the deviations in the lower percentile are directly proportional to those of the area of the tail of the distribution (p_1), while those of the upper percentile are proportional to p_2 but of opposite sign. We

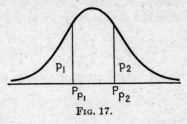

Fig. 17.

may, therefore, take the correlation between the percentiles to be the same numerically as that between the areas p_1 and p_2 but of opposite sign. Our problem, then, is to get a value for the r between the proportions p_1 and p_2.

If there is a deficiency of observations below the lower percentile, so that in the sample in question the area below P_{p_1} differs from the true proportion by δ_1, that deficiency may be expected to be offset by a surplus above apportioned to the other categories in proportion to their respective sizes. Thus p_2 will have a positive increment δ_2 of such size that

$$\delta_2 = -\frac{p_2}{q_1}\delta_1$$

where q_1 is $(1 - p_1)$ and is, therefore, the whole area within which the δ_1 increment is to be apportioned. Thus $-(p_2/q_1)$ is the regression coefficient of δ_2 on δ_1. The coefficient of correlation is (see page 111) the regression coefficient multiplied by the ratio of the standard deviations of the two series. Therefore

$$r_{\delta_1\delta_2} = r_{p_1p_2} = -\frac{p_2}{q_1}\cdot\frac{\sigma_{q_1}}{\sigma_{p_2}} = -\frac{p_2}{q_1}\cdot\frac{\sqrt{(p_1q_1/N)}}{\sqrt{(p_2q_2/N)}}$$

$$= -\frac{\sqrt{p_2^2p_1q_1}}{\sqrt{q_1^2p_2q_2}} = -\sqrt{\frac{p_1p_2}{q_1q_2}} \quad \begin{array}{l}\text{(r between proportions in}\\ \text{cells in the same distri-}\\ \text{bution)}\end{array} \quad (76)$$

Since, as said above, the r between percentiles is the same numerically as that between the tails marked off by them but of opposite sign,

$$r_{P_{p_1}P_{p_2}} = \sqrt{\frac{p_1 p_2}{q_1 q_2}} \qquad \text{(Coefficient of correlation between percentiles in the same distribution)} \qquad (77)$$

Ordinarily we shall be concerned only with ranges between symmetrically placed points, *i.e.*, between points equally distant from their respective ends of the distribution. In this case $p_1 = p_2$ and $q_1 = q_2$, so that $r = p/q$. Furthermore, in this case the standard errors of the two percentiles are equal, so that

$\sigma_{P_{p_1}}$ or $\sigma_{P_{p_2}} = \frac{\sigma}{z}\sqrt{\frac{pq}{N}}.$ We may then simplify our formula for the standard error of a range as follows:

$$\sigma^2_{P_{p_2}-P_{p_1}} = \sigma^2_{P_p} + \sigma^2_{P_p} - 2r_{P_{p_1}P_{p_2}}\sigma_{P_p}\sigma_{P_p} = 2\sigma^2_{P_p}(1 - r_{P_{p_1}P_{p_2}})$$

$$\sigma_{P_{p_2}-P_{p_1}} = \sigma_{P_p}\sqrt{2(1 - r_{P_{p_1}P_{p_2}})} \quad \begin{array}{l}\text{(Standard error of the range}\\ \text{between symmetrically}\\ \text{placed percentiles)}\end{array} \quad (78)$$

With this formula let us find the standard error of Q, the semi-interquartile range, often called the *quartile deviation*. (Notice that Q is very different from Q_1.) Q is half the range between Q_1 and Q_3, that is, half the range between the 25th and the 75th percentiles. Sigma of the 25th and also of the 75th percentile is $\frac{\sigma}{z}\sqrt{\frac{(.75)(.25)}{N}}.$ The r between these two percentiles is $.25/.75$, which equals .333. From our tables in the Appendix z is found to be 0.3178. Substituting these values, we get

$$\sigma_{Q_3-Q_1} = \frac{\sigma}{0.3178}\sqrt{\frac{(.75)(.25)}{N}} \cdot \sqrt{2(1 - .3333)}$$

$$= \frac{1.5734\sigma}{\sqrt{N}}$$

Since Q is half of the interquartile range its standard error will be half as large. Therefore, dividing by 2, we get

$$\sigma_Q = \frac{0.7867\sigma}{\sqrt{N}} = \frac{1.166Q}{\sqrt{N}} \quad \begin{array}{l}\text{(Standard error and probable}\\ \text{error of } Q, \text{ the semi-inter-}\\ \text{quartile range)}\end{array} \quad (79)$$

$$\text{P.E.}_Q = \frac{0.5306\sigma}{\sqrt{N}} = \frac{0.7867Q}{\sqrt{N}}$$

D was defined above as the range between the 1st and the 9th decile points, *i.e.*, between the 10th and the 90th percentiles.

The substitutions required in the formula for getting its standard error are as follows:

$$\sigma_D = \frac{\sigma\sqrt{(.10)(.90)}}{.1755\sqrt{N}}\ \sqrt{2(1 - .1111)} = \frac{2.2792\sigma}{\sqrt{N}} = \frac{3.38Q}{\sqrt{N}}$$

$$\text{P.E.}_D = \frac{1.54\sigma}{\sqrt{N}} = \frac{2.28Q}{\sqrt{N}} \qquad \begin{array}{c}\text{(Probable error of the 10th}\\ \text{to 90th percentile range)}\end{array} \quad (80)$$

We shall give without proof the value shown by Kelley for the standard error of an average deviation:

$$\sigma_{\text{A.D.}} = \frac{0.6\sigma}{\sqrt{N}} = \frac{0.9Q}{\sqrt{N}} \qquad \begin{array}{c}\text{(Standard and probable errors}\\ \text{of the average deviation)}\end{array} \quad (81)$$

$$\text{P.E.}_{\text{A.D.}} = \frac{0.4066\sigma}{\sqrt{N}} = \frac{0.6Q}{\sqrt{N}}$$

If we put the standard error of each of the measures of variability in terms of the magnitude of the variability measure itself, we can get a clear idea as to which measure is most stable and therefore most desirable when other considerations are equal. In doing this we shall need to know the equivalents between σ and each of the other measures of variability. Q equals, of course, 0.6745σ. On page 81 it is shown that A.D., in a normal distribution, equals 0.7979σ. The relation between D and σ is found as follows. By referring to Table XLIII in the Appendix we find that when $q = .10$, $x = 1.2816$. The x's are in terms of σ's of a normal distribution of unit area and unit standard deviation. Thus from the 10th percentile to the mean is 1.2816σ. From the 10th percentile to the 90th is twice as far. Thus D, the whole range from the 10th to the 90th percentile, is 2.5632σ. Therefore, replacing σ's by their equivalents in other statistics, we have

$$\sigma_\sigma = \frac{\sigma}{\sqrt{2N}} = \frac{0.707\sigma}{\sqrt{N}}$$

$$\sigma_{\text{A.D.}} = \frac{0.6028\sigma}{\sqrt{N}} = \frac{0.756\ \text{A.D.}}{\sqrt{N}}$$

$$\sigma_D = \frac{2.279\sigma}{\sqrt{N}} = \frac{0.889D}{\sqrt{N}}$$

$$\sigma_Q = \frac{0.7867\sigma}{\sqrt{N}} = \frac{1.166Q}{\sqrt{N}}$$

It is thus shown that the standard deviation is the most reliable of the customarily employed variability measures, the average deviation next, then D and last of all Q. Of course, all these computations turn upon the assumption of a normal distribution. In practice with small distributions these relations may not hold in precisely the same way.

THE STANDARD ERROR OF A COEFFICIENT OF CORRELATION

In the lithoprinted edition of this book we gave a derivation of the formula for the standard error of r. But the derivation was rather lengthy; consequently, limitation of space compels us to omit it from this edition and to refer to the earlier edition those readers who are interested in following the proof. The formula derived there is the following customary one:

$$\sigma_r = \frac{1 - r^2}{\sqrt{N}} \qquad \text{(Standard error of } r\text{)} \qquad (82)$$

$$\text{P.E.}_r = 0.6745 \frac{1 - r^2}{\sqrt{N}} \qquad \text{(The probable error of } r\text{)} \qquad (82a)$$

The derivation involves the following assumptions: recti-linearity of regression in both arrays; homoscedasticity in both arrays; and mesokurtosis ($\beta_2 = 3$) in the sample in both arrays. These assumptions are rather hazardous, and the distortion is made far worse by the fact that the distribution of r's from random samples is highly skew for arithmetically large r's. It is however satisfactory for large samples and for small or moderate sized r's.

Soper[1] has shown that, by avoiding certain assumptions and approximations in the above type of development, a somewhat better approximation can be made to the standard error of a coefficient of correlation as follows:

$$\sigma_r = \frac{1 - \rho^2}{\sqrt{N - 1}} \left[1 + \frac{11\rho^2}{4(N - 1)} \right] \qquad \begin{array}{l} \text{(Second approxima-} \\ \text{tion to the stand-} \\ \text{ard error of } r\text{)} \end{array} \qquad (83)$$

where ρ is the true correlation (that from the whole population). Note that this ρ has nothing to do with ranks correlation, for which it is customary to employ the same symbol. In practice

[1] SOPER, H. E., "On the Probable Error of a Coefficient of Correlation to a Second Approximation," *Biometrika*, Vol. 9, pp. 91–115 (1913).

we would not know ρ and would need either to estimate it by the rather complicated formula given below or substitute r for it. We show below that, in samples of reasonable size, r is, on the average, a close approximation to ρ.

But what we most often need in practice is not the standard error of the r computed from our sample but the standard error of r for samples of the same size when the true r is zero. For most often we wish to know whether we could reasonably expect to have obtained as large r as we did if the true r is zero. The formula for the standard error when the true r is zero follows readily from the formula quoted above from Soper; it is

$$\sigma_r = \frac{1}{\sqrt{N-1}} \qquad \begin{array}{c}\text{(Standard error of } r \text{ where} \\ \text{the true } r \text{ is zero)}\end{array} \qquad (84)$$

In this case the distribution of random samples is symmetrical about zero and may be regarded as normal except for very small samples. This formula should be used much more than is now the case. It is always the pertinent one when what we wish to show is that our obtained r differs reliably from zero.

r's from Small Samples.—There is always a slight bias in r computed from a sample less than the whole population. Fisher[1] gives the relation between an r from a sample and the "most likely" population value as follows:

$$\hat{\rho} = r - \frac{r(1-r^2)}{2(N-1)}\left[1 - \frac{1-5r^2}{4(N-1)}\right] \qquad \begin{array}{c}\text{(Most likely pop-} \\ \text{ulation equiva-} \\ \text{lent of an } r)\end{array} \qquad (85)$$

This correction would be very small with more than 25 pairs of observations and wholly negligible with N's of 50 or more. It always reduces slightly the arithmetic value of r, except when $r = \pm 1.00$ or when $r = 0$, at which points $\hat{\rho} = r$. But the correction is always far less than the probable error.

It is also true that the distribution of correlation coefficients in random samples around a true r is not normal. Of course, that distribution is skew for samples of all sizes as ρ departs from zero; but in addition the distribution of t (the ratio of r to its standard error estimated from a sample) is leptokurtic, so that the use of the normal curve values gives somewhat erroneous

[1] FISHER, R. A., "On the Probable Error of a Coefficient of Correlation Deduced from a Small Sample," *Metron*, Vol. 1, No. 4., p. 9 (1921).

interpretations of the reliability, especially in small samples. According to Fisher, t obtained by the following expression is distributed in the same manner as Student's ratio on the hypothesis that the true r is zero:

$$t = \frac{r}{\sqrt{(1 - r^2)/(N - 2)}}$$

$$= \sqrt{\frac{r^2(N-2)}{1 - r^2}} \qquad \text{(Student's } t \text{ for the reliability of } r \text{ when estimated from the sample)} \qquad (86)$$

Fisher does not offer the denominator in the middle expression above as a formula for the standard error of r; he merely shows that the best estimate that can be made from a single sample of the probability of obtaining by chance an r of the size of the one in hand (or larger) *if the true correlation is zero* is given by the t determined by formula (86) when used with Student's distribution. The table, which we give on pages 488 to 492, is to be entered with $n = (N - 2)$, and Table XLVI must be used to supplement Table XLV if precise probabilities are wanted and n exceeds 20. But for reasonably large n's the normal curve tables give good enough estimates except for very high odds (very low probabilities). *On the average*, formula (84) will give practically the same values as formula (86) except where N is as small as 25 or less, and the former is much easier to use since it is independent of r and the reliability of a whole column of r's from the same population can be indicated once for all since only the N is involved.

Fisher makes much of handling small samples, hence his emphasis on such formulas as (86) which differ in outcome appreciably from the classical ones only in the case of small samples. He characteristically carries the computation of an r to four decimal places, even when computed from 10 to 20 pairs of observations and when the standard error is of the order of .20. Then, because he employs formula (86) instead of (82) for the t, he speaks of his method as "exact." But the research worker must not be misled into thinking that any such legerdemain permits him to calculate coefficients of correlation from 10 or 20 pairs of observations and have meaningful results just because he employs some trick "correction" formula. No statistic is more dependable than the observations upon which it is based, for any correction formula makes the obtained statistic its starting point. Correlations from 10 pairs of observations are practically useless regardless of any "correction" formulas, unless they are from extremely stable variates such as means of large classes.

TRANSFORMING r INTO z'

In view of the fact that the distribution of r is limited to ± 1, random samples for a given ρ become highly skew at the two ends. Furthermore, it becomes harder and harder to raise an r through successive equal units as perfect correlation is approached, so that a difference of (say) .10 means far more near the upper or lower limit than it means near zero. To remedy this, Fisher has proposed that, for certain computational and comparison purposes, we use instead of r the hyperbolic arctangent of r, which he calls z but which, following Tippett, we shall designate z' because it is not exactly the same as the z employed for testing significance in analysis of variance.

$$\tanh^{-1} r = z' = \tfrac{1}{2}[\log_e (1 + r) \\ - \log_e (1 - r)] \quad \substack{\text{(Fisher's formula for} \\ \text{translating } r \text{ into } z)} \quad (87)$$

$$= \frac{2.3026}{2} [\log_{10} (1 + r) - \log_{10} (1 - r)]$$

z' can take values from zero to infinity and can take either the plus or the minus sign. Fisher derives[1] for the distribution of random samples of z' the following measures of skewness and of kurtosis:

$$\beta_1 = \frac{\rho^2}{(N - 1)^3} \left(\rho^2 - \frac{9}{16}\right)^2 + \cdots$$

$$\beta_2 = 3 + \frac{32 - 3\rho^4}{16(N - 1)} + \frac{128 + 112\rho^2 - 57\rho^4 - 9\rho^6}{32(N - 1)^2}$$

Thus β_1, although depending somewhat upon ρ, is nearly equal to zero so that the distribution is nearly symmetrical; and β_2, while also somewhat dependent upon ρ, is nearly equal to 3. Because for a normal distribution β_1 equals 0 and β_2 equals 3, Fisher claims that the distribution of random samples of z' is "nearly normal." In his *Statistical Methods for Research*

[1] *Ibid.*, p. 14.

Workers, Fisher gives for the standard error of z'

$$\sigma_{z'} = \frac{1}{\sqrt{N-3}}$$
$\quad$ (Approximate formula for the standard error of z') $\quad$ (88)

which is independent of z' and consequently of r. But that is only an approximation. The more complete formula is[1]

$$\sigma_{z'} = \frac{1}{\sqrt{N-1}}\left[1 + \frac{4-\rho^2}{2(N-1)}\right.$$

$$+ \frac{176 - 21\rho^2 - 21\rho^4}{48(N-1)^2} + \cdots \left.\right]^{\frac{1}{2}} \text{(Standard error of } z') \quad (88a)$$

Thus the standard error of z' is somewhat dependent upon the z', since z' is a function of ρ. E. S. Pearson and his associates have made several empirical studies of the distribution of z' and its standard deviation[2] and find that the full formula agrees rather closely with the actual distribution and that the approximate formula does moderately well.

The mean departure of the average z' from the true z' is not zero; the z' has a slight bias as follows:

$$\bar{z}' - \zeta' = \frac{\rho}{2(N-1)}\left[1 + \frac{1+\rho^2}{8(N-1)} \cdots \right] \quad (88b)$$

In precise work with z' this requires that a small correction be made to the obtained z', which is approximately $\dfrac{\rho}{2(N-1)}$, and which must be subtracted arithmetically from the z' obtained by formula (87).

There are some advantages to the use of z'.

1. The fact that z's in random samples are distributed almost normally along the whole range makes the interpretation of the standard error more meaningful and legitimate. Regardless of the size of the sample, the interpretation may be made in terms of the normal curve.

2. Unit increments of z' have nearly the same meaning (in terms of difficulty of attaining them) all along their range, while

[1] *Ibid.*, pp. 13–14.

[2] PEARSON, EGON S., "Further Experiments on the Sampling Distribution of the Correlation Coefficient," *J. Amer. Statistical Assoc.*, Vol. 27, pp. 121–128; see also *Biometrika*, Vol. 21, pp. 257*ff*.

r's do not. This fact makes adding, subtracting, or averaging z''s more legitimate processes than are like processes with r's.

3. If one is insistent upon showing how sample r's would spread at the level of his obtained r rather than around a true r of zero, the only really correct way of showing it is by translating his r to z' and interpreting the z' in terms of the $\sigma_{z'}$. For the distribution of r's around any other point than zero is neither normal nor symmetrical.

On the other hand z' has limitations of which cognizance must be taken.

1. Its reliability formulas (when in usable form) are approximations, just as are those of r.

2. z' is only an intermediate statistic; the final result must be in terms of r. For z' has only an artificial meaning while r has a straightforward and practical meaning: *viz.*, the slope of the best-fitting line when the variabilities have been equalized.

3. The advantage from the standpoint of standard error is academic rather than practical. The main situation in which we are concerned about the standard error is when we wish to know whether the r we have in hand might have arisen by chance when the true r is zero. But samples of r when ρ is zero are distributed as symmetrically as z' is, and nearly as normally, and the formula for the standard error is also independent of r [formula (84)]. Since r at this point has all the advantages of z', the awkwardness of the transformation may be avoided.

4. It is legitimate to add or to subtract z''s only when we can assume that they are estimates from the same population. It would not do, for example, to average z''s for the correlation between intelligence tests and academic achievement when the intelligence was measured by different tests and on somewhat different types of students. When needing a central tendency for a number of r's it would be much better to take the median, and the median z' would correspond exactly to the median r, so that nothing whatever would be gained by the transmutation.

5. If we add or subtract z''s in correlated samples and test the significance of the sum or the difference, we shall lose accuracy by reason of not knowing the tail of the formula involving correlation (see pages 160 to 162). For the r between z''s is not known. The loss from this cause might well be greater than any gain from using z' instead of r.

ADDITIONAL RELIABILITY FORMULAS

For the standard error of β_1 or β_2, see H. L. Reitz, *Handbook of Mathematical Statistics*, page 96, or Karl Pearson, *Tables for Statisticians and Biometricians*, Tables 37 and 38. For many additional standard-error formulas, see Kurtz and Dunlap, *Handbook of Statistical Nomographs, Tables, and Formulas*, pages 103 to 140.

Exercises

1. Find the P.E. of the mean in Table I, page 43, and in Table II, page 45. Interpret these statistics.
2. Find the standard error of the medians for these same two distributions, and compare them with the standard errors of the means.
3. Find the value of the 10th percentile in Table I, and compute its standard error.
4. The norm for the seventh grade in a certain arithmetic test is 48. If a typical sample of 36 of your pupils makes a mean of 45 and a standard deviation of 12, what are the odds that the true mean for your school is up to norm?
5. What are the odds that the true mean for this particular sample is up to norm, if the reliability of the test is 0.89?
6. From how large a population must an r of .20 have been computed if it is to be as much as three times its standard error?
7. Develop a formula for the standard error of V (the coefficient of variation). Suggestion: take logarithmic derivatives, remember that the correlation between means and standard deviations is zero, and free your final formula from all terms except V and N. Compare your formula with the accepted one (which you will find in Holzinger's text and in several others).

References for Further Study

DICKEY, J. W.: "On the Reliability of a Standard Score," *J. Educ. Psychol.*, Vol. 21, pp. 547–549.

DOUGLASS, H.: and F. COZENS, "On Formulae for Estimating the Reliability of Test Batteries," *J. Educ. Psychol.*, Vol. 20, pp. 369–377.

FISHER, R. A.: "On the Probable Error of a Coefficient of Correlation Deduced from a Small Sample," *Metron*, Vol. 1, pp. 1–32.

———: "On the Distribution of the Coefficient of Correlation," *Biometrika*, Vol. 10, pp. 507–521.

HUFFAKER, C. L.: "Errors of the Mean Due to Sampling and to Measurement," *J. Educ. Psychol.*, Vol. 19, pp. 643–649.

———: "Probable Error of the Accomplishment Quotient," *J. Educ. Psychol.*, Vol. 21, pp. 550–551.

———: "Formulas for Probable Errors of Coefficients of Correlation," *J. Amer. Statistical Assoc.*, Vol. 24, pp. 170–173.

KONDO, T., "The Theory of the Sampling Distribution of Standard Deviations," *Biometrika*, Vol. 22, pp. 36–64.

PEARSON and FILON: "Mathematical Contributions to the Theory of Evolution," *Proc. Roy. Soc. (London)*, Series *A*, Vol. 191, pp. 229–311. (An important article, giving many standard error formulas.)

WILKS, S. S.: "The Standard Error of the Mean of Matched Samples," *J. Educ. Psychol.*, Vol. 22, pp. 205–208.

WILSON, E. B.: "The Probable Error of Correlation Results," *Proc. Amer. Statistical Assoc.*, March, 1929, Suppl. pp. 90–93.

CHAPTER VI

THE RELIABILITY OF DIFFERENCES

The reliability of differences is an even more important matter than the reliability of statistics of separate groups. For customarily we wish to make comparisons and then we need to know, when we find differences by such comparisons, whether they can be explained on the basis of chance fluctuations alone or whether they indicate true differences.

THE STANDARD ERROR OF THE DIFFERENCES BETWEEN MEANS

We may regard our means as deviations from the means of all the samples of their respective series, and this will simplify the algebra. If S is the number of samples we get, by the ordinary definition of standard deviation when the items are in deviation form,

$$\sigma^2_{m_x - m_y} = \frac{\Sigma(m_x - m_y)^2}{S} = \frac{\Sigma m_x^2}{S} + \frac{\Sigma m_y^2}{S} - \frac{2\Sigma m_x m_y}{S}$$

The first term is $\sigma^2_{m_x}$ and the second term $\sigma^2_{m_y}$. In the third term we shall multiply both the numerator and denominator by $\sigma_{m_x}\sigma_{m_y}$ and have

$$\sigma^2_{m_x - m_y} = \sigma^2_{m_x} + \sigma^2_{m_y} - \frac{2\Sigma m_x m_y}{S\sigma_{m_x}\sigma_{m_y}} \cdot \sigma_{m_x}\sigma_{m_y}$$

As a part of the last term we now have the r between the means, so that we may rewrite the expression as follows:

(A) $$\sigma^2_{m_x - m_y} = \sigma^2_{m_x} + \sigma^2_{m_y} - 2r_{m_x m_y}\sigma_{m_x}\sigma_{m_y}$$

We have next to seek a simpler value for the r between the means, which appears as a disturbing factor in formula (A). If we let $x_1, x_2, x_3, \ldots, x_n$, represent the successive scores within a sample of the x series and a similar arrangement represent the scores in the corresponding y series and we conceive these scores as deviations from the means of the whole aggregate of samples in their respective series (as we must if we are to be consistent here with the conception of the means as deviations employed above),

160

we shall have

$r_{m_x m_y}$

$$= \frac{\dfrac{\Sigma(x_1 + x_2 + x_3 + \cdots + x_n)}{n} \dfrac{(y_1 + y_2 + y_3 + \cdots + y_n)}{n}}{S\sigma_{m_x}\sigma_{m_y}}$$

$$= \frac{\Sigma(x_1 + x_2 + x_3 + \cdots + x_n)(y_1 + y_2 + y_3 + \cdots + y_n)}{n^2 S\sigma_{m_x}\sigma_{m_y}}$$

When we multiply together the two factors in the numerator, we shall get two types of products, those involving the paired items and those involving cross products between nonpaired items, as follows:

$r_{m_x m_y}$

$$= \frac{\Sigma(x_1 y_1 + x_2 y_2 + x_3 y_3 + \cdots + x_n y_n) + \Sigma(x_1 y_2 + x_1 y_3 + \cdots + x_2 y_1 + \cdots + x_n y_{n-1})}{n^2 S\sigma_{m_x}\sigma_{m_y}}$$

It would not be far from correct to say, as is customarily done, that the second type of products sum to zero since the items that are multiplied together are uncorrelated. But that is not strictly true. We have a situation precisely like the one encountered in our preceding chapter in connection with the standard error of a mean (page 131). If carried through a process similar to the one employed there, our development would arrive at the following:

$$n\sigma_{m_x}\sigma_{m_y} r_{m_x m_y} = \frac{\Sigma xy_N}{N}\left(1 - \frac{n-1}{N-1}\right)$$

Dividing through by the coefficient of r, and then substituting the value we found for the standard error of a mean,

$$r_{m_x m_y} = \frac{\Sigma xy_N \left(1 - \dfrac{n-1}{N-1}\right)}{Nn\sigma_{m_x}\sigma_{m_y}}$$

$$= \frac{\Sigma xy_N \left(1 - \dfrac{n-1}{N-1}\right)}{Nn\left(\dfrac{\tilde{\sigma}_x}{\sqrt{n}}\sqrt{1 - \dfrac{n-1}{N-1}}\right)\left(\dfrac{\tilde{\sigma}_y}{\sqrt{n}}\sqrt{1 - \dfrac{n-1}{N-1}}\right)}$$

Since the n is the same for each sample and the N constant throughout our problem, certain factors containing these terms will cancel, and we are left with

$$r_{m_x m_y} = \frac{\Sigma xy}{N \tilde{\sigma}_x \tilde{\sigma}_y}$$

Since N is the total population, Σxy the sum of the products of paired items for this total population, and $\tilde{\sigma}_x \tilde{\sigma}_y$, respectively, the standard deviations of the two total populations, we have

$$r_{m_x m_y} = \rho_{xy} \qquad \text{(Coefficient of correlation between means in correlated series)} \qquad (89)$$

Thus it is proved that, for all samples combined, the r between means of successive constituent samples equals the correlation of the paired scores for the whole population. We do not know the ρ for the large population N, but we may take our r_{xy} from the sample in hand to represent it for our purpose. Substituting r_{xy} for $r_{m_x m_y}$ in formula (A), page 160, and extracting the square root of both sides of the equation,

$$\sigma_{m_x - m_y} = \sqrt{\sigma_{m_x}^2 + \sigma_{m_y}^2 - 2r_{xy}\sigma_{m_x}\sigma_{m_y}} \qquad \text{(Standard error of the difference between two means)} \qquad (90)$$

This is the formula that should always be used when calculating the standard error of the difference between means of groups matched on some criterion so as to involve the presence of an element of correlation between the groups compared. Unfortunately the tail of this formula, containing the r, is often omitted, in consequence of which the standard errors as calculated are too high. Of course, if the two series should be uncorrelated, the r would be zero, and the formula would become, since the third term would amount to zero,

$$\sigma_{m_x - m_y} = \sqrt{\sigma_{m_x}^2 + \sigma_{m_y}^2} \qquad \text{(Standard error of the difference between two means in case of uncorrelated series)} \qquad (91)$$

In either of these formulas the value of σ_m^2 as developed on pages 133 to 135 of this volume is to be substituted. It was shown there that, if the successive samples are to be chosen at random from a large population, $\sigma_{m_x}^2 = \tilde{\sigma}_x^2 / N$; if the successive samples are matched with one another on a true criterion so that they are correlated with one another, then

$$\sigma_{m_x}^2 = \left(\frac{\tilde{\sigma}_x^2}{N}\right)(1 - r_{x_1 x_2}),$$

where the r is the reliability coefficient of the measuring instrument; if the successive samples are matched with one another on a fallible criterion so that they are correlated with one another by reason of being correlated with the criterion, then

$$\sigma_{m_x}^2 = \left(\frac{\tilde{\sigma}_x^2}{N}\right)(1 - r_{x_1 x_2}^2),$$

where the r is the coefficient of correlation between the matching criterion and one of the samples. Using first the simplest of these cases, we have, by substituting in formula (90),

$$\sigma_{m_x-m_y} = \sqrt{\frac{\tilde{\sigma}_x^2 + \tilde{\sigma}_y^2 - 2r_{xy}\tilde{\sigma}_x\tilde{\sigma}_y}{N}} \qquad \begin{array}{l}\text{(Standard error of the dif-}\\ \text{ference between means}\\ \text{of two series correlated}\\ \text{with each other but suc-}\\ \text{cessive samples in the}\\ \text{same series random ones)}\end{array} \qquad (92)$$

Note that the N belongs under the radical sign.[1]

This is the form that is likely to be most needed in practice. For when, say in an experiment, we wish to compare the mean success of our two groups, we ordinarily wish to know what could be expected to happen if we drew at random other groups, subject only to the condition that they be matched with each other, and put them through the same experiment. Nevertheless we might have involved the other types of situations, and we shall include them here for the sake of making the issue thoroughly clear. Suppose, for example, we measured the difference in attainment in arithmetic between a seventh-grade group of pupils under one teacher and a seventh-grade group under another teacher and meant by our statement of the reliability of the obtained difference what could be expected to happen if we took many measures of the same kind of these same two groups. Then the formula next to be stated would be appropriate. Substituting for σ_m^2 in the case of successive groups matched on a true criterion (because in each series the groups are the same in the successive samples), we get[2]

[1] This form holds only if the N is the same in both the series. Otherwise we must write

$$\sigma_{m_x-m_y} = \sqrt{\frac{\tilde{\sigma}_x^2}{N_x} + \frac{\tilde{\sigma}_y^2}{N_y} - \frac{2r_{xy}\tilde{\sigma}_x\tilde{\sigma}_y}{\sqrt{N_x N_y}}}$$

[2] The r_{mm} would be zero between two series of means which remain on a constant level except for random fluctuations in successive samples.

$$\sigma_{m_x - m_y} = \sqrt{\frac{\tilde{\sigma}_x^2(1 - r_{x1f})}{N_x} + \frac{\tilde{\sigma}_y^2(1 - r_{y1f})}{N_y}} \qquad (93)$$

(Standard error of a difference between means when successive samples are matched on a true criterion)

If the samples are not the same pupils repeating the experiment but instead they are pupils of the same ability as those upon whom the first experiment was done (if, that is, they are always matched with the original groups in their own series on a fallible criterion, so that the successive groups would always have the same educational age or the same general intelligence or the same socioeconomic status as those of the earlier experiment), then the formula would become[1]

$$\sigma_{m_x - m_y} = \sqrt{\frac{\tilde{\sigma}_x^2(1 - r_{cx}^2)}{N_x} + \frac{\tilde{\sigma}_y^2(1 - r_{cy}^2)}{N_y}} \qquad (94)$$

(Standard error of a difference between means when successive samples are matched with the initial one on a "fallible" criterion)

Where the groups between which differences of means are taken have been matched by matching individuals, which is the case in well set up experiments (see page 448), the standard error of the difference between the means can be put into a form far simpler for computational purposes than the above. For here we have paired scores so that the differences may be taken between these paired scores, and operation with these d's makes unnecessary the computation of a coefficient of correlation. Recall the formula for an r, which we developed on page 101,

$$r = \frac{\sigma_x^2 + \sigma_y^2 - \sigma_d^2}{2\sigma_x\sigma_y}$$

We shall substitute this value for r in formula (92), cancel terms that permit canceling, and find an extremely simple formula resulting.

$$\sigma_{m_x - m_y}^2 = \frac{\sigma_x^2 + \sigma_y^2 - 2\frac{(\sigma_x^2 + \sigma_y^2 - \sigma_d^2)}{2\sigma_x\sigma_y}\sigma_x\sigma_y}{N - 1}$$

[1] This is the formula given by Lindquist, although he does not indicate the limitation under which it must be used. See *J. Educ. Psychol.*, Vol. 22, pp. 197-204 (1931).

$$\sigma^2_{m_x-m_y} = \frac{\sigma^2_d}{N-1}$$

$$\sigma_{m_x-m_y} = \frac{\sigma_d}{\sqrt{N-1}}$$

(Standard error of the difference between means in terms of the differences between paired scores) (95)

The $(N-1)$ instead of N is important in small samples, and in very small samples t should be used with Student's distribution instead of the normal distribution.

Thus, in the case we shall ordinarily be dealing with (successive samples chosen at random but the two series matched in each sample), the standard error of the difference between the means of paired groups turns out to be merely the standard deviation of the differences between paired scores divided by the square root of the number of such paired scores. Although this formula relieves the worker of the necessity of computing any r between the series, it takes full account of the value of the r. In a later chapter on the technique of controlled experimentation we shall show that there are many additional advantages accruing from this arrangement beyond the one of ease of operation. If the two series are not correlated, the r that equals zero will automatically take care of itself just as well as any other r. We shall show an example of this method of computing the standard error of the difference between means by utilizing a table from a controlled experiment on the effect upon achievement in geometry from requiring failing pupils to remain after school hours.[1] In the first column are shown the "standard scores" (z scores) of both members who made a pair indicating their prospective capacity to learn, the "free" group on the left, and the "kept" on the right. The other columns give in succession the score on the test earned through the semester by the "free" pupils, the score by the "kept" pupils, and the differences. It is this last column from which we compute our standard error.

The difference between the means of the two groups is $(15.8 - 15.4 = 0.4)$. The standard deviation of the column of differences is found, by calculation, to be 3.28. This divided by the square root of 22, which is the number of cases minus 1 (to take account of the fact that the numerator is σ instead of $\tilde{\sigma}$), will give the standard error of the difference between the means.

---

[1] From a master's thesis at Pennsylvania State College by Bertha A. Swartz.

3.28 divided by $\sqrt{22}$ gives 0.7. Thus while the difference is 0.4, its standard error is 0.7, so that the difference is only 0.6 of its standard error. From this comparison we conclude, therefore, that, while there is a slight difference found against

TABLE XI.—ILLUSTRATING THE COMPUTATION OF THE STANDARD ERROR OF A DIFFERENCE

Matching scores		Attainment scores		Differences
Free	Kept	Free	Kept	
1.63	1.64	22	16	6
1.24	1.19	21	21	0
0.98	0.94	18	15	3
0.74	0.68	16	16	0
0.55	0.58	16	20	− 4
0.54	0.49	17	19	− 2
0.37	0.37	18	13	5
0.12	0.13	15	16	− 1
0.30	0.45	17	17	0
0.09	0.13	16	16	0
0.24	−0.04	14	13	1
−0.24	−0.20	14	18	− 4
−0.25	−0.25	14	17	− 3
−0.33	−0.33	17	11	6
−0.37	−0.39	16	15	1
−0.40	−0.59	18	13	5
−0.54	−0.37	14	14	0
−0.33	−0.29	9	16	− 7
−0.13	−0.13	16	14	2
−0.81	−0.90	10	13	− 3
−0.91	−0.91	14	14	0
−1.24	−1.40	15	12	3
−1.92	−1.69	16	15	1
Means........	......	15.8	15.4	0.4

keeping after school, it is a difference of practically no statistical significance.

It is suggested that the reader work out the standard error of the difference between the means for this problem by the long formula (92) and prove to himself that the two formulas give identical results and that the short method is far more economical. The short method necessitates pairing individuals but so does the calculation of the r for the long method. However, in some problems involving very large numbers of cases, or in cases where the n is different in the two populations, it may be enough to determine our r from a sample of the whole population, in which formula (90) may be more economical.

Standard Error of the Difference between Mean Gains.—Very frequently we have a situation in which we measure *gains* made by groups through a period of time and wish to determine the statistical significance of the difference between the mean gains of two groups. Thus we may be interested in comparing the mean gain in speed of reading made in a semester by a group of pupils of given average mental age with the mean gain made by a control group that has had no such drills but which control group has been matched with the drill group on some such index of learning ability as IQ's. This is a more complex problem than the one where we merely compare one mean with another. Letting x represent the scores of the one group (in deviation form) and y those of the other group, 1 indicating the scores at the beginning of the period and 2 those at the end, the following formula would state our case:

$$\sigma^2_{(m_{x_2}-m_{x_1})-(m_{y_2}-m_{y_1})} = \frac{\Sigma(m_{x_2} - m_{x_1} - m_{y_2} + m_{y_1})^2}{S}$$

If the reader will square the polynomial of the four terms and carry through a process of substitutions parallel to the one we did above in connection with the standard error of a mean, he will arrive at the following formula:

$$\sigma_{(m_{x_2}-m_{x_1})-(m_{y_2}-m_{y_1})} = \frac{1}{\sqrt{N}} (\tilde{\sigma}^2_{x_1} + \tilde{\sigma}^2_{x_2} + \tilde{\sigma}^2_{y_1} + \tilde{\sigma}^2_{y_2}$$

$$- 2r_{x_1 x_2}\tilde{\sigma}_{x_1}\tilde{\sigma}_{x_2} - 2r_{y_1 y_2}\tilde{\sigma}_{y_1}\tilde{\sigma}_{y_2} + 2r_{x_2 y_1}\tilde{\sigma}_{x_2}\tilde{\sigma}_{y_1} - 2r_{x_2 y_2}\tilde{\sigma}_{x_2}\tilde{\sigma}_{y_2}$$

$$+ 2r_{x_1 y_2}\tilde{\sigma}_{x_1}\tilde{\sigma}_{y_2} - 2r_{x_1 y_1}\tilde{\sigma}_{x_1}\tilde{\sigma}_{y_1})^{\frac{1}{2}}$$

(Standard error of the difference between mean gains by correlated groups)   (96)

This is the correct formula which must be used for exactness when employing the conventional method. Lindquist gives this formula with the last four terms of the tail omitted.[1] It is true that, since two of them are positive and two negative, they would largely cancel one another; but not completely so,

[1] LINDQUIST, F. E., "On the Determination of Reliability in Comparing the Final Mean-scores of Matched Groups," *J. Educ. Psychol.*, Vol. 20, p. 105.

unless the two groups are independent. We shall show that an immensely simpler formula is identical in value with this long one. Using the same symbolism as above,[1]

$$(x_2 - x_1) - (y_2 - y_1) = (g_x - g_y) = d_g$$

the difference in gain in the case of one particular individual. Summing for all individuals in the group and dividing by N,

$$\left(\frac{\Sigma x_2}{N} - \frac{\Sigma x_1}{N}\right) - \left(\frac{\Sigma y_2}{N} - \frac{\Sigma y_1}{N}\right) = \left(\frac{\Sigma g_x}{N} - \frac{\Sigma g_y}{N}\right) = \left(\frac{\Sigma d_g}{N}\right)$$

Therefore, by reason of the meaning of a mean,

$$(m_{x_2} - m_{x_1}) - (m_{y_2} - m_{y_1}) = (m_{g_x} - m_{g_y}) = m_{d_g}$$

We may now express, for a series of samples, the standard deviation of each of the quantities between which equality is indicated in the above equation. Since the items that constitute the sigmas for the three series involved in the above equation are severally equal, the sigmas obtained from them must be equal. Therefore,

$$\sigma_{(m_{x_2}-m_{x_1})-(m_{y_2}-m_{y_1})} = \sigma_{(m_{g_x}-m_{g_y})} = \sigma_{m_{d_g}}$$

But the standard error of any mean, including, of course, the standard error of the mean of the d's involved in the last expression at the right in the equation last above, equals the standard deviation of the distribution divided by the square root of the number of items. Therefore, $\sigma_{m_{d_g}}$ equals $\tilde{\sigma}_{d_g}/\sqrt{N}$, where d stands for the differences between the paired gains between the x and the y series of the sample in hand. Thus we obtain a very simple formula for the standard error of the difference between mean gains in correlated series, parallel to the one for means, as follows:

$$\sigma_{(m_{g_x}-m_{g_y})} = \frac{\tilde{\sigma}_{d_g}}{\sqrt{N}} \qquad \text{(Short formula for the standard error of the difference between mean gains in correlated series)} \qquad (97)$$

Sometimes the statistical significance of the sum of means is wanted instead of the difference. Sometimes, too, what is

[1] A derivation along the same lines as that given on p. 164 is also available here; but the proof is considerably more lengthy and the simple derivation given here seems sufficient.

wanted is the standard error of the sum of gains instead of their difference, especially in rotation experiments. Whatever the combination of means involved, the worker can make his own formula by constructing a polynomial from the combination of means designated and setting up a formula parallel in structure to our long ones (90) and (96), carefully watching the signs. But in every case of matched groups, no matter how complicated the combination of means required, a corresponding short formula may be employed, which will be algebraically identical with the long one and will involve the full force of each r, by merely performing for each combination of paired variates the algebraic additions called for among the means, taking the standard deviation of these sums, and dividing this standard deviation by the square root of N.   Thus

$$\sigma_{(m_1 \pm m_2 \pm m_3 \pm m_4 \pm \cdots \pm m_k)} = \frac{\tilde{\sigma}_s}{\sqrt{N}} \quad \begin{array}{l}\text{(The standard error of any} \\ \text{combination of means in} \\ \text{the case of matched groups)}\end{array} \quad (98)$$

The operation of these formulas will be further illustrated in connection with a later chapter on control ed experimentation.

Interpretation of the Standard Error of the Difference between Means.—Perhaps it may be well to pause here again to consider the interpretation of the standard error of a difference between means.   The interpretation is essentially similar to that of the standard error of a mean except that we are interested almost exclusively in the relation of our difference to a hypothetical difference of zero.   We shall take as our concrete example the one shown in the table from Miss Swartz's study of keeping after school, page 166.   Here the difference was 0.4 and the standard error of the difference 0.7, showing a slight advantage for not keeping after school.   We are interested in knowing what the chances are that,

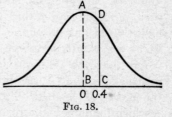

Fig. 18.

with further sampling, the advantage may not descend to zero and pass to the other side.   We are interested, then, in the hypothesis that the true mean may lie as low as zero. We shall construct a normal distribution of assumed differences with the mean at zero.   If the true mean of all the differences were at zero and the standard error of that mean were 0.7, some differences would go as high as the 0.4 we obtained from our sample, *viz.*, all those above CD. In the trapezoid $ABCD$ with a base of $0.4/0.7 = 0.6\sigma$ there lie 22.5 per cent of all the cases in the distribution. Thus above the point C, at which our obtained difference lies, would be $50 - 22.5$ equals 27.5 per cent of the cases, while below that point would lie the 50 per cent in the lower half of the distribution plus the 22.5 in the trapezoid or 72.5 per cent of the cases. So out of every 100 samples 27.5 would be expected to give differences of 0.4 or higher even though the true difference were zero, while the other 72.5 would give differences of less than that. If, however, the true difference is as low as zero, something has happened to us in this experiment that would happen only 27.5 times out of 100. The chances are 72.5 to 27.5, or 2.6 to 1, against such a coincidence. These chances are something, but they fall far below giving us practically complete assurance that we have not gotten the advantage on the side we did merely by reason of chance fluctuation; hence we say that the difference has negligible statistical significance.

This is the type of interpretation that we shall practically always want to place upon the standard error of a difference. A number of writers of elementary textbooks on statistics give for practice elaborate problems about the chances that the true difference is not less than a certain amount or more than a certain amount or between certain specified amounts when the obtained difference and the standard error are specified amounts. But such problems are rather artificial; the authors of this book have never yet encountered a practical research problem in which such interpretations were needed. Besides, it will be found that the solutions intended by these writers for their artificial problems turn upon placing the *obtained* difference at the middle of the distribution—a wholly unwarranted procedure —which fundamental error makes fairly simple the statement of a solution that, while not impossible, is difficult and awkward when correctly put.

What we have said about the interpretation of the reliability of a difference between means will hold true for all the other differences we shall discuss throughout the remainder of this chapter—subject to what is said later about small samples.

STUDENT'S DISTRIBUTION FOR SMALL SAMPLES

Since the N in the example we have been using here is rather small (23 cases), it will constitute a good one for showing the application of Student's distribution for small samples and for comparing the interpretation by the small-sample technique with that for large samples. The assumption we made above that a large number of means (or differences, or other statistics) could be expected to group themselves in a normal distribution about the true value holds approximately for small samples as well as for large ones. If we could divide the deviation of the mean (or other statistic) by the true standard deviation of the whole population of such statistic to get t, the t's would also be normally distributed. However, we do not know this population standard deviation but must use instead an estimate of it, s. When t's are obtained by dividing the deviation of a statistic by s instead of $\tilde{\sigma}$, their distribution is no longer normal. In 1908 an English scholar who modestly signed his name Student worked out mathematically the distribution[1] of t (which he called z) when thus obtained by dividing the deviation of a mean from the hypothetical true value by the standard deviation of the sample instead of by $\tilde{\sigma}$. He dealt with the distribution of means, including in particular the mean of a set of paired differences like that of our illustrative exercise. But it is now known that the same distribution holds for other statistics as well.[2] The distribution is symmetrical about the true value, just as the normal distribution is; but it is more leptokurtic than the normal distribution and is different for each n. As n increases, the distribution approaches normality. The reason is that s, the estimate of the population variability, becomes a better and better estimate of $\tilde{\sigma}$ as n increases in size and s approaches $\tilde{\sigma}$ as n approaches infinity.

Student found the standard deviation of his distribution to be $1/\sqrt{N-3}$. His β_2 differs somewhat from the 3 of the normal distribution but rapidly approaches 3 as N increases.[3] In his

---

[1] STUDENT, "The Probable Error of a Mean," *Biometrika*, Vol. 6, pp. 1–25 (1908).

[2] For a more detailed, and yet simple, discussion of the small-sample technique we suggest L. H. C. Tippett, *The Methods of Statistics*, Williams and Norgate, 1937, Chap. 5.

[3] $\beta_2 = 3 + \dfrac{6}{N-5}$.

original article he carried his table only to $N = 10$, showing that beyond that point a good approximation is reached by dividing the σ of the sample by $\sqrt{N-3}$ instead of by $\sqrt{N-1}$ and using the normal curve tables. But later (1917) he extended his table to $N = 30$, and still later (1925) Fisher, with Student's blessing, redeveloped Student's integral in terms of $(N-1)$, and Student made new tables. It is these 1925 tables from which our tables in the Appendix (Tables XLV and XLVI) are taken, although we table the tail of the distribution from t to plus infinity while Student tables the area under the curve from minus infinity to t, so that our values are his subtracted from one. Our table gives directly the probability of obtaining, on the basis of chance alone, a t as large as the one in hand deviating in the same direction from the hypothetical value as the one in our sample.

Student carried his 1925 table only to $n = 20$ ($n' = N = 21$). His reason was that beyond that number the shape of his distribution was so nearly normal that the normal curve tables give good enough results, provided one divides the standard deviation of the sample by $\sqrt{N-3}$ instead of by $\sqrt{N-1}$. But Student provided a supplementary table for dealing with n's above 20, if precise probabilities are wanted. We reproduce this as Table XLVI. It involves interpolating from an n of infinity as follows:

$$p = p_\infty + \frac{c_1}{n} + \frac{c_2}{n^2} + \frac{c_3}{n^3} + \frac{c_4}{n^4}$$

where p is the desired probability, p_∞ is the value given in the last column of Table XLV for $n =$ infinity, and the c's are given in the body of Table XLVI. Although Student's tables, which were published in *Metron* (Rome, Italy) in 1925, have been little used and little known by American research workers, they contain the bases for the most precise interpretation of probabilities anywhere available for the type of application for which they were intended. (Student reports that the corrections provided in his table of c values, our Table XLVI, give approximations to the order of 0.000005.) Fisher's table of the distribution of Student's t, which is the one best known in contemporary practice, is intended for hurried use in making rough interpretations. Both have a place among research tools. We shall show how to use both tables, employing the data from Miss Swartz's experiment for the purpose. We shall compare the values from

TABLE XII.—FISHER'S TABLE OF THE DISTRIBUTION OF t FOR CERTAIN PROBABILITY LEVELS[1]

n	$P = 0.9$	0.8	0.7	0.6	0.5	0.4	0.3	0.2	0.1	0.05	0.02	0.01
1	0.158	0.325	0.510	0.727	1.000	1.376	1.963	3.078	6.314	12.706	31.821	63.657
2	0.142	0.289	0.445	0.617	0.816	1.061	1.386	1.886	2.920	4.303	6.965	9.925
3	0.137	0.277	0.424	0.584	0.765	0.978	1.250	1.638	2.353	3.182	4.541	5.841
4	0.134	0.271	0.414	0.569	0.741	0.941	1.190	1.533	2.132	2.776	3.747	4.604
5	0.132	0.267	0.408	0.559	0.727	0.920	1.156	1.476	2.015	2.571	3.365	4.032
6	0.131	0.265	0.404	0.553	0.718	0.906	1.134	1.440	1.943	2.447	3.143	3.707
7	0.130	0.263	0.402	0.549	0.711	0.896	1.119	1.415	1.895	2.365	2.998	3.499
8	0.130	0.262	0.399	0.546	0.706	0.889	1.108	1.397	1.860	2.306	2.896	3.355
9	0.129	0.261	0.398	0.543	0.703	0.883	1.100	1.383	1.833	2.262	2.821	3.250
10	0.129	0.260	0.397	0.542	0.700	0.879	1.093	1.372	1.812	2.228	2.764	3.169
11	0.129	0.260	0.396	0.540	0.697	0.876	1.088	1.363	1.796	2.201	2.718	3.106
12	0.128	0.259	0.395	0.539	0.695	0.873	1.083	1.356	1.782	2.179	2.681	3.055
13	0.128	0.259	0.394	0.538	0.694	0.870	1.079	1.350	1.771	2.160	2.650	3.012
14	0.128	0.258	0.393	0.537	0.692	0.868	1.076	1.345	1.761	2.145	2.624	2.977
15	0.128	0.258	0.393	0.536	0.691	0.866	1.074	1.341	1.753	2.131	2.602	2.947
16	0.128	0.258	0.392	0.535	0.690	0.865	1.071	1.337	1.746	2.120	2.583	2.921
17	0.128	0.257	0.392	0.534	0.689	0.863	1.069	1.333	1.740	2.110	2.567	2.898
18	0.127	0.257	0.392	0.534	0.688	0.862	1.067	1.330	1.734	2.101	2.552	2.878
19	0.127	0.257	0.391	0.533	0.688	0.861	1.066	1.328	1.729	2.093	2.539	2.861
20	0.127	0.257	0.391	0.533	0.687	0.860	1.064	1.325	1.725	2.086	2.528	2.845
21	0.127	0.257	0.391	0.532	0.686	0.859	1.063	1.323	1.721	2.080	2.518	2.831
22	0.127	0.256	0.390	0.532	0.686	0.858	1.061	1.321	1.717	2.074	2.508	2.819
23	0.127	0.256	0.390	0.532	0.685	0.858	1.060	1.319	1.714	2.069	2.500	2.807
24	0.127	0.256	0.390	0.531	0.685	0.857	1.059	1.318	1.711	2.064	2.492	2.797
25	0.127	0.256	0.390	0.531	0.684	0.856	1.058	1.316	1.708	2.060	2.485	2.787
26	0.127	0.256	0.390	0.531	0.684	0.856	1.058	1.315	1.706	2.056	2.479	2.779
27	0.127	0.256	0.389	0.531	0.684	0.855	1.057	1.314	1.703	2.052	2.473	2.771
28	0.127	0.256	0.389	0.530	0.683	0.855	1.056	1.313	1.701	2.048	2.467	2.763
29	0.127	0.256	0.389	0.530	0.683	0.854	1.055	1.311	1.699	2.045	2.462	2.756
30	0.127	0.256	0.389	0.530	0.683	0.854	1.055	1.310	1.697	2.042	2.457	2.750
∞	0.12566	0.25335	0.38532	0.52440	0.67449	0.84162	1.03643	1.28155	1.64485	1.95996	2.32634	2.57582

[1] This table is taken by permission from *Statistical Methods for Research Workers* by R. A. Fisher, Oliver & Boyd, Edinburgh, and attention is drawn to the larger collection of tables in *Statistical Tables* by R. A. Fisher and F. Yates, Oliver & Boyd, Edinburgh.

both of these tables with the values from the normal distribution. Let us consider first Student's table.

The N in Miss Swartz's experiment was 23 ($n = 22$), and the t was given (page 166) as 0.6 in round numbers but more precisely should be 0.572. In the normal curve for a t of 0.572 we have in the upper tail of the distribution (Table XLIV) 0.2836, which means that we could expect to get as large difference as we did in favor of the "free" class about 28 per cent of the times (28 times in 100) even if the true difference was zero. We now compare that with the probability indicated by Student's distribution. Going to Student's table (page 489), we do not find a column for $n = 22$. So we must interpolate as stated above, which we do from the last column in Table XLV aided by Table XLVI. Since we do not have a row for $t = 0.572$, we must find values for $t = 0.5$ and then for $t = 0.6$ and interpolate. For $t = 0.5$,

$$p = 0.3085375 + \frac{0.0550102}{22} - \frac{0.008509}{22^2} - \frac{0.00697}{22^3} + \frac{0.0022}{22^4}$$
$$= 0.3110$$

For $t = 0.6$, by the corresponding formula, $p = 0.2773$. By linear interpolation between these for $t = 0.572$, $p = 0.2852$, to four decimal places. More exact work would require more refined methods of interpolation than the linear one. But practical purposes in research would probably never require such refinement.

In this problem the discrepancy between the results by using Student's distribution and those by using the normal curve is wholly negligible; the probability is 0.2852 by the one method and 0.2836 by the other. But the discrepancy would be much greater farther out in the tail of the distribution. For example, if the n is 40 and $t = 4.0$, the odds by the normal curve table are 32,000 to 1 while those indicated by Student's table are only 7,500 to 1, which is a tremendous discrepancy. If the odds are very high and it seems worth while to state them, they should be determined from Student's table rather than from a table of the normal distribution integral even though the n reach several hundred observations. Otherwise the estimated odds may be greatly exaggerated. (See page 170 for meaning of odds in contrast with probability.)

We shall now illustrate the use of Fisher's table with the same data. We give this table on page 173. Since Fisher's table is intended for only hurried, rough interpretations, it gives values at only certain significance levels, and it is sufficient to estimate the probability in relation to these levels. We enter Table XII, page 173, with $n = 22$ and follow along row 22 until we come as near as we can to 0.572, which is the value of our t. Under column headed 0.6 we find a t of 0.532 and under column headed 0.5 a t of 0.686. Since our t of 0.572 lies between these two, we say that the probability is somewhere between .60 and .50. This is the probability of getting *as bad arithmetic fit* as we did, even though the true difference were zero. That is, it gives the probability of getting on the basis of chance fluctuation a t that deviates *either positively or negatively* from zero as far as the one we have in hand, hence it gives the sum of the areas in both the upper and the lower tail of the distribution of t's outside the range $\pm t$. To find the probability of a divergence in the same direction from zero as that of our sample and hence to make the interpretation comparable with that made above, we must divide these entries by two. Doing this, we find the probability to be somewhere between .25 and .30, which agrees with the determination of .2852 from Student's table. Fisher's table makes no provision for probabilities lower than 0.01 (or .005 on one side), which corresponds to odds of 199 to 1, nor for n's higher than 30.

The probability of a true difference beyond zero in the above problem is so low that we were not justified in elaborating upon it in the refined manner we employed. We did that merely to illustrate the method. The proper thing would have been to dismiss the difference as insignificant immediately upon finding the very low t, or at any rate to investigate only roughly the probability of a true difference above zero. Many people believe that a point of reference should be set up as a norm for acceptable reliability. For many years American students have set a t of 3 as such standard. They called a difference reliable if it was three or more times its standard error and unreliable if it fell below that point. That is a very exacting standard; it demands that the odds be at least 740 to 1 that the true difference is above zero in the direction of the obtained one before it be accepted as reliably established. The practice that follows the

Fisher lead puts acceptable reliability in terms of fixed probabilities rather than in terms of fixed abscissa values, so that the technique may be extended to small samples as well as to large. As we saw above, the area in the tail of the distribution of t is dependent upon the size of the samples, and so it is convenient to keep the probability constant while n changes. Most of the Fisher tables are constructed on the principle that we care only to know if the probability is as low as 5 per cent, or if as low as 1 per cent, that the difference could have arisen by chance. If it reaches 5 per cent, he calls it significant; and if it reaches 1 per cent, he calls it highly significant.   In view of the manner in which the Fisher tables are constructed, his 5 per cent corresponds, in the case of a normal distribution, to a t of 1.96 and his 1 per cent to a t of 2.58.

There may be some practical convenience in having some such commonly understood points of reference to mark "limits of confidence."   But we wish emphatically to warn our readers that any such limits are entirely arbitrary.   Nothing happens at these points that is unique.   Reliability is a matter of degree; the larger the t the higher the reliability.   To employ these points of reference mechanically is quite misleading and unwarranted. On the contrary, to state the issue in terms of probabilities and secondarily to observe that the ratio falls short of, or reaches, the conventionally accepted standards, is an effective way of preventing one's thinking from becoming overmechanical.

If, instead of caring to test the hypothesis that the true difference may be zero, the worker is interested in determining the limits between which he may claim, with a given degree of confidence, that the true difference lies, he should recall what was said on pages 137 to 139 about fiducial limits.

THE STANDARD ERROR OF ANY DIFFERENCE

Since the formulas for the standard errors of all differences are fundamentally alike, we may as well consider at once the general case. Let α stand for any statistic we please (mean, standard deviation, coefficient of correlation, proportion, or what not) and ω for any other statistic, whether of the same class or of a different class.   Then, if we conceive these as deviations from the means of their respective series,

$$\sigma^2_{\alpha-\omega} = \frac{\Sigma(\alpha - \omega)^2}{S} = \frac{\Sigma\alpha^2}{S} + \frac{\Sigma\omega^2}{S} - \frac{2\Sigma\alpha\omega}{S}$$

In the expression farthest to the right, the first term is σ^2_{α}, and the second is σ^2_{ω}. We can put the third into a form that involves an r if we multiply both the numerator and denominator by $\sigma_\alpha\sigma_\omega$. Making these substitutions, we have

$$\sigma^2_{\alpha-\omega} = \sigma^2_{\alpha} + \sigma^2_{\omega} - 2\frac{\Sigma\alpha\omega}{S\sigma_\alpha\sigma_\omega} \cdot \sigma_\alpha\sigma_\omega$$

The reader will recognize in the expression $\Sigma\alpha\omega/S\sigma_\alpha\sigma_\omega$ the value $r_{\alpha\omega}$. Substituting this and taking the square root

$$\sigma_{\alpha-\omega} = \sqrt{\sigma^2_{\alpha} + \sigma^2_{\omega} - 2r_{\alpha\omega}\sigma_\alpha\sigma_\omega} \qquad \text{(Standard error of any difference)} \qquad (99)$$

In all our further developments we shall need only to substitute our particular statistics for the α and the ω. The standard errors of the individual statistics were given in our preceding chapter. Our new task will center in finding a value for the $r_{\alpha\omega}$ for the several statistics so that we may substitute it in the general formula. If we were concerned with the sum of statistics rather than with their difference, $(\alpha + \omega)$ would replace $(\alpha - \omega)$ in the above development, and we would have

$$\sigma_{\alpha+\omega} = \sqrt{\sigma^2_{\alpha} + \sigma^2_{\omega} + 2r_{\alpha\omega}\sigma_\alpha\sigma_\omega} \qquad \text{(Standard error of any sum)} \qquad (100)$$

THE NULL HYPOTHESIS

Formula (99) and adaptations from it operate on the principle that the two classes compared might be different, and hence we estimate for each its own variance. We next concern ourselves with both the extent of the difference and, perhaps, with the possibility that the true difference might go down as far as zero, or even have the opposite sign from the one obtained in the sample. We could, however, start with the assumption that the two samples may have arisen merely as chance fluctuations in drawing samples from the same homogeneous population and that, as such, there could be no difference between them except what such chance fluctuation could explain. This is the null hypothesis, as applied to differences. It can, of course, be extended to include the average difference among a plurality of classes (as in analysis of variance) or to the reliability of a single statistic (as when we wish to ask whether an observed r could have arisen out of a situation in which the true r is zero), or to other types of situations.

Our problem would then become that of testing the null hypothesis—of confirming or refuting it. Since we assume that we are dealing with a homogeneous population to which all of our classes really belong as samples, the true $\tilde{\sigma}$ of the numerator of our standard-error formula will be the same for all samples and can best be predicted by averaging the moments from the several samples. Thus, for our two samples,

$$ s^2 = \frac{\Sigma x_1^2 + \Sigma x_2^2}{(N_1 - 1) + (N_2 - 1)} = \frac{\Sigma x_1^2 + \Sigma x_2^2}{N_1 + N_2 - 2} $$

where each x is taken as a deviation from the mean of its own class, and N is the number of individuals in a sample. Since the s would be the same for both classes and the classes would be conceived as independent samples, the s could come outside the radical, and we would have, for the standard error of a difference between means,[1]

$$ \sigma_{m_1 - m_2} = s \sqrt{\frac{1}{N_1} + \frac{1}{N_2}} \qquad \begin{array}{l}\text{(Standard error of a difference}\\ \text{between means, assuming}\\ \text{the null hypothesis)}\end{array} \qquad (101) $$

Other difference formulas would take corresponding forms.

It is entirely possible to think of the reliability of differences thus in terms of the null hypothesis. Its essence consists in speculating upon how far sample statistics might reach from zero in a homogeneous population and whether some samples from such population might reach as high or as low as the one in hand. If so, there can be no assurance that a real difference between two populations exists because the behavior of a single one could possibly have given rise to the apparent difference between the samples. Such procedure may serve rough purposes well enough, and some people think it is a little easier to handle than the more refined methods of classical statistics. But it sometimes leads into rather farfetched and awkward consequences. Fisher points out that it sometimes enhances the value of t and thus leads to a more exacting test than legitimate; and also that it may give results so discordant with those of

---

[1] Student's t table is to be entered with $n = N_1 + N_2 - 2$.

the correct method that one or the other must be ignored.[1]   The
more general methods, discussed earlier in this chapter and later,
obviate these aberrations.   In the problem cited in this paragraph, for example, in which Fisher finds discrepancy between
Student's formula and formula (101) above, completely consistent
results would have been obtained if he had used the formula
correctly taking account of the correlation element [formula (90)]
and Student's formula [which is the same as our formula (95)].
Formula (90) is the absolutely general case; formulas of the type
of (91) are specialized in the sense that they apply only where
there is no correlation; and formulas of the type of (101) represent the still more limited case where it is not too farfetched
to assume that a combination of the moments from the several
samples can predict a variance common to them.   The more
general case adds so little extra labor that it does not seem to us
worth while to employ the cruder method of the null hypothesis.
To envisage the behavior of statistics in successive samples;
to take cognizance of the influence of correlation in restricting
the fluctuations of those samples; to estimate for each statistic
its own most likely population value instead of merely averaging
the two together; to raise the question whether with very large
populations these means might occupy the same position so that
the difference would be zero; and to raise corresponding questions
about the variabilities of the samples, about their skewness and
kurtosis, and about the possible extent of differences with which
other arrays correlate with each of the factors; all seems much
more satisfying and meaningful than merely to say that, if there
were a homogeneous population giving rise to samples of a certain
size, some of these random samples might show as great differences as the one we have in hand.   Certainly that is true if the
samples are large enough to give any dependability to the
statistics in hand—say, 30 or more cases in each sample.
      These are two different approaches, and each has its plausi-
bility.   The null hypothesis is especially useful for rough exploratory research in which relatively small samples are used.   For
constructive research, especially with large samples, the more
elaborate techniques of classical statistics are needed.   We
continue with the elaboration of these, developing the applications of formula (99) to the several types of statistics.

[1] FISHER, R. A., *Statistical Methods*, 7th ed., pp. 129, 133.

STANDARD ERROR OF THE DIFFERENCE
BETWEEN STANDARD DEVIATIONS

In formula (99), page 177, we provided for the standard error of any difference. For our present purpose we need only substitute in this general formula σ_x for α and σ_y for ω. We shall then have

$$\sigma_{(\sigma_x - \sigma_y)} = \sqrt{\sigma^2_{\sigma_x} + \sigma^2_{\sigma_y} - 2r_{\sigma_x\sigma_y}\sigma_{\sigma_x}\sigma_{\sigma_y}}$$

We know the sigmas of the sigmas ($\sigma_\sigma = \sigma/\sqrt{2N}$), so that we require only the coefficient of correlation between standard deviations in series of correlated arrays. We shall now proceed to determine a value for $r_{\sigma_x\sigma_y}$. It is most convenient to approach that through $r_{\sigma^2_x\sigma^2_y}$ and then to return to the unsquared σ's.

We shall take our x's and y's as deviations from the means of their respective samples; but the x^2's and the y^2's will, of course, not then be in deviation form. Our formula for r will be

$$r_{\sigma^2_x\sigma^2_y} = \frac{S\Sigma\left(\frac{\Sigma x^2}{N} \cdot \frac{\Sigma y^2}{N}\right) - \frac{\Sigma\Sigma x^2}{N} \cdot \frac{\Sigma\Sigma y^2}{N}}{\left[S\Sigma\left(\frac{\Sigma x^2}{N}\right)^2 - \left(\Sigma\frac{\Sigma x^2}{N}\right)^2\right]^{\frac12}\left[S\Sigma\left(\frac{\Sigma y^2}{N}\right)^2 - \left(\Sigma\frac{\Sigma y^2}{N}\right)^2\right]^{\frac12}}$$

where S is the number of samples and N the population within each sample. But it will be observed that in this expression all our quantities are of the form $\Sigma x^2/N$ or $\Sigma y^2/N$. The former is the expression for the mean of the x^2's and the latter for the mean of the y^2's. We have, therefore, a case of the r between means of samples, which was shown (page 162) to equal the r between the variates within a sample. We may, therefore, write

$$(B) \quad r_{\sigma^2_x\sigma^2_y} = \frac{N\Sigma x^2 y^2 - \Sigma x^2 \cdot \Sigma y^2}{\sqrt{N\Sigma(x^2)^2 - (\Sigma x^2)^2}\sqrt{N\Sigma(y^2)^2 - (\Sigma y^2)^2}}$$

$$= \frac{N\Sigma x^2 y^2 - N^2\sigma^2_x\sigma^2_y}{\sqrt{N\Sigma x^4 - N^2\sigma^4_x}\sqrt{N\Sigma y^4 - N^2\sigma^4_y}}$$

In the lithoprinted edition of this book we showed that

$$\frac{\Sigma x^2 y^2}{N} = \sigma^2_x\sigma^2_y(1 - r^2 + \beta_2 r^2),$$

so that, assuming that $\beta_2 = 3$, $\Sigma x^2 y^2 = N\sigma^2_x\sigma^2_y(1 + 2r^2)$. We shall shortly substitute this value in the r formula. But first let us find a simpler value for Σx^4 and Σy^4 of the denominator.

In a normal distribution $\beta_2 = 3$.

$$\beta_2 = \frac{\Sigma x^4}{N(\sigma^2)^2}.$$

Therefore, clearing of fractions, $\Sigma x^4 = 3N\sigma_x^4$. Similarly

$$\Sigma y^4 = 3N\sigma_y^4.$$

Substituting these three values in the r formula, we have,

$$r_{\sigma^2_x \sigma^2_y} = \frac{N[N\sigma_x^2\sigma_y^2(1 + 2r^2)] - N^2\sigma_x^2\sigma_y^2}{\sqrt{N(3N\sigma_x^4) - N^2\sigma_x^4}\sqrt{N(3N\sigma_y^4) - N^2\sigma_y^4}}$$

$$= \frac{N^2\sigma_x^2\sigma_y^2(1 + 2r^2) - N^2\sigma_x^2\sigma_y^2}{\sqrt{3N^2\sigma_x^4 - N^2\sigma_x^4}\sqrt{3N^2\sigma_y^4 - N^2\sigma_y^4}}$$

The term $N^2\sigma_x^2\sigma_y^2$ can be canceled out of the numerator and the denominator, so that the expression will simplify to

$$r_{\sigma^2_x \sigma^2_y} = \frac{1 + 2r^2 - 1}{\sqrt{3 - 1}\sqrt{3 - 1}} = \frac{2r^2}{\sqrt{2}\sqrt{2}} = r_{xy}^2$$

This is the coefficient of correlation between the sigmas squared. What we desire, however, is the r between the sigmas, not that between the sigmas squared. Unfortunately no simple formula can be given for the relation between the r between measures and the r between those measures squared. It depends upon the origin from which the squared measures are taken. We can show, by a process of development which it is scarcely worth while to reproduce here, that, assuming homoscedasticity and mesokurtosis,

$$r_{x^2y^2} = \sqrt{1 - \frac{\sigma_{y_e}^2}{\sigma_y^2}\frac{(\sigma_{y_e}^2 + 2m_y^2)}{(\sigma_y^2 + 2m_y^2)}}, \quad \begin{array}{l}(r \text{ between squared measures} \\ \text{in terms of } r \text{ between the} \\ \text{measures}\end{array} \quad (102)$$

where σ_{y_e} is the standard deviation of a column in the correlation table while σ_y is the standard deviation of the whole y distribution. As the m increases indefinitely in comparison with the σ's, the fraction involving the parentheses approaches 1 in value, and our expression becomes

$$r_{x^2y^2} = \sqrt{1 - \frac{\sigma_{y_e}^2}{\sigma_y^2}}$$

But this is also the formula for r_{xy}. In our particular application, the mean will customarily be large in comparison with the variabilities, so that we may take the r between the sigmas squared to be substantially the same as the r between the sigmas. Therefore

$$r_{\sigma_x \sigma_y} = r_{xy}^2 \qquad \text{(Coefficient of correlation between standard deviations in correlated series)} \qquad (103)$$

Substituting this value in the formula for the standard error of the difference between standard deviations, given at the opening of this section, and employing numerical subscripts,

$$\sigma_{\sigma_1 - \sigma_2} = \sqrt{\sigma^2_{\sigma_1} + \sigma^2_{\sigma_2} - 2r_{12}^2 \sigma_{\sigma_1} \sigma_{\sigma_2}} \qquad \begin{array}{l}\text{(Standard error of the} \\ \text{difference between} \\ \text{standard deviations)}\end{array} \qquad (104)$$

If the N is the same in the two series, we may conveniently substitute $\sigma/\sqrt{2N}$ for σ_σ and have

$$\sigma_{\sigma_1 - \sigma_2} = \sqrt{\left(\frac{\sigma_1^2 + \sigma_2^2 - 2r_{12}^2 \sigma_1 \sigma_2}{2N}\right)} \qquad (104a)$$

The application of this formula to an experimental problem will be illustrated in our chapter on experimentation, pages 455 to 466. See those pages also for a different formula for small samples.

THE STANDARD ERROR OF THE DIFFERENCE BETWEEN PROPORTIONS

In applying our general formula for the standard error of any difference we need only to know the r between proportions in correlated arrays, since we already know the standard errors of the separate proportions (page 145). If, in computing proportions, we look upon each individual as scoring one point when present and no points when absent, as is the customary way, a proportion equals $\Sigma x/N$, where N is the whole population and Σx is the number present in the count. The mean score would also be $\Sigma x/N$, where the symbols have the same meaning. The correlation between proportions would, therefore, be the same as the correlation between means, which we have already shown to be equal to the correlation between the variates within the two matched samples. That is, $r_{p_x p_y} = r_{xy}$. Our formula would then become

$$\sigma_{p_x-p_y} = \sqrt{\sigma_{p_x}^2 + \sigma_{p_y}^2 - 2r_{xy}\sigma_{p_x}\sigma_{p_y}}$$

$$= \sqrt{\left(\frac{p_x q_x}{N_x} + \frac{p_y q_y}{N_y} - 2r_{xy}\sqrt{\frac{p_x q_x p_y q_y}{N_x N_y}}\right)}$$

(Standard error of the difference between proportions in the case of matched groups)   (105)

In groups selected from the two populations at random instead of matched on some criterion correlated with the outcome with regard to which we are measuring proportions, the r would be zero, and the tail of the formula would drop off, so that we would have

$$\sigma_{p_x-p_y} = \sqrt{\left(\frac{p_x q_x}{N_x} + \frac{p_y q_y}{N_y}\right)}$$ (106)

It is seldom that the former of these formulas can be employed, for it is seldom that we know the correlation factor when dealing with proportions. The possibility of its use may be illustrated from a study by Freeman and Hoefer on the influence of motion pictures upon conduct.[1] They match two groups of children on information and intelligence test scores, then they show to one group motion pictures propagandizing for clean teeth. After the lapse of sufficient time to permit the instruction to function, they ascertain, among other things, what proportion of each group possessed toothbrushes. It was found that 99.48 per cent of the group that had seen the motion pictures owned toothbrushes while 97.65 per cent of the nonmovie group possessed them. The investigators do not report the coefficient of correlation between the two groups in respect to owning toothbrushes when matched for information and intelligence; it would need to be computed by the tetrachoric method described on page 366. Let us assume, for purposes of illustration, that this r turned out to be .30. We would then have (since per cents are proportions multiplied by 100)

$$\sigma_{p_x-p_y} = \left[\frac{(99.48)(.52)}{192} + \frac{(97.65)(2.35)}{170}\right.$$
$$\left. - 2(.30)\sqrt{\frac{(99.48)(.52)(97.65)(2.35)}{(192)(170)}}\right]^{\frac{1}{2}}$$

[1] FREEMAN, FRANK N., and CAROLYN HOEFER, "An Experimental Study of the Influence of Motion Pictures on Behavior," *J. Educ. Psychol.*, Vol. 22, pp. 411-425 (1931).

which equals 1.12 per cent. The difference itself is 1.83 per cent, so that the ratio of the difference to its standard error is 1.63. This is to be interpreted in the same manner as in our illustration with the difference between means, page 169. Referring to our table, page 486, we find that a ratio of 1.63 indicates chances of 18.2 to 1 that a real difference exists in favor of the children who had been instructed by means of the motion pictures. If we did not employ the tail to the formula but instead ignored the correlation element, we would get from the first two terms a standard error of 1.27. This would give a ratio of 1.44 between the difference and its standard error, which would indicate chances of 12.5 to 1 that a real difference exists in favor of the motion-picture group.

We shall illustrate the application of the second formula (106) from a study made by C. N. Rabold on the differences between country pupils and town pupils.[1] Rabold ascertained, among 38 other things, what proportion of 71 high-school pupils who came from the open country and of 65 pupils who came from a small city are employed after school hours. He found the proportion to be 57 per cent for the country and 51 per cent for the town, a difference of 6 per cent. Is this sufficient difference to indicate that repeated sampling of the same kind of populations would continue to show differences on the same side and that the theoretical (true) difference obtained from an infinitely large population would show a larger proportion of country pupils of this type of population employed after school hours than of town pupils? Since the groups selected were random ones, the formula without the correlation element is the correct one to use in getting an answer to the question about reliability. Substituting our particular values for the symbols,

$$\sigma_{p_x-p_y} = \sqrt{\frac{(.57)(.43)}{71} + \frac{(.51)(.49)}{65}} = .085$$

Thus, while the difference is 6 per cent the standard error of that difference is 8.5 per cent. The difference is only 0.7 of its standard error. A ratio of 0.7 between a difference and its standard error indicates chances of only 3.1 to 1 that the true difference lies in the same direction. This is extremely low

[1] RABOLD, C. N., and C. C. PETERS, "How Country Pupils Differ from Town Pupils," *J. Ed. Sociol.*, Vol. 3, pp. 297–306.

statistical significance, so that we must conclude that we cannot trust a difference so small in comparison with its standard error as proof that more country pupils are employed after school than town pupils.

THE STANDARD ERROR OF THE DIFFERENCE BETWEEN TWO COEFFICIENTS OF CORRELATION

Substituting r's for the α and the ω in our general formula, we get

$$\sigma_{r_{12}-r_{34}} = \sqrt{\sigma_{r_{12}}^2 + \sigma_{r_{34}}^2 - 2r_{r_{12}r_{34}}\sigma_{r_{12}}\sigma_{r_{34}}} \qquad (107)$$

From our previous chapter we know the σ's of the r's. We need only a value for the r between two r's. We would scarcely be justified here in taking the space necessary to develop these required formulas. Pearson and Filon[1] give them for the two cases as follows: (1) the case in which the same array occurs as one factor in both the r's; and (2) the case in which the four arrays are different. But all the arrays are somehow correlated with one another; otherwise there would be no correlation between the r's. The first case is as follows:

$$r_{r_{12}r_{13}} = r_{23} - \frac{r_{12}r_{13}(1 - r_{23}^2 - r_{12}^2 - r_{13}^2 + 2r_{12}r_{13}r_{23})}{2(1 - r_{12}^2)(1 - r_{13}^2)} \qquad (108)$$

(Coefficient of correlation between two r's having one array in common)

The other case involves a considerably longer formula, as follows:

$$r_{r_{12}r_{34}} = \begin{cases} [(r_{13} - r_{12}r_{23})(r_{24} - r_{23}r_{34})] \\ + [(r_{14} - r_{13}r_{34})(r_{23} - r_{13}r_{12})] \\ + [(r_{13} - r_{14}r_{34})(r_{24} - r_{14}r_{12})] \\ + [(r_{14} - r_{12}r_{24})(r_{23} - r_{24}r_{34})] \end{cases} \left[\frac{1}{2(1 - r_{12}^2)(1 - r_{34}^2)} \right]$$

(Coefficient of correlation between two r's in correlated series, no   (108a) array in common)

We shall illustrate the operation of these formulas with data from a study by H. Clair Henry on the reliability and validity of the consistent-response method of scoring a true-false test

[1] PEARSON, KARL, and L. N. G. FILON, "Mathematical Contributions to the Theory of Evolution," *Trans. Roy. Soc.* (*London*), Series *A*, Vol. 191, pp. 259, 262.

as compared with that of the rights-minus-wrongs method.[1]
He scored the Peters Test of General Information according to
the rules for this test, *viz.*, a credit for an item if a pupil responded
to it twice correctly when stated in different ways and no penalty
for wrongs, and also by the conventional rights-minus-wrongs
method, computed validity and reliability coefficients by both
methods, and examined the differences for sign and for statistical
significance. As one test of validity he correlated the scores
on the test by both methods with the recorded IQ's of the
pupils. We shall consider his trial with 90 senior high-school
students. Evidently this problem comes under our first case
since, in each of the two scorings, marks were correlated with the
same array, *viz.*, the intelligence quotients. We shall call the
IQ array 1; the R-W array 2; and the consistent-response array 3.
The correlations Henry found were as follows: $r_{12} = .76$; $r_{13} = .84$;
and $r_{23} = .89$. The consistent-response method showed a higher
correlation with intelligence quotients by $(.84 - .76) = .08$.
Is this a significant difference? We shall apply to it our formula (108).

$$r_{r_{12}r_{13}}$$

$$= .89 - \frac{(.76)(.84)[1 - .89^2 - .76^2 - .84^2 + 2(.76)(.84)(.89)]}{2(1 - .76^2)(1 - 84^2)}$$

$$= .773$$

Putting this value for the r into our standard-error formula we
have

$$\sigma_{r_{12}-r_{13}}$$

$$= \sqrt{\frac{(1 - .76^2)^2}{90} + \frac{(1 - .84^2)^2}{90} - 2(.733)\frac{(1 - .76^2)(1 - .84^2)}{90}}$$

$$= .03$$

Thus the standard error of the difference is .03 while the
difference is .08, making a ratio of 2.67. This indicates chances
of 263 to 1 of a true difference in favor of the consistent-response
method of scoring. If we disregard the correlation between the
r's and employ the formula in the customary manner without the
tail, we get a standard error of .054 and a ratio of 1.48 between
the difference and its standard error. This indicates chances

[1] An unpublished master's thesis at Pennsylvania State College, 1932.

of only 13 to 1 that a true difference is in favor of the consistent-response method.   Evidently, if we had depended upon the short formula which ignores the correlation element between the r's, we would have greatly underestimated the reliability of our difference.

In illustration of our second case we shall use Henry's figures for the difference between the reliability coefficients by the two methods of scoring for 100 college sophomores.   In this case he correlated scores from form A of the test with those for form B by each of the two methods.   The arrays were numbered as follows: 1 is the scores on form A by the rights-minus-wrongs method; 2, the scores on form B by the rights-minus-wrongs method; 3, the scores on form A by the consistent-response method; and 4, the scores on form B by the consistent-response method. The reliability coefficient by the rights-minus-wrongs method would be r_{12}, while that for the consistent-response method would be r_{34}.   We are interested in the difference between these two r's. The values of the several r's needed in the formula are as follows: $r_{12} = .52$; $r_{34} = .64$; $r_{13} = .61$; $r_{23} = .36$; $r_{14} = .43$; $r_{24} = .61$. When these values for the r's are put into formula (108a), $r_{r_{12}r_{34}}$ turns out to be .334.   When this value of r is used in the general formula for the standard error of the difference between two r's [Eq. (107)], the standard error is found to be .08, giving a ratio of 1.5 between the difference and its standard error and indicating chances of 14 to 1 of a true difference in favor of the consistent-response method of scoring.   If the r between the r's is ignored, the standard error of the difference is .096, the ratio 1.25, and the chances of a true difference in the same direction 8.5 to 1.   The use of the tail to the formula here makes less difference than in the previous case because the inter-correlations are rather low.

Thus, to be strictly correct, one needs to employ the formula for the standard error of a difference between r's that takes account of the r between the r's.   But we have taken the position that standard errors of r's are not to be taken so seriously as they customarily are, and this would extend to the standard error of the difference between the r's.   Since the tail of the formula involves the computation of additional r's probably not needed otherwise in the problem and since we are on rather uncertain ground here, most people will probably wish to continue to

employ the approximately correct formula that ignores the tail
containing the r between the r's.   In this form

$$\sigma_{r_{12}-r_{24}} = \sqrt{\sigma^2_{r_{12}} + \sigma^2_{r_{24}}} \qquad \text{(Standard error of the difference between two } r\text{'s in unmatched series, or when the force of the matching is ignored)} \qquad (109)$$

But when one uses this abbreviated formula where the element
of matching is present, he should recognize that his obtained
standard error is probably too high, and possibly much too high.

The Significance of a Difference between z's.—The z' technique (see page 155) is especially recommended by Fisher for
testing the significance of a difference between r's.   We shall,
therefore, apply it to testing the significance of the difference
between the z' values of the r's we tested on page 186 by formulas
(107) and (109).   The formula is the customary one of type
(99) with the correlation factor omitted.   It is, as inspection
of the formula for the standard error of z' [formula (88) page 156]
would indicate,

$$t = \frac{z'_{12} - z'_{13}}{\sqrt{\dfrac{1}{N_{12} - 3} + \dfrac{1}{N_{13} - 3}}} \qquad \text{(Standard error ratio for the difference between two } z\text{'s)} \qquad (110)$$

We need first to obtain the z' value for each of the r's.   If
a table of hyperbolic functions is available, such as is printed
in the *Handbook of Chemistry and Physics*, the hyperbolic arc
tangent of r may be read directly from it, and that is z'.   Or
tables covering certain ranges of z' may be found in Fisher's
manual and in some other books.   If no such tables are available,
the values must be obtained by the use of tables of logarithms
as indicated by formula (87), page 155.   By the use of the table
of hyperbolic functions in the *Handbook of Chemistry and Physics*
we get as z' for our r's

$$r_{12} = .76; \ z'_{12} = 0.9962$$
$$r_{13} = .84; \ z'_{13} = 1.2212$$

$$t = \frac{0.9962 - 1.2212}{\sqrt{\dfrac{1}{90 - 3} + \dfrac{1}{90 - 3}}} = -1.48$$

Thus we get as our ratio of the difference between the z's and
the standard error of that difference 1.48, which is to be inter-

preted by use of the normal curve functions in our familiar manner. That is exactly the same ratio as we obtained on page 186 by the use of the standard formula [Eq. (109)], and both ratios are to be interpreted in exactly the same manner. So for all our extra labor we gained nothing, *in this problem,* by transmuting to z's; and we lost all the additional precision that formula (107) gave us. We cannot use with z' a formula of the type of (107) because the r between z's is unknown.

Exercises

1. From the data given in Table IV, pages 58 to 61, ascertain whether girls differ from boys in grade-point average; in scores in history. How reliable are these differences? (Note that these are random groups, hence no correlation element is present.)

2. Match girls and boys for general intelligence scores; *i.e.*, for each girl find a boy with the same, or nearly the same, intelligence test score. Then see whether there are sex differences in grade-point average when the groups are thus matched for general intelligence. Do likewise with history scores and with scores on the other sections of the test. How significant are these differences? (Remember that now the correlation element is present.)

3. How do the sexes compare in variability: (1) when random groups are taken? (2) when groups are matched for general intelligence?

4. Are there significant differences in the extent to which the scores in the several functions correlate with general intelligence test scores?

5. Revert to the matched groups of Exercise 2. Compute for each of the sexes the r between intelligence test scores and science scores (or other array in which you are most interested). Is there a statistically significant difference between the r for girls and that for boys? [Remember that here the matching element is present and hence formula (108) applies. It is considered that the scores on the matching element are perfectly correlated between the two groups, so that a single subscript may refer to either set.]

6. From these same matched groups compute the r between history scores for boys and those for girls and also the r between science scores for boys and those for girls. Is there a statistically significant difference between these r's? [Note that here formula (108a) applies.]

References for Further Study

DICKEY, J. W.: "Reliability of Integration Index Differences," *J. Educ. Psychol.*, Vol. 22, pp. 209–211.

FISHER, R. A.: "The Mathematical Distributions Used in Common Tests of Significance," *Econometrika*, Vol. 3, pp. 353–365.

————: "Applications of Student's Distribution," *Metron*, Vol. 5, pp. 90–104. (A short but important article generalizing Student's method.)

HOTELLING, H.: "The Generalization of Student's Ratio," *Ann. Mathematical Statistics*, Vol. 2, pp. 359–378.

JACKSON, DUNHAM: "Mathematical Principles in the Theory of Small Samples," *Amer. Mathematical Monthly*, Vol. 42, pp. 344–364.

KOLODZIEJCZYK, S.: "An Important Class of Statistical Hypotheses," *Biometrika*, Vol. 27, pp. 161–190.

RIETZ, H. L.: "Comments on Application of Recently Developed Theory of Small Samples," *J. Amer. Statistical Assoc.*, Vol. 26, pp. 150–158.

STUDENT: "The Probable Error of a Mean," *Biometrika*, Vol. 6, pp. 1–25.

WISHART, JOHN: "The Generalized Product-moment Distribution in Samples from a Multivariate Population," *Biometrika*, Vol. 20, pp. 32–52.

CHAPTER VII

INFERRING COEFFICIENTS OF CORRELATION FOR CHANGED CONDITIONS

THE GENERALIZED SPEARMAN PROPHECY FORMULA

We shall first develop a general formula for the correlation of the sum of corresponding scores in a sets of similar arrays in an x series and the sum of corresponding scores in b sets of similar arrays in a y series. The reader is asked to follow critically the development in this section because it will be made the basis of the derivation of practically all the formulas of this chapter.

Let x_1, x_2, x_3, . . . , x_a be scores made by one individual in the x series (which may be such measures as estimates by judges as well as scores on an objective test), and let y_1, y_2, y_3, . . . , y_b be this same individual's scores in the y series. Let these all be conceived as deviations from the means of their respective arrays. Then, employing our product-moment correlation formula in the shape,

$$r = \frac{\Sigma xy}{\sqrt{\Sigma x^2 \cdot \Sigma y^2}}$$

we get for our particular type of data

$$r_{(x_1+x_2+x_3\cdots+x_a)(y_1+y_2+y_3+\cdots+y_b)}$$
$$= \frac{\Sigma(x_1 + x_2 + x_3 + x_4 + \cdots + x_a)(y_1 + y_2 + y_3 + y_4 + \cdots + y_b)}{\sqrt{\Sigma(x_1 + x_2 + x_3 + x_4 + \cdots + x_a)^2 \cdot \Sigma(y_1 + y_2 + y_3 + y_4 + \cdots + y_b)^2}}$$

Multiplying together our polynomials in the numerator and squaring those in the denominator as indicated, placing the summation sign with each member instead of before the expressions as wholes, and using a more abbreviated symbolism for the r between sums,

$$r_{s_x s_y} = \frac{\Sigma x_1 y_1 + \Sigma x_1 y_2 + \cdots + \Sigma x_1 y_b + \Sigma x_2 y_1 + \Sigma x_2 y_2 + \cdots + \Sigma x_3 y_1 + \cdots + \Sigma x_a y_b}{\sqrt{(\Sigma x_1^2 + \Sigma x_2^2 + \cdots + \Sigma x_a^2 + \Sigma x_1 x_2 + \cdots)(\Sigma y_1^2 + \Sigma y_2^2 + \Sigma y_3^2 + \cdots + \Sigma y_1 y_2 + \Sigma y_1 y_3 + \cdots)}}$$

Since we are considering the sum of *similar* samples, we may take the sigmas within the x series to be essentially equal to one another, and likewise we may take the sigmas within the y series to be substantially equal to one another. Let us then divide both numerator and denominator of the right-hand member of the equation by $n\sigma_x\sigma_y$, these being the typical standard deviations of the series to which they belong and the n being the number of cases in any one sample. We shall then have

$$r_{s_x s_y} = \cfrac{\begin{aligned}&\frac{\Sigma x_1 y_1}{n\sigma_x\sigma_y} + \frac{\Sigma x_1 y_2}{n\sigma_x\sigma_y} + \frac{\Sigma x_1 y_3}{n\sigma_x\sigma_y} + \cdots\\[4pt] &\qquad + \frac{\Sigma x_2 y_1}{n\sigma_x\sigma_y} + \frac{\Sigma x_2 y_2}{n\sigma_x\sigma_y} + \frac{\Sigma x_2 y_3}{n\sigma_x\sigma_y} + \cdots\end{aligned}}{\sqrt{\left(\dfrac{\Sigma x_1^2}{n\sigma_x^2} + \dfrac{\Sigma x_2^2}{n\sigma_x^2} + \dfrac{\Sigma x_3^2}{n\sigma_x^2} + \cdots + \dfrac{\Sigma x_1 x_2}{n\sigma_x^2} + \dfrac{\Sigma x_1 x_3}{n\sigma_x^2} + \cdots\right)\left(\dfrac{\Sigma y_1^2}{n\sigma_y^2} + \dfrac{\Sigma y_2^2}{n\sigma_y^2} + \cdots + \dfrac{\Sigma y_1 y_2}{n\sigma_y^2} + \dfrac{\Sigma y_1 y_3}{n\sigma_y^2} + \cdots\right)}}$$

We have above two types of product moments: those of the type $\Sigma x_1 y_1 / n\sigma_x\sigma_y$ and those of the type $\Sigma x_1 x_2 / n\sigma_x^2$ or $\Sigma y_1 y_2 / n\sigma_y^2$. The latter represent the correlations within the series of x measures or within the series of y measures, being the intercorrelations among the samples within each set. The former represent the intercorrelations between the x samples and the y samples. Since the samples are assumed to be similar within each set, we may represent the first type of product moments as $\bar{r}_{xy}$, the average intercorrelation between the samples, or simply as r_{xy} on the assumption that these intercorrelations are reasonably well represented by any r_{xy} that we may have at hand. Those of the second type we may represent as r_{11x} and r_{11y}, the average intercorrelation among the samples within each set.

Evidently there are in the numerator ab of the r_{xy}'s because each element of the x series, of which there are a in number, enters into combination with each element of the y series of which there are b. But in the denominator each enters into combination with one less than the whole series (itself being excluded by reason of having been used in the x^2 or y^2 element); therefore the number will be $a(a-1)$ or $(a^2 - a)$ on the left and $(b^2 - b)$ on the right. Each expression of the type $\Sigma x^2 / n\sigma_x^2$ equals 1, since it is equivalent to σ_x^2 / σ_x^2, and there are a of these on the left and b of them on the right. Keeping in mind all these equivalents, we may write

$$r_{s_a s_b} = \frac{ab\bar{r}_{xy}}{\sqrt{a + (a^2 - a)r_{1Ix}} \sqrt{b + (b^2 - b)r_{1Iy}}}$$

(Coefficient of correlation between the
sum of a samples of an x function and   (111)
the sum of b samples of a y function)

This is the r between sums. Since we may divide either or both arrays in any correlation problem by any constant or constants without changing the value of r, the r between averages is precisely the same as the r between sums. The formula for the r between the average scores in a samples of x measurements and b sets of corresponding y measurements, where the samples are similar within their own series, is thus precisely the same as the above for sums. But, when we quote it as the r between averages, we shall employ for the r the symbol $r_{\bar{a}_x \bar{b}_y}$.

RELIABILITY OF AVERAGES

We have two main types of applications for these formulas. The first is the type where x and y are the same function. This is the case where a number of judges make estimates on a group of individuals and we are concerned to know how closely the averages of these estimates may be expected to correlate with the sum of estimates made by these same judges, or by others similar to them, on another sample of individuals similar to the first sample. It is also the case where we have the average intercorrelation of a number of forms of a test in hand and wish to judge how closely the scores obtained from the sum of these forms in hand could be expected to correlate with the sums or the averages from any given number of similar forms to be obtained in the future. This is the problem of reliability. In this type of application all the forms may be taken as similar, so that all intercorrelations are of the type r_{1I}, whether obtained within set a or within set b. Under these conditions formula (111) becomes

$$r_{\bar{a}\bar{b}} = \frac{abr_{1I}}{\sqrt{a + (a^2 - a)r_{1I}} \sqrt{b + (b^2 - b)r_{1I}}}$$

(Predicted correlation between the averages from a
forms of a test and the averages from b forms of   (112)
the same test)

If $a = b$, formula (112) becomes

$$r_{\bar{a}\bar{a}} = \frac{ar_{1I}}{1 + (a - 1)r_{1I}}$$
(Predicted correlation between the average scores from a forms of a test and a other forms of the same test) 　(113)

If a is 2, this formula becomes

$$r_{2I} = \frac{2r_{1I}}{1 + r_{1I}}$$
(Spearman-Brown formula for predicting the reliability of a test of doubled length) 　(114)

Formula (114) is the one we employ when we split a test into two halves (as odds and evens), get the correlation between these two halves, and then step this up to a prediction of what the r could be expected to be if taken between the whole of the test and another whole test instead of between the halves. It is very widely employed in calculating the reliability coefficient of a test. Mathematically it indicates what should be obtained by correlating two forms of a test, provided those forms are as closely similar as the two halves are. But in practice it will be found to give slightly higher correlations than those obtained by correlating two forms. This is because, in the case of split halves from the same test, conditions are precisely the same for the two halves—same condition of health for a pupil on the two halves, same degree of understanding of the instructions, same motivation, etc.—while with different forms, given on different days or even in sequence on the same day, the conditions may not be the same for the two forms. These inequalities in the degree and manner to which changed conditions affect different pupils will tend to lower the correlation between forms. Sometimes a third method is employed in order to ascertain the reliability coefficient of a test: to readminister the same form of the test after an interval. By this method the coefficient tends to be raised by reason of the element of overlapping. Thus reliability coefficients are highest when the same form of the test is repeated at a reasonably short interval, next highest by the split-halves method, and lowest by the correlation of scores from different forms.

Let us return to our general reliability formula [Eq. (111)] and carry it through one more step of development; let us make b infinitely large. We shall then have the predicted correlation between the average scores from a forms of a test, or the average estimates by a judges, and the averages from an infinite number. This average from an infinite number may be called the *true* scores, and the r between the a forms and the infinite number may be called the *correlation of the obtained averages with the true averages*. An examination of the formula will show that we cannot substitute infinity for b directly because that would give us infinity in both numerator and denominator, infinity over infinity, which is indeterminate in value. We shall, therefore, divide both numerator and denominator by b, remembering that this must become b^2 when dividing under the radical sign. Then

$$r_{\overline{ab}} = \frac{ar_{1I}}{\sqrt{a + (a^2 - a)r_{1I}}\ \sqrt{\frac{1}{b} + \left(1 - \frac{1}{b}\right)r_{1I}}}$$

The $1/b$ equals zero, since the denominator is infinity. Therefore,

$$r_{\overline{a\infty}} = \frac{ar_{1I}}{\sqrt{a + (a^2 - a)r_{1I}}\ \sqrt{r_{1I}}} = \frac{ar_{1I}}{\sqrt{ar_{1I} + (a^2 - a)r_{1I}^2}}$$

(Predicted correlation between the average scores
from a forms of a test and the true scores)   (115)

We shall illustrate the application of some of these formulas from a study by one of the authors of the influence of motion pictures on standards of morality.[1] The investigation of motion pictures involved the necessity of giving them ratings on the degree of divergence from the mores with the guidance of certain scales having quantitative indices. With these scales in hand three judges made ratings of the scenes that fell within selected areas. We shall take as a sample the ratings on the treatment of children by parents. The average intercorrelation of the ratings by the three judges, computed by the method to be described in our next section, was .862. When this is entered into formula (113), we get, as the predicted correlation between the averages of the ratings for the several films from these three judges and the averages from another three of the same general type, the following:

$$r_{\overline{aa}} = \frac{3 \cdot .862}{1 + (3 - 1).862} = .949$$

[1] PETERS, CHARLES C., *Motion Pictures and Standards of Morality*, The Macmillan Company, 1933.

Employing formula (115) for the correlation between the averaged ratings from the three judges and those to be expected from an infinite number, we get

$$r_{a_\infty} = \frac{3 \cdot .862}{\sqrt{3 \cdot .862 + (3^2 - 3).862^2}} = .974$$

The meaning of this last correlation is that, for most practical purposes where the average intercorrelation among judges is as high as .862, three judges are sufficient; for then the joint estimates agree to the extent of an r of .974 with the true estimates that one would obtain from an unlimited number of judges. This is as close agreement as we would ordinarily demand. If, however, we decide that we would be satisfied with an r that is no less than, say, .99, we could put this value into our formula on the left and the known average intercorrelation on the right, and determine the number of judges (a) required to give that r by solving the equation for a.

Lengthening a test increases its validity as well as its reliability. If we measure validity in terms of the correlation of the test with an outside criterion and assume that there is one form of the criterion, formula (111) becomes

$$r_{c(ax)} = \frac{a \bar{r}_{cx}}{\sqrt{a + (a^2 - a)r_{11}}}$$

(Predicted correlation between a criterion and the sum or average of a forms of a test)   (116)

AVERAGE INTERCORRELATION

Average intercorrelations were called for in the formulas of the preceding section. A great deal of labor would be involved in computing these in the regular way, especially when the number of forms to be intercorrelated becomes considerable. Fortunately there is available a very simple method of computing an average intercorrelation if we may assume equal variabilities in the arrays among which the average intercorrelations are sought.

Let s be the sum of the corresponding items across all the arrays in the case of one individual. Then, if 1, 2, 3, . . . , a number the columns, $s = x_1 + x_2 + x_3 + \cdots + x_a$. Squaring, summing for all the individuals (N), and dividing by their number,

$$\frac{\Sigma s^2}{N} = \frac{\Sigma(x_1 + x_2 + x_3 + \cdots + x_a)^2}{N}$$

Squaring the polynomial and putting the summation sign and the N with each term, we have

$$\frac{\Sigma s^2}{N} = \frac{\Sigma x_1^2}{N} + \frac{\Sigma x_2^2}{N} + \frac{\Sigma x_3^2}{N} + \cdots + \frac{\Sigma x_1 x_2}{N} + \frac{\Sigma x_1 x_3}{N}$$
$$+ \cdots + \frac{\Sigma x_2 x_3}{N} + \cdots + \frac{\Sigma x_{a-1} x_a}{N}$$

The term on the left of the equation is the standard deviation squared of the sums of scores by individuals. The items of the first type on the right are expressions for the standard deviation squared of the column (*i.e.*, is, by forms or judges). Since we are assuming equal variabilities among our arrays, we may call any one of them σ_i^2, meaning the standard deviation squared of an individual array. (An array is the set of scores assigned to the individuals by a single judge or achieved on a single form of the test.) There are obviously a of these σ_i^2's, a being the number of arrays; since we have assumed them sufficiently similar to be treated as averages, their sum is $a\sigma_i^2$. We shall also treat the product moments as averages. In order to make r's out of them we must, of course, multiply each by $\sigma\sigma/\sigma\sigma$, so that each will give us $r\sigma^2$. There are $(a^2 - a)$ of these, as in the previous development. Using a symbol to indicate that these are *averages* and summing them as such, our equation becomes,

$$\sigma_{s_a}^2 = a\sigma_i^2 + (a^2 - a)\sigma_i^2 r_{1I} \quad \begin{array}{l}\text{(The variance of the sum of}\\ \ a \text{ similar correlated arrays)}\end{array} \quad (117)$$

Transposing and solving for r_{1I},

$$r_{1I} = \frac{\sigma_s^2 - a\sigma_i^2}{\sigma_i^2(a^2 - a)} = \frac{(\sigma_s^2/\sigma_i^2) - a}{a^2 - a} \quad \begin{array}{l}\text{(Average intercorrela-}\\ \text{tion among } a \text{ arrays}\\ \text{of equal variability)}\end{array} \quad (118)$$

The a is, of course, the number of arrays correlated. The σ_i^2 is best found array by array, then these σ^2's averaged. If all the scores are thrown together into a single frequency table for the calculation of the σ_i, the additional assumption must be made that the means of the arrays are equal. This is likely to be a more disturbing factor than the assumption of equal variabilities. For averaging the variances of the a different arrays, the following formula is convenient. Notice that, since the N is the number of items, it is the same for all the arrays.

$$\sigma_i^2 = \frac{1}{a}\left[\frac{N\Sigma X_1^2 - (\Sigma X_1)^2}{N^2} + \frac{N\Sigma X_2^2 - (\Sigma X_2)^2}{N^2}\right.$$
$$\left. + \frac{N\Sigma X_3^2 - (\Sigma X_3)^2}{N^2} \cdots\right]$$

$$\sigma_i^2 = \frac{N(\Sigma X_1^2 + \Sigma X_2^2 + \Sigma X_3^2 \cdots) - (\overline{\Sigma X}_1^2 + \overline{\Sigma X}_2^2 + \overline{\Sigma X}_3^2 \cdots)}{aN^2}$$

$$\sigma_i^2 = \frac{N\Sigma\Sigma X^2 - \Sigma\overline{\Sigma X}_i^2}{aN^2}$$

TABLE XIII.—RATINGS ON 25 PUPILS BY 16 FELLOW PUPILS ON
SOCIAL-MINDEDNESS

Pu.	Ratings by 16 fellow pupils																S	Av.
1	5	5	5	5	3	5	5	5	5	4	5	5	5	5	3	4	74	4.6
2	5	3	4	3	3	3	4	4	3	3	2	2	4	5	2	4	54	3.4
3	5	4	4	4	3	3	3	4	4	4	3	3	5	3	5	5	62	3.9
4	5	5	5	5	3	4	4	4	5	2	5	5	5	5	4	4	70	4.4
5	4	3	3	5	3	3	2	4	3	2	3	4	3	1	3	5	51	3.2
6	5	4	3	5	3	5	3	3	4	4	3	3	4	5	5	4	63	3.9
7	3	3	3	4	1	5	2	4	2	2	5	5	2	5	5	4	55	3.4
8	5	4	4	5	3	5	1	3	3	3	3	3	5	4	5	4	60	3.7
9	3	3	3	3	1	2	3	3	1	3	1	1	3	3	3	3	39	2.4
10	3	3	3	5	1	2	2	4	2	2	1	1	3	3	2	1	38	2.4
11	5	1	2	1	1	1	4	3	1	2	2	2	1	3	3	1	33	2.1
12	5	4	3	5	3	5	4	4	4	4	3	3	5	5	2	5	64	4.0
13	5	4	3	3	3	5	3	3	5	4	5	5	2	5	5	5	65	4.1
14	3	2	3	1	1	1	3	4	1	1	3	3	1	3	2	4	36	2.2
15	5	4	3	3	1	3	2	3	3	3	5	5	4	5	5	4	58	3.5
16	4	3	2	5	3	4	2	4	5	3	5	5	5	4	3	4	61	3.7
17	5	4	4	5	1	3	3	4	3	3	4	4	4	5	5	4	61	3.7
18	5	4	3	5	3	5	4	3	4	2	5	5	5	1	5	5	64	4.0
19	4	4	3	4	1	3	1	3	2	2	2	2	2	3	3	3	41	2.6
20	2	3	3	5	1	3	3	3	3	2	2	2	4	1	3	1	41	2.6
21	5	4	5	5	5	5	3	4	5	5	5	5	5	5	5	5	76	4.7
22	3	3	4	5	3	3	2	2	2	3	2	4	4	3	1	1	45	2.8
23	3	2	2	4	1	1	2	3	3	2	3	3	2	3	1	1	36	2.2
24	4	4	4	2	1	2	4	4	2	2	3	3	3	1	5	4	48	3.0
25	5	4	4	5	3	3	3	3	5	3	3	5	3	5	5	5	64	4.0
ΣX	106	87	85	102	55	84	72	88	80	70	83	88	89	90	90	90		
ΣX^2	472	323	307	456	153	328	232	320	300	218	319	354	359	378	372	374		

Table XIII is a table of ratings made by 16 high-school pupils on 25 of their fellow pupils on the trait of social-mindedness. The ratings are on a scale of 1 to 5, with each stage defined by a description. The illustration is from the "Survey of On-coming Youth in Pennsylvania" conducted by Harlan Updegraff. At the foot of each column we give the "makings" of the standard deviation of the individual ratings and in the two columns at the right the "makings" of the standard deviation of the sums and also of the averages. The computations are given a few lines below. For $\Sigma\Sigma X$ we add along the columns all the separate ΣX elements, and for $\Sigma\overline{\Sigma X}_i^2$ we similarly add the $\overline{\Sigma X}^{2}$'s of the separate columns. For the sums, column ΣX_s is necessarily the same as $\Sigma\Sigma X$, which is 1,359. For the sums column ΣX_s^2 is 77,763. The student may himself wish to solve the problem by way of averages. The computations by way of the sums follow:

$$\sigma_i^2 = \frac{N\Sigma\Sigma X^2 - \Sigma\overline{\Sigma X}_i^2}{aN^2} = \frac{25 \cdot 5{,}265 - 117{,}597}{16 \cdot 25^2} = 1.4$$

$$\sigma_s^2 = 155.5$$

$$r_{1I} = \frac{(\sigma_s^2/\sigma_i^2) - a}{a^2 - a} = \frac{(155.5/1.4) - 16}{16^2 - 16} = .396$$

$$r_{\overline{aa}} = \frac{ar_{1I}}{1 + (a - 1)r_{1I}} = \frac{16 \cdot .396}{1 + 15 \cdot .396} = .913$$

Usually when one is dealing with such data as those to which this section relates, especially when in the form of ratings, he will have in hand the averages for the individuals rated in addition to the sums, or perhaps only the averages. Formula (118) may then take the shape,

$$r_{1I} = \frac{(a^2\sigma_{av}^2/\sigma_i^2) - a}{a^2 - a} = \frac{(a\sigma_{av}^2/\sigma_i^2) - 1}{a - 1} \qquad (119)$$

In this form it is possible to estimate roughly the reliability of the ratings from the range of the averages and an estimate of the variability of the individual ratings. In the survey from which the above illustration was taken, it was necessary to detect, and to hold out for further investigation, those rooms in which the ratings seemed to have been unreliably made. Because there were hundreds of rooms, actual calculation would have been far too slow. We observed that the individual ratings had, usually, a standard deviation of about 1, and we took the standard deviation of the averages to be about one-fourth of the range. We, therefore, looked over the averages from the 30 or more pupils in a room, recorded the highest and the lowest of these, divided this by four, and substituted in formula (119), or mentally made the substitution. Suppose, for example, the averages in a particular room ranged from 1.22 to 3.18, and there were 30 judges contributing to the rating. We would have, as a rough estimate of the intercorrelation,

$$r_{1I} = \frac{30 \left(\dfrac{3.18 - 1.22}{4} \right)^2 - 1}{30 - 1} = \frac{6.20}{29} = .21$$

And the reliability of the average of the 30 ratings would be

$$r_{\overline{a}\overline{a}} = \frac{a r_{1I}}{1 + (a - 1) r_{1I}} = \frac{(30)(.21)}{1 + (29)(.21)} = .86$$

If one prefers, he may use the split-halves method for determining reliability in such situations as we have been referring to in the above paragraphs. That is, one may break the set of raters into two approximately equal chance halves, get an array of sums or of averages from each of these halves, determine the coefficient of correlation between these halves, and apply formula (114). If the assumptions mentioned in this section have been fully met, the outcome will be identical by way of the split-halves method with that obtained by way of the average-intercorrelation method, as the reader may wish to convince himself by a little exercise in algebraic manipulation.

Average Intercorrelation from Ranks.—If our data are in the form of ranks, we can put formula (118) in a different shape, simpler for operative purposes, by taking advantage of the fact that the standard deviation of any set of ranks is known. We treated that matter on page 107. Since the σ_i^2 is the standard deviation of a set of N ranks, $\sigma_i^2 = (N^2 - 1)/12$. We need yet a more convenient value for σ_s^2. The average of a set of N ranks is the sum of the first and the last divided by 2; that is, $(N + 1)/2$. Each array has this as its average rank score. Therefore all the a arrays together have as the sum of all their scores $N \cdot a$ times this average. That is,

$$\Sigma S = Na\left(\frac{N+1}{2}\right), \text{ and } \frac{\Sigma S}{N} = a\left(\frac{N+1}{2}\right).$$

Remembering the general formula for a standard deviation in terms of scores, $\sigma_x^2 = (\Sigma X^2/N) - (\Sigma X/N)^2$, or $(\Sigma X^2/N) - M^2$, we have in the case of our data, $\sigma_S^2 = \frac{\Sigma S^2}{N} - \frac{a^2(N+1)^2}{4}$. The a has the same meaning and value as before. Substituting in formula (118) the equivalents just found for the two types of σ's, we have

$$r_{1\prime} = \frac{\frac{\Sigma S^2}{N} - \frac{a^2(N+1)^2}{4} - \frac{a(N^2-1)}{12}}{\frac{(N^2-1)}{12}(a^2-a)}$$

Rearranging the order of terms and placing all the terms of the numerator over 12 as a common denominator, we have

$$r_{1\prime} = \frac{\frac{-a(N^2-1)}{12} - \frac{3a^2(N+1)^2}{12} + \frac{12\Sigma S^2}{12N}}{\frac{(N^2-1)}{12}(a^2-a)}$$

Canceling certain terms and breaking the fraction into three component ones, we get

$$r_{1\prime} = \frac{1}{1-a} - \frac{3a(N+1)}{(N-1)(a-1)} + \frac{12\Sigma S^2}{aN(N^2-1)(a-1)}$$

By some rearrangement of terms this can be put into the form given by Kelley as follows:

$$r_{1\prime} = 1 - \frac{a(4N+2)}{(a-1)(N-1)} + \frac{12\Sigma S^2}{a(a-1)(N^2-1)N} \quad (120)$$
(Average intercorrelation among arrays expressed in ranks)

Although this formula is somewhat long, all the terms in it have a conventional meaning, and it is easily applied in practice. It involves no special assumptions.

INTRACLASS CORRELATION

In formulas (118) and (119) for average intercorrelation the columns were treated as possibly somewhat different from one another. Consequently, we took their contributions to σ_i^2 from deviations from their own several means. But suppose we could be sure that these columns were alike, except for chance fluctuation. Suppose, for example, we had a number of trees represented by the rows and measurements of samples of the leaves from each spread through the rows. That would place the different trees in place of the 25 pupils and the leaves in place of the 16 raters. Then, since the leaves would not have been assigned to columns in any systematic manner, the columns would tend all to have the same means and the same variabilities. It would then make no appreciable difference whether we computed the σ's of the columns from their own means or from the grand mean. The same thing would be true if we had, say, measurements of the texture of the teeth of brothers spread through the rows and the families to which they belonged represented by the columns. In this situation we could use formula (119) with σ_i^2 computed from deviations from the grand mean. Such an average r between sets of members of which the pairs belong to the same class is called an *intraclass correlation*. It is evidently a special form of average intercorrelation in which sufficient confidence can be put in the assumption that the classes are alike (apart from chance fluctuation) that the deviations may be taken from the mean of the combined classes rather than from the means of the several classes. On this assumption Harris's formula[1] for intraclass correlation reduces to our formula (119). Of course, intraclass correlations can be computed directly from a correlation table by entering each pair twice, entering a member's score on the y axis at one entry and on the x axis at the second entry, then computing the r from the combined table. The outcome is the same as if formula (119) were used, but the process becomes too laborious beyond several pairs of classes. The worker must take warning that the technique of calculating intraclass correlations is highly sensitive to the fulfillment of its assumptions; if the classes are not really alike, so that the assumption of equal means is not fulfilled, highly distorted results may follow.[2]

[1] Quoted by Fisher, *Statistical Methods for Research Workers*, 7th ed., p. 220.

[2] *Ibid.*, p. 235, for an example in which the intraclass correlation technique leads to the inference that the r is negative when observation of the table, or calculation of the average intercorrelation among the columns or among the rows shows that the average intercorrelation of the classes is markedly positive.

CORRECTING A COEFFICIENT OF CORRELATION
FOR ATTENUATION

Virtually always in practice when we compute a coefficient of correlation between two arrays, we are correlating measures of imperfect reliability. To the extent to which our measures are unreliable, our obtained correlation is too low; if there were no reliability at all in our measures of one or both of the traits, we would get a zero correlation no matter how highly the traits were really correlated intrinsically, *i.e.*, if truly measured. We have a legitimate interest, therefore, in asking ourselves how much higher the true correlation is than the one we have obtained from our fallible measures. To find this correction is to "correct our r for attenuation." A formula for this purpose is easily derived after the manner employed in the second section of this chapter. Since we want the "true" correlation, we must have the correlation of the average scores from an all-but-infinite number of forms of each of the tests with which we are dealing. Making our starting point formula (111) in the first section of this chapter, we must therefore make both a and b infinite. As a preliminary step to doing this, we shall divide both numerator and denominator of the fraction by ab, and get

$$r_{af_x, bf_y} = \frac{\bar{r}_{xy}}{\sqrt{\frac{1}{a} + \left(1 - \frac{1}{a}\right) r_{1Ix}} \sqrt{\frac{1}{b} + \left(1 - \frac{1}{b}\right) r_{1Iy}}}$$

As a and b approach infinity, we shall have left

$$r_{x_\infty, y_\infty} = \frac{\bar{r}_{xy}}{\sqrt{r_{1Ix} r_{1Iy}}} \quad \text{(Formula for a coefficient of correlation corrected for attenuation)} \quad (121)$$

The r_{1Ix} and the r_{1Iy} are the reliability coefficients of the two tests, respectively. The $\bar{r}_{xy}$ is the average correlation between any number of samples of measures of the x and the y functions. But in practice we ordinarily have in hand only one pair of samples, and we must take this as representing the r between the functions obtained with fallible measures. Therefore the r corrected for attenuation is merely the obtained r divided by the square root of the product of the reliability coefficients of the measures. This formula is applicable, of course, not only to tests of the objective, verbal type but to any sort of estimates or other fallible measures. Sometimes this correction results in an r greater than 1.00. This is because the $\bar{r}_{xy}$ obtained from our particular sample is not the one we would have obtained from the average of a considerable number of samples but is an abnormally high variant. It is the practice to write no corrected r's as higher than 1.00 even though the correction gives mathematically a higher one.

THE RELATION BETWEEN TRUE AND FALLIBLE SCORES

This section merely extends the technique employed in the preceding one. For certain theoretical purposes we may wish to know certain relations between true and fallible scores (the latter being defined as the scores obtained from a relatively short instrument of measurement so that it yields results that vary somewhat from sample to sample and the former is defined as the scores yielded by an instrument applied an infinite number of times and the average taken so that the scores have been completely stabilized). We shall consider first the r between scores on a single sample of x measures and an infinite number of measurements of a y function. This will give us the r between fallible scores and a true criterion. Making the general formula [Eq. (111)] our starting point, b is to be infinite and a is to equal 1. Dividing numerator and denominator by b, we have

$$r_{\bar{a}x\bar{b}y} = \frac{a\bar{r}_{xy}}{\sqrt{a + (a^2 - a)r_{11x}} \sqrt{\frac{1}{b} + \left(1 - \frac{1}{b}\right)r_{11y}}}$$

Substituting 1 for a and infinity for b, we have

$$r_{x,y_\infty} = \frac{\bar{r}_{xy}}{\sqrt{1 + (1^2 - 1)r_{11x}} \sqrt{0 + (1 - 0)r_{11y}}}$$

$$r_{x,y_\infty} = \frac{\bar{r}_{xy}}{\sqrt{r_{11y}}} \qquad \text{(Correlation between a fallible score and a true criterion)} \qquad (122)$$

The r_{11y} is the reliability coefficient of the instrument that is to constitute the infallible criterion—computed from fallible samples of it which we have in hand. The $\bar{r}_{xy}$ is the obtained correlation between fallible measures of the two correlated functions. In order to get the r between true scores and a fallible criterion, we would need only to make the proper interchanges in the formula.

We shall next take the case of correlation between a single sample and the average of an infinite number of samples of the *same* function. Here we proceed in the same manner as in the preceding paragraph; but the $\bar{r}_{xy}$, the r_{1Ix}, and the r_{1Iy} are the same sort of correlations (since the x series and the y series are similar measures of the same function), so that all the r's of the formula will be r_{1I}.   Then

$$r_{af,bf} = \frac{ar_{1I}}{\sqrt{a + (a^2 - a)r_{1I}}\,\sqrt{\frac{1}{b} + \left(1 - \frac{1}{b}\right)r_{1I}}}$$

Substituting infinity for b and 1 for a, we have

$$r_{1\infty} = \frac{r_{1I}}{\sqrt{1}\,\sqrt{r_{1I}}} = \frac{r_{1I}}{\sqrt{r_{1I}}}$$

Reducing this by dividing the numerator by the denominator, we have

$$r_{1\infty} = \sqrt{r_{1I}} \qquad \substack{\text{(Index of reliability—the correlation}\\ \text{between fallible and true scores of}\\ \text{the same function)}} \qquad (123)$$

Thus the correlation between a set of fallible scores and a set of true scores of the same function is the square root of the average intercorrelation among the samples, *i.e.*, the square root of the reliability coefficient of the test.   This r between obtained scores and hypothetical true scores of a function is called the *index of reliability* in contrast with the *coefficient of reliability* of the test.   It is claimed by many persons that such index of reliability is a fairer formula in terms of which to state the reliability of a measure than is the coefficient of reliability.

Can we estimate an individual's true score from the fallible score we have in hand for him?   We shall see.   We have already learned how to estimate a score in a second series from a score in a first series, knowing the σ's of the two and the coefficient of correlation between them.   We make our estimate by means of the regression equation in score form, for which the formula was given on page 111.   It is $Y = r_{xy}(\sigma_y/\sigma_x)(X - M_x) + M_y$. For us the Y is to be the true score, σ_y the standard deviation of a set of true scores, σ_x the standard deviation of the sample we have in hand, and r_{xy} is to be $r_{1\infty}$.   Our formula then becomes

$$\overset{\infty}{X} = r_{1\infty} \frac{\sigma_x^\infty}{\sigma_x}(X - M_x) + M_x^\infty$$

So far as we know M_x^∞ is the same as M_x. We, therefore, know everything required by our regression equation except σ_x^∞. We shall now find that. Taking the square root of both sides of formula (117) we get

$$\sigma_{s_a} = \sigma_i\sqrt{a + (a^2 - a)r_{1I}}$$

This is the standard deviation of the sum of a sets of samples. We may get the standard deviation of the average of a samples by dividing the sum by a, remembering that we must make this a^2 when dividing under the radical sign.

$$\sigma_{\frac{s}{a}} = \sigma_i\sqrt{\frac{1}{a} + \left(1 - \frac{1}{a}\right)r_{1I}} \qquad \begin{array}{l}\text{(Standard deviation of the}\\ \text{average of } a \text{ correlated}\\ \text{measurements of the same}\\ \text{function)}\end{array} \quad (124)$$

Now let a approach infinity. We shall then have,

$$\sigma_\infty = \sigma_i\sqrt{0 + (1 - 0)r_{1I}}$$

$$\sigma_\infty = \sigma_i\sqrt{r_{1I}} \quad \text{(Standard deviation of a set of true scores)} \quad (124a)$$

We are now ready to substitute in our regression equation.

$$\overset{\infty}{X} = \frac{\sigma_x\sqrt{r_{1I}}}{\sigma_x} \cdot \sqrt{r_{1I}}(X - M_x) + M_x = r_{1I}(X - M_x) + M_x$$

By a rearrangement of terms this may be written in a form that is more convenient for operative purposes as follows:

$$\overset{\infty}{X} = r_{1I}X + (1 - r_{1I})M_x \qquad \begin{array}{l}\text{(Formula for a true score in}\\ \text{terms of a fallible score}\\ \text{and the reliability coeffi-}\\ \text{cient of the test)}\end{array} \quad (125)$$

What is the standard error involved in estimating a true score from a fallible criterion? We can easily determine. Our general formula for the standard error of estimate is

$$\sigma_{est y} = \sigma_y\sqrt{1 - r_{xy}^2}.$$

We wish now to have y become a true measure instead of a fallible one. There are two cases: the first is the one in which we want the standard error of estimate of a true score from a fallible score of the same function. Here y is to be replaced by

x_∞, so that we shall have

$$\sigma_{\text{est}_{x_\infty}} = \sigma_{x_\infty}\sqrt{1 - r_{1\infty}^2}$$

From our preceding developments we know that $\sigma_\infty = \sigma_x\sqrt{r_{1I}}$, that $r_{1\infty} = \sqrt{r_{1I}}$, and that, therefore, $r_{1\infty}^2 = r_{1I}$. Making these substitutions, we get,

$$\sigma_{\text{est}_{x_\infty}} = \sigma_x\sqrt{r_{1I}}\sqrt{1 - r_{1I}}$$
$$\sigma_{\text{est}_{x_\infty}} = \sigma_x\sqrt{r_{1I} - r_{1I}^2}$$

(Standard error of estimate of a true score from a fallible score of the same function)   (126)

We can make the converse approach and get the scatter of the fallible scores in hand around the true scores. This is called the *standard error of measurement* and is used considerably in interpreting reliability coefficients. Here x represents the true scores and y the fallible ones, and we have

$$\sigma_{(\text{Meas.})} = \sigma_y\sqrt{1 - r_{1\infty}^2} = \sigma_y\sqrt{1 - r_{1I}}$$

(Standard error of measurement)   (127)

P.E. is $.6745\sigma$. Therefore, employing the expression P.E.$_{\text{Meas.}}$ for the probable error of a fallible score when estimated from a true criterion,

$$\text{P.E.}_{(\text{Meas.})} = .6745\sigma\sqrt{1 - r_{1I}}$$

(Probable error of measurement)   (127a)

where, again, r_{1I} is the reliability coefficient of the test and σ is the standard deviation of the sample in hand.

The other case is where we wish to obtain the standard error of prediction of a true score in one function from a fallible score in another. The reader will be able to see, by proper substitutions in our basic formulas, that, when the x series and the y series are different,

$$\sigma_{\text{est}_{y_\infty}} = \sigma_y\sqrt{r_{1I_y} - r_{1I_y}\frac{r_{xy}^2}{r_{1I_y}}}$$
$$\sigma_{\text{est}_{y_\infty}} = \sigma_y\sqrt{r_{1I_y} - r_{xy}^2}$$

(Standard error of estimate of a true score in one function from a fallible score in another function)   (128)

Here the r_{1I_y} is the reliability coefficient of the y measure taken from the samples of it we have in hand, the σ_y is the standard deviation of the sample set of fallible measures, and the r_{xy} is the coefficient of correlation between fallible measures of the x function and fallible measures of the y function which we have in hand from our pair of samples.

The reader should take warning that the true scores about which we have been talking in these sections, the r's between true scores, and the σ's of true scores are to be taken as only hypothetical entities, useful for theoretical purposes. One is not justified in taking the theoretical true score calculated for a pupil to be necessarily his *correct* score. It is only that the *average* of the true scores made by individuals who earned the same score on a fallible measure as that attained by him would be the true score estimated for him. His own might diverge widely from the estimated one. Neither should we substitute true sigmas for obtained ones in practical computations or use the "r corrected for attenuation" in applied regression equations or in the multiple or partial correlation problems we shall treat in our next chapter.

CORRECTING A COEFFICIENT OF CORRELATION FOR HETEROGENEITY

It is well known that, other things being equal, the size of a coefficient of correlation is very much affected by the heterogeneity of the population on which it is computed. Suppose we were to select 25 representative persons ranging from one year of age to twenty-four years and to compute a coefficient of correlation between their ages and weights. The r would be very high, perhaps .90 or .95. Suppose, now, we select twenty-five representative persons of ages approximately thirteen to fourteen years—say a random sample from the pupils of the eighth grade in school—and compute a coefficient of correlation between the ages and weights of this more homogeneous population. The r would be very low. The same contrast holds in other types of data. When the coefficient of reliability of a test is given, it is important to know through what range of talent the test was given from which the r was computed. The same is true of a coefficient of correlation between intelligence test scores and scores on an academic achievement test, or an r between measures of any other two functions. To be comparable, two r's must have been computed from populations of the same degree of heterogeneity or there must be some method of correcting one of the r's so as to indicate what it would probably be if computed from the same type of population as that from which the one was derived with which it is being compared.

Kelley[1] has developed a formula for correcting an r for a range of talent different from that of another with which it is to be compared; in other words, for inferring what an r would be in one range of talent knowing its size in another range of talent. We shall employ a somewhat different approach from his but arrive at the same result. We take first the case of reliability.

Let x be a score (in deviation form) in the narrow range and x_∞ the corresponding true score. Then

$$x - x_\infty = d; \; x^2 - 2xx_\infty + x_\infty^2 = d^2$$

$$\frac{\Sigma x^2}{N} - \frac{2\Sigma xx_\infty}{N} + \frac{\Sigma x_\infty^2}{N} = \frac{\Sigma d^2}{N}; \; \sigma_x^2 - 2r_{xx_\infty}\sigma_x\sigma_{x_\infty} + \sigma_{x_\infty}^2 = \sigma_d^2$$

Similarly, let X and X_∞ be paired deviation scores in the wide range. Then, by the same process, if Σ represent the standard deviation in the wide range and R the coefficient of correlation,

$$\Sigma_X^2 - 2R_{XX_\infty}\Sigma_X\Sigma_{X_\infty} + \Sigma_{X_\infty}^2 = \Sigma_D^2$$

But, if the test is equally as effective in the narrow range as it is in the wide one, the distribution of differences between fallible and corresponding true scores will be the same in the two ranges,[2] so that σ_d^2 will equal Σ_D^2. Therefore,

$$\sigma_x^2 - 2r_{xx_\infty}\sigma_x\sigma_{x_\infty} + \sigma_{x_\infty}^2 = \Sigma_X^2 - 2R_{XX_\infty}\Sigma_X\Sigma_{X_\infty} + \Sigma_{X_\infty}^2$$

Substituting the values of r_{xx_∞} and σ_{x_∞} from formulas (123) and (124a), we have

$$\sigma_x^2 - 2\sqrt{r_{1I}}\sigma_x\sigma_x\sqrt{r_{1I}} + \sigma_x^2 r_{1I} = \Sigma_X^2 - 2\sqrt{R_{1I}}\Sigma_X\Sigma_X\sqrt{R_{1I}} + \Sigma_X^2 R_{1I}$$

$$\sigma_x^2 - 2r_{1I}\sigma_x^2 + \sigma_x^2 r_{1I} = \Sigma_X^2 - 2R_{1I}\Sigma_X^2 + \Sigma_X^2 R_{1I}$$

$$\sigma_x^2(1 - r_{1I}) = \Sigma_X^2(1 - R_{1I}); \; \frac{\sigma_x^2}{\Sigma_X^2} = \frac{1 - R_{1I}}{1 - r_{1I}}$$

$$\frac{\sigma_x}{\Sigma_X} = \frac{\sqrt{1 - R_{1I}}}{\sqrt{1 - r_{1I}}} \qquad \text{(Formula for correcting a reliability coefficient for heterogeneity)} \qquad (129)$$

From this formula it is easy to calculate either coefficient, know-

---

[1] KELLEY, T. L., *Statistical Method*, The Macmillan Company, 1923, pp. 221–223.

[2] This is identical with Kelley's assumption that the standard error of measurement is the same in both ranges. For the differences locate the items in the columns of the correlation surface, and, if the items that constitute the columns of the two surfaces are similarly placed, the variabilities of the columns under the two conditions will be the same.

ing the other and knowing the standard deviations in both the wide and the narrow range of talent.

This formula relates only to the case of reliability. The development will not work through in nearly so simple a manner in the case of inter-function correlation. In the latter case, assuming that the scatter ("variance") of the distribution of true scores in the one function from their corresponding true scores in the other function is the same in the narrow range as it is in the broad one, we would have the following rather complicated formulas:

$$\frac{\sigma_y}{\Sigma_y} = \frac{\sqrt{R_{1I_y} - (R_{xy}^2/R_{1I_x})}}{\sqrt{r_{1I_y} - (r_{xy}^2/r_{1I_x})}}; \text{ and } \frac{\sigma_x}{\Sigma_x} = \frac{\sqrt{R_{1I_x} - (R_{xy}^2/R_{1I_y})}}{\sqrt{r_{1I_x} - (r_{xy}^2/r_{1I_y})}}$$

(Formula for correcting inter-function
r's for heterogeneity) (130)

But these formulas involve the reliability coefficients of the measurements in both functions for both ranges. Often, if not usually, information regarding these will not be available. But we can do well enough with the much simpler formula developed below, which works with obtained scores rather than with true scores.

Let us assume that the standard errors of estimate are the same in the narrow range as in the wide one (see pages 112 to 113). That is,

$$\sigma_y \sqrt{1 - r_{xy}^2} = \Sigma_y \sqrt{1 - R_{xy}^2}$$

Dividing through this equation by $\Sigma_y \sqrt{1 - r_{xy}^2}$, we get

$$\frac{\sigma_y}{\Sigma_y} = \frac{\sqrt{1 - R_{xy}^2}}{\sqrt{1 - r_{xy}^2}}$$

similarly

(Approximate formula for
correcting inter-function (131)
r's for heterogeneity)

$$\frac{\sigma_x}{\Sigma_x} = \frac{\sqrt{1 - R_{xy}^2}}{\sqrt{1 - r_{xy}^2}}$$

These formulas demand no information regarding the reliabilities, and we shall shortly show that they work well enough in practice.

Kelley's formula for correcting a coefficient of correlation for heterogeneity has been severely challenged. Holzinger[1] gives

[1] HOLZINGER, KARL J., *Statistical Methods for Students in Education*, Ginn and Company, 1928, p. 254.

an illustration in which an r of .01 is increased to an R of .75 by doubling the size of the standard deviation and expresses doubt whether such an extreme change from merely doubling the variability could be reasonably expected. Odell (though not in criticism) gives an illustration in which he infers a negative correlation for a narrow range from a positive one for a wider range of talent. But both of these examples are hypothetical cases, and neither is a case likely to be ever encountered in practice. There are, in fact, limits to the extent to which variabilities may change by merely extending the range from which scores are drawn, which limitation neither Holzinger nor Odell seems to recognize. The variability of the whole y distribution cannot become less than that of a single column of the correlation chart (assuming homoscedasticity), for the y distribution must be made up of scores summed across the columns. The standard deviation of a column is $\sigma_y\sqrt{1 - r_{xy}^2}$. If the R of the heterogeneous population is below .87, it is impossible for the σ of the homogeneous population to be as small as half the large sigma. The absurdities involved in certain hypothetical cases will be found to turn upon ignoring this limitation.

However, in view of the challenge to Kelley's formula, we subjected it to empirical test. R. S. Hovis[1] secured evidence which indicates high validity for both formulas (129) and (131). One type of data he used was measurements of the relation of height and weight in children, based upon tables published in *Biometrika* from some Glasgow surveys. Ten different populations were employed, each with ranges from four to eight years when massed into heterogeneous populations and with a range of a single year for the homogeneous populations. In the narrow ranges the populations ranged in number from 255 to 1,445 and averaged about 800. Since measures of height and weight have nearly perfect reliability, formula (130) would reduce to (131). In 34 trials R's predicted by formula (131) missed the corresponding ones actually computed from the consolidated tables by an average of only .0189 when the algebraic signs of the deviations were disregarded and by only +.0048 when the signs were considered. But formula (129) gave just as good a prediction;

[1] Hovis, R. S., "An Evaluation and Comparison of Two Formulae for Correcting Coefficients of Correlation for Heterogeneity," master's thesis, Pennsylvania State College, 1935.

here the average error was .0172 when signs were disregarded and .0014 when signs were considered.

In a second study Hovis employed correlations between parts I and II of the Otis Classification Test (general intelligence and academic achievement), the homogeneous populations having a single grade range and the heterogeneous one a six-grade range. In these measurements the reliabilities were lower but still good. Out of 40 trials with formula (131) the predicted R missed the computed one by an average of .0129 when algebraic signs were disregarded and by .0097 when signs were considered. Formula (129) gave average errors of .0115 and .0065, respectively. Thus in both these studies these formulas for correcting r's for heterogeneity proved highly valid, and formula (129) was as good as formula (131), even though formula (129) does not theoretically apply to inter-function correlation.

REMOVING THE SPURIOUS ELEMENT IN CORRELATION DUE TO OVERLAPPING

A student of one of the writers was attempting to find the coefficient of correlation between college grades for a single year and those for other years. His data were in a form that gave the average number of grade points earned by each student during the junior year and the average up to the end of this same year. In the grading system in question quality points of 0, 1, 2, or 3 are given in each course; an average of these points for the year, obtained by multiplying the number of points awarded for a course by the number of "hours" in the course, summing for all courses of the year, and dividing by the aggregate number of hours carried during the year; and a similar point average computed "up-to-date." Our student could not obtain the average of the two preceding years excluding the junior year without considerable extra work. When he correlated the junior year averages with those of the 3-year period including the junior year, his r was .92, which was obviously spuriously high. It was spuriously high on account of the fact that the array which was to be used as a criterion included the array which was to be correlated with it. How could he remove this spurious element due to overlapping and ascertain what would have been the r if the overlapping element could have been removed from the accumulated point averages before computing the coefficient of correlation? We developed for this purpose a formula which applies to any sort of case where averages are employed and the criterion average includes the factor to be correlated with it. We shall use the following notation:

x = accumulated point average for all three years
y = point average 1 year less—to end of sophomore year
z = point average for the junior year alone
a = the number of years combined in x—in this case **3**.

For the sake of simplicity of development we shall take the x, y, and z as deviations from the means of their respective series. It can easily be shown that, if the means of the constituent arrays are all equal, the relations among the deviations will be the same as the corresponding relations among the scores; and a little later we shall show that the effects of inequalities among means, too, cancel out in this problem, so that we commit no error by developing our formula in terms of deviations rather than in terms of scores.

$(a - 1)$ years were involved in making up the point averages of y. Therefore, for any particular student,

$$x = \frac{y(a - 1) + z}{a}$$

Clearing of fractions,

$$ax = y(a - 1) + z$$

Multiplying through by z,

$$axz = yz(a - 1) + z^2$$

Summing for all students in the problem and dividing by their number,

$$a \frac{\Sigma xz}{N} = \frac{\Sigma yz}{N}(a - 1) + \frac{\Sigma z^2}{N}$$

The product moments can be reduced to r's, as done repeatedly in this book, by multiplying both numerators and denominators of the fractions by the two required σ's. Doing this, and using σ_z^2 for $\Sigma z^2/n$, we have

$$ar_{xz}\sigma_x\sigma_z = r_{yz}\sigma_y\sigma_z(a - 1) + \sigma_z^2$$

We want a value for r_{yz}.   Transposing, and solving for this, we get

$$r_{yz}\sigma_y\sigma_z(a-1) = ar_{xz}\sigma_x\sigma_z - \sigma_z^2; \ r_{yz} = \frac{a\sigma_x r_{xz} - \sigma_z}{(a-1)\sigma_y} \qquad (132)$$

Roughly, we might take the σ's to be equal, in which case our formula would reduce to $r_{yz} = (ar_{xz} - 1)/(a - 1)$.   But, in view of our showing in formula (124), the standard deviation of an average of correlated arrays is less than that of one of the component arrays and less than that of the average of a smaller number of arrays; to take the σ's as equal would give us a predicted r that would be somewhat too high.   We shall do better, therefore, not to assume equality of σ's in the formula even though we have reason to believe that the variabilities of the point averages are about the same in each year.   We know, as a by-product from the calculation of r_{xz}, the σ_x and the σ_z.   We do not know σ_y, and to compute it directly would make us too much trouble, since we would need to make up a set of averages for the $(a - 1)$ composite which is just what we are trying to avoid. But we can easily develop a formula for getting this standard deviation through elements we already know.   In any one student's case,

$$y = \frac{ax - z}{(a-1)}, \text{ and } y^2 = \frac{a^2 x^2 - 2axz + z^2}{(a-1)^2}$$

Summing for all individuals and dividing by their number,

$$\frac{\Sigma y^2}{N} = \frac{1}{(a-1)^2}\left[\frac{a^2 \Sigma x^2}{N} - 2a\frac{\Sigma xz}{N} + \frac{\Sigma z^2}{N}\right]$$

$$\sigma_y^2 = \frac{a^2\sigma_x^2 - 2ar_{xz}\sigma_x\sigma_z + \sigma_z^2}{(a-1)^2}$$

$$\sigma_y = \frac{1}{(a-1)}\sqrt{a^2\sigma_x^2 - 2ar_{xz}\sigma_x\sigma_z + \sigma_z^2}$$

(Standard deviation of the average of $(a - 1)$ arrays
in terms of the average of a arrays and 1 array)   (133)

We may now substitute this in formula (132) and have

$$r_{yz} = \frac{a\sigma_x r_{xz} - \sigma_z}{\sqrt{a^2\sigma_x^2 - 2ar_{xz}\sigma_x\sigma_z + \sigma_z^2}}$$

(Coefficient of correlation between the averages from $(a - 1)$ arrays and 1 array in terms of the averages from a arrays and 1 array)   (134)

We shall now correct for overlapping the spuriously high correlation found by our student. His r_{xz} was .92; σ_x was .47; and σ_z was .53. a was 3. Substituting these values in our formula we get,

$$r_{yz} = \frac{3 \cdot .47 \cdot .92 - .53}{\sqrt{9 \cdot .47^2 - 2 \cdot 3 \cdot .92 \cdot .47 \cdot .53 + .53^2}} = .811$$

This same general type of problem often confronts the investigator when he wishes to determine the relative validities of different tests by correlating the scores of each with the average of all the others, or when he wishes to learn which of several judges is best by ascertaining which judge's estimates correlate most highly with the average of all the others. It is much bother to make up each time a new average, omitting a different test or a different judge in turn. In order to save this labor, the same average of all is ordinarily kept for all the correlations, and each test or set of estimates is in turn correlated with this composite. But the r's thus obtained are spuriously high, because of the element of overlapping due to the inclusion in the total of the scores to be correlated with it. We can remove this spurious element by the use of the formula developed above.

But it will prove far easier to work with sums of scores than with averages, since an additional operation is required to reduce a sum to an average. A formula for sums instead of averages can be developed along the same lines, but more simply. We shall develop it in terms of scores rather than in terms of deviations, so as to fulfill our promise to show that inequality of means among the constituent arrays does not affect the formula.

$X =$ the score for an individual in the sum of all the arrays

$Y =$ the score of an individual in the sum of $(a - 1)$ arrays, the excluded one being the Z array

$Z =$ the score of an individual in the one array which we wish to correlate with the Y sum

$a =$ the whole number of arrays included in X

Then, for any one individual,

$$X = Y + Z$$

Multiplying through by Z,

$$XZ = YZ + Z^2$$

Summing for all individuals and dividing by their number, $(\Sigma XZ/N) = (\Sigma YZ/N) + (\Sigma Z^2/N)$. We must now subtract from each term the correction required to make it conform to the formula for an r or for a σ when taken in terms of scores rather than in terms of deviations. We may legitimately do this provided we compensatingly add these same terms.

$$\left(\frac{\Sigma XZ}{N\sigma_x\sigma_z} - \frac{M_xM_z}{\sigma_x\sigma_z}\right)\sigma_x\sigma_z = \left(\frac{\Sigma YZ}{N\sigma_y\sigma_z} - \frac{M_yM_z}{\sigma_y\sigma_z}\right)\sigma_y\sigma_z$$

$$+ \left(\frac{\Sigma Z^2}{N} - M_z^2\right) - M_xM_z + M_yM_z + M_z^2$$

$$r_{xz}\sigma_x\sigma_z = r_{yz}\sigma_y\sigma_z + \sigma_z^2 - M_xM_z + M_yM_z + M_z^2$$

transposing and solving for r_{yz},

$$r_{yz} = \frac{r_{xz}\sigma_x\sigma_z - \sigma_z^2 + (M_xM_z - M_yM_z - M_z^2)}{\sigma_y\sigma_z}$$

Before proceeding further we shall show that the M's in the parentheses aggregate zero. Since for each individual

$$Y = X - Z,$$

$\Sigma Y = \Sigma X - \Sigma Z$, and therefore $M_y = M_x - M_z$. Substituting this equivalent for the M_y in the parentheses, we get

$$M_xM_z - (M_zM_x - M_z^2) - M_z^2 = M_xM_z - M_xM_z$$
$$+ M_z^2 - M_z^2 = 0.$$

In view of the fact that the M's aggregate zero and cancel out, we have, upon canceling the σ_z from numerator and denominator, $r_{yz} = (r_{xz}\sigma_x - \sigma_z)/\sigma_y$.

We must now find a value for σ_y in terms of X and Z, as in our previous development.

$$Y = X - Z; \frac{\Sigma Y^2}{N} = \frac{\Sigma X^2}{N} - \frac{2\Sigma XZ}{N} + \frac{\Sigma Z^2}{N}$$

Adding and compensatingly subtracting the necessary quantities to make our terms σ's or r's when the items are taken as scores rather than as deviations,

$$\left(\frac{\Sigma Y^2}{N} - M_y^2\right) = \left(\frac{\Sigma X^2}{N} - M_x^2\right) - 2\left(\frac{\Sigma XZ}{N\sigma_x\sigma_z} - \frac{M_xM_z}{\sigma_x\sigma_z}\right)\sigma_x\sigma_z$$

$$+ \left(\frac{\Sigma Z^2}{N} - M_z^2\right) - M_y^2 - 2M_xM_z + M_z^2 + M_x^2$$

$$\sigma_y^2 = \sigma_x^2 + \sigma_z^2 - 2r_{xz}\sigma_x\sigma_z - (M_y^2 + 2M_xM_z - M_x^2 - M_z^2).$$

Before proceeding further, we shall show that the M's in the parentheses aggregate zero. $M_y = M_x - M_z$. Substituting this in the parentheses,

$$(M_x^2 - 2M_xM_z + M_z^2 + 2M_xM_z - M_x^2 - M_z^2) = 0.$$

We have left, therefore, as the value of σ_y,

$$\sigma_y = \sqrt{\sigma_x^2 + \sigma_z^2 - 2r_{xz}\sigma_x\sigma_z} \qquad \begin{array}{l}\text{(Standard deviation of the}\\ \text{sum of } (a-1) \text{ arrays in}\\ \text{terms of the sum of } a\\ \text{arrays and of 1 array)}\end{array} \quad (135)$$

We may now substitute this value of σ_y in the formula in which it occurs above and get as our completed formula

$$r_{yz} = \frac{r_{xz}\sigma_x - \sigma_z}{\sqrt{\sigma_x^2 + \sigma_z^2 - 2r_{xz}\sigma_x\sigma_z}} \qquad \begin{array}{l}\text{(Coefficient of correlation between}\\ \text{the sums from } (a-1) \text{ arrays and}\\ \text{1 array in terms of the sums from}\\ a \text{ arrays and 1 array)}\end{array} \quad (136)$$

In the case of averages, with which this section opened, we would have experienced the same behavior as between scores and deviations that we did in the case of summed series; *i.e.*, inequalities of means in the individual arrays would have canceled out leaving us the same formula when operating with items in score form as when operating in deviation form. None of the formulas involve any special assumptions. They can be counted upon to give the same r's as would have been obtained by separating the arrays before computing the coefficient of correlation and are very convenient methods of correcting r's for overlapping.

SPURIOUS INDEX CORRELATION

Another condition under which coefficients of correlation may be spuriously high is when each of the paired items is divided by a factor that is correlated with them. Thus, when we correlate IQ's and EQ's we have

$$r\left(\frac{\text{M.A.}}{\text{C.A.}} \frac{\text{E.A.}}{\text{C.A.}}\right)$$

Here both mental age and educational age are divided by chronological age. If C.A. were a constant the division would, of course, have no effect upon the correlation. But it is not a constant; it varies from pair to pair in a way that involves correlation with the numerator of its fraction. This involves a community between the two arrays that appreciably affects the correlation. The remedy here is to compute the coefficient of correlation between M.A. and E.A. with C.A. held constant by the technique of partial correlation. This will be discussed in our next chapter.

A corresponding thing happens when AQ's and IQ's are correlated. Here the common factor, mental age, enters as numerator in one of the variables and denominator in the other. The effect is characteristically a negative correlation between intelligence quotient and educational quotient (see reference to Douglass and Huffaker at end of this chapter).

Exercises

1. Have the members of the class in which you are participating, or have at least three teachers, rate specimens of handwriting, or of sewing, or of art on one of the scales available for such purpose. Determine the reliability of the ratings. Calculate how many judges would be needed to give a reliability coefficient of .97.

2. Have the members of the class estimate the weights of one another and determine both the reliability and the validity of the estimates.

3. In a similar spirit have persons give character ratings on classmates or on fraternity brothers, or have teachers rate their pupils on character traits, and ascertain the reliability of the ratings. Try different techniques for making these ratings specific and objective and ascertain effect upon reliability.

4. In a particular situation the r between history scores and geography scores is found to be .78. The history test has a reliability coefficient of .87 and the geography test a reliability coefficient of .91. Correct the r between history and geography for attenuation.

5. In a range of eight grades a certain intelligence test has a reliability coefficient of .98. What should it be expected to be for a single grade if the standard deviation for the eight grades combined is 32 and that for the single grade in question is 23?

6. In Table IV, pages 58 to 61, compute the r between scores on English literature and total English scores (which include those on literature). By means of formula (136) determine what the r should be between scores on literature and scores on the remainder of the test excluding literature; i.e., remove the spurious effect of the overlapping. Finally, actually subtract the literature scores from the total, compute the correlation, and see how your r from the actual net scores compares with the inferred one.

References for Further Study

DOUGLASS, HARL R.: "Note on the Correctness of Certain Error Formulas," *J. Educ. Psychol.*, Vol. 20, pp. 434–437; Vol. 21, pp. 621–624.

————, and C. L. HUFFAKER: "Correlation between Intelligence Quotient and Accomplishment Quotient," *J. Appl. Psychol.*, Vol. 13, pp. 76–80.

DUNLAP, J. W., and E. E. CURETON: "Note on the Standard Error of a Reliability Coefficient for a Different Range of Talent," *J. Educ. Psychol.*, Vol. 20, pp. 705–706.

EDGERTON, H. A., and H. A. TOOPS: "Formula for Finding the Average Inter-correlation of Unranked Raw Scores without Having Any of the Individual Inter-correlations," *J. Educ. Psychol.*, Vol. 19, pp.131–138.

HARRIS, J. A.: "On the Calculation of Intra-class and Inter-class Correlations," *Biometrika*, Vol. 9, pp. 446–472.

HOLZINGER, KARL, and CLAYTON: "Further Experiments in the Application of Spearman's Prophecy Formula," *J. Educ. Psychol.*, Vol. 16, pp. 289–299; Vol. 14, pp. 302–305.

MAY, MARK A.: "A Method for Correcting Coefficients of Correlation for Heterogeneity," *J. Educ. Psychol.*, Vol. 20, pp. 417–423.

NEIFELD, M. R.: "A Study of Spurious Correlation," *J. Amer. Statistical Assoc.*, Vol. 22, pp. 331–338.

RUCH, ACHERSON, and JACKSON: "Empirical Study of the Spearman-Brown Formula as Applied to Educational Test Material," *J. Educ. Psychol.*, Vol. 17, pp. 309–313.

CHAPTER VIII

PARTIAL AND MULTIPLE CORRELATION

The title to this chapter is likely to lead the reader to fear that he will find treated at this point a very complicated and a very mysterious topic. If he is already acquainted with the treatment of this matter in elementary texts in statistics, his experience there is likely to have confirmed this impression, especially in view of the rather forbidding-looking formulas that enter into the technique. But, in fact, partial regression and partial and multiple correlation are very simple in principle and parallel at every point simple regression and simple correlation as treated in Chap. IV. The reader should observe this parallelism as he progresses through the chapter.

NATURE AND USE OF THE MULTIPLE REGRESSION EQUATION

We may best approach the problem of the nature and use of the multiple regression equation through some illustrations. An agriculturalist wishes to predict from conditions that obtain up to the end of May what will most likely be the number of bushels of wheat produced per acre in July. This yield will be influenced by several known factors, such as, (1) the aggregate number of inches of rainfall through April and May, (2) the number of days of sunshine through these months, (3) the average temperature through these months. But these are not of equal importance as factors. In making his estimate, he must multiply each by an index number that will most closely accord with its relative degree of importance in affecting the yield of wheat. These several indices are the regression coefficients.

Again, we wish to predict a student's grade in school from several factors known in advance. These factors are such as the following: (1) his intelligence score; (2) time spent in study; (3) health; (4) the socioeconomic status of the home in which he lives. If we wish to predict his scholarship most closely, we may not give equal consideration to each of these factors, but must multiply the scores on each by a coefficient growing out of its relative importance as a factor in producing the result in which we are interested. A critical problem becomes for us, then, the problem of ascertaining what are the relative degrees of importance with which the several components enter in the determination of the criterion; *i.e.*, finding the several regression coefficients. Or we may merely wish to know the relative weights of the factors as an evidence of their relative importance. Many such problems confront the educational and social research worker, such as: To what extent do stature, intelligence, quickness of decision, and breadth of scholarship contribute to leadership? In what relative degrees do hours spent in formal drill, in browsing, in listening to lectures, in going to movies contribute to one's knowledge of history? And countless others. These relative weights are found by essentially the same procedure as the coefficients which are mentioned above. Or, perhaps, we may wish to put the matter in terms of coefficients of correlation because these are more familiar than regression coefficients. We shall then wish to find the extent of correlation between each of our several causative factors and our criterion when the influence of the other factors is ruled out. These correlations which express what may be expected to be the relation between one of a team of factors and a criterion when the influence of the other members of the team is held constant, we call the coefficients of partial correlation. We shall see later that they are very closely akin to the regression coefficients and that they may be derived by essentially the same machinery. Perhaps we may wish to know what is the maximum accuracy with which we could predict a criterion by combining a number of predictive factors each with its "best weight"; how high a correlation, *i.e.*, we could get in the case of our illustration between scholarship and our four contributing factors listed above taken jointly if we combined these in the best possible proportion. This maximum correlation that may be expected from combining a team of factors is called the *coefficient of multiple correlation*. It may be derived directly from the regression coefficients. When, too, the technique of computing partial correlations can be made sufficiently simple to permit its use by the rank and file of research workers, we shall find it a feasible substitute for parallel-group experimentation where we cannot control certain disturbing variables in our

experiment but can rule out their influence upon our findings by
the partial correlation technique. It is clear, therefore, that,
if we can get hold of the secret of finding partial regression
coefficients, we shall have at our command an extremely useful
tool in all our research.

DERIVATION OF THE FUNDAMENTAL "NORMAL EQUATIONS"

Our problem, you remember, is to find multipliers for a team
of scores that will give each of the scores best weight in predicting
(or producing) a criterion score. Let us put this in the form of
an equation. Let us suppose that x_0 is the score of a particular
student in scholarship (taken as a deviation from the mean of
the scholarship scores rather than as a raw score), and x_1, x_2, x_3,
and x_4 are the same student's scores on intelligence, socioeconomic
status, health, and attendance, respectively. Then

$$(A) \qquad x_0 = b_1x_1 + b_2x_2 + b_3x_3 + b_4x_4$$

where the b's are the coefficients by which we must multiply the
several scores. We do not, of course, know the values of these
b's; their values are just the very things we are seeking. But it
is one of the beauties of algebra that it permits us to play with
quantities, even if we do not yet know their numerical values;
we merely designate them by letters and handle them as such until
we can reach the point where we shall have found values for
them. We know that there is *some* value by which we must
multiply x_1 in order to give it its best weight, and also some value
for each of the other coefficients, and we merely set b's for these
values then proceed to search for the numerical equivalents for
the b's as our regression coefficients.

But we have probably measured intelligence, socioeconomic
status, health, and attendance in terms of different units, so that
our x's in the different series are of unlike meaning. To carry
them along in this way will cause unnecessary cumbersomeness.
Let us, therefore, reduce all of our scores to "standard measures"
which have everywhere the same meaning; we can easily return
to ordinary scores when we wish. To get standard measures we
merely divide each deviation score by the standard deviation of
the array to which it belongs. We shall let z's stand for the scores
in standard measures. Then

$$z_0 = \frac{x_0}{\sigma_0}, \; z_1 = \frac{x_1}{\sigma_1}, \; z_2 = \frac{x_2}{\sigma_2}, \text{ etc.}$$

We shall also use β's for the regression coefficients with standard measures instead of small b's.   Our equation then becomes

$$\bar{z}_0 = \beta_1 z_1 + \beta_2 z_2 + \beta_3 z_3 + \beta_4 z_4$$

In order to generalize our equation, we merely extend it out toward the right to any number of factors.

(B) $$\bar{z}_0 = \beta_1 z_1 + \beta_2 z_2 + \beta_3 z_3 + \cdots + \beta_n z_n$$

Now, if only we could apply some algebraic procedure to this equation, we might find the values of our several β's.   But we are blocked by the fact that we have only one equation and in it a number of unknowns—all the β's.   We are helpless in this sort of situation until we have as many independent equations as unknown quantities.   Is there any way out?

Yes, there is a way out, a way of getting as many equations as we need, but it involves a little calculus.

We have drawn a little horizontal line above the z_0 in the preceding equation.   That is to indicate that it would be the value computed (estimated from the combination on the right). Each score thus estimated from the right side of the equation, when the β's are so determined as to give the best prediction on the average, would miss the corresponding student's actual score a little.   The error in any one case would be $z_0 - \bar{z}_0$.   If we substitute for $\bar{z}_0$, its value from Eq. (B), we have[1]

$$z_0 - \bar{z}_0 = z_0 - (\beta_1 z_1 + \beta_2 z_2 + \beta_3 z_3 + \beta_4 z_4 + \cdots + \beta_n z_n)$$

Now it is a principle of mathematics that for best fit the sum of the squares of the errors should be a minimum.   We shall, therefore, square both sides of our equation and indicate by the summation sign that we have passed from considering a single score to the consideration of all the scores, because they all obey the same laws.   Indicating the square on the left and squaring out the term on the right, we have

$$\begin{aligned}
\Sigma(z_0 - \bar{z}_0)^2 = \Sigma(&z_0^2 + \beta_1^2 z_1^2 + \beta_2^2 z_2^2 + \beta_3^2 z_3^2 + \cdots + \beta_n^2 z_n^2 \\
&- 2z_0 z_1 \beta_1 - 2z_0 z_2 \beta_2 - 2z_0 z_3 \beta_3 - \cdots - 2z_0 z_n \beta_n \\
&+ 2z_1 z_2 \beta_1 \beta_2 + 2z_1 z_3 \beta_1 \beta_3 + 2z_1 z_4 \beta_1 \beta_4 + \cdots + 2z_1 z_n \beta_1 \beta_n \\
&+ 2z_2 z_3 \beta_2 \beta_3 + 2z_2 z_4 \beta_2 \beta_4 + 2z_2 z_5 \beta_2 \beta_5 + \cdots + 2z_2 z_n \beta_2 \beta_n + \cdots)
\end{aligned}$$

[1] The procedure here is identical in character with that involved in the Pearson product-moment formula, p. 95.

Now, as was stated above, we want the values of the β's to be such that the right-hand member of our equation will be a minimum. We must, therefore, differentiate it and set its derivative equal to zero. But, since our equation contains a number of independent variables (the several β's), we must resort to partial differentiation, $i.e.$, we must differentiate separately for each of the variables in turn. Differentiating first with respect to β_1 (and remembering that every term will drop out of our derivative that does not contain a β_1), we have

$$\Sigma(2\beta_1 z_1 z_1 - 2z_0 z_1 + 2\beta_2 z_1 z_2 + 2\beta_3 z_1 z_3 + 2\beta_4 z_1 z_4 + \cdots$$
$$+ 2\beta_n z_1 z_n) = 0$$

We shall now place the summation sign with each of the elements within the parentheses, which is a legitimate way of summating a complex quantity, and also divide through our equation by $2N$. Then we have

$$\beta_1 \frac{\Sigma z_1 z_1}{N} - \frac{\Sigma z_0 z_1}{N} + \beta_2 \frac{\Sigma z_1 z_2}{N} + \beta_3 \frac{\Sigma z_1 z_3}{N} + \beta_4 \frac{\Sigma z_1 z_4}{N} + \cdots$$
$$+ \beta_n \frac{\Sigma z_1 z_n}{N} = 0$$

But remember that z_1 equals x_1/σ_1, z_2 equals x_2/σ_2, etc. Therefore $\Sigma z_1 z_2/N$ equals $\Sigma x_1 x_2/N\sigma_1\sigma_2$. But this, it will be observed, is the formula for the Pearson r. For all such quantities in our equation we may, therefore, substitute r's with the proper subscripts. We shall then have (remembering that r_{11} represents perfect self-correlation, which is equal to unity)

$$\beta_1 - r_{01} + \beta_2 r_{12} + \beta_3 r_{13} + \beta_4 r_{14} + \cdots + \beta_n r_{1n} = 0$$

We must next differentiate in the same way for each of the other β's. The result will be n equations similar in symmetry with the one above. Transposing the terms preceded by the minus sign, we have the following as our set of "normal equations":

$$r_{01} = \beta_1 + \beta_2 r_{12} + \beta_3 r_{13} + \beta_4 r_{14} + \beta_5 r_{15} + \beta_6 r_{16} + \cdots + \beta_n r_{1n}$$
$$r_{02} = \beta_1 r_{12} + \beta_2 + \beta_3 r_{23} + \beta_4 r_{24} + \beta_5 r_{25} + \beta_6 r_{26} + \cdots + \beta_n r_{2n}$$
$$r_{03} = \beta_1 r_{13} + \beta_2 r_{23} + \beta_3 + \beta_4 r_{34} + \beta_5 r_{35} + \beta_6 r_{36} + \cdots + \beta_n r_{3n}$$
$$r_{04} = \beta_1 r_{14} + \beta_2 r_{24} + \beta_3 r_{34} + \beta_4 + \beta_5 r_{45} + \beta_6 r_{46} + \cdots + \beta_n r_{4n}$$
$$r_{0n} = \beta_1 r_{1n} + \beta_2 r_{2n} + \beta_3 r_{3n} + \beta_4 r_{4n} + \beta_5 r_{5n} + \beta_6 r_{6n} + \cdots + \beta_n$$

Our concern from the first was to find values for our β's. We have now found our way of doing so. We have as many equations in our set as we have independent variables. It is, therefore, in principle, a very simple matter to solve these equations and find the values of our β's. All that there is to any special method of computing regression coefficients is some method of simplifying the solution of a set of simultaneous equations Practically every reader has solved such problems in high-school algebra, and you might be interested in trying on this set of equations the methods you have learned there, substituting numerical values, of course, for the r's. But you will find the job extremely complex if you use more than two or three variables. The labor mounts rapidly with an increase in the number of equations and becomes enormous after four or five.

THE MOST ECONOMICAL METHODS FOR COMPUTING REGRESSION COEFFICIENTS

The principal trick in working with regression equations is to command some economical method of solving these equations. In the texts on statistics the method customarily explained involves doing in turn a series of partial sigmas and partial r's, each time reducing the partials to a lower order by one. This is the method developed by Yule, which we may call the *partial correlations method*. But this process gets immensely complicated beyond three or four variables and also involves working with what for the layman are magical procedures the meaning of which he does not grasp. There is needed a simpler and more meaningful method.

Various persons have devised schemes for reducing the labor involved in solving such sets of simultaneous equations. As early as 1855 Gauss developed a method of shortening the process by successive trials and approximations. The determinants treated in texts in college algebra afford a convenient method for solving simultaneous equations for those who are familiar with them. Within the past ten years Truman Kelley developed an indirect method for attacking this particular problem of regression coefficients which he called first *the approximation method* and later, in a further developed form, *the iteration method*. But these approximation methods are also difficult to learn and very baffling to laymen. Peters and Wykes[1] set forth a completed-

---

[1] PETERS and WYKES, "Completed Determinants Method," *J. Educ. Res.*, Vol. 24, pp. 44–52.

determinants method making available to laymen the method of determinants in a form that makes no demand that the worker know the algebra of determinants.

The Doolittle method was developed by M. H. Doolittle, of the U.S. Coast and Geodetic Survey, about 1857. Up to this time but little attention has been given to it in texts on educational statistics, although such books as those of Mills and of Ezekiel have presented it. For any considerable number of variables it is by far the best method available. We shall turn now to an explanation of it and to certain work sheets embodying it. The Doolittle method takes advantage of the fact that our set of equations is symmetrical to multiply each, as it is used, by such factor that, when the equations are added, certain terms at the left aggregate zero and are thus eliminated. In this way the number of terms is rapidly reduced to a single unknown, which can then be directly calculated. Thereafter the process must be reversed and substitutions progressively made until all of the unknowns have been found. In the following work sheets, set up by Mrs. Wykes, the procedure is indicated step by step. Our work sheet extends to ten variables, but beyond that number the student can make his own formulas by induction from the steps used up to ten variables. Evidence given in the series of articles, of which the one just referred to is the second, shows that the completed-determinants method is the most economical one up to four variables and that beyond that point the Doolittle method is by far the most economical.

WORK SHEETS FOR THE DOOLITTLE METHOD

The directions on the accompanying sheet are so explicit that no difficulty should be encountered in understanding them. An illustration will be given after the work sheet has been given and explained. It is to be noted that each row (line) has a number and each column a designating letter. These numbers and letters are used in the directions.

The 1 found in the first row and column of each new section is considered in all calculations. It has been placed there permanently because that is always the value of the item in that place.

The work sheet is prepared for calculations up to a ten-variable problem. For any larger number of variables the reader can extend the work sheet by induction from the steps so far

Work Sheet for the Doolittle Method

Directions	A	B	C	D	E	F	G	H	J	I	X
1 Insert values for r's	1	r_{12}	r_{13}	r_{14}	r_{15}	r_{16}	r_{17}	r_{18}	r_{19}	$-r_{01}$	ΣA to I
2 Divide line 1 by -1											
3 Insert values for r's		1	r_{23}	r_{24}	r_{25}	r_{26}	r_{27}	r_{28}	r_{29}	$-r_{02}$	ΣB to I
4 Multiply items in line 1, B to I, by B_2											
5 Add algebraically lines 3 and 4											
6 Divide line 5 by negative B_5											
7 Insert values for r's			1	r_{34}	r_{35}	r_{36}	r_{37}	r_{38}	r_{39}	$-r_{03}$	ΣC to I
8 Multiply items in line 1, C to I, by C_2											
9 Multiply items in line 5, C to I, by C_6											
10 Add algebraically lines 7, 8, 9											
11 Divide line 10 by negative C_{10}											
12 Insert values for r's				1	r_{45}	r_{46}	r_{47}	r_{48}	r_{49}	$-r_{04}$	ΣD to I
13 Multiply items in line 1, D to I, by D_2											
14 Multiply items in line 5, D to I, by D_6											
15 Multiply items in line 10, D to I, by D_{11}											
16 Add algebraically lines 12, 13, 14, 15											
17 Divide line 16 by negative D_{16}											
18 Insert values for r's					1	r_{56}	r_{57}	r_{58}	r_{59}	$-r_{05}$	ΣE to I
19 Multiply items in line 1, E to I, by E_2											
20 Multiply items in line 5, E to I, by E_6											
21 Multiply items in line 10, E to I, by E_{11}											
22 Multiply items in line 16, E to I, by E_{17}											
23 Add algebraically lines 18, 19, 20, 21, 22											
24 Divide line 23 by negative E_{23}											
25 Insert values for r's						1	r_{67}	r_{68}	r_{69}	$-r_{06}$	ΣF to I
26 Multiply items in line 1, F to I, by F_2											
27 Multiply items in line 5, F to I, by F_6											
28 Multiply items in line 10, F to I, by F_{11}											
29 Multiply items in line 16, F to I, by F_{17}											
30 Multiply items in line 23, F to I, by F_{24}											
31 Add algebraically lines 25, 26, 27, 28, 29, 30											
32 Divide line 31 by negative F_{31}											
33 Insert values for r's							1	r_{78}	r_{79}	$-r_{07}$	ΣG to I
34 Multiply items in line 1, G to I, by G_2											
35 Multiply items in line 5, G to I, by G_6											
36 Multiply items in line 10, G to I, by G_{11}											
37 Multiply items in line 16, G to I, by G_{17}											
38 Multiply items in line 23, G to I, by G_{24}											
39 Multiply items in line 31, G to I, by G_{32}											
40 Add algebraically lines 33, 34, 35, 36, 37, 38, 39											
41 Divide line 40 by negative G_{40}											
42 Insert values for r's								1	r_{89}	$-r_{08}$	ΣH to I
43 Multiply items in line 1, H to I, by H_2											
44 Multiply items in line 5, H to I, by H_6											
45 Multiply items in line 10, H to I, by H_{11}											
46 Multiply items in line 16, H to I, by H_{17}											
47 Multiply items in line 23, H to I, by H_{24}											
48 Multiply items in line 31, H to I, by H_{32}											
49 Multiply items in line 40, H to I, by H_{41}											
50 Add algebraically lines 42, 43, 44, 45, 46, 47, 48, 49											
51 Divide line 50 by negative H_{50}											
52 Insert values for r's									1	$-r_{09}$	ΣJ to I
53 Multiply items in line 1, J to I, by J_2											
54 Multiply items in line 5, J to I, by J_6											
55 Multiply items in line 10, J to I, by J_{11}											
56 Multiply items in line 16, J to I, by J_{17}											
57 Multiply items in line 23, J to I, by J_{24}											
58 Multiply items in line 31, J to I, by J_{32}											
59 Multiply items in line 40, J to I, by J_{41}											
60 Multiply items in line 50, J to I, by J_{51}											
61 Add algebraically lines 52, 53, 54, 55, 56, 57, 58, 59, 60											
62 Divide line 61 by negative J_{61}											

Substitute values from above table for symbols in following equations (β's for each equation found when each variable in turn is solved for) and solve equations for the regression coefficients, $\beta_1, \beta_2, \beta_3, \ldots \beta_k$.

$\beta_9 = I_{62}$

$\beta_8 = (\beta_9)J_{51} + I_{51}$

$\beta_7 = (\beta_9)J_{41} + (\beta_8)H_{41} + I_{41}$

$\beta_6 = (\beta_9)J_{32} + (\beta_8)H_{32} + (\beta_7)G_{32} + I_{32}$

$\beta_5 = (\beta_9)J_{24} + (\beta_8)H_{24} + (\beta_7)G_{24} + (\beta_6)F_{24} + I_{24}$

$\beta_4 = (\beta_9)J_{17} + (\beta_8)H_{17} + (\beta_7)G_{17} + (\beta_6)F_{17} + (\beta_5)E_{17} + I_{17}$

$\beta_3 = (\beta_9)J_{11} + (\beta_8)H_{11} + (\beta_7)G_{11} + (\beta_6)F_{11} + (\beta_5)E_{11} + (\beta_4)D_{11} + I_{11}$

$\beta_2 = (\beta_9)J_6 + (\beta_8)H_6 + (\beta_7)G_6 + (\beta_6)F_6 + (\beta_5)E_6 + (\beta_4)D_6 + (\beta_3)C_6 + I_6$

$\beta_1 = (\beta_9)J_2 + (\beta_8)H_2 + (\beta_7)G_2 + (\beta_6)F_2 + (\beta_5)E_2 + (\beta_4)D_2 + (\beta_3)C_2 + (\beta_2)B_2 + I_2$

presented. For anything less than a ten-variable problem, columns not needed should be cut off (marked out) beginning with the J column. Thus, work would be continued only through the H column for a nine-variable problem, through the G column for an eight variable, and so on. (The criterion is always counted as one of the variables.) In all cases, no matter what the number of variables, the I column is used.

The lower sections also disappear *in toto* with a smaller number of variables than ten. They will disappear below that section where the column with your highest-numbered r subscript terminates in a 1. But this will not bother you; it will take care of itself.

In the back solution, provided for at the foot of the work sheet, rows and columns also disappear with a smaller number of variables. Beginning at the top of the set of back-solution equations, draw a line through each β on the left side of the equations that has a subscript for which you have no corresponding r subscript. Extend this line all the way across, thus striking out the whole equation constituting that line. Then strike out all the columns that have had their respective I's eliminated with the eliminated rows. The remaining elements are all that are needed in the back solution, discussed in our next paragraph.

You need now only find the values of the several β's in these back-solution equations at the foot of the work sheet. They are the regression coefficients you are seeking, each corresponding with a similarly numbered element in your r's. The value of the topmost one is indicated directly in your equation; the others are obtained by successive substitutions in the equations that follow.

The X column in the work sheet is the check for correctness. Its use is optional, but, if it is not used, the problem should be done simultaneously by two different workers and their results compared from time to time, or should be done by the same person twice on different work sheets, perfect consistency being required.

The check is to be used as follows: the capital sigma is the summation sign, meaning that you should add together all the items in the line between the limits named, including the limits. The X column is to be included each time you are told to multiply,

add, or divide lines.   But carefully note this exception: before multiplying any summated item in the X column by the factor used as a multiplier throughout the line, subtract from this summation all the items in that line lying to the left of the column with which the multiplications in that line started.   For example, in line 14 you are told to "multiply items in line 5, D to I, by D_6." When you extend this multiplication into the X column you must first subtract from the value standing at X_5 the values at C_5 and B_5 before multiplying the remainder by D_6.   It amounts to the same thing to sum the line only from the column in which the multiplier is found.   A corresponding thing must be done at lines 4, 8, 9, 13, and every other place where such a multiplication is called for.[1]

Before proceeding further, we shall do an example, since the directions for using the work sheets seem to be hard to follow before concrete illustration and easy to follow thereafter.   We shall use a study by Miss Dessa E. Gresser on "The Factors Conditioning Comprehension of Literature in the Senior High School."[2]   One finds some pupils who have difficulty in comprehending the literature they read.   One feels at a loss to know what to do for them until one knows what are the factors that cause the failure to comprehend.   Miss Gresser undertook to ascertain what some of these factors are and with what weight they severally contribute toward the ability to comprehend. It is to this sort of problem that the partial regression technique lends itself as a tool.

The factors considered by Miss Gresser were

1. Speed of reading.
2. Knowledge of grammar.
3. Range of general information.
4. Knowledge of vocabulary.

Each of these abilities was measured by suitable tests and scores on each obtained for each pupil used in the research.   The criterion, ability to comprehend literature, was similarly meas-

---

[1] The spacing in the work sheet on p. 227 is too small to permit operations on the page unless with a very sharp pencil.   For a work sheet with wider spacing the worker should copy this one on a larger scale or send to the authors for copies.

[2] A master's thesis at the Pennsylvania State College 1932.   Abstracted in *Penn. State Studies in Educ.* No. 8.

ured by the Stanford Test of Comprehension of Literature. The following zero-order correlations were obtained among these four factors and the criterion, for the last of which we use the subscript 0 and for the others the numbers indicated above.

$$r_{01} = .334 \quad r_{12} = .370 \quad r_{23} = .642 \quad r_{34} = .735$$
$$r_{02} = .416 \quad r_{13} = .396 \quad r_{24} = .578$$
$$r_{03} = .653 \quad r_{14} = .567$$
$$r_{04} = .691$$

We must now insert these values for the several r's in the proper places in the work sheet and do what the work sheet says. The reader should carefully verify all the steps, then use this example as a model. In using the work sheet, (opposite page) we omit all parts we do not need for a problem of this length.

The results we get at the foot of the work sheet are the partial regression coefficients. What do they mean? They serve two sorts of purposes. One of these is to show us the relative weights of the four factors in contributing to ability to comprehend literature. These weights are speed of reading, $-.0691$; knowledge of grammar, $-.0857$; range of information, $+.3530$; and knowledge of vocabulary, $+.5203$. The first two are substantially equal to zero, so that we may say grammar (as measured by the Kirby test) and ability to read rapidly do not contribute significantly to ability to comprehend literature when these are separated from the force they get by overlapping general information and knowledge of vocabulary. The other two contribute heavily, vocabulary making a larger net contribution than general information. These weights are not to be confused with percentages; they cannot be expected to add up to $+1$. They are the slopes of the respective regression lines relating the criterion with each of the factors in turn, when the influence of the other factors involved in the problem (but not additional disturbing factors) are held constant and provided the factors are measured in units of equal variability.

The second use is prediction of scores in the criterion from a knowledge of scores in each of the contributing factors. If we take our measures in z scores, we can predict the score a student is most likely to make in comprehension from his scores in the four other tests by the regression equation

$$z_0 = -.0691z_1 - .0857z_2 + .3530z_3 + .5203z_4$$

But it is only in those cases where we are dealing with scores that have the same variability in all distributions—like z scores,

DOOLITTLE WORK SHEET

Miss Gresser's Data—Arranged for Obtaining $\beta_{04\cdot123}$

Directions	A	B	C	D	I	X
1 Insert values for r's	1	r_{12}.370	r_{13}.396	r_{14}.567	$-r_{01}-.334$	$+1.9990$
2 Divide line 1 by -1	-1	$-.370$	$-.396$	$-.567$	$+.334$	
3 Insert values for r's		1	r_{23}.642	r_{24}.578	$-r_{02}-.416$	$+1.8040$
4 Multiply items in line 1, B to I, by B_2		$-.1369$	$-.1465$	$-.2098$	$+.1236$	$-.3696$
5 Add algebraically lines 3 and 4		$+.8631$	$+.4955$	$+.3682$	$-.2924$	$+1.4344$
6 Divide line 5 by negative B_5		-1	$-.5741$	$-.4266$	$+.3388$	-1.6619
7 Insert values for r's			1	r_{34}.735	$-r_{03}-.653$	$+1.0820$
8 Multiply items in line 1, C to I, by C_2			$-.1568$	$-.2245$	$+.1323$	$-.2490$
9 Multiply items in line 5, C to I, by C_6			$-.2845$	$-.2114$	$+.1679$	$-.3280$
10 Add algebraically lines 7, 8, and 9			$+.5587$	$+.2991$	$-.3528$	$+.5050$
11 Divide line 10 by negative C_{10}			-1	$-.5353$	$+.6315$	$-.9039$
12 Insert values for r's				1	$-r_{04}-.691$	$+.3090$
13 Multiply items in line 1, D to I, by D_2				$-.3215$	$+.1894$	$-.1321$
14 Multiply items in line 5, D to I, by D_6				$-.1571$	$+.1247$	$-.0323$
15 Multiply items in line 10, D to I, by D_{11}				$-.1601$	$+.1889$	$+.0287$
16 Add algebraically lines 12, 13, 14, and 15				$+.3613$	$-.1880$	$+.1733$
17 Divide line 16 by negative D_{16}				-1	$+.5203$	$-.4797$

Substitute values from above table for symbols in the following equations (β's for each equation found when each variable in turn is solved for) and solve equations for the regression coefficients, β_1, β_2, β_3, and β_4.

$$\beta_4 = I_{17} = +.5203$$
$$\beta_3 = (\beta_4)(D_{11}) + I_{11} = (.5203)(-.5353) + .6315 = +.3530$$
$$\beta_2 = (\beta_4)(D_6) + (\beta_3)(C_6) + I_6 = (.5203)(-.4266) + (.3530)(-.5741)$$
$$+ .3388 = -.0857$$
$$\beta_1 = (\beta_4)(D_2) + (\beta_3)(C_2) + (\beta_2)(B_2) + I_2 = -.0691$$

T scores, ranks, or percentiles—that our predicting equation remains so simple.   If we have scores of unequal variabilities, we must take account of the sigmas.   If our measures are in terms of deviations from the means of their respective arrays, our regression equation would become

$$\bar{x}_0 = \sigma_0\left(- .0691 \frac{x_1}{\sigma_1} - .0857 \frac{x_2}{\sigma_2} + .3530 \frac{x_3}{\sigma_3} + .5203 \frac{x_4}{\sigma_4}\right)$$

If we wish to put this in terms of raw scores instead of deviations, we must substitute $(X_1 - M_1)$ for x_1, $(X_2 - M_2)$ for x_2, etc. We shall then have, as our regression equation,

$$\bar{X}_0 = \sigma_0\left(- .0691 \frac{X_1}{\sigma_1} - .0857 \frac{X_2}{\sigma_2} + .3530 \frac{X_3}{\sigma_3} + .5203 \frac{X_4}{\sigma_4}\right) - K$$

where K is given by the following expression (which may be calculated once for all the scores):

$$K = \sigma_0\left(- .0691 \frac{M_1}{\sigma_1} - .0857 \frac{M_2}{\sigma_2} + .3530 \frac{M_3}{\sigma_3} + .5203 \frac{M_4}{\sigma_4}\right) - M_0$$

The $\bar{X}_0$ in this equation is the score predicted for an individual from the team at the right. Let us take the following hypothetical data from Miss Gresser's study. A boy made the following scores:

1. Speed of reading, 100.
2. Grammar, 30.
3. General information, 90.
4. Vocabulary, 80.

What score may he be expected to make in comprehension of literature? We shall take the means and the standard deviations of our several factors to be as follows:

	Mean	Standard Deviation
1. Reading......................	96	30
2. Grammar...................	35	6
3. Information................	96	20
4. Vocabulary.................	92	30
0. Comprehension.............	63	22

Putting these values in our score-form regression equation, we predict for this boy:

$$\bar{X}_0 = 22(-.0691\tfrac{100}{30} - .0857\tfrac{30}{6} + .3530\tfrac{90}{20} + .5203\tfrac{80}{30})$$
$$- 22(-.0691\tfrac{96}{30} - .0857\tfrac{35}{6} + .3530\tfrac{96}{20} + .5203\tfrac{92}{30})$$
$$+ 63 = 57.5$$

Thus for the boy in question we forecast a score of 57.5 in comprehension, which is 5.5 points below the average.

In this particular problem the prediction function is not an important one; the value of the regression technique lies rather in its ability to show the relative weights of the contributing factors in explaining success in the comprehension of literature. But, if we wished to predict the probable academic success of a candidate for admission to college, so that we might select or reject him as a promising or unpromising candidate, or if as a basis for vocational guidance we wished to forecast the degree of a person's success in each of several vocations, the prediction function might become one of great importance. As a preliminary to the use of a regression equation for prediction purposes, we must, of course, have had previous measurements of success in the criterion and in each of the predicting factors, on the basis of which we have been able to compute the necessary correlations. Assuming that these r's will hold for future samples of the population, we employ measurements of certain factors we can get now as a basis for prophesying scores in a criterion that, for the particular individuals for whom we are attempting to forecast, can come into existence only in the future.

So far in this discussion we have put our formulas in particular terms—in terms of the number of variables and the particular coefficients of correlation in Miss Gresser's problem. We shall now state the formulas in general terms. First is the case in which we use z scores, or other types of scores of the same variability in all our arrays:

$$\bar{z}_0 = \beta_{01 \cdot 23 \ldots k} z_1 + \beta_{02 \cdot 134 \ldots k} z_2 \qquad \text{(Regression equation in}$$
$$+ \cdots + \beta_{0k \cdot 1234 \ldots} z_k \qquad \text{terms of } z \text{ scores)} \qquad (137)$$

Next we take the case where scores are worked in terms of deviations from the means of their respective arrays but the variabilities of the several arrays are different. This involves merely substituting x/σ, for z.

$$\bar{x}_0 = \sigma_0 \left(\beta_{01 \cdot 234 \ldots k} \frac{x_1}{\sigma_1} + \beta_{02 \cdot 134 \ldots k} \frac{x_2}{\sigma_2} \right. \qquad \text{(Partial regression}$$
$$\left. + \cdots + \beta_{0k \cdot 123 \ldots} \frac{x_k}{\sigma_k} \right) \qquad \begin{array}{l}\text{equation in de-} \\ \text{viation terms)}\end{array} \qquad (138)$$

Finally we have the case where the several series are measured in terms of unequal variabilities and where we are working with raw scores. For this we replace x by $(X - M_x)$.

$$\bar{X}_0 = \sigma_0 \left(\beta_{01 \cdot 234 \cdots k} \frac{X_1}{\sigma_1} + \beta_{02 \cdot 134 \cdots k} \frac{X_2}{\sigma_2} + \cdots + \beta_{0k \cdot 1234 \cdots} \frac{X_k}{\sigma_k} \right)$$

$$- \sigma_0 \left(\beta_{01 \cdot 234 \cdots k} \frac{M_1}{\sigma_1} + \beta_{02 \cdot 134 \cdots k} \frac{M_2}{\sigma_2} + \cdots + \beta_{0k \cdot 1234 \cdots} \frac{M_k}{\sigma_k} \right)$$

$$+ M_0 \qquad \text{(Partial regression equation in terms of raw scores)} \qquad (139)$$

PARTIAL CORRELATION

When developing the formula for the Pearson product-moment coefficient of correlation (page 96), we had occasion to notice the relation between a coefficient of correlation and a regression coefficient. When b_{xy} stands for the regression coefficient of x on y and r_{xy} stands for the coefficient of correlation between these two arrays, we saw that $r_{xy} = b_{xy}(\sigma_y/\sigma_x)$. The b, we said, is the slope of the line in terms of whatever units happen to be employed in measuring the x and the y, while the r is the slope of the line of regression relating the paired variables when the variabilities of the two arrays have been made equal. A precisely parallel thing is true of partial correlation. The partial regression coefficient, which we learned above to find, is the slope of the line relating the paired measures in a criterion and some other factor *when the influence of certain other factors has been ruled out* but when our units of measurement are not necessarily of equal variability. However, corresponding to the case of the zero order r's, the coefficient of partial correlation is defined as the slope of this regression line *when the variabilities of the two arrays have been made equal.*[1] Consequently, employing $\beta_{01 \cdot 2}$ to represent a partial regression coefficient of the second order, $r_{01 \cdot 2}$ to represent the corresponding partial correlation coefficient, $\sigma_{0 \cdot 12}$ (called the

---

[1] The reader must not be misled into thinking that, if we start with z scores or other units of equal variability as we did in developing our partial regression formulas, we avoid this distinction by having only equal variabilities all the way along. As a matter of fact, whenever we partial out the influence of a factor, we (normally) lessen the variability of whatever we have left, and the amount of such reduction differs for different factors. So that, when we arrive at the point at which we wish to deal with partial correlations, we have unequal variabilities regardless of the nature of the measurements with which we started.

partial standard deviation) to be the standard deviation of the criterion scores when the effects of the inclusion of factors 1 and

DOOLITTLE WORK SHEET

Miss Gresser's Data—Arranged for Obtaining $\beta_{40\cdot123}$

1	Insert values for r's	1	r_{12} .370	r_{13} .396	r_{14} .334	$-r_{01}$ −.567	+1.5330
2	Divide line 1 by −1	−1	−.370	−.396	−.334	+.567	−1.5330
3	Insert values for r's		.1	r_{23} .642	r_{24} .416	$-r_{02}$ −.578	+1.4800
4	Multiply items in line 1, B to I, by B_2		−.1369	−.1465	−.1236	+.2098	−.1972
5	Add algebraically lines 3 and 4		+.8631	+.4955	+.2924	−.3682	+1.2828
6	Divide line 5 by negative B_5		−1	−.5741	−.3388	+.4266	−1.4862
7	Insert values for r's		1	r_{34} .653	$-r_{03}$ −.735	+.9180
8	Multiply items in line 1, C to I, by C_2			−.1568	−.1323	+.2245	−.0645
9	Multiply items in line 5, C to I, by C_6			−.2845	−.1679	+.2114	−.2409
10	Add algebraically lines 7, 8 and 9			+.5587	+.3528	−.2991	+.6126
11	Divide line 10 by negative C_{10}			−1	−.6315	+.5353	−1.0961
12	Insert values for r's			1	$-r_{04}$ −.691	+.3090
13	Multiply items in line 1, D to I, by D_2			−.1115	+.1894	+.0778
14	Multiply items in line 5, D to I, by D_6			−.0991	+.1247	+.0257
15	Multiply items in line 10, D to I, by D_{11}			−.2228	+.1889	−.0339
16	Add algebraically lines 12, 13, 14, and 15			+.5666	−.1880	+.3786
17	Divide line 16 by negative D_{16}			−1	+.3318	−.6682

Substitute values from above table for symbols in the following equations (β's for each equation found when each variable in turn is solved for), and solve equations for the regression coefficients, β_1, β_2, β_3, and β_4.

$\beta_4 = I_{17} = +.3318$ (When working for $r_{04\cdot123}$, the only regression coeffi-
$\beta_3 = (\beta_4)(D_{11}) + I_{11}$ cient needed from this sheet is β_4)
$\beta_2 = (\beta_4)(D_6) + (\beta_3)(C_6) + I_6$
$\beta_1 = (\beta_4)(D_2) + (\beta_3)(C_2) + (\beta_2)(B_2) + I_2$

2 have been ruled out, and $\sigma_{1\cdot02}$ to be a similar standard deviation for factor 1, we have

$$r_{01\cdot2} = \beta_{01\cdot2} \frac{\sigma_{1\cdot02}}{\sigma_{0\cdot12}}$$

and correspondingly,

$$r_{10\cdot2} = \beta_{10\cdot2} \frac{\sigma_{0\cdot12}}{\sigma_{1\cdot02}}$$

The $r_{01\cdot2}$ is precisely the same as the $r_{10\cdot2}$, since the former is the regression of factor 0 upon factor 1 and the latter the regression of factor 1 on factor 0; and these are the same in the case of the r's. But that is not true in the case of the β's. Let us now multiply these two equations together. We shall get the partial r squared, since the two of these have the same value. The fractions containing the partial sigmas cancel, since one is the reciprocal of the other. Hence,

$$r_{01\cdot2} = \sqrt{\beta_{01\cdot2} \cdot \beta_{10\cdot2}} \tag{140}$$

The general case is obviously similar.

$$r_{0k\cdot1234\ldots} = \sqrt{\beta_{0k\cdot1234\ldots}\beta_{k0\cdot1234\ldots}} \quad \text{(The partial correlation coefficient)} \tag{141}$$

Thus the partial r may be obtained by taking the square root of the product of the two corresponding partial regression coefficients. One of these, $\beta_{0k\cdot1234\ldots}$, we have already learned how to compute. The other differs from this only in having the 0 and the k interchanged, where the 0 is the criterion factor and the k is any other factor in which we are at the moment interested. Hence all we need to do is to interchange the position of these two variables in the work sheet, then find the new regression coefficient in precisely the same manner as we did the original one. The easiest way in which to avoid confusion in this interchange is to write out a table of new equivalents for the original correlations. Suppose, for example, you wish in a four-variable problem to shift factor 3 into the criterion place in exchange for factor 0. You must substitute a 0 for each 3 and a 3 for each 0.

$$\text{New } r_{01} = \text{old } r_{13}$$
$$r_{02} = r_{23}$$
$$r_{03} = r_{03}$$
$$r_{13} = r_{01}$$
$$r_{23} = r_{02}$$

Any correlations not containing 0 or 3 are unaffected. Having substituted the new values for the coefficients, forget about it, and do just what the work sheet says, as before. The new β

is found at the position in your work sheet exactly corresponding with that of the old one. Multiply this new β by the old one that stood at a corresponding position in the original work sheet, take the square root of the product, and you will have the required coefficient of partial correlation. Your radical will, of course, have the ambiguous sign, as all square roots do. Affix to the root the sign of the partial β's from which it was derived. Both of the β's will always have the same sign if the work has been correctly done. This process must be repeated as many times as there are partial r's to be determined.

If only one partial r is required, as is often the case, give the factor involving it the highest number of the set, and thus place it in the column nearest the right of the work sheet (except, of course, the criterion). Then all except a very few of the calculations will be the same as the one involved in the original work sheet and much labor will be saved. We are giving on an accompanying page a sample of the work. We have drawn double lines around the parts that involve new computations. If the reader will compare this work sheet with the one on which the partial regression coefficient for factor 4 in Miss Gresser's problem was computed, he will see that all the others reappear here in precisely the same form as there, but some of them in different positions. In order to show this, we have copied all the work but blocked in with heavy lines the only elements it would really be necessary to copy, for the sake of the new operations or for the new check.

The partial r is $\sqrt{.5203 \cdot .3318} = .415$. This is the coefficient of correlation between knowledge of vocabulary and ability to comprehend literature when the factors of speed of reading, knowledge of grammar, and general information are held constant. It will be observed that the partial r does not differ very much from the partial β.

Let us again get in mind the meaning of partial regression and of partial correlation in order that we may raise the question of the value of knowing each. The partial r shows the slope of the line relating our factors when the influence of certain other factors is eliminated *and the variabilities of the residual scores have been equalized* as between the criterion and the factor being correlated with it. The partial β is the slope of this same line without equalization of the variabilities of the residual scores but with equal initial variabilities.   In other words, the standard deviations of the measures in terms of which we take our original measurements are equal in the case of the partial β's, but the partial standard deviations (which we shall discuss shortly) are not necessarily equal.   It is here suggested that, since partial β's are simpler in meaning than partial r's, since they are easier to compute by our technique (although the reverse was true by the old Yule method), and since they are not likely to differ much from partial r's, it would be preferable as a rule to make our showings in terms of partial β's rather than in terms of partial r's.   We can take initial measurements in terms of equal standard deviations, but partial standard deviations exist only theoretically.   To ask how factors as we can know them are related to one another when the overlapping elements have been removed seems to be more sensible and meaningful than to ask how they would be related if they could be measured in terms adjusted for a variability that is never concretely accessible but that can exist only in imagination.   Nevertheless, in spite of the greater convenience of partial β's, statistical workers will need to make some use of partial r's because people are more accustomed to thinking in terms of coefficients of correlation than in terms of regression coefficients.   But when partial regression coefficients are announced as evidences of closeness of relation between criterion and factor, or as evidence of the relative amounts of such relation among the several factors, they should be β's, not b's; $i.e.$, they should be the regression coefficients with variabilities equalized as these come from our work sheets.   If they are otherwise announced, as is sometimes done, it is impossible for a reader to interpret them without supplementary information about the variabilities of the criterion and of the several related factors, and even then the interpretation is rather awkward.

MULTIPLE CORRELATION

The coefficient of multiple correlation is the r to be expected between scores on our criterion and the scores predicted for the individuals by the partial regression equation.   It is, thus, the r between the criterion as actually obtained and the criterion as predicted from the whole team of related factors, each multiplied by its regression coefficient.   Since the regression coefficients represent the best possible weights for prediction purposes, the multiple r is the highest r that could be obtained between the team on the one hand and the criterion on the other. For multiple correlation we customarily employ the capital R rather than the lower case r. A formula for multiple R is very easily developed.

At the opening of this chapter we let $\bar{z}_0$ stand for such predicted score on the criterion and gave as its value

$$\bar{z}_0 = \beta_1 z_1 + \beta_2 z_2 + \beta_3 z_3 + \cdots + \beta_n z_n$$

where the subscripts are simply more abbreviated ways of indicating the partial β's than we used earlier in the chapter. Since all of these are in deviation form, and since the multiple R is, as said above, the coefficient of correlation between the calculated z_0 and the observed one, we have, as our formula for multiple correlation,

$$R = \frac{\Sigma z_0 \bar{z}_0}{N \sigma_{z_0} \sigma_{\bar{z}_0}} = \frac{\Sigma z_0 (\beta_1 z_1 + \beta_2 z_2 + \beta_3 z_3 + \cdots + \beta_n z_n)}{N \sigma_{z_0} \sigma_{\bar{z}_0}}$$

Multiplying through the equation by $\sigma_{z_0} \sigma_{\bar{z}_0}$ and placing the N and the Σz_0 with each of the terms instead of with the expression as a whole, we have

$$R \sigma_{z_0} \sigma_{\bar{z}_0} = \frac{\beta_1 \Sigma z_0 z_1}{N} + \frac{\beta_2 \Sigma z_0 z_2}{N} + \frac{\beta_3 \Sigma z_0 z_3}{N} + \cdots + \frac{\beta_n \Sigma z_0 z_n}{N}$$

On the right we have formulas for $\beta_1 r_{01}$, $\beta_2 r_{02}$, etc. But the value on the left side of the equation demands examination. $\sigma_{z_0} = 1$, for it is the standard deviation of a full set of standard measures, and the standard deviation of any full set of standard measures is 1.[1] The $\sigma_{\bar{z}_0}$ is not quite so simple. It is not the standard deviation of a full set of z scores but of the z_0 scores that are calculated as lying on the regression line. We must find a value for such a standard deviation. We shall take first the general case, in deviation form.

---

[1] This may be easily proved as follows:

$$\sigma_z^2 = \frac{\Sigma z^2}{N} = \frac{(\Sigma x^2 / \sigma_x^2)}{N} = \frac{\Sigma x^2}{N \sigma_x^2} = \frac{\sigma_x^2}{\sigma_x^2} = 1$$

$$\bar{y} = r \frac{\sigma_y}{\sigma_x} x$$

$$\bar{y}^2 = r^2 \frac{\sigma_y^2}{\sigma_x^2} x^2$$

$$\frac{\Sigma \bar{y}^2}{N} = r^2 \frac{\sigma_y^2}{\sigma_x^2} \frac{\Sigma x^2}{N}$$

$$\sigma_{\bar{y}}^2 = r^2 \frac{\sigma_y^2}{\sigma_x^2} \sigma_x^2 = r^2 \sigma_y^2$$

$$\sigma_{\bar{y}} = r \sigma_y$$

Thus the standard deviation of scores calculated as lying on a rectilinear regression line is r times the standard deviation of the whole set of scores. When we parallel this with the case we want, we have

$$\sigma_{\bar{z}_0} = R \sigma_{z_0}$$

But $\sigma_{z_0} = 1$. Therefore $\sigma_{\bar{z}_0} = R$. Making in our last R equation (above) all of these substitutions we get,

$$R^2 = \beta_1 r_{01} + \beta_2 r_{02} + \beta_3 r_{03} + \cdot \cdot \cdot + \beta_n r_{0n}$$

Taking the square root and substituting again the more complete and conventional subscripts for the β's and for R,

$$R_{0 \cdot 123 \ldots k} = \sqrt{\beta_{01 \cdot 234 \ldots k} r_{01} + \beta_{02 \cdot 134 \ldots k} r_{02} + \cdot \cdot \cdot + \beta_{0k \cdot 1234 \ldots} r_{0k}}$$
(Coefficient of multiple correlation)   (142)

Normal account must, of course, be taken of algebraic signs.

When we apply this formula to the data of Miss Gresser's problem, we find a multiple correlation coefficient of .73. The highest zero-order coefficient was .691. The multiple correlation coefficient is always higher than the highest zero-order one in the team, and the gain by using the multiple regression technique for purposes of prediction is indicated by the amount by which the multiple correlation is increased over the highest simple one. A multiple correlation of .73 means that, if measurements of a group were taken on the four factors related in the problem to comprehension of literature and composite scores made for pupils by multiplying their scores on the several tests by the optimum weights indicated by the partial regression coefficients, these scores would predict standings in comprehension of literature with an accuracy represented by a coefficient of correlation of .73.

A problem where prediction is relatively more important than it is in this problem of Miss Gresser's is a small one done at Pennsylvania State College having to do with prediction of college success by a battery of objective tests given in high school. The Carnegie Foundation for the Advancement of Teaching gave to high-school seniors in Pennsylvania such a battery of tests. When these were worked up with grades in the freshman year of our School of Engineering as criterion, they showed the zero-order r's and the partial β's set opposite them as follows:

Variate	r	β
Mathematics........................	.55	.4383
Physical science.....................	.61	.4401
American history....................	.23	.1127
Foreign language....................	.44	.2234
Otis intelligence test................	.40	.0644
English.............................	.28	−.1632

This battery yields, by application of our formula, a multiple correlation coefficient of .78. The reader may compare this again with the highest zero-order correlation and ask himself whether in attempting to predict college success it is worth while to make a battery of all these test factors rather than to predict by means of one of them.

PARTIAL SIGMAS

The reader will surely be impressed, as we proceed, with the complete parallelism between simple and partial correlation. All that we said on pages 110 to 123 by way of interpreting the meaning of a coefficient of correlation applies with equal force to partial and multiple correlation. The same is true of what we said in that chapter about prediction by means of the simple regression equation. We learned there that, when we predict by means of a simple regression equation, we miss somewhat the actual scores we are attempting to predict. The standard deviation of these errors we called the standard error of estimate. The formula for its amount was $\sigma_{\text{est}_y} = \sigma_y \sqrt{1 - r_{xy}^2}$. A parallel thing is true of prediction by means of the partial regression equation. Let us run through a development of a formula for this. Let x_0 be an obtained score on the criterion and $\bar{x}_0$ be a score for the same individual predicted from the team of factors, each with its best weight. Then in any particular case the error will be $(x_0 - \bar{x}_0)$. We need the standard deviation of these errors. We shall treat them, as usual, in deviation form.

$$\sigma^2_{(x_0 - \bar{x}_0)} = \frac{\Sigma(x_0 - \bar{x}_0)^2}{N} = \frac{\Sigma x_0^2}{N} - \frac{2\Sigma x_0 \bar{x}_0}{N} + \frac{\Sigma \bar{x}_0^2}{N}$$

$$= \frac{\Sigma x_0^2}{N} - \frac{2\Sigma x_0 \bar{x}_0}{N \sigma_{x_0} \sigma_{\bar{x}_0}} \sigma_{x_0} \sigma_{\bar{x}_0} + \frac{\Sigma \bar{x}_0^2}{N}$$

$$= \sigma^2_{x_0} - 2R\sigma_{x_0}\sigma_{\bar{x}_0} + \sigma^2_{\bar{x}_0}$$

But we showed a few moments ago that $\sigma_{\bar{x}_0} = R\sigma_{x_0}$. Making this substitution in the two places where the $\sigma_{\bar{x}_0}$ occurs, we have

$$\sigma^2_{\text{est}_R} = \sigma^2_{x_0} - 2R^2\sigma^2_{x_0} + R^2\sigma^2_{x_0}$$

$$= \sigma^2_{x_0} - R^2\sigma^2_{x_0}$$

$$= \sigma^2_{x_0}(1 - R^2)$$

$$\sigma_{\text{est}_R} = \sigma_{x_0}\sqrt{1 - R^2}$$

Replacing the symbol on the left by one that is more conventional in this connection and using our more familiar symbol with the same meaning for the σ on the right, we have

$$\sigma_{0 \cdot 1234 \cdots k} = \sigma_0\sqrt{1 - R^2_{0 \cdot 1234 \cdots k}}$$

(Formula for partial sigma, the standard error of estimate in partial regression) (143)

This is the theoretical standard deviation of the scatter of the scores predicted by the team from the regression line. If the reader will hold in his mind's eye a correlation chart, it is the measure of the scatter of the columns in such chart when the scores are all placed in the columns to which they properly belong as determined by all the other factors that make up the team. Whatever scatter still remains in these columns is due to factors additional to the ones caught in the team; if all had been included, there would be no scatter in the columns and the R would be perfect. In the chart of simple (zero-order) correlation, too, the standard error of estimate is, as we previously saw, the standard deviation of the columns when the scores have been grouped homogeneously with respect to the criterion factor, i.e., of the y scores when they have been grouped into columns of like x values. This standard error of estimate in multiple regression is called, as indicated above, the *partial sigma*. Analogously the standard error of estimate might have been called a partial sigma. Indeed it is sometimes written $\sigma_{1\cdot2}$ and called a partial sigma of the first order while the $\sigma_{1\cdot234\cdots n}$ is called a partial sigma of the nth order.

SOME COMPLETED FORMULAS

For any large number of variables, formulas for partial correlation and for partial regression coefficients become extremely complicated. But it is convenient to have such formulas, couched in terms of only zero-order correlations, for three or four variable problems. Beyond that point the worker should employ the Doolittle work sheets provided earlier in this chapter. The formulas given below might readily have been worked out with these work sheets, using general terms instead of arithmetical quantities, so that no new principles would be involved. As a matter of convenience, however, they were worked out by the method of determinants, which is another method of solving sets of simultaneous equations.[1]

FORMULAS FOR REGRESSION COEFFICIENTS

$$\beta_{01\cdot2} = \frac{r_{01} - r_{02}r_{12}}{1 - r_{12}^2}; \; \beta_{02\cdot1} = \frac{r_{02} - r_{01}r_{12}}{1 - r_{12}^2} \tag{144}$$

$$\beta_{01\cdot23} = \frac{r_{01}(1 - r_{23}^2) - r_{02}(r_{12} - r_{13}r_{23}) + r_{03}(r_{12}r_{23} - r_{13})}{(1 - r_{23}^2) - r_{12}(r_{12} - r_{13}r_{23}) + r_{13}(r_{12}r_{23} - r_{13})} \tag{145}$$

$$\beta_{02\cdot13} = \frac{r_{02}(1 - r_{13}^2) - r_{01}(r_{12} - r_{13}r_{23}) - r_{03}(r_{23} - r_{12}r_{13})}{(1 - r_{23}^2) - r_{12}(r_{12} - r_{13}r_{23}) + r_{13}(r_{12}r_{23} - r_{13})} \tag{145a}$$

$$\beta_{03\cdot12} = \frac{r_{01}(r_{12}r_{23} - r_{13}) - r_{02}(r_{23} - r_{12}r_{13}) + r_{03}(1 - r_{12}^2)}{(1 - r_{23}^2) - r_{12}(r_{12} - r_{13}r_{23}) + r_{13}(r_{12}r_{23} - r_{13})} \tag{145b}$$

FORMULAS FOR PARTIAL CORRELATION COEFFICIENTS

$$r_{01\cdot2} = \frac{r_{01} - r_{02}r_{12}}{\sqrt{(1 - r_{02}^2)}\sqrt{(1 - r_{12}^2)}} \tag{146}$$

$$r_{02\cdot1} = \frac{r_{02} - r_{01}r_{12}}{\sqrt{(1 - r_{01}^2)}\sqrt{(1 - r_{12}^2)}} \tag{146a}$$

$$r_{01\cdot23} = \frac{r_{01}(1 - r_{23}^2) - r_{02}(r_{12} - r_{13}r_{23}) + r_{03}(r_{12}r_{23} - r_{13})}{\sqrt{2r_{02}r_{03}r_{23} + 1 - r_{02}^2 - r_{03}^2 - r_{23}^2}\sqrt{1 - r_{23}^2 - r_{12}(r_{12} - r_{13}r_{23}) + r_{13}(r_{12}r_{23} - r_{13})}} \tag{147}$$

[1] Such formulas for problems up to five variables are given in an article by Peters and Wykes in the *J. Educ. Res.*, Vol. 24, pp. 44–52 (June, 1931).

$r_{02 \cdot 13}$

$$= \frac{r_{02}(1 - r_{13}^2) - r_{01}(r_{12} - r_{13}r_{23}) - r_{03}(r_{23} - r_{12}r_{13})}{\sqrt{2r_{01}r_{03}r_{13} + 1 - r_{01}^2 - r_{03}^2 - r_{13}^2}} \quad (147a)$$
$$\sqrt{1 - r_{23}^2 - r_{12}(r_{12} - r_{13}r_{23}) + r_{13}(r_{12}r_{23} - r_{13})}$$

$r_{03 \cdot 12}$

$$= \frac{r_{01}(r_{12}r_{23} - r_{13}) - r_{02}(r_{23} - r_{12}r_{13}) + r_{03}(1 - r_{12}^2)}{\sqrt{2r_{01}r_{02}r_{12} + 1 - r_{01}^2 - r_{02}^2 - r_{12}^2}} \quad (147b)$$
$$\sqrt{1 - r_{23}^2 - r_{12}(r_{12} - r_{13}r_{23}) + r_{13}(r_{12}r_{23} - r_{13})}$$

RELIABILITY FORMULAS

The reliability formulas for partial and multiple correlation are closely parallel to those for zero-order r's and b's and are interpreted and applied in precisely the same manner. The standard errors are given below. The P.E. is in each case, of course, equal to .6745 times the standard error.[1]

$$\sigma_{r_{01 \cdot 234 \cdots n}} = \frac{1 - r_{01 \cdot 234 \cdots n}^2}{\sqrt{N}} \quad (148)$$

$$\sigma_{\beta_{01 \cdot 234 \cdots n}} = \frac{\sqrt{1 - R_{0 \cdot 1234 \cdots n}^2}}{\sqrt{N}\sqrt{1 - R_{1 \cdot 234 \cdots n}^2}} \quad (149)$$

$$= \frac{\sqrt{(1 - R_{0 \cdot 123 \cdots}^2)(1 - \beta_{01 \cdot 23 \cdots}\beta_{10 \cdot 23 \cdots})}}{\sqrt{N}\sqrt{1 - R_{1 \cdot 0234 \cdots}^2}}$$

$$\sigma_{b_{01 \cdot 234 \cdots n}} = \frac{\sigma_0 \sqrt{1 - R_{0 \cdot 123 \cdots}^2}}{\sqrt{N}\sigma_1 \sqrt{1 - R_{1 \cdot 234 \cdots}^2}} \quad (150)$$

$$\sigma_{R_{0 \cdot 123 \cdots n}} = \frac{1 - R_{0 \cdot 1234 \cdots n}^2}{\sqrt{N}} \quad (151)$$

POSSIBILITIES AND PRECAUTIONS

Under proper conditions the partial regression technique is a very valuable tool of research. It has been employed extensively in agricultural research and in psychological and educational investigations. It has especially promising possibilities as a tool for research in sociology and economics. The partial correlation technique can be made a substitute for controlled experimentation, in addition to the two uses discussed earlier in this chapter. In controlled experimentation we make two

[1] For small samples N should be replaced by $(N - a)$, where a is the number of arrays intercorrelated (including the criterion), when the t is to be used with Student's distribution for testing the hypothesis that the true regression or correlation coefficient may be zero.

groups—an experimental and a control—equivalent by selection, then apply an experimental factor to the former group while withholding it from the latter. Thus we are enabled to learn how, when all other pertinent conditions are held constant by selection and manipulation, the experimental factor is related to certain measured outcomes which we use as a criterion of success. In partial correlation we hold all of a set of factors except one constant in order that we may determine the relation between this one and a criterion, but we hold the disturbing ones constant by statistical analysis rather than by actual selection and manipulation. There are many situations, especially in social science research, where we are not at liberty actually to manipulate the conditions; we must accept them as they come, with all their entanglements. Here the disturbing factors may be held constant by the partial correlation technique, and thus the equivalent of a controlled experiment may become feasible. The effect of high tariffs on imports, for example, cannot, under present notions of the function of governments, be studied by a scientifically controlled experiment, but it might be investigated by the partial-correlation method.

But some precautions must be noted regarding this technique. Partial correlations are notoriously affected by errors in measurement. The final values of the partials turn upon small differentials in the zero-order r's, especially as the number of variables increases. It is, therefore, very important that the validity and the reliability of the basic r's be high, and the more so if the number of variables is considerable. Hence to justify the application of this technique to problems of more than three or four variables, the number of cases upon which the r's are based must be large. The formulas as we have given them assume, too, rectilinearity of regression between all the correlated arrays. It is possible to have corresponding formulas for curvilinear regressions, but the formulas would be necessarily very complex. Under certain circumstances it might be feasible to translate raw scores that involve curvilinear relations into new ones between which the regressions would be rectilinear, then compute partial r's in terms of these transmuted scores.

Exercises

1. In 1919 six objective tests were administered to 900 freshmen entering the engineering school of Purdue University. The purpose was to ascertain which test individually and what combination of tests would best predict college success as indicated by grades made in the freshman year. The following correlations resulted. Calculate the "weight" with which each should be entered in the team, and the multiple R. Find the partial r of intelligence with scholarship and all standard errors.

	Fresh-man scholar-ship	Arith-metic	Alge-bra	Geom-etry	Intelli-gence	Physics	Tech. infor-mation
Arithmetic....	.51	—	.54	.45	.55	.58	.46
Algebra.......	.46	.54	—	.38	.38	.38	.24
Geometry.....	.374	.45	.38	—	.22	.43	.45
Physics........	.39	.58	.38	.43	.28	—	.41
Technical information......	.293	.46	.24	.45	.34	.41	—
Intelligence....	.343	.55	.38	.22	—	.28	34

2. The following table of intercorrelations was taken from an article in *The School Review* for March, 1924. The number of pupils involved in the study was 213. Compute from it the weights of the several relevant factors in predicting success in algebra (you to decide which ones are relevant), the multiple R, and the reliabilities of the statistics you calculate.

	Achieve-ment test scores	Kuhl-man intelli-gence	Ter-man intelli-gence	Trait ratings	Teacher ratings on apti-tude	Lee algebra apti-tude
Teacher's marks......	.538	.481	.437	.599	.593	.459
Achievement-test scores.............		.559	.472	.388	.531	.624
Kuhlman intelligence..			.834	.359	.440	.690
Terman intelligence...				.287	.341	.564
Trait ratings.........					.525	.286
Teacher ratings on apti-tude..............						.474

3. By the partial regression technique determine the weight of each of the factors in Table IV in predicting final grade-point average.

4. Determine the multiple correlation between the team of factors involved in Exercise 3 and final grade-point average.

5. Compute the partial r between at least one of the tests of Exercise 3 and final grade-point average.

References for Further Study

BURKS, BARBARA: "On the Inadequacy of the Partial and Multiple Correlation Technique," *J. Educ. Psychol.*, Vol. 17, pp. 532–554, 625–630.

EZEKIEL, MORDICAI: "A Method of Handling Curvilinear Correlations for Any Number of Variables," *J. Amer. Statistical Assoc.*, Vol. 19, pp 431–453.

FISHER, R. A.: "On the Influence of Rainfall on the Yield of Wheat at Rothamsted," *Trans. Roy. Soc. (London)*, Series *B*, Vol. 213, p. 91.

GRIFFIN, H. D.: "Nomographs for Correcting Simple and Multiple Correlation Coefficients," *J. Amer. Statistical Assoc.*, Vol. 25, pp. 316–319.

HOLZINGER, KARL J.: "On Tetrad Differences with Overlapping Variables," *J. Educ. Psychol.*, Vol. 20, pp. 91–97.

LARSON, S. C.: "Shrinkage of the Coefficient of Multiple Correlation," *J. Educ. Psychol.*, Vol. 22, pp. 45–55.

PEARSON, KARL: "On the Partial Correlation Ratio," *Proc. Roy. Soc. (London)*, Series *A*, Vol. 91, p. 492 (1915).

SPEARMAN, C.: "Disturbers of Tetrad Differences," *J. Educ. Psychol.*, Vol. 21, pp. 559–573.

WATKINS, R. J.: "The Use of Coefficients of Net Determination in Testing the Economic Validity of Correlation Results," *J. Amer. Statistical Assoc.*, Vol. 25, pp. 191–197.

WISHART, J.: "The Mean and Second Moment Coefficient of the Multiple Correlation Coefficient," *Biometrika*, Vol. 22, pp. 353–367. (Distribution of sample R's when the true R is zero.)

YULE, G. U.: *An Introduction to the Theory of Statistics*, Charles Griffin and Company, Ltd., 1919, Chap. 12.

CHAPTER IX

MULTIPLE-FACTOR ANALYSIS

TETRAD-DIFFERENCE TECHNIQUE

Under the leadership of Spearman there was developed, comparatively recently, a technique for investigating the presence of a general factor running through three or more sets of variables. The usual combination is of four variables, hence the name *tetrad differences;* though the technique may be extended into "pentads" or into combinations involving an even larger number of variables. Spearman's original purpose was to investigate a hypothesis that "intelligence" may be explained by a common g factor plus a number of specific factors. But the tetrad difference technique may be utilized in a variety of research situations additional to the one for which it was first employed.

Since this technique has to do with the presence of a factor common to different sets of variables and hence with an element of overlapping among the factors, it is most natural to take our point of departure for the development of the formulas from our treatment of correlation as percentage of overlapping between the correlated variables, page 121. On that page we saw that if two variables, x and y, have in them a common factor, c, while the other elements of the two are unique rather than common, then

$$r_{xy} = \frac{\sigma_c^2}{\sigma_x \sigma_y}$$

This may be separated into two factors, so that we may write

$$r_{xy} = \frac{\sigma_c}{\sigma_x} \cdot \frac{\sigma_c}{\sigma_y}$$

In this connection it will be more convenient for us to employ numerical subscripts rather than literal ones and also to use a simpler symbol for each expression of the form, σ_c/σ_x. Let us, therefore, write

$$r_{12} = \frac{\sigma_c}{\sigma_1} \cdot \frac{\sigma_c}{\sigma_2} = \alpha_1 \alpha_2$$

where α_1 stands for σ_c/σ_1 and α_2 for σ_c/σ_2.

Suppose, now, we have not only two variables to which the element c is common but four. Then all four of these are inter-correlated through the common element, c, so that

$$r_{12} = \frac{\sigma_c}{\sigma_1} \cdot \frac{\sigma_c}{\sigma_2} = \alpha_1 \alpha_2; \quad r_{23} = \frac{\sigma_c}{\sigma_2} \cdot \frac{\sigma_c}{\sigma_3} = \alpha_2 \alpha_3$$

$$r_{13} = \frac{\sigma_c}{\sigma_1} \cdot \frac{\sigma_c}{\sigma_3} = \alpha_1 \alpha_3; \quad r_{24} = \frac{\sigma_c}{\sigma_2} \cdot \frac{\sigma_c}{\sigma_4} = \alpha_2 \alpha_4$$

$$r_{14} = \frac{\sigma_c}{\sigma_1} \cdot \frac{\sigma_c}{\sigma_4} = \alpha_1 \alpha_4; \quad r_{34} = \frac{\sigma_c}{\sigma_3} \cdot \frac{\sigma_c}{\sigma_4} = \alpha_3 \alpha_4$$

We may now combine certain of these equations by multiplication so as to make the resulting products equal to the same thing in all the combinations.

$$r_{12}r_{34} = \alpha_1\alpha_2\alpha_3\alpha_4 \qquad r_{14}r_{23} = \alpha_1\alpha_2\alpha_3\alpha_4 \qquad r_{13}r_{24} = \alpha_1\alpha_2\alpha_3\alpha_4$$

If, now, we subtract in pairs and designate our tetrads by the symbols indicated below, we have

$$t_{1234} = r_{12}r_{34} - r_{13}r_{24} = 0 \qquad (152)$$
$$t_{1243} = r_{12}r_{34} - r_{14}r_{23} = 0 \qquad (152a)$$
$$t_{1342} = r_{13}r_{24} - r_{14}r_{23} = 0 \qquad (152b)$$

Three additional tetrads could be made, but the other three would be only these with the signs reversed, so that it is unnecessary for us to write them here.

It is thus seen that, if a common element c runs through all of four sets of variables, the differences between certain pairs of products of the r's is zero. Consequently, when we find such differences to be zero, that finding indicates the presence of such general factor. While this converse proposition does not follow from our proof, Spearman[1] gives a proof that it is true. It is important to note that all the intercorrelations must be determined solely by the common element c. There may not be between any pair of elements of the tetrad any further common element than c or the r involved will be higher than the presence

[1] SPEARMAN, C., The Abilities of Man, The Macmillan Company, 1927, Appendix, pp. iii–vi. (This proposition has, however, been challenged.)

of the c alone would explain; and, wherever the two elements occur between which there is a higher correlation than that mediated by the c, the product will be raised or lowered in value so that it will no longer equal that of the correlations paired with it in the tetrad. Our development assumes, then, that the factors are entirely uncorrelated except through the common element c.

Spearman approaches the tetrad formulas through partial correlations and arrives at the same result as we gave in our three tetrads above.[1] Since his development is short, we shall reproduce it here, with changes in terminology, by way of further confirmation.

Let $r_{12 \cdot c}$ denote the correlation between factors 1 and 2 if the influence of the common factor were eliminated. Then, according to our formula, page 243,

$$r_{12 \cdot c} = \frac{r_{12} - r_{1c} r_{2c}}{\sqrt{1 - r_{1c}^2} \sqrt{1 - r_{2c}^2}}$$

But we are assuming, as said above, that c constitutes all the elements common to factors 1 and 2, so that 1 and 2 are uncorrelated except through c. Therefore $r_{12 \cdot c}$ equals zero. Hence

$$\frac{r_{12} - r_{1c} r_{2c}}{\sqrt{1 - r_{1c}^2} \sqrt{1 - r_{2c}^2}} = 0; \; r_{12} - r_{1c} r_{2c} = 0; \; r_{12} = r_{1c} r_{2c}$$

Going through the same sort of process for $r_{13 \cdot c}$, $r_{14 \cdot c}$, $r_{23 \cdot c}$, $r_{24 \cdot c}$, $r_{34 \cdot c}$, we get

$$r_{13} = r_{1c} r_{3c}; \; r_{23} = r_{2c} r_{3c}; \; r_{34} = r_{3c} r_{4c}$$
$$r_{14} = r_{1c} r_{4c}; \; r_{24} = r_{2c} r_{4c}$$

We may now combine these equations in pairs by division and have

$$\frac{r_{12}}{r_{13}} = \frac{r_{1c} r_{2c}}{r_{1c} r_{3c}} = \frac{r_{2c}}{r_{3c}}; \frac{r_{24}}{r_{34}} = \frac{r_{2c} r_{4c}}{r_{3c} r_{4c}} = \frac{r_{2c}}{r_{3c}}$$

Since both fractions at the extreme left in the above sets are equal to the same thing, they are equal to each other. Hence

$$\frac{r_{12}}{r_{13}} = \frac{r_{24}}{r_{34}}; \; r_{12} r_{34} = r_{13} r_{24}; \; \text{and} \; r_{12} r_{34} - r_{13} r_{24} = 0$$

[1] *Ibid.*, Appendix, p. iii.

By bringing in, in this manner, all the combinations permitted, we would arrive at precisely the same set of tetrads as concluded our first development. It is, then, established that, following the proposition by Spearman cited above, if the indicated tetrad differences equal zero, there is an element common to all four of the factors. But these differences would be precisely zero only in the rarest of instances—only when we had an unusual stroke of luck or when our measures were perfectly reliable. Because of errors of measurement these differences will deviate from zero even when there is present a common factor, and our only concern must be whether they deviate more from zero than the chance involved in fluctuations from sampling would explain. Hence we need a formula for the P.E. of a tetrad difference. Although it would be feasible to compute P.E.'s for each tetrad separately, that procedure is scarcely practicable since the number of tetrads involved in most practical applications is likely to be of considerable size. To meet this situation, Spearman proposes the following formula for the average P.E. from a set of tetrad differences:[1]

$$\overline{\text{P.E.}}_t = \frac{1.349}{\sqrt{N}} \sqrt{\bar{r}^2 (1 - \bar{r})^2 + (1 - R)s^2}$$

(Average probable error of a
set of tetrad differences) (153)

where $\bar{r}$ denotes the mean of all the intercorrelations, s is the standard deviation of all the r's from their mean, and

$$R = 3\bar{r}\, \frac{n - 4}{n - 2} - 2\bar{r}^2 \frac{n - 6}{n - 2},$$

the n being the number of variables intercorrelated while N is the number of individuals in the population. In order to refute the hypothesis that the true tetrad may be zero, an obtained tetrad should be at least four times its P.E.

In the previous edition of this book we carried the treatment of tetrad differences further, deriving formulas for the probable error and for the correlation of the common factor with each of the constituent tests and giving an illustration of the use and interpretation of this technique. We are curtailing the treatment here and referring the interested reader to this earlier

[1] *Ibid.*, Appendix, p. xi.

edition and to such more specialized books as Kelley's *Crossroads in the Mind of Man* and Spearman's *Abilities of Man,* because the tetrad-difference technique is now being largely superseded in this country by the multiple-factor analysis technique, which is more generalized.	But the tetrad-difference technique still has a limited field of usefulness.	The first factor loadings in the factor-analysis method are (before "rotation") exactly the same in value as the r's between the common factor and the several tests in the Spearman tetrad-difference technique.	However, the generalized multiple-factor method does not impose the restriction of no correlation except through the common factor, and it has a much more efficient way of finding and evaluating additional group factors.

THE NATURE OF MULTIPLE-FACTOR ANALYSIS

Within the past few years several methods of multiple-factor analysis have been developed which give substantially equivalent results.	Of these the two major alternative ones are those by L. L. Thurstone and Harold Hotelling.	Both Burt and Tryon have developed rather major variations on these methods, and there have been a host of minor variations.	In fact the technique of multiple-factor analysis is still (1940) so much in the making that it is not feasible to foresee into what form it will ultimately settle.	There is also still some skepticism regarding the ultimate value of the present methods of multiple-factor analysis in practical research, although all who have worked with them have found them fascinating in theory and in mathematical manipulation.	Nevertheless, the technique has enlisted widespread interest and extensive use in research.

We could not possibly take the space in this book to explain all or even the major methods of multiple-factor analysis.	The interested reader will need to follow them through the original expositions by their authors, or through more comprehensive secondary accounts (see references at end of chapter).	Of these latter, Thomson's *The Factorial Analysis of Human Abilities* is at present the most comprehensive single-volume account, and it is readable and authoritative.

Of all the methods Thurstone's centroid method is at present the most widely known and the most extensively used.	We shall, since we must choose only one, confine our exposition to it.

Thurstone's exposition of this method is carried in terms of matrix algebra and the geometry of hyperspace, and its reading is beyond the ability of a layman in mathematics and difficult even for those of fair mathematical training[1]. But, fortunately, for every geometrical argument there is possible a parallel analytic (algebraic) argument; and we have succeeded in developing exactly the same argument in a very simple algebraic form. For the satisfaction of those who have read Thurstone's presentation, we shall show the parallelism of the two derivations in footnotes, so far as our argument proceeds. We do not go into all the ramifications reported by Thurstone, by any means; but for every one of them that is couched in geometrical form there is a parallel and equally cogent analytical form. It is only the *derivation* of the formulas in our presentation that differs from Thurstone's; the arithmetic is exactly the same; and, of course, the outcomes are the same. We shall take this occasion to say, however, that, if the reader wishes to be at home in the literature of mathematical statistics, he must learn the geometry of hyperspace because so many of the fundamental developments in statistics are couched in terms of it.

What is multiple-factor analysis? When we measure such a trait as "general intelligence," we may not be measuring a unitary attribute. It is conceivable that we are catching in the measured trait a component of reading ability, another component of ability to visualize geometric forms, of ability to see relations, etc. It is likely that different tests of what is supposed to be this same function will measure each of these constituent factors with different degrees of effectiveness (validity). Multiple-factor analysis attempts to determine how many such independent factors are needed to account for our scores as revealed by their behaviors in a set of intercorrelations from a number of tests which are alleged to be tests of the same function and to determine how heavily each of the tests is weighted with each of these factors. A basic consideration to keep in mind is that these factors are to be uncorrelated with one another (because otherwise they would not be independent) and that we wish to account for the test scores with the smallest possible number of factors and hence wish to take out on each successive trial the maximum possible load.

[1] THURSTONE, L. L., *The Vectors of Mind*, University of Chicago Press, 1935.

THE BASIC EQUATIONS

Let 1 and 2 stand for two different abilities possessed by an individual, and let z_1 and z_2 be standard scores indicating the true amount of these abilities possessed by him. Let a_1 and a_2 be the corresponding weightings (percentages of perfect validity) with which test a measures these abilities. Then, if Z is the individual's standard score on the test as a whole,

(A) $$Z_a = a_1z_1 + a_2z_2$$

And for a second test, b,

(B) $$Z_b = b_1z_1 + b_2z_2$$

Multiplying (A) by (B),

$$Z_aZ_b = a_1b_1z_1^2 + a_2b_2z_2^2 + a_1b_2z_1z_2 + a_2b_1z_1z_2$$

Summing for the whole population and dividing by N,

$$\frac{\Sigma Z_aZ_b}{N} = a_1b_1 \frac{\Sigma z_1^2}{N} + a_2b_2 \frac{\Sigma z_2^2}{N} + a_2b_1 \frac{\Sigma z_1z_2}{N} + a_1b_2 \frac{\Sigma z_1z_2}{N}$$

The value on the left of the equation is r_{ab}, because the mean of the paired products of z scores is the coefficient of correlation. $\Sigma z^2/N$ is the variance (σ^2) of a set of z scores, hence equal to 1. Furthermore, the two abilities are uncorrelated, by hypothesis, so that $\Sigma z_1z_2/N$, which is the coefficient of correlation between them, equals zero. Therefore

$$r_{ab} = a_1b_1 + a_2b_2 + 0 + 0$$

If there were more tests,

$$r_{ac} = a_1c_1 + a_2c_2; \; r_{bd} = b_1d_1 + b_2d_2; \text{ etc.}$$

Square Eq. (A), sum, and divide by N, and observe that the variances are 1 and that the abilities are uncorrelated.

$$Z_a^2 = a_1^2z_1^2 + a_2^2z_2^2 + 2a_1a_2z_1z_2$$
$$\frac{\Sigma Z_a^2}{N} = a_1^2 \frac{\Sigma z_1^2}{N} + a_2^2 \frac{\Sigma z_2^2}{N} + 2a_1a_2 \frac{\Sigma z_1z_2}{N}$$
$$a_1^2 + a_2^2 = 1$$

If there is an error factor and a specific factor, uncorrelated with the others, denoted by e and s, respectively,

$$a_1^2 + a_2^2 + a_e^2 + a_s^2 = 1$$
$$a_1^2 + a_2^2 = 1 - (a_e^2 + a_s^2) = 1 - a_0^2 = h^2$$

the communality of the test. The reliability coefficient of the test would be exactly the same as the communality except for specific factors. By reason of these the reliability is likely to be a little higher than the communality, but at any rate the communality has the reliability coefficient as its upper limit.

FINDING THE FIRST FACTOR LOADINGS

We wish now to find the values for the factor loadings on the several tests. That is, we wish to find values for a_1, a_2, b_1, and b_2. Moreover, we want to account for the test scores with the smallest number of factors that is possible. Hence we wish to take out each time the maximum loading for each factor isolated. In order to extend our problem a little further than above and yet keep within convenient limits, let us assume three abilities and up to k tests. These may be laid out and summed as below.

k will stand for any test. k_1 will be any test loading in factor 1, k_2 any loading in factor 2, etc. Σk_1 will be the sum of the factor loadings in all the tests combined in respect to factor 1, etc.

$$r_{aa} = a_1 a_1 + a_2 a_2 + a_3 a_3$$
$$r_{ab} = a_1 b_1 + a_2 b_2 + a_3 b_3$$
$$\underline{r_{ak} = a_1 k_1 + a_2 k_2 + a_3 k_3}$$
$$\Sigma r_{ak} = a_1 \Sigma k_1 + a_2 \Sigma k_2 + a_3 \Sigma k_3$$

Doing a similar thing for the correlations of each other test with all the other tests, then summing for these partial sums, and letting Σr be $\Sigma \Sigma r_{kk}$, and therefore the sum of all the intercorrelations,

(C)

$$\Sigma r_{ak} = a_1 \Sigma k_1 + a_2 \Sigma k_2 + a_3 \Sigma k_3$$
$$\Sigma r_{bk} = b_1 \Sigma k_1 + b_2 \Sigma k_2 + b_3 \Sigma k_3$$
$$\underline{\Sigma r_{kk} = k_1 \Sigma k_1 + k_2 \Sigma k_2 + k_3 \Sigma k_3}$$
$$\Sigma r = \Sigma k_1 \Sigma k_1 + \Sigma k_2 \Sigma k_2 + \Sigma k_3 \Sigma k_3$$
$$\Sigma r = \overline{\Sigma k_1}^2 + \overline{\Sigma k_2}^2 + \overline{\Sigma k_3}^2$$

Now comes the crux of our development. We want $\overline{\Sigma k_1}$ to be a maximum. Therefore $\overline{\Sigma k_2}$ and $\overline{\Sigma k_3}$ must equal zero, because if either differed from zero by any amount, whether positive or negative, the value when squared would be positive and hence would reduce the value of $\overline{\Sigma k_1^2}$ and violate our assumption that $\overline{\Sigma k_1}$ is to be a maximum.[1]   Therefore

(D) $$\overline{\Sigma k_1^2} = \Sigma r, \text{ and } \Sigma k_1 = \sqrt{\Sigma r}$$

From (C) it follows that $a_1 \Sigma k_1 = \Sigma r_{ak}$, because the two other terms in equation (C) must be zero for the reason given above. Substituting from (D),

$$a_1 \sqrt{\Sigma r} = \Sigma r_{ak}; \; a_1 = \frac{\Sigma r_{ak}}{\sqrt{\Sigma r}}$$

Similarly,

$$b_1 = \frac{\Sigma r_{bk}}{\sqrt{\Sigma r}}, \text{ etc.} \tag{154}$$

We have now reached the climax of our development and are ready to apply our technique to a concrete problem and to find numerical values for the first factor loading.   In Table XIV are

TABLE XIV.—INTERCORRELATIONS AMONG THE TEN TESTS
(Sometimes Called the *Correlational Matrix*)

	a	b	c	d	e	f	g	h	i	j
a	(.834)	.544	.500	.488	.545	.642	.834	.715	.453	.366
b	.544	(.544)	.282	.293	.320	.352	.473	.450	.272	.101
c	.500	.282	(.529)	.483	.381	.438	.498	.529	.359	.301
d	.488	.293	.483	(.656)	.571	.648	.563	.656	.368	.332
e	.545	.320	.381	.571	(.622)	.622	.568	.595	.365	.344
f	.642	.352	.438	.648	.622	(.729)	.703	.729	.419	.269
g	.834	.473	.498	.563	.568	.703	(.834)	.723	.507	.364
h	.715	.450	.529	.656	.595	.729	.723	(.729)	.621	.457
i	.453	.272	.359	.368	.365	.419	.507	.621	(.621)	.393
j	.366	.101	.301	.332	.344	.269	.364	.457	.393	(.457)
Σr_{kk_1}	5.921	3.631	4.300	5.058	4.933	5.551	6.067	6.204	4.378	3.384
k_1	.842	.517	.612	.719	.702	.790	.863	.882	.623	.481

$$\Sigma r = 49.427; \; \sqrt{\Sigma r} = 7.030433; \; \frac{1}{\sqrt{\Sigma r}} = 0.1422387$$

displayed intercorrelations among ten tests designated by the first ten letters of the alphabet.   In the conventional literature such a table is called the *correlational matrix;* but it is nothing but a systematic arrangement of the correlations of every test

---

[1] This is the first departure of our derivation from Thurstone's.   Making $\overline{\Sigma k_1^2}$ a maximum is identical in principle with the fact that passing the axis through the centroid necessarily makes the projections on axis I a maximum and the projections on the other axes a minimum.

in the series with every other test. Thus r_{ab} is .544, r_{fd} is .648, etc. The formula we just derived, (154), states that we must add all the r's in the first column for Σr_{ak}, all in the second column for Σr_{bk}, etc. Those sums are entered in the row labeled Σr_{kk1} in the table. Formula (154) also says that we must get the first factor loading in test a, (a_1), by dividing Σr_{ak} by the square root of the sum of all the intercorrelations in the table. This sum is 49.427 and its square root is 7.030433. But it will be easier to multiply by the reciprocal of 7.030433 than to divide by the number itself. The reciprocal is 0.1422387. Multiplying Σr_{ak} (which is 5.921) by this we get .842. That is the weighting of factor 1 in test a. Similarly, multiplying in turn the summation at the foot of each column by 0.1422387, we get the weightings of factor 1 in each of the nine other tests, as shown in the last row of the table.

Examination of Table XIV will show certain correlations enclosed in parentheses, the ones constituting the diagonal of the matrix. They are the estimated communalities, referred to earlier in this chapter. In a full set of intercorrelations there would appear such values as r_{aa}, r_{cc}, etc. These would be the self-correlations of the tests in respect to the factors common to the tests which still remain. But they are seldom known. Even if we had reports on the reliabilities of the tests, these reliability coefficients would not be exactly the same as the communalities wanted, because the reliability coefficients would be raised above the communalities by reason of the presence of a factor specific to the several pairs of tests in addition to those factors common to all the tests. Thus the communality is a little lower than the reliability coefficient. It is also true that any inter-function correlation is somewhat lower than the reliabilities of the correlated tests, except for chance fluctuation. So the highest inter-function correlation is not a bad guess at the communality. Hence, following Thurstone, we hunt in column a of Table XIV the highest r in the column and write it in the diagonal as the communality. For r_{aa} that is .834. We do likewise in each of the other columns in the table.

FINDING A SECOND FACTOR

In the development with which we opened this section, we had equations of the type

$$r_{ab} = a_1b_1 + a_2b_2 + a_3b_3$$

We know the values of r_{ab}, of a_1, and of b_1, because we were given the former and have just found the latter two. Transposing so as to get these known values on one side of the equation, we have

$$a_2b_2 + a_3b_3 = r_{ab} - a_1b_1 \qquad (155)$$

That is, if there are in the measures any other common factors than 1, there will be certain residuals in the correlations after factor 1 has been removed. These residuals are found in the manner indicated by Eq. (155). In this particular case the residual remaining as $a_2b_2 + a_3b_3$ would be found by substituting the value of r_{ab} and the obtained values of a_1 and b_1.

$$r_{ab\cdot1} = .544 - (.842)(.517) = +.109$$

The residual we write in the proper space to represent r_{ab} in the table of first residuals, Table XV. But instead of writing its sign directly by the r value, we shall enter it at the top of the cell space directly at the left of it. That is done because we shall later wish to make some changes in these temporary signs. Similarly

$$r_{ac\cdot1} = .500 - (.842)(.612) = -.015$$
$$r_{cd\cdot1} = .483 - (.612)(.719) = +.043$$

and so on with all the others. We enter all of these in the table headed First Residuals in the cells immediately to the left of the respective residuals (Table XV). This process includes the residual communalities, entered in the diagonal in parentheses.

Now we wish to isolate from this table of residuals a second common factor. The argument is precisely the same as it was in the case of factor 1, so that we should be able to employ a second time the same technique. We proceed, therefore, to add our successive columns of r's as we added the columns of Table XIV. But a strange thing happens; all sums come out zero, or practically so. Some further algebraic manipulation would show us that all these sums *must* be zero if our arithmetic has been correct. Of course, not only would the sums of the separate columns be zero but the sum of all the intercorrelations would be zero, since this latter sum is obtained by summing the column totals. Thus, when we attempt to get our second factor load-

Table XV.—First Residuals

The matrix is symmetric; the parenthetical values are the diagonal entries.

	a (x_2)	b (x_1)	c	d	e	f	g (x_3)	h	i	j
a_{x_2}	(.125) +.118	+.109	+.015	+.118	+.046	+.023	+.107	+.028	+.071	+.039
b_{x_1}	+.109	(.277) +.148	+.034	+.079	+.042	+.056	+.027	+.006	+.050	+.148
c	+.015	+.034	(.155) +.048	+.043	−.048	−.045	+.030	−.011	−.022	+.007
d	+.118	+.079	+.043	(.138) +.118	+.066	+.080	+.058	+.021	−.080	−.014
e	+.046	+.042	−.048	+.066	(.130) +.072	+.068	+.038	−.024	−.072	+.006
f	+.023	+.056	−.045	+.080	+.068	(.106) +.111	−.022	+.032	−.073	−.111
g_{x_3}	+.107	+.027	+.030	+.058	+.038	−.022	(.089) +.107	+.039	+.030	+.051
h	+.028	+.006	−.011	+.021	−.024	+.032	+.039	(−.050) .072	+.072	+.032
i	+.071	+.050	−.022	−.080	−.072	−.073	+.030	+.072	(.233) +.093	+.093
j	+.039	+.148	+.007	−.014	+.006	−.111	+.051	+.032	+.093	(.225) .148

Summary block (Σ_0, Σ_{-1}, Σ_{-2}, Σ_{-3}, k_1, k_2):

	Summary values (in order)
a	+.001, −.124, −.342, +.556, +.674, +.359, −.359
b	−.002, −.279, +.279, +.497, +.551, +.699, +.373, −.373
c	−.000, −.155, −.087, −.057, +.003, +.051, +.027, +.027
d	−.001, −.139, −.019, +.255, +.371, +.489, +.261, +.261
e	−.000, −.130, +.046, +.046, +.122, +.194, +.103, +.103
f	−.000, +.106, −.006, +.052, +.008, +.119, +.063, +.063
g	−.001, −.090, −.144, −.358, +.465, +.248, −.248
h	−.001, +.049, +.061, +.117, +.195, +.267, +.142, +.142
i	−.000, −.233, −.133, +.009, +.069, +.162, +.086, +.086
j	+.000, +.225, +.071, +.149, +.251, +.399, +.213, +.213

ings, each of them will be 0/0. This is an indeterminate expression and will get us nowhere. We must try some scheme of avoiding this pitfall.

In this dilemma Thurstone has proposed that we change the signs of some of the tests. Any test score may be either positive or negative according to the way in which it is oriented. If, for example, a positive score means "tactful," the same score with the negative sign would mean "tactless." It is, therefore, entirely legitimate to imagine all scores on the test reversed in sign, so far as the remaining factors are concerned.[1] The fact that we could not in practice reverse the part of the score that remains after taking out of it factor 1 need not bother us, because we are making the change merely conceptually and shall return to the original sign when our purpose has been met. To change the sign of all scores in one of the arrays will change the sign of its correlation with every other array. We shall change the signs of such tests as will let us take out of our correlations at the next attempt the largest possible loading. There are several methods of doing this, but we shall choose that one of Thurstone's proposals which gives unique results; i.e., one that could be followed in precisely the same manner by persons working entirely independently.

We shall sum the residuals (Table XV) algebraically by columns, not including the communalities, entering the sums in row Σ_{-0}. After all the columns have been thus summed, we shall find the one having the highest negative sum.[2] In this trial that is test b. We mark x_1 above that column to help

---

[1] Our changing some of the signs in the first and second residuals is identical with Thurstone's procedure. But, whereas in a geometrical system one must think of reflecting the test vector from one hemisphere to the opposite one, we merely think what would happen algebraically if we changed the signs of all the items of one of the variables when computing an r between it and another.

[2] In the geometric system one passes the axis through the most dense cluster of points. "If an observer were stationed at the origin and he could see in space of $(r - 1)$ dimensions, he would discover clustering of the points if a second factor is conspicuously present . . . We want the second axis to go in that direction." (Thurstone, A Simplified Method, pp. 4–5). The precise equivalent in our system is the choice of the column that aggregates arithmetically large r's. For arithmetically high correlations make a clustering of points, since the correlations are expressed by the cosines of the angles between the direction vectors, and large cosines mean small angles.

us remember that we chose it first for "reflection." We now "reflect" (change all signs in) test b, entering the new signs just below the original ones in the narrow column at the left. But, having changed the signs of the r's involving b in the column, we must, of course, change them also in row b, indicating that fact by an x_1 after the b. Now we again sum our columns, disregarding communalities, and get a new row of sums, Σ_{-1}. In that row the greatest negative value is in the column for test a. So we change the signs of all correlations in column a and in row a, indicating by an x_2 that we have done so. After summing again, we reflect test g. Upon summing after that change, we find that all the signs are positive. We are now through with the process of reflection as far as this table is concerned.

But before we proceed further, we shall look to our communalities. In fact it would have been better to do this before reflecting any signs, just as soon as we had tested the correctness of our arithmetic by finding that the columns sum to zero. We enclose in parentheses the communalities we brought over from the previous table to show that we shall have no further use for them. The argument about what our communalities shall be in this table is exactly the same as that advanced in connection with Table XIV. So here again we take as our communality in a column the highest inter-function correlation in that column, entering it in the diagonal with positive sign. All communalities must be positive in sign because they are self-correlations, no matter whether the inter-function correlations from which they were inferred were positive or negative. It would not really be wrong to use the residual communalities standing in parentheses. If our guess about the communality in Table XIV had been correct, the residual would be correct. But, since our first estimate was merely a guess, we choose not to trust it very far but make a new estimate by taking for the communality the highest inter-function residual in the column.

With these changes in signs and in communalities completed, we place our final signs in front of the residual correlations and proceed to find a second set of weightings by exactly the same technique as we employed before in getting factor 1 loadings. These stand in the row labeled k_2. But they are the values with some reversed signs. In order to get back to the values actually used in the tests, we must reverse the signs for all those tests for which we changed signs to get them. That is, we must reverse the signs of the obtained factor loadings for tests a, b, and g. The corrected loadings are given in the last row of the table.

FINDING A THIRD FACTOR

Our argument continues to recur in the same form. We left off above with

$$r_{ab \cdot 1} = a_2 b_2 + a_3 b_3$$

Transposing

$$a_3 b_3 = r_{ab \cdot 1} - a_2 b_2 \tag{156}$$

That is, there may still remain in our correlations certain residuals, owing to a remaining factor or factors. We know $r_{ab \cdot 1}$, a_2, and b_2, from Table XV, so that we can find the residual by exactly the same technique as we used in getting the first residuals,

$$r_{ab \cdot 12} = r_{ab \cdot 1} - a_2 b_2 = .109 - (+.359)(+.373) = -.025$$

We write this in the proper place in the table of second residuals (Table XVI). Notice that we use the final signs in the r's, even if some are reversed as compared with their original values, and the k_2 values *before the last correction* in the factor loadings. But we must keep track of the number of reversals of each test so that we may ultimately restore the original signs. Continuing the process started for the one cell just above, we get the remainder of the residuals for our Table XVI entirely analogously to the manner in which we got the first residuals for Table XV. Then we test our arithmetic by summing the columns, algebraic signs considered and communalities included. If the arithmetic is correct, all columns will sum to zero, or practically so. If not, we must discover the error before proceeding further. We then proceed just as in Table XV with the reflection of tests, achieving all positive signs after five reflections. Of course, if it appeared clear that we could not reach all positive signs, we would stop reflecting when we had attained that goal as nearly as feasible. Then, if not before, we put in new communalities and get the k_3 and the k_{3a} rows of loadings in the same manner as in Table XV.

TABLE XVI.—SECOND RESIDUALS

	x_4 a	b	c	x_3 d	x_2 e	x_1 f	x_6 g	h	i	j
$a\,x_4$	(.011) +.040	+.025	−.005	+.024	+.009	+.000	+.018	+.023	−.040	+.037
b	+.025	(.009) +.069	+.024	+.018	−.004	−.033	+.066	−.047	+.018	+.069
c	−.005	+.024	(.047) +.051	−.036	+.051	+.047	−.023	−.015	−.024	+.001
$d\,x_3$	+.024	+.018	−.036	(.050) +.102	+.039	+.064	−.007	+.016	+.102	+.070
$e\,x_2$	+.009	−.004	+.051	+.039	(.061) +.081	+.062	+.012	+.039	+.081	+.016
$f\,x_1$	+.000	−.033	+.047	+.064	+.062	(.107) +.124	−.038	−.023	+.078	+.124
$g\,x_5$	+.018	+.066	−.023	−.007	+.012	−.038	(.045) +.066	−.004	−.009	+.002
h	+.023	−.047	−.015	+.016	+.039	−.023	−.004	(.052) +.060	+.060	+.002
i	−.040	+.018	−.024	+.102	+.081	+.078	−.009	+.060	(.086) +.102	+.075
j	+.037	+.069	+.001	+.070	+.016	+.124	+.002	+.002	+.075	(.103) +.124
Σ_0	+.000	+.001	−.001	+.000	+.000	+.002	−.002	−.001	−.003	+.001
Σ_{-1}	+.011	−.008	−.048	−.050	−.061	−.105	−.047	−.051	−.083	−.102
Σ_{-2}	−.011	−.074	+.046	+.178	+.185	+.105	+.029	−.097	+.073	+.146
Σ_{-3}	−.007	−.082	+.148	+.256	+.185	+.229	+.005	+.019	+.235	+.178
Σ_{-4}	+.055	+.046	+.076	+.256	+.263	+.357	+.019	+.013	+.439	+.318
Σ_{-5}	+.055	+.004	+.066	+.304	+.281	+.357	−.017	+.059	+.359	+.392
Σr^2	+.091	+.136	+.020	+.290	+.305	+.281	+.017	+.051	+.341	+.396
k_3	+.131	+.205	+.071	+.392	+.386	+.405	+.083	+.111	+.443	+.520
k_{3c}	+.079	+.124	+.043	+.237	+.233	+.244	+.050	+.067	+.267	+.314
	+.079	+.124	+.043	+.237	+.233	+.244	+.050	+.067	+.267	+.314

$\Sigma r = 2.747$ $\sqrt{\Sigma r} = 1.65740761$ $\dfrac{1}{\sqrt{\Sigma r}} = 0.603351881$

We can continue to do this through as many factors as we wish, until our residuals are so small that they are obviously due to chance.

TRANSFORMING THE VALUES

(Equivalent to Rotating the Axes)

Now we collect all our weightings so far determined into a summary table—Table XVII. (Pay no attention now to the numbers in parentheses; we shall refer to these later.) The columns appear to belong to two different systems; all weightings in factor 1 have positive signs, but about half of the entries in factors 2 and 3 have negative signs. It may be possible to make the three factors more comparable by transforming all of them to the same sort of system, having the same zero point. As a matter of fact there is no unique solution to a multiple-factor problem; an infinite number of different values would satisfy the fundamental equations if only these values maintain the right relations *inter se*. So, in order to have a unique solution, let us impose the condition that all the weightings shall be positive (so far as possible) and that the number of zero loadings shall be maximized. We can control this last condition at least to the extent that each column except one shall have at least one zero and (if a positive manifold is possible) that its loadings shall run from zero up. But we must, of course, keep our two basic types of equations intact as to total value. If the primed symbols represent new values, it must remain true that

$$a_1'b_1' + a_2'b_2' + a_3'b_3' = a_1b_1 + a_2b_2 + a_3b_3$$

because each of these must equal r_{ab}, which has a fixed value. Also

$$a_1'^2 + a_2'^2 + a_3'^2 = a_1^2 + a_2^2 + a_3^2 = h_{123}^2$$

because these are the communalities, and they have fixed values which may not be changed capriciously. Of course, the corresponding equations must hold for the other tests. But we may shift values within the equations, provided the values of the equations as wholes are kept intact. (This is Thurstone's principle of rotation of axes.) But to attack the problem of transforming all factor loadings at once gets us into complicated algebra. So we shall hold one factor constant while we manipulate the other two, then hold one of the first pair constant while we manipulate the left over one paired with one of the prior factors. (This is Thurstone's principle of rotating about one axis at a time.)[1] Taking the first two factors while holding factor 3 constant,

$$a_1'^2 + a_2'^2 = a_1^2 + a_2^2 = h_{a12}^2$$

Let a_2' equal 0. Then

$$a_1'^2 + 0 = a_1^2 + a_2^2 = h_{a12}^2$$

Hence $a_1' = h_{a12}$. Again

$$a_1'b_1' + a_2'b_2' = a_1b_1 + a_2b_2$$

Since $a_2' = 0$,

$$a_1'b_1' = a_1b_1 + a_2b_2; \text{ and hence } b_1' = \frac{a_1b_1 + a_2b_2}{a_1'}$$

We could now get new values for a_1', a_2', and b_1', since all the required values in these equations are known. For any other required new loadings we could get new values by constructing similar equations involving them.

Although we could use the above types of formula for getting a set of transformed values, we can simplify them further for computational purposes by a little algebraic manipulation. Reproducing them in generalized form, where k may stand for any test and m may stand for the test with the lowest factor loading in the independent function when corrected for uniqueness (i.e., when the loading has been divided by the square root of the communality, i.e., when divided by h_{k12}), we have

$$(E) \qquad k_1' = \frac{m_1k_1 + m_2k_2}{m_1'}$$

The m_1, m_2, and m_1' will recur in the computation for each row, so we may as well make the required divisions once for the whole set of tests. Letting m_1/m_1' be represented by m_{10} and m_2/m_1' by m_{20}, (E) becomes

$$k_1' = m_{10}k_1 + m_{20}k_2 \qquad (157)$$

[1] For a new scheme by which several rotations can be made simultaneously see L. L. Thurstone, "A New Rotational Method in Factor Analysis," *Psychometrika*, Vol. 3, pp. 199–218 (1938).

For k_2' we draw in addition upon the following two propositions:

(F) $\qquad m_1^2 + m_2^2 = h_{m12}^2$. Since $m_2' = 0$, $m_1' = h_{m12}$

Hence dividing formula (F) by $m_1'^2$,

(G) $\qquad\qquad\qquad\qquad m_{10}^2 + m_{20}^2 = 1$

(H) $\qquad\qquad\qquad\qquad k_1^2 + k_2^2 = h_{k_{12}}^2$

Multiply (G) by (H), then subtract formula (157) squared,

$$m_{10}^2 k_1^2 + m_{20}^2 k_1^2 + m_{10}^2 k_2^2 + m_{20}^2 k_2^2 = h_{k_{12}}^2$$
$$\underline{m_{10}^2 k_1^2 + 2 m_{10} m_{20} k_1 k_2 + m_{20}^2 k_2^2 = k_1'^2}$$
$$m_{10}^2 k_2^2 - 2 m_{10} m_{20} k_1 k_2 + m_{20}^2 k_1^2 = (h_{k_{12}}^2 - k_1'^2) = k_2'^2$$

Taking square root,
$$k_2' = m_{10} k_2 - m_{20} k_1 \qquad\qquad (158)$$

Formulas (157), and (158) are the ones we use for getting the new weighting in the rotated system.[1]

We shall make a numerical application of these formulas to the transformation of values in factors 1 and 2, columns headed 1 and 2 in Table XVII, substituting for k the several tests in succession and letting factor 1 be the dependent one and factor 2 the independent one. We want the values in factor 2 to be so transformed that they will extend from zero up in the plus direction.

Test b has the lowest negative loading in factor 2 when corrected for uniqueness, $i.e.$, when divided by h_{b12}. Consequently,

---

[1] Our algebraic system of transforming loadings is identical in outcome with Thurstone's rotation in hyperspace. Ordinarily the rotating must be done about one axis at a time. Parallel to this, we transform two columns at a time. Guilford (p. 489) quotes from Thurstone the following formulas for computing new loadings, and the bases for these formulas are laid in Thurstone's *Vectors*, pp. 203–205:

$$k_1' = k_1 \cos \phi + k_2 \sin \phi$$
$$k_2' = k_2 \cos \phi - k_1 \sin \phi$$

where ϕ is the angle of rotation. If the reader will visualize, or actually construct, a plotting of the tests on a plane for two reference vectors, will rotate the axes so as to make axis I pass through the test with the lowest negative loading, m, he will find that m_{10} is cos ϕ and that m_{20} is sin ϕ. With these substitutions our formulas become identical with those of Thurstone's rotational system.

let it be m.

$b_2' = 0$, by hypothesis. Hence $b_1' = \sqrt{b_1^2 + b_2^2} = h_{b_{12}} = +.638$

$$m_{10} = \frac{b_1}{b_1'} = \frac{.517}{.638} = .811; \text{ and } m_{20} = \frac{b_2}{b_1'} = \frac{-.373}{.638} = -.585$$

For each new factor 1 loading we shall need to multiply the original factor loading by m_{10}, which is $+.811$, and add to that

TABLE XVII.—FACTOR LOADINGS BEFORE ROTATION
(Starting Factor Loadings in Parentheses)

	1	2	3	h^2
a	$+.842$ (.8)	$-.359$ (.3)	$+.079$ (.1)	.844 (.74)
b	$+.517$ (.7)	$-.373$ (.0)	$-.124$ (.1)	.422 (.50)
c	$+.612$ (.3)	$+.027$ (.3)	$+.043$ (.3)	.377 (.27)
d	$+.719$ (.3)	$+.261$ (.4)	$-.237$ (.6)	.641 (.61)
e	$+.702$ (.5)	$+.103$ (.4)	$-.233$ (.3)	.558 (.50)
f	$+.790$ (.6)	$+.063$ (.3)	$-.244$ (.5)	.688 (.70)
g	$+.863$ (.7)	$-.248$ (.4)	$+.050$ (.3)	.809 (.74)
h	$+.882$ (.7)	$+.142$ (.5)	$+.067$ (.3)	.803 (.83)
i	$+.623$ (.4)	$+.086$ (.5)	$+.267$ (.0)	.467 (.41)
j	$+.481$ (.2)	$+.213$ (.6)	$+.314$ (.0)	.375 (.40)

the product of the corresponding factor 2 loading by m_{20}, which is $-.585$; add these products algebraically. For this purpose it is convenient to write $+.811$ beneath the factor 1 column and $-.585$ beneath the factor 2 column, where reference can be easily made to them. For the new factor 2 loadings each original loading in factor 2 must be multiplied by m_{10} and from that must be subtracted the product of m_{20} and the corresponding original factor 1 loading. For this purpose it is most convenient to write, under column 1, m_{20} *with reversed sign* $(+.585)$; and, under column 2, m_{10} $(+.811)$; then *add* the products algebraically as before. We shall illustrate a few of these sums of products.

$a_1' = m_{10}a_1 + m_{20}a_2 = (.811)(.842) + (-.585)(-.359) = .893$
$c_1' = m_{10}c_1 + m_{20}c_2 = (.811)(.612) + (-.585)(+.027) = .481$
$a_2' = m_{10}a_2 - m_{20}a_1 = (.811)(-.359) - (-.585)(.842) = .201$
$c_2' = m_{10}c_2 - m_{20}c_1 = (.811)(+.027) - (-.585)(.612) = .380$

After thus transforming the loadings of factors 1 and 2 with factor 3 held constant, we proceed in the same manner to trans-

form loadings in factors 3 and 1 with factor 2 held constant.
The results of these transformations are shown in Tables XVII,

TABLE XVIII.—FACTOR LOADINGS AFTER ONE ROTATION

	1	2	3	h^2
a	+.893	+.201	+.079	.844
b	+.638	0	−.124	.422
c	+.481	+.380	+.043	.378
d	+.430	+.632	−.237	.640
e	+.509	+.494	−.233	.557
f	+.604	+.513	−.244	.688
g	+.845	+.303	+.050	.808
h	+.632	+.631	+.067	.802
i	+.455	+.434	+.267	.467
j	+.265	+.454	+.314	.375

XVIII, and XIX. Notice that in all the tables the communalities (h^2) remain the same within the limit of accuracy determined

TABLE XIX.—FACTOR LOADINGS AFTER TWO ROTATIONS
(Starting Factor Loadings in Parentheses)

	1	2	3	h^2
a	+.744 (.8)	+.201 (.3)	+.501 (.1)	.845 (.74)
b	+.619 (.7)	.0 (.0)	+.200 (.1)	.423 (.50)
c	+.401 (.3)	+.380 (.3)	+.270 (.3)	.378 (.27)
d	+.491 (.3)	+.632 (.4)	+.0 (.6)	.641 (.61)
e	+.558 (.5)	+.494 (.4)	+.042 (.3)	.557 (.50)
f	+.647 (.6)	+.513 (.3)	+.078 (.5)	.688 (.70)
g	+.716 (.7)	+.303 (.4)	+.452 (.3)	.809 (.74)
h	+.521 (.7)	+.631 (.5)	+.364 (.3)	.802 (.83)
i	+.270 (.4)	+.434 (.5)	+.454 (.0)	.467 (.41)
j	+.080 (.2)	+.454 (.6)	+.403 (.0)	.375 (.40)

by the number of decimal places to which the computations have
been carried. To sum the squares along the rows and thus find
the h^2's unchanged is an important check on the correctness
of the arithmetic.

INTERPRETATION OF APPLIED FACTOR ANALYSIS

We shall now speak of the numbers in parentheses in Tables
XVII and XIX. They are the known loadings which the process

should have given back if it has a realistic meaning.   They grow
out of an effort on the part of one of the authors to test empirically
the validity of multiple-factor analysis.   We arbitrarily set
weightings for each of ten "tests" in each of three common
factors and then added for each test a specific factor weighting
that would make the communalities nearly 1.00.   Then we made
four independent tosses of 12 pennies for each of 100 hypothetical "subjects," one toss to represent his real ability in each
of the four factors.   Thus a subject achieved a "score" on a
test which was the sum of the number of heads turned up for
him in each of the four fundamental abilities multiplied by
the loading assigned to those abilities for the particular tests.
Suppose, for example, subject 1 had a score of 6 heads in factor
1, 3 in factor 2, 5 in factor 3, and 7 in the specific factor for test a.
In test a the assigned loadings were .8 for factor 1, .3 for factor 2,
.1 for factor 3, and .5 for the specific factor.   His score on test a
would be $(6)(.8) + (3)(.3) + (5)(.1) + (7)(.5) = 9.7$, multiplied
by 10 to avoid decimals $= 97$.   Thus scores were made up for
all of the 100 hypothetical subjects for each of the ten tests.
Intercorrelation coefficients were then computed among these
tests and entered in Table XIV.   This duplicates the situation
to which factor analysis attempts to get back by mathematical
analysis.

It will be observed that there is a fair amount of agreement
between these "starting" values and the ones which accrued
from the analysis.   The coefficients of correlation between
starting values and final values are

BEFORE ROTATION

	Factor 1	Factor 2	Factor 3
r	.63	.70	$-.78$

AFTER TWO ROTATIONS

r	.84	.73	$-.72$

These are highly significant r's, though they are less than
perfect.

But notice the negative r for factor 3.   That is a phenomenon
of great importance to the practical worker, although little

attention seems to have been given to it in America. It is just
as possible for any factor (except the first) to come out with
the signs of all factor loadings reversed as with the correct
signs. That is inherent in the mathematics of the situation.
An inspection of Tables XVII and XVIII will reveal that the
reversal of all signs in any one of the three columns, or in all of
them, would not affect the cross products and hence would not
affect the power of the factor loadings to give back the correct
correlations and the correct communalities. Consider

$$a_1b_1 + a_2b_2 + a_3b_3 = r_{ab}$$

Perform this operation with factor loadings from Table XVII
and get r_{ab}. Now suppose all signs in any one of the factors
were reversed and again compute r_{ab}. It will be found to be
unchanged. Thus, reversed signs will support precisely the
same matrix of correlations and the same communalities as
correct signs. Thompson has observed and commented upon
this phenomenon in connection with both Thurstone's and
Hotelling's method. This uncertainty about signs certainly
complicates the interpretation of the outcomes from multiple-
factor analysis. We must be prepared to take an arithmetically
large loading in a test as indicating that the test *discriminates*
with respect to the factor, a large negative weighting having
possibly the same meaning as a large positive one.

If we could know that the signs are reversed, we could rotate
out this reversal. If in Table XVIII we had transformed factors
3 and 2 instead of 3 and 1, with 2 the dependent one, we would
have let $b_3 = 0$, and the transformation technique explained on
pages 264 to 268 would have resulted merely in changing all
signs in factor 3 and shifting it into column 2, while it would have
left unchanged the weights in factor 3 but shifted them into
column 2. Then another transformation of 3 and 2 with 2
dependent and a final transformation of 2 and 1 to get rid of a
small negative loading in test b would have yielded a wholly
positive manifold in much closer agreement with the known
original loadings than those of Table XIX, all having correct
signs. By this procedure the r's would be as follows:

Between final first factor loadings and original weighting, $+.92$.
Between final second factor loadings and original weightings, $+.95$.
Between final third factor loadings and original weightings, $+.90$.

These are very high r's, and show high validity for the technique. The reason they fall below 1.00 is probably on account of unreliability due to sampling in our penny tossing and on account of the approximation involved in taking the highest inter-function r of a column as the communality.

In the geometrical method the equivalent of what we did in the transformation mentioned on page 270 is to rotate the axes through 90 deg. All the signs of any factor can always be reversed by rotating through 90 deg. But the hitch is that we never can know with certainty whether thus rotating through 90 deg. will bring us nearer the truth or farther from it. We are on highly speculative ground and can only do in this respect what looks most plausible. In the geometrical method the worker merely rotates his axes graphically until he gets what looks like most plausible results. In our empirical work with our method of transformation we appear to have gotten best results in a three-factor table by first transforming factors 2 and 1 with 1 dependent, then factors 3 and 2 with 2 dependent, and finally factors 2 and 1 with 1 dependent. An analogous procedure with more factors would be to transform the factors in successive overlapping pairs beginning at the first, each time making the earlier of the pair the dependent one; then repeat the process in the same order to eliminate remaining negative terms. But, while we see a glimmer of theoretical basis for this, a satisfactory theoretical basis for determining a unique method of transformation or rotation still awaits discovery.

The reader is urged to try this type of transformation on our Table XVII as an exercise; and he is especially challenged to seek to discover some theoretical basis for a unique solution.

An Applied Example

But the fact that our situation was a made-to-order one made the procedure in the above example work out very smoothly. It was easy to get in it a positive manifold (all positive loadings) and a common factor because the situation had been set up that way. But not all practical applications work out so neatly as that. If the tests are of such a nature that some of them are inherently negatively intercorrelated in respect to any one factor, it will be impossible to get a positive manifold. Such is the case, for example, in the Bernreuter Personality Inventory,

where some of the items measuring presence of neurotic tempera-
ment are so stated as to require a plus mark in the scoring while
others are so stated as to require a negative mark. Here we
could get a positive manifold in a matrix made from the items
only if we transposed the scoring key so that all items would be
oriented in the same direction.

Another condition under which we may fail to get a positive
manifold is when the tests are short or populations small, so
that the r's have low reliability and some weightings are negative by chance. Among the exercises at the end of this chapter
we give a table of intercorrelations among a set of tests used
for predicting achievement in the Engineering School at the
Pennsylvania State College. These resulted in the factor loadings of Table XX as taken from the original work sheets. When
the technique of rotation described above was applied to this
table, factors 1 and 2 being transformed with the others held
constant, two small negative values occurred in factor 1 at the
first rotation. Thus there was little promise from further
rotations of other factors in the same direction involving factor 1.
When other rotations were made about the most promising axes,
they also involved some negative values; hence a positive manifold could not be achieved, and the best that could be done to
make the factors comparable in meaning was to balance them
against one another in such a way that each would have about
the same extent of negative signs. This is shown in Table XXI.

This difficulty is much more easily resolved in the graphical
method of rotation than in our algebraic method. The Thurstone practice does not take the meaning of a positive manifold
strictly; it accepts as zero small negative loadings, attributing
them to unreliability. So, loadings down to −.20, or even down
to −.40 if the population is not large, are accepted as not violating
the principle of a positive manifold. The axes are rotated until
they pass through the densest cluster of points, within the
liberal definition of positive manifold just mentioned. This
sort of process is more awkward by our algebraic procedure
because it is not easy to see which test (other than the lowest
one) to select for a zero loading. But really it makes little
difference, provided the differential rotation is not great, because
within reasonable limits the loadings of the tests within each
factor remain in the same relative order so that the interpretation

of the outcome is unaffected. But if the worker wishes to try the more flexible graphical method of rotation as a hint of which test to accept as the one with zero loading, he can get directions for this process from the books by Guilford and by Thurstone, which are listed in the bibliography at the end of this chapter. However, no matter what method of rotation is employed, we cannot determine whether or not there is a general factor common to all the tests; the indeterminism of the methods of rotation forestalls that, unless the general factor is very prominent.

The foregoing account shows how arbitrary are the arithmetic loadings when conditions cannot be imposed that determine a unique solution. They are equally arbitrary by our algebraic method and by the Thurstone geometrical method. As a matter of fact, the exact arithmetic weightings are not in themselves important; what we want to know is which tests go together as possessing the ability to measure a certain one or more of the fac-

TABLE XX.—ORIGINAL FACTOR LOADINGS (BEFORE ANY ROTATION) FROM NINE TESTS INTENDED TO PREDICT ACADEMIC SUCCESS

Tests	Factors				
	1	2	3	4	h^2
1. Number completion......	+.405	−.359	+.360	−.124	.438
2. English usage...........	+.183	−.289	−.102	−.194	.165
3. Scientific information.....	+.264	−.312	−.299	−.189	.292
4. Arithmetic problems.....	+.301	−.268	+.087	+.394	.325
5. MacQuarrie block........	+.546	+.423	+.282	−.079	.563
6. Thurstone-Jones sketching	+.531	+.142	+.150	−.80	.331
7. Thurstone-Jones cards....	+.550	+.305	+.084	−.114	.416
8. Detroit pulleys..........	+.364	+.103	−.324	−.126	.264
9. Minnesota form board....	+.354	+.312	−.131	+.342	.357

tors. For purely survey measurement purposes it would be satisfactory that a given test stand relatively high on all factors. But for diagnostic purposes it is desirable that we find tests which are high in ability to measure one of the factors while being very low (ideally zero) in weightings in the other factors. In the geometric system this is sometimes studied by plotting the positions of the tests on a plane if there are two factors or on a sphere if there are three—sticking hatpins in a ball and studying their relation to the spherical triangle generated by the 90-deg.

central angles between the vectors. Beyond three factors the process cannot be carried graphically. But, as a matter of fact, all these relations show up by merely inspecting Tables XX and XXI, or Tables XVII and XIX. We want, for a diagnostic battery, tests which agree in being high on one factor and low on the others. Failing this, we select as nearly as possible according to this principle. If the system lends itself well to this selection, our task will be a straightforward one. Under these circumstances in the geometric form the tests plotted on a hyper-

TABLE XXI.—FACTOR LOADINGS ON THE SAME TESTS AFTER
THREE ROTATIONS

Tests	Factors				
	1	2	3	4	h^2
1. Number completion......	+.433	−.128	+.368	+.314	.438
2. English usage............	+.370	+.068	−.076	+.133	.165
3. Scientific information....	+.407	+.241	−.186	+.184	.292
4. Arithmetic problems.....	−.047	+.024	+.138	+.550	.324
5. MacQuarrie block.......	+.018	+.325	+.669	−.101	.564
6. Thurstone-Jones sketching	+.167	+.292	+.462	+.072	.332
7. Thurstone-Jones cards....	+.111	+.413	+.481	−.046	.416
8. Detroit pulleys..........	+.166	+.487	0	0	.265
9. Minnesota form board....	−.308	+.435	+.213	+.166	.357

surface would prevailingly fall around the vertices of a hyper-polygon (of a plane triangle if two factors, of a spherical triangle if three, etc.). The problem would then be said to exhibit "simple structure." If a test or tests were not high in one factor and low in the others but were moderate in several or in all, then such test would not fall at the vertex, or even along the side, of the hyperpolygon but somewhere within the polygon; then the system would lack simple structure. But such relations can also be sensed directly from the table of weightings; indeed, with a little practice and insight into trigonometry, one can soon become quite adept at picturing just how the tests would fall if corrected for uniqueness (weightings divided by h in the table of original values) and plotted on a hypersurface.

These observations prove the secondary character of the whole process of rotation. The configuration of points representing

the placement of the tests on the hypersurface would be precisely the same if plotted from the original loadings (Table XVII
or XX) as if plotted after any kind and amount of rotation.
For this configuration of points is determined by the intercorrelations among the tests, and those are given in the data and cannot be changed. We get different arithmetic weightings only
by looking "down" upon these points from different positions,
and hence getting different "projections." Inspection of
Table XVII in relation to Table XIX and of Table XX in relation
to Table XXI will reveal substantially the same story before
and after rotation. Especially in all except the first factor the
tests relatively high before rotation are prevailingly the same as
those relatively high after rotation. In Tables XVII and XIX
the r between original loadings and those after rotation is .71 in
factor 1; .93 in factor 2; and .86 in factor 3. It is factor 1 that
suffers most from failure to rotate. As it stands, it is likely to
be deceptive as to the extent of the presence of a common factor.
In Table XX it looks as if all the tests have a common factor
(factor 1), but that disappears in Table XXI, after rotation.
We, therefore, recommend rotation as facilitating interpretation,
but we point out that its function is a secondary one.

After analyzing a correlational matrix for its factors, it is
natural to try to interpret the meaning of these factors. This
must perforce be a speculative process. We observe which
tests are high in a factor and which low, and in which factors
each is high and each low, and then try upon this showing our
hypothetical interpretation. In Mercer's study, involved in
Tables XX and XXI, factor 1 (Table XXI) looks like a verbal
academic-information ability, since English usage and scientific
information play up high in it and the visualizing and manipula-
tive tests have low weightings. Factor 2 is clearly ability to
deal with visual space relations. Factor 4 seems to be mathematical problem-solving ability, since it is very high in arithmetic
problems, moderate in number completion, and low in the
visualizing tests. Factor 3 is harder to name; it is high in the
MacQuarrie block tests and moderately high in number completion and in the Thurstone-Jones sketching and card tests.
Perhaps it is an ability to grasp rational space relations. But
what was said above about the possibility of reversed signs in
some of the factors might upset these interpretations.

It must be remembered that the factor loadings from a particular sample are subject to considerable uncertainty on account of unreliability of measurement, especially with the higher numbered factors, although reliability formulas for the factor loadings have not yet been developed. On account of the probability of fluctuations in weightings of particular tests from sample to sample and the uncertainty about signs, speculation as to the nature of the factors must be regarded as highly tentative.

THE RELATION OF FACTOR ANALYSIS TO A CRITERION

The factor analysis technique, as employed above and as usually employed, suffers from the lack of a criterion. Only such factors emerge as are entered in the battery. They are thus entered because they are alleged to be measures of a certain function. So the analysis shows only what the tests have in common, not necessarily what are the factorial components of the trait alleged to be measured. By contrast with this, the multiple-regression technique gets weightings for factors in relation to their importance in the team in predicting a criterion (see pages 220 to 230). It would be feasible to put a criterion in with the battery in multiple-factor analysis; then it could be discovered how largely the criterion itself is weighted with each of the factors; and those factors could be made the basis for selecting tests with which the criterion is heavily weighted.[1] As Exercise 3, page 278, we give Mercer's criterion r's (the r of each test with academic achievement). We suggest that the student add these as a tenth row and a tenth column to the correlational matrix and see with what factor loadings the criterion (academic success) emerges.

THE HOTELLING METHOD

The Thurstone centroid method, which we set forth in this chapter, has a long lead in practice over any other method. At the time this book goes to press it has been used in research applications probably a hundred times as frequently as any rival method (excluding the older Spearman tetrad-difference technique). But some people think that the method developed by

[1] At the suggestion of the senior author Henry L. Sisk did this. See "A Multiple Factor Analysis of Mental Abilities in the Freshman Engineering Curriculum," *J. Psychol.*, Vol. 9, pp. 165–177 (1939).

Hotelling and furthered by Kelley may prove in the end to be superior. The exposition of the Hotelling method is given by its authors in terms of hyperspace geometry, just as Thurstone's is. We judge that the arithmetic work is roughly the same in both methods. But the Hotelling method calls for no rotation of axes, for which reason its solutions are unique.[1] Furthermore, some headway has been made in deriving standard-error formulas for the Hotelling factors. But as yet there is no certain evidence upon which to base a choice. Thomson says on this point:

It will be seen from these first chapters that the different systems of factors proposed by different schools of "factorists" have each their own advantages and disadvantages, and it is really impossible to decide between them without first deciding why we want to make factorial analyses at all.

We cannot here take space to discuss a second method. The interested reader is referred to Thomson's semipopularized account of the several methods and to the publications by Hotelling and by Kelley in the bibliography at the end of this chapter.

Exercises

1. By the tetrad-difference technique determine whether or not there is an element common to all the measures involved in Table IV, pages 58 to 61, and determine the correlation of each test with this common element. Venture an interpretation as to what this common element is.

2. The table (page 278) from a dissertation by Margaret Mercer, gives a set of intercorrelations among certain tests presumably related to success in the Engineering School of the Pennsylvania State College. Find how many factors are represented, calculate the factor loadings, and compare your findings with those given earlier in this chapter.

3. The following are the correlation coefficients of each of the above tests with academic success (grade-point averages) in the Engineering School. Put these criterion scores in the matrix as a tenth row and a tenth column, recompute the loadings, and see which tests are loaded with the same factors with which the criterion is heavily loaded. Interpret.

Tests...	1	2	3	4	5	6	7	8	9
r's......	.250	.400	.348	.387	.277	.311	.328	.239	.128

[1] But E. B. Wilson and Jane Worcester challenge the psychological meaningfulness of the Hotelling factors. See "Note on Factor Analysis," *Psychometrika*, Vol. 4, pp. 133–148 (June, 1939).

TABLE XXII.—INTERCORRELATIONS AMONG NINE ABILITY MEASURES

Test	1	2	3	4	5	6	7	8	9
1. Number completion.......	—	.158	.144	.279	.205	.144	.214	.083	−.089
2. English usage.	.158	—	.196	.030	−.029	.100	.024	.020	−.056
3. Scientific information.......	.144	.196	—	.109	−.085	.158	.002	.194	.010
4. Arithmetic problems......	.279	.030	.109	—	.058	.053	.027	.021	.195
5. MacQuarrie block.........	.205	−.029	−.085	.058	—	.426	.412	.262	.234
6. Thurstone-Jones sketching...........	.144	.100	.158	.053	.426	—	.317	.006	.227
7. Thurstone-Jones card....	.214	.024	.002	.027	.412	.317	—	.245	.269
8. Detroit pulleys	.083	.020	.194	.021	.262	.006	.245	—	.179
9. Minnesota form board....	−.089	−.056	.010	.195	.234	.227	.269	.179	—

References for Further Reading

BURT, C. L.: "Methods of Factor Analysis with and without Successive Approximation," *Brit. J. Educ. Psychol.*, Vol. 7, pp. 172–195 (1937).

GUILFORD, J. P.: *Psychometric Methods*, McGraw-Hill Book Company, Inc., 1936, Chap. 14.

HOTELLING, H.: "Analysis of a Complex of Statistical Variables into Principal Components," *J. Educ. Psychol.*, Vol. 24, pp. 417–441, 498–520.

———: "Simplified Calculation of Principal Components," *Psychometrika*, Vol. 1, pp. 27–35.

———: "Relation between Two Sets of Variates," *Biometrika*, Vol. 28, pp. 322–377 (1936). (Canonical Correlation.)

KELLEY, T. L.: *The Essential Traits of Human Life*, Harvard University Press, 1935.

———: *Crossroads in the Mind of Man*, Stanford University, 1928.

Psychometrika, nearly every number has one or more important technical articles on multiple-factor analysis.

SPEARMAN, C.: *The Abilities of Man*, The Macmillan Company, 1927.

THOMSON, GODFREY H.: *The Factorial Analysis of Human Abilities*, Houghton Mifflin Company, 1939.

THURSTONE, L. L.: *The Vectors of Mind*, University of Chicago Press, 1935.

———: "Primary Mental Abilities," *Psychometric Monograph* No. 1.

TRYON, R. C.: *Cluster Analysis Correlation Profile and Orthometric (Factor) Analysis for the Isolation of Unities in Mind and Personality*, Edwards Brothers, 1939.

CHAPTER X

THE NORMAL PROBABILITY CURVE

Derivation of the Formula.—In the algebra of chance it is shown that if each of n independent events has p chances to occur and q chances to fail, the total combinations of successes and failures is prophesied by the binomial expansion

$$(q + p)^n = q^n + nq^{n-1}p^1 + \frac{n(n-1)}{1 \cdot 2} q^{n-2}p^2 + \cdots + p^n \quad (159)$$

where the exponent of the p expresses the number of successes and that of the q the number of failures, and the coefficients represent the relative frequencies with which each of these combinations of successes and failures is likely to occur. Any particular term in the expansion represents the probability of the occurrence of the number of successes indicated by the exponent of p in that particular term. If p and q are equal, indicating an equal probability of success or failure (half the times the chance of success, the other half of failure), the binomial becomes

$$\left(\frac{1}{2} + \frac{1}{2}\right)^n = \left(\frac{1}{2}\right)^n + n\left(\frac{1}{2}\right)^{n-1}\left(\frac{1}{2}\right)^1 + \frac{n(n-1)}{1 \cdot 2}\left(\frac{1}{2}\right)^{n-2}\left(\frac{1}{2}\right)^2$$
$$+ \cdots + \left(\frac{1}{2}\right)^n$$

Since $\left(\frac{1}{2}\right)^{n-r}\left(\frac{1}{2}\right)^r = \left(\frac{1}{2}\right)^n$, this expression obviously becomes

$$\left(\frac{1}{2} + \frac{1}{2}\right)^n = \left(\frac{1}{2}\right)^n + n\left(\frac{1}{2}\right)^n + \frac{n(n-1)}{1 \cdot 2}\left(\frac{1}{2}\right)^n + \cdots + \left(\frac{1}{2}\right)^n$$

There is much in genetics to suggest this as descriptive of the operation of determiners in controlling growth. Determiners in the body cells are inherited from the two parents, and, on the law of chance in mating, in the long run a determiner for the presence of a trait more favorable than the average is equally likely to be present or absent. When present, such a determiner contributes something toward the characteristics we measure as success—height in a cornstalk, quickness of reaction, intelligence, or academic success in a pupil. It is plausible enough that these composite characteristics may be the outcome of the operation of many determiners for elemental constituent traits obeying singly the principle of equal probability of presence or absence and obeying jointly the principle of chance described by the binomial expansion. In like manner, behavior that is not the expression of the chance combination of elemental traits in the reaction of a biological organism but is the product of a combination of elemental factors or forces, each unit of which obeys the laws of chance, or behavior that is the result of an aggregation of constituent units each of which is determined according to laws of chance (as groups composed of the sort of individuals we have been discussing) may be expected to conform to this same principle of chance combinations as expressed in the binomial expansion.

At any rate the composite traits or conditions we measure in educational statistics and in most other statistical applications arrange themselves with remarkable frequency in distributions that conform to this principle—which we call normal distribution. Consequently, the assumption of normality of distribution underlies much of our statistical work. The curve of a normal distribution is a peculiar bell-shaped one with which all students are already familiar. It will be the essential burden of this chapter to prove that the formula for the curve is

$$y = \frac{N}{\sigma\sqrt{2\pi}}\, e^{-\frac{x^2}{2\sigma^2}}$$

Since the normal distribution is of such fundamental importance in statistics and since the student makes so much of its mathematical properties, the reader will wish to see a development of its equation.

From our previous discussion of the binomial expansion we have seen that the successive terms,

$$\left(\frac{1}{2}\right)^n, \; n\left(\frac{1}{2}\right)^n, \; \frac{n(n-1)}{1\cdot 2}\left(\frac{1}{2}\right)^n, \; \frac{n(n-1)(n-2)}{1\cdot 2\cdot 3}\left(\frac{1}{2}\right)^n, \; \cdots,$$

$$\frac{n(n-1)(n-2)(n-3)\cdots(n-s+1)}{1\cdot 2\cdot 3\cdots s}\left(\frac{1}{2}\right)^n, \; \cdots, \; \left(\frac{1}{2}\right)^n$$

represent the probabilities of the occurrence of 0, 1, 2, 3, . . . s, . . . , or n successes, respectively. The last factor of the factorial expression in the denominator of each term represents the number of successes predicted by that particular term. We shall refer to these binomial terms as ordinates and to the corresponding numbers of successes as scores. Our problem then becomes that of obtaining an equation which will express the dependency of ordinate upon score value.

In Fig. 19 we have plotted "number of successes" along the horizontal axis and corresponding "probability of success"

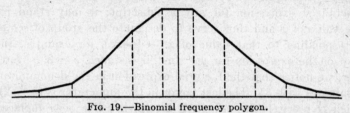

FIG. 19.—Binomial frequency polygon.

along the vertical axis. The extremities of successive ordinates are joined in order to obtain the resulting frequency polygon.

The Y measurements are ordinates corresponding to the X measurements which stand for the different score values or number of successes. For example, y_3 represents graphically the probable frequency of the occurrence of the score value x_3.

For the sake of clearness we shall list our set of scores together with their respective probabilities in the ordinate-abscissa notation. Our set is composed of

$$y_0 = \left(\frac{1}{2}\right)^n, \text{ the probability of a score of value 0, or } x_0$$

$$y_1 = n\left(\frac{1}{2}\right)^n, \text{ the probability of a score of value 1, or } x_1$$

$$y_2 = \frac{n(n-1)}{1\cdot 2}\left(\frac{1}{2}\right)^n, \text{ the probability of a score of value 2, or } x_2$$

$$y_3 = \frac{n(n-1)(n-2)}{1\cdot 2\cdot 3}\left(\frac{1}{2}\right)^n, \text{ the probability of a score of value}$$
$$3, \text{ or } x_3$$

. . . .

$$y_s = \frac{n(n-1)(n-2)\cdots(n-s+1)}{1\cdot 2\cdot 3\cdots s}\left(\frac{1}{2}\right)^n,$$

the probability of a score of value s, or x_s

. . . .

$y_{n-1} = n \left(\dfrac{1}{2}\right)^n$, the probability of a score of value $n - 1$, or x_{n-1}

$y_n = \left(\dfrac{1}{2}\right)^n$, the probability of a score of value n, or x_n

Unless the reader is skilled in the manipulation of algebraic expressions, he may perhaps find difficulty at first in understanding how the expressions for y_s was obtained. Notice that s is a generalized expression for any y subscript; it may stand for any value of x and thus serve to designate the group of scores corresponding to that value of x. Observe, for example, the form of the expression for y_3. In this instance, $s = 3$. Moreover, we notice that the factorial expression in the denominator terminates with 3. The last factor in the numerator is $(n - 2)$, which is precisely $(n - 3 + 1)$, in which s has been replaced by 3. Since the expression gives the desired quantity for any particular chosen value of s, we are led by induction to the general expression for y_s. (The reader should verify the expression for $s = 4, 5, 6$, etc.)

The general expression for y_s can be written in a more simplified form by multiplying both numerator and denominator by the quantity

$$(n - s)(n - s - 1)(n - s - 2)(n - s - 3) \; \cdots \; 3 \cdot 2 \cdot 1,$$

which is, of course, $(n - s)!$ The equation for y_s becomes

$$y_s = \frac{n(n - 1)(n - 2) \; \cdots \; (n - s + 1)(n - s)(n - s - 1)}{(1 \cdot 2 \cdot 3 \; \cdots \; s)(n - s)(n - s - 1)}$$
$$\frac{\cdots \; 3 \cdot 2 \cdot 1}{\cdots \; 3 \cdot 2 \cdot 1} \left(\frac{1}{2}\right)^n$$

which in terms of factorials may be written

$$y_s = \frac{n!}{s!(n - s)!} \left(\frac{1}{2}\right)^n \qquad \text{[Probability of a score } s \text{ in the binomial } (\tfrac{1}{2} + \tfrac{1}{2})^n] \qquad (160)$$

Now suppose that in our development n is very large and for convenience is even and equal to $2r$. Then the probability of the occurrence of exactly r successes would be y_r and would be expressed by the equation

$$y_r = \frac{2r!}{r!(2r-r)!}\left(\frac{1}{2}\right)^{2r}$$

in which n has been replaced by $2r$,

$$y_r = \frac{2r!}{r!\,r!}\left(\frac{1}{2}\right)^{2r} \quad \text{[Probability of obtaining exactly } r \text{ successes in the binomial } (\frac{1}{2}+\frac{1}{2})^{2r}] \quad (161)$$

The task of evaluating the expression for y_r becomes laborious for even small values of r when substitution is made directly into the formula. A good approximation can be obtained, however, by using Stirling's approximation formulas for factorials. Stirling's formula is as follows:

$$n! = e^{-n}n^{n+\frac{1}{2}}(2\pi)^{\frac{1}{2}} \text{ (Approx.)} \quad \text{(Stirling's approximation formula for factorials)} \quad (162)$$

We shall apply Stirling's formula to evaluate Eq. (161). Making the substitution and remembering that in the numerator of (161) $2r$ must be used as the n of the approximation formula and that in the denominator we use r, we find

$$y_r = \frac{e^{-2r}(2r)^{2r+\frac{1}{2}}(2\pi)^{\frac{1}{2}}}{e^{-r}r^{r+\frac{1}{2}}(2\pi)^{\frac{1}{2}}e^{-r}r^{r+\frac{1}{2}}(2\pi)^{\frac{1}{2}}}\left(\frac{1}{2}\right)^{2r}$$

Upon simplifying by canceling terms that are common to both numerator and denominator, we are left with the formula

$$y_r = \frac{1}{(\pi r)^{\frac{1}{2}}} \quad \text{[Approximate probability of obtaining exactly } r \text{ successes in the binomial } (\frac{1}{2}+\frac{1}{2})^{2r}] \quad (163)$$

Equation (163) gives a very good approximation to the probability of obtaining exactly r successes out of the range of $2r$ scores. It denotes, therefore, the ordinate at the mean of the binomial distribution since we are taking $n=2r$.

In developing the equation for the normal curve, we are seeking an expression that will hold for all points in the distribution of scores on either side of the mean value. If we let x be the distance from the mean of the distribution to any other given point, then $r+x$ or $r-x$ will represent the score whose probability or ordinate value we are looking for. This amounts to finding an expression for exactly $r+x$ successes or a score of $r+x$ in the binomial distribution.

Substituting $r + x$ for s and $2r$ for n in the general formula (160), we have

$$y_x = \frac{2r!}{(r + x)![2r - (r + x)]!}\left(\frac{1}{2}\right)^{2r}$$

or

$$y_x = \frac{2r!}{(r + x)!(r - x)!}\left(\frac{1}{2}\right)^{2r} \quad \begin{array}{l}\text{[Probability of a score } x \\ \text{units from the mean in} \\ \text{the binomial } (\frac{1}{2} + \frac{1}{2})^{2r}]\end{array} \quad (164)$$

We now come to the task of evaluating Eq. (164). Before applying the approximation formula, it is convenient to rearrange the form of the equation by multiplying and dividing the right-hand member by $r! \, r!$ We make this change and write

$$y_x = \left[\frac{2r!}{r!\,r!}\left(\frac{1}{2}\right)^{2r}\right]\frac{r!\,r!}{(r + x)!(r - x)!}$$

The expression within brackets is the same as Eq. 161 which we have already found to be $1/(\pi r)^{\frac{1}{2}}$.
Hence,

(A)
$$y_x = \frac{1}{(\pi r)^{\frac{1}{2}}}\frac{r!\,r!}{(r + x)!(r - x)!}$$

The factor $\dfrac{r!\,r!}{(r + x)!(r - x)!}$ is evaluated by applying the Stirling approximation formula. The task is rather long and involves detailed simplification. It is left to the student as an exercise in algebraic manipulation.[1] It is sufficient to say here that its value is approximately $e^{-\frac{x^2}{r}}$. Substituting this value in (A) we have as our approximation formula for the probability of the occurrence of a deviation x in the binomial distribution $(\frac{1}{2} + \frac{1}{2})^{2r}$

(B)
$$y_x = \frac{1}{(\pi r)^{\frac{1}{2}}} e^{-\frac{x^2}{r}}$$

Replacing r in (B) by its equal $n/2$,

$$y_x = \frac{1}{\left(\pi\frac{n}{2}\right)^{\frac{1}{2}}} e^{-\frac{2x^2}{n}}$$

[1] HINT: Take logarithms of the expression, use Stirling's approximation formula for the factorials, simplify, and then take the antilogarithms.

which reduces to

$$y_x = \sqrt{\frac{2}{\pi n}}\, e^{-\frac{2x^2}{n}} \qquad \begin{array}{l}\text{[Approximate probability of a score } x \\ \text{units from the mean in the binomial} \\ (\frac{1}{2}+\frac{1}{2})^n]\end{array} \qquad (165)$$

We show on page 298 that for a point binomial $\sigma^2 = npq$. In this development $p = q = \frac{1}{2}$; so that $\sigma^2 = n/4$, or $n = 4\sigma^2$. Substituting $4\sigma^2$ for n in Eq. (165) and dropping the subscript from y to denote that we shall assume the formula to hold continuously throughout the range of x values, we have

$$y = \sqrt{\frac{2}{\pi 4\sigma^2}}\, e^{-\frac{2x^2}{4\sigma^2}}$$

which reduces to

$$y = \frac{1}{\sqrt{2\pi}\sigma}\, e^{-\frac{x^2}{2\sigma^2}} \qquad \begin{array}{l}\text{(Approximation equation for the point} \\ \text{binomial)}\end{array} \qquad (166)$$

Formula (166) expresses the probability, within the limits of Stirling's formula, for the point binomial for n very large.

Mathematicians often make a more direct approach to the normal curve equation by setting up a differential equation of the form

$$\frac{dy}{dx} = -Cxy$$

which satisfies certain conditions which we know to be true for the normal curve. The integration is performed as follows:

$$\frac{dy}{dx} = -Cxy$$

Separating the variables,

$$\frac{dy}{y} = -Cx\, dx$$

Integrating,

$$\log y = -C\frac{x^2}{2} + K$$

Solving for y,

$$y = Ae^{-\frac{Cx^2}{2}}$$

As was shown in the previous edition of this book (pages 231 to 234),

$$A = \frac{1}{\sigma\sqrt{2\pi}} \text{ and } C = \frac{1}{\sigma^2}$$

whence

$$y = \frac{1}{\sigma\sqrt{2\pi}} e^{-\frac{x^2}{2\sigma^2}} \qquad \text{(Normal probability function)} \quad (167)$$

This is precisely the same as formula (166). We see, therefore, that our approximation formula, (166), expressing the point binomial probability is precisely the formula for the normal curve.

The right-hand member of formula (167) can be factored as

$$\frac{1}{\sigma} \left(\frac{1}{\sqrt{2\pi}} e^{-\frac{x^2}{2\sigma^2}} \right)$$

in which the quantity within parentheses is usually denoted by the letter z. Values of z have been tabulated for various values of x/σ_x. But from the above expression it is evident that

$$(C) \qquad\qquad y = \frac{1}{\sigma} z$$

So if our distribution has unit area and unit standard deviation, $y = z$ and the z values are merely the ordinates of a normal distribution of unit area and unit standard deviation. The equation for z would, of course, be

$$(D) \qquad\qquad z = \frac{1}{\sqrt{2\pi}} e^{-\frac{x^2}{2}}$$

If N is the total area under the curve, instead of unity, the equation of the normal curve becomes

$$y = \frac{N}{\sigma\sqrt{2\pi}} e^{-\frac{x^2}{2\sigma^2}} \quad \text{(Normal probability curve of area } N) \quad (167a)$$

Equation (167a) follows from the fact that the area obtained by integration would be N times that obtained by integrating (D), which we shall see is unity.

PROPERTIES OF THE NORMAL PROBABILITY CURVE

Modal Ordinate.—At the origin, that is when $x = 0$, formula (167) becomes

$$y = \frac{1}{\sqrt{2\pi}\sigma} e^0 = \frac{1}{\sqrt{2\pi}\sigma}. \quad \text{(For } e^0 = 1\text{)}$$

This tells us that $\dfrac{1}{\sqrt{2\pi}\sigma}$ is the value of the y ordinate at the middle of the distribution because we have measured our x deviations from this middle point. If we designate this modal ordinate by y_0, the normal curve equation may be written

(E) $$y = y_0 e^{-\frac{x^2}{2\sigma^2}}$$

Area under the Normal Curve.—Since we began the development with the expansion of the binomial $(\frac{1}{2} + \frac{1}{2})^n$, the sum of all the ordinates of the binomial is unity; for $(\frac{1}{2} + \frac{1}{2})^n = (1)^n = 1$. This means that the curve whose equation is (166) should by analogy obey the condition

$$\int_{-\infty}^{+\infty} \frac{1}{\sqrt{2\pi}\sigma} e^{-\frac{x^2}{2\sigma^2}} dx = 1$$

i.e., the area under the curve from a distance infinitely far to the left of the y axis to a distance infinitely far to the right of the same axis should equal unity.

The x^2 term in the integrand assures us that the curve is symmetrical with respect to the y axis; for no matter whether x is positive or negative, its square must necessarily be positive. Thus the area under the curve between the limits $-\infty$ and $+\infty$ is the same as twice the area under the curve between the limits 0 and $+\infty$. Letting A denote the area under the curve, we may write

$$A = 2 \int_0^{+\infty} \frac{1}{\sqrt{2\pi}\sigma} e^{-\frac{x^2}{2\sigma^2}} dx$$

Since $\dfrac{1}{\sqrt{2\pi}\sigma}$ is the height of the ordinate at the origin and represents, therefore, the mode of the distribution, it is a constant quantity in any given distribution. We may, consequently, remove it from beneath the integral sign without affecting the integration involved.   Then our expression for the area may be written

$$A = \frac{2}{\sqrt{2\pi}\sigma} \int_0^{+\infty} e^{-\frac{x^2}{2\sigma^2}} dx$$

It so happens that the evaluation of the integral appearing in this last equation involves the application of certain advanced mathematical functions which, if introduced at this time, might serve to confuse the reader.   It is listed among the standard types in most integral tables and its value is given as $\sqrt{2\pi}\sigma/2$. We see that this value is the reciprocal of the coefficient of the integral itself in the equation directly above.   The product of the two quantities, of course, is unity; and we see that $A = 1$.

Standard Deviation of a Normal Distribution.—We have observed elsewhere that in the case of a finite number of discrete variates the standard deviation is defined by the relation $\sigma^2 = \Sigma x^2/N$, where x denotes a deviation and N the number of scores.   The analogous definition in the case of the continuous normal distribution which extends infinitely far to the left and to the right of the mean is $\sigma^2 = \dfrac{\int_{-\infty}^{+\infty} yx^2 dx}{N}$, where y denotes the predicted frequency $\left(y = \dfrac{N}{\sqrt{2\pi}\sigma} e^{-\frac{x^2}{2\sigma^2}}\right)$ of the deviation x, and N denotes the total number of deviations—area under the curve.

Mean Deviation of the Tail of a Normal Distribution.—One of the many important properties of the normal curve involves the expression for the mean deviation of a truncated portion of a normal distribution.   It will be of value, therefore, to develop a formula for this quantity.   We shall deal with the normal distribution of unit area and unit standard deviation.

Let d represent the mean deviation, q the proportion of cases in the distribution from the point of truncation x_1 on to ∞.   The ordinate value of any point in this section of the area will, of course, be z.   Then, since by the definition of a mean we must sum all deviations and divide by their number, our problem of finding d will be that of evaluating the expression

$$d = \frac{\int_{x_1}^{\infty} zx\, dx}{q}$$

When we replace the z appearing under the integral sign by its equal given in (D), our expression for d becomes

$$d = \frac{\displaystyle\int_{x_1}^{\infty} \frac{1}{\sqrt{2\pi}} e^{-\frac{x^2}{2}} x\, dx}{q}$$

In order to facilitate the integration involved in the above equation, let us insert a minus sign before the x appearing as one of the factors under the integral sign and compensate for this change by inserting another minus sign before the integral sign. Then

$$d = \frac{-\displaystyle\int_{x_1}^{\infty} \frac{1}{\sqrt{2\pi}} e^{-\frac{x^2}{2}} (-x) dx}{q}.$$

Aside from the constant $1/\sqrt{2\pi}$, which may be taken outside the integral sign and which does not enter into the integration, our integral to be evaluated between the limits x_1 and ∞ is of the type form $\int e^u du$, in which form $u = -x^2/2$ and $du = -x\,dx$. Now we know that $\int e^u du = e^u$ (see page 35). Hence,

$$d = \frac{-\left[\dfrac{1}{\sqrt{2\pi}} e^{-\frac{x^2}{2}}\right]_{x_1}^{\infty}}{q}$$

Upon evaluating the quantity in the numerator between the designated limits, we find that for the upper limit (∞) the quantity approaches zero,[1] and for the lower limit (x_1) the quantity obtained is $(1/\sqrt{2\pi})e^{-\frac{x_1^2}{2}}$, which is the value of z (say z_1) at the point x_1. When the complex expression in the numerator above is replaced by its equal z_1, we obtain, therefore,

$$d = \frac{z_1}{q} \qquad \begin{array}{c}\text{(Mean deviation of the tail of a} \\ \text{normal distribution)}\end{array} \qquad (168)$$

Mean Deviation of a Portion of a Normal Distribution.—We shall now develop a formula for the mean deviation of a portion

---

[1] The reader will observe that because of the negative sign appearing before the exponent of e the whole factor will approach zero with increasingly large values of x, because the e with a negative exponent in the numerator is the same as the e with a positive exponent in the denominator of a fraction.

of a unit normal distribution included between two designated points of division.

Let q_1 be the proportion of cases lying beyond the point x_1, and let q_2 be the proportion of cases lying beyond the point x_2. Then the area (proportion of cases) between x_1 and x_2 is $q_1 - q_2$. Hence, from our definition of a mean we may write

$$d = \frac{\int_{x_1}^{x_2} zx\,dx}{q_1 - q_2}$$

We may, of course, replace z by its equal as given by (D) and rewrite the equation for d as follows:

$$d = \frac{\int_{x_1}^{x_2} \frac{1}{\sqrt{2\pi}} e^{-\frac{x^2}{2}} x\,dx}{q_1 - q_2}$$

We have already integrated the numerator of the above expression (page 289). Making use of this value, we may write

$$d = \frac{\left[-\frac{1}{\sqrt{2\pi}} e^{-\frac{x^2}{2}} \right]_{x_1}^{x_2}}{q_1 - q_2}$$

Substituting the upper and lower limits, we now have

$$d = \frac{\frac{1}{\sqrt{2\pi}} e^{-\frac{x_1^2}{2}} - \frac{1}{\sqrt{2\pi}} e^{-\frac{x_2^2}{2}}}{q_1 - q_2}$$

The individual terms of the numerator of this last equation are nothing more than z_1 and z_2, respectively. Hence

$$d = \frac{(z_1 - z_2)}{(q_1 - q_2)},$$

or, if we call the proportion of cases lying in the sector between z_1 and z_2, q, then

$$d = \frac{z_1 - z_2}{q} \qquad \begin{array}{l}\text{(Mean deviation of a portion of a normal}\\ \text{distribution of unit area and unit}\\ \text{standard deviation)}\end{array} \qquad (168a)$$

where z_1 is always the left-hand ordinate bounding the portion of the distribution and z_2 is the right-hand ordinate.

THE VALUES OF β_1 AND β_2 FOR A NORMAL DISTRIBUTION

Throughout many of our developments we have had occasion to say that $\beta_1 = 0$ and $\beta_2 = 3$ in a normal distribution. We shall now give the proof for these values of the β's.

We have the following definition for β_1:

$$\beta_1 = \frac{(\Sigma x^3 / N)^2}{\sigma^6}$$

In the summation of the x^3's the frequency must, of course, be considered. Remembering that the frequency at any value of x is the corresponding y, we may express the above for a normal distribution as follows:

$$\beta_1 = \frac{\left[\frac{1}{N} \int_{-\infty}^{+\infty} \frac{N}{\sigma\sqrt{2\pi}} e^{-\frac{x^2}{2\sigma^2}} x^3 dx \right]^2}{\sigma^6} = \frac{\left[\int_{-\infty}^{+\infty} \frac{1}{\sigma\sqrt{2\pi}} e^{-\frac{x^2}{2\sigma^2}} x^3 dx \right]^2}{\sigma^6}$$

We are now led to the evaluation of the integral appearing in the numerator of this fraction. For this purpose we shall resort to the familiar "parts" method. We have

$$\int u \, dv = uv - \int v \, du$$

(see page 38), where $\int u \, dv$ represents the integral we are to evaluate. Let $dv = \frac{1}{\sigma\sqrt{2\pi}} e^{-\frac{x^2}{2\sigma^2}} x \, dx$, and let $u = x^2$. Then, multiplying both numerator and denominator by σ and indicating the integration,

$$\int dv = v = \int \frac{\sigma}{\sqrt{2\pi}} e^{-\frac{x^2}{2\sigma^2}} \frac{x}{\sigma^2} \, dx$$

The integral on the right is only a slight modification of the one already found. It is

$$\frac{-\sigma}{\sqrt{2\pi}} e^{-\frac{x^2}{2\sigma^2}}$$

The differential for our expression for u is $du = 2x \, dx$. When we substitute the values of u, v, and du into the parts formula, $\int u \, dv = uv - \int v \, du$, the integral in question becomes, after due consideration of sign changes and noticing that $u\,dv$ is the expression in the β formula above for which we are integrating,

$$\int_{-\infty}^{+\infty} \frac{1}{\sigma\sqrt{2\pi}}\, e^{-\frac{x^2}{2\sigma^2}}\, x^3 dx = \left[\frac{-\sigma}{\sqrt{2\pi}}\, e^{-\frac{x^2}{2\sigma^2}}\, x^2 + \int \frac{2\sigma}{\sqrt{2\pi}}\, e^{-\frac{x^2}{2\sigma^2}}\, x\, dx \right]_{-\infty}^{+\infty}$$

We must now integrate the second term of the expression within the brackets. In order to do this it is convenient to make certain algebraic adjustments so that we may apply the same standard integral form we have just used. If we divide the x factor appearing under the integral by $-\sigma^2$, our integral becomes at once of the form $\int e^u du$. If the reader will perform the task, he will find that the second term of the brackets becomes

$$\frac{-2\sigma^3}{\sqrt{2\pi}}\, e^{-\frac{x^2}{2\sigma^2}}$$

Now the value of the quantity at the left of the equation will be that value obtained by evaluating the two right-hand terms between the limits $-\infty$ and $+\infty$. Since the first of these terms contains an even power of x, it will have the same value at $+\infty$ and $-\infty$, so that the value at the upper limit minus the value at the lower limit will be zero. Since the exponent of the e in the second term has the negative sign which would have the effect of putting it in the denominator with a positive exponent and leaving in the numerator the constant $2\sigma^3/\sqrt{2\pi}$, the entire term will also approach zero for increasing values of x whether positive or negative. Therefore the whole numerator of the fraction to which β_1 is equated (called the *third moment* or μ_3) is equal to zero, since it equals the two members on the right of the equation which sum to zero. We would, therefore, have

$$\beta_1 = \frac{(0)^2}{\sigma^6} = 0 \qquad \text{(β_1 for a normal distribution)} \quad (169)$$

In this development it has been incidentally shown that $\Sigma x^3/N$, called μ_3, equals zero in a normal distribution. It can be readily shown that every other odd moment of a normal distribution also equals zero.

The following relation defines β_2.

$$\beta_2 = \frac{\mu_4}{(\sigma^2)^2} = \frac{(\Sigma x^4/N)}{\sigma^4}$$

Expressed in terms of the integral, this becomes, for a normal distribution,

$$\beta_2 = \cfrac{\dfrac{1}{N} \displaystyle\int_{-\infty}^{+\infty} \dfrac{N}{\sigma\sqrt{2\pi}} e^{-\frac{x^2}{2\sigma^2}} x^4 dx}{\sigma^4}$$

Canceling the N's and clearing of fractions,

$$\sigma^4\beta_2 = \int_{-\infty}^{+\infty} \frac{1}{\sigma\sqrt{2\pi}} e^{-\frac{x^2}{2\sigma^2}} x^4 dx$$

Apply the method of parts, letting $u = x^3$ and

$$dv = e^{-\frac{x^2}{2\sigma^2}} x\, dx.$$

Then

$$v = \int dv = -\sigma^2 \int e^{-\frac{x^2}{2\sigma^2}} \frac{x}{-\sigma^2} dx = -\sigma^2 e^{-\frac{x^2}{2\sigma^2}}$$

Furthermore, since $u = x^3$, $du = 3x^2 dx$. Upon substituting in the parts formula, $\int u\, dv = uv - \int v\, du$, and at the same time remembering that the constant factor $\dfrac{1}{\sigma\sqrt{2\pi}}$ is to be carried along throughout the entire process, we have

$$\beta_2\sigma^4 = \left[\frac{-\sigma^2}{\sigma\sqrt{2\pi}} x^3 e^{-\frac{x^2}{2\sigma^2}} + \frac{3\sigma^2}{\sigma\sqrt{2\pi}} \int e^{-\frac{x^2}{2\sigma^2}} x^2 dx \right]_{-\infty}^{+\infty}$$

We observe that the first term within brackets is of the order x^3/e^{x^2}. When we let x approach the infinite limits, this term takes on the indeterminate form ∞/∞. We must, therefore, resort to a method of evaluating indeterminate forms provided by the calculus, but which we did not discuss in our calculus chapter. This method consists in differentiating repeatedly the numerator for a new numerator and the denominator for a new denominator until finally a meaningful value is found, when substitution of limits is made into the last of the series of expressions thus obtained. The reader may easily verify that after differentiating three times in this manner we obtain the expression

$$\frac{6}{12xe^{x^2} + 8x^3 e^{x^2}}$$

Since this expression contains a constant in the numerator, its value will be zero when x equals $+\infty$ or $-\infty$. Hence the first term becomes zero when evaluated between the limits $-\infty$ and $+\infty$. Let us now examine the second term. It may be written

$$3\sigma^2 \int_{-\infty}^{+\infty} \frac{1}{N} \frac{N}{\sigma\sqrt{2\pi}}\, e^{-\frac{x^2}{2\sigma^2}}\, x^2 dx$$

The value of the integral is σ^2, so that the whole expression is equal to $3\sigma^4$. Substituting this in our equation above for $\beta_2\sigma^4$ and dividing through the equation by σ^4, we have

$$\beta_2\sigma^4 = 3\sigma^4$$

$$\beta_2 = 3 \qquad (\beta_2 \text{ for a normal distribution}) \quad (170)$$

Since the numerator of our β_2 equation was μ_4, it has followed from our development that, in a normal distribution, $\mu_4 = 3\sigma^4$.

POINTS OF INFLECTION ON THE NORMAL CURVE

In the calculus it was shown that a condition for a point of inflection upon a curve is that the second derivative be equal to zero. If, then, we set the expression for the second derivative equal to zero, we are in a position to solve the resulting equation for the values of the independent variable which satisfy that condition.

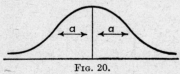

Fig. 20.

Now let us consider the equation of the normal curve and investigate the values of x which give us the points of inflection. In the accompanying diagram, we wish to find the distance a. According to the argument given in the calculus, we must differentiate the equation of the normal curve twice and set the result equal to zero. Upon solving this final equation for x, we shall find those values which give the position of the point of inflection. The computation is as follows:

The equation $y = \frac{N}{\sigma\sqrt{2\pi}}\, e^{-\frac{x^2}{2\sigma^2}}$ is of the form $y = Ae^v$, where A is a constant coefficient and v is a variable exponent. Since the constant multiplier does not enter into the differentiation and since the derivative of the form e^v is $e^v(dv/dx)$ (see page 24), we may write our first differentiation $(dy/dx) = Ae^v(dv/dx)$. The right-hand side of the expression for the first derivative is seen to be a product of the two functions e^v and dv/dx with the constant A again appearing as a multiplier. Remembering that the derivative of a product is equal to the first times the derivative of the second plus the second times the derivative of the first, the reader will readily observe that the expression for the second derivative becomes

$$\frac{d^2y}{dx^2} = A \left[e^v \frac{d^2v}{dx^2} + e^v \left(\frac{dv}{dx} \right)^2 \right]$$

We must now set the expression for the second derivative equal to zero and solve for x in order to find the points of inflection. Before doing so, however, we must replace the derivatives appearing in the right-hand member by their equals as determined from the replacement of the letter v for the more complex exponent appearing in the normal equation. We have that

$$v = -\frac{x^2}{2\sigma^2}$$

$$\frac{dv}{dx} = -\frac{x}{\sigma^2} \text{ (see page 7—differentiation of } x^n)$$

$$\frac{d^2v}{dx^2} = -\frac{1}{\sigma^2}$$

Making these substitutions into the expression for (d^2y/dx^2) and equating the expression to zero,

$$A \left[e^{-\frac{x^2}{2\sigma^2}} \left(-\frac{1}{\sigma^2} \right) + e^{-\frac{x^2}{2\sigma^2}} \left(-\frac{x}{\sigma^2} \right)^2 \right] = 0$$

The constant A may, of course, be divided out. Since the factor $e^{-\frac{x^2}{2\sigma^2}}$ cannot equal zero for any finite value of x, it may likewise be divided out. Thus we are left with the following equation from which to determine the value of x that will be a point of inflection:

$$-\frac{1}{\sigma^2} + \frac{x^2}{\sigma^4} = 0$$

Dividing both sides by $1/\sigma^2$ and transposing,

$$\frac{x^2}{\sigma^2} = 1$$

Hence $x^2 = \sigma^2$, and $x = \pm\sigma$

We have, therefore, discovered that the points of inflection of the normal curve lie at a distance of one σ to the right and to the left of the mean.

Mean and Standard Deviation of the Point Binomial.—In our development of the formula for the normal curve, we began with the binomial expansion, the successive terms of which represent the occurrence of 0, 1, 2, etc., successes. We saw that for increasingly large numbers of events (the n of the exponent of the binomial), the distribution of successes approached nearer and nearer the normal form when p and q are equal. Often, however, we are in a position to deal with distributions of which we know the p and the q and the n as determined by sampling. It is convenient, therefore, to have a formula for the standard deviation in terms of these quantities.

Let us begin by making a table of our assumed scores. Since each term of the expansion represents the probability of the occurrence of a particular score, the frequency of each score will be the product of the probability of its occurrence and N, the total number of scores. With this in mind, we may display our table as follows:

(x)	(f)	(fx)	(fx^2)
0	Nq^n	0	0
1	$Nnq^{n-1}p$	$Nnq^{n-1}p$	$Nnq^{n-1}p$
2	$N\dfrac{n(n-1)}{2!}q^{n-2}p^2$	$N\dfrac{n(n-1)}{1}q^{n-2}p^2$	$N\dfrac{2n(n-1)}{1}q^{n-2}p^2$
3	....	....	....
.	....	....	....
.	....	....	....
.	....	....	....
n	Np^n	Nnp^n	Nn^2p^n

From this table we obtain the mean and standard deviation of the distribution expressed by the point binomial by calculating the quantities given in the definitions of these measures. We have, upon adding the elements of column (fx) and dividing by N

$$M = \frac{\Sigma fx}{N} = \frac{1}{N}\left[Nnq^{n-1}p + \frac{Nn(n-1)q^{n-2}p^2}{1}\right.$$
$$\left. + N\frac{n(n-1)(n-2)}{2!}q^{n-3}p^3 + \cdots + \cdots + Nnp^n\right]$$

We may factor out of each term in the brackets the quantity Nnp. Doing this, we may write

$$M = \frac{\Sigma fx}{N} = \frac{Nnp}{N} \left[q^{n-1} + \frac{(n-1)q^{n-2}p}{1} \right.$$

$$\left. + \frac{(n-1)(n-2)}{2!} q^{n-3}p^2 + \cdots + \cdots + p^{n-1} \right]$$

The expansion now left within the brackets is that of the binomial $(q+p)^{n-1}$ and therefore equals 1, for $q + p = 1$. Hence, we have, after canceling the N appearing in both numerator and denominator of the fraction, that

$$M = np \qquad\qquad \text{(Mean of the point binomial)} \quad (171)$$

From the definition of standard deviation

$$\sigma^2 = \frac{\Sigma fx^2}{N} - \left(\frac{\Sigma fx}{N} \right)^2$$

The second term in this expression becomes, in view of the development just above, n^2p^2. Our problem now is to find $\Sigma fx^2/N$. Adding column (fx^2), and dividing by N, we write

$$\frac{\Sigma fx^2}{N} = \frac{1}{N} \left[Nnq^{n-1}p + N \frac{2n(n-1)}{1} q^{n-2}p^2 \right.$$

$$\left. + N \frac{3n(n-1)(n-2)}{2!} q^{n-3}p^3 + \cdots + \cdots + Nn^2p^n \right]$$

Factor out of each term within brackets the quantity Nnp.

$$\frac{\Sigma fx^2}{N} = \frac{Nnp}{N} \left[q^{n-1} + \frac{2(n-1)}{1} q^{n-2}p + \frac{3(n-1)(n-2)}{2!} q^{n-3}p^2 \right.$$

$$\left. + \cdots + \cdots + np^{n-1} \right]$$

The expression now appearing within the brackets may be written as the sum of two series by properly grouping certain terms and portions of terms. That is, we may write

$$\left[q^{n-1} + \frac{2(n-1)}{1} q^{n-2}p + \frac{3(n-1)(n-2)}{2!} q^{n-3}p^2 \right.$$

$$\left. + \cdots + np^{n-1} \right] = \left\{ q^{n-1} + \frac{(n-1)}{1} q^{n-2}p \right.$$

$$+ \frac{(n-1)(n-2)}{2!} q^{n-3}p^2 + \cdots + p^{n-1} \right\} + \left\{ (n-1)q^{n-2}p \right.$$

$$\left. + \frac{2(n-1)(n-2)}{2!} q^{n-3}p^2 + \cdots + (n-1)p^{n-1} \right\}$$

The expression within the first set of braces is the expansion of the binomial $(q + p)^{n-1}$ and therefore equals 1. We may factor $(n-1)p$ out of the second set of braces and write this expression as $(n-1)p\{q^{n-2} + (n-2)q^{n-3}p + \cdots + p^{n-2}\}$. The expansion appearing within this final set of braces is that of the binomial $(q + p)^{n-2}$ and therefore equals 1. Thus we find the value of the expression given in brackets above is $1 + (n-1)p$. Hence,

$$\frac{\Sigma f x^2}{N} = \frac{Nnp}{N} [1 + (n-1)p]$$

$$\frac{\Sigma f x^2}{N} = np(1 + np - p)$$

$$\frac{\Sigma f x^2}{N} = np + n^2p^2 - np^2$$

We are now in a position to substitute our values of $\Sigma f x^2/N$ and $(\Sigma f x/N)^2$ into the formula for σ^2. Making these substitutions, we obtain

$$\sigma^2 = np + n^2p^2 - np^2 - n^2p^2$$

Collecting, we have $\sigma^2 = np - np^2$. Factor the right-hand member. $\sigma^2 = np(1 - p)$. But since $q + p = 1$, we have that $1 - p = q$. Therefore, $\sigma^2 = npq$. And

$$\sigma = \sqrt{npq} \qquad \text{(Standard deviation of the point binomial)} \quad (172)$$

Shape, Symmetry, Extent, and Slope of the Normal Curve.— We have already pointed out in our previous discussion that the normal curve is a symmetric bell-shaped curve whose slope at equal distances to the right and to the left of the mean is theoretically always the same. Furthermore, the curve changes from convex to concave at a distance of σ on each side of the mean.

An additional property of the normal curve is its approach to the x axis as we go out farther and farther in either direction. This asymptotic approach may readily be demonstrated mathematically by considering the form of the equation and observing that because of the negative exponent of the term e,

the equation may be written $y = (N/\sigma\sqrt{2\pi})(1/e^{+\frac{x^2}{2\sigma^2}})$. Now, as we take increasingly large values of x in absolute value (either positive or negative), the denominator of the fraction on the right involving x^2 becomes larger and larger, and as a consequence the right-hand member becomes smaller and smaller. This amounts to saying that y approaches zero as x increases without bound. Hence we see that, although for most practical purposes the normal curve is taken to include all the cases between 3.5σ or 4.0σ in either direction from the mean, this is not the actual situation if a sufficiently large sample of the total normal population were available.

The Principle of Least Squares.—In the development of many statistical formulas we have found it necessary at times to minimize the sum of the squares of errors resulting from the use of observed rather than the actual scores. Because this procedure plays such an important part in so many developments and because its application is so universal, the advanced student of statistics will wish to examine the principle upon which it rests.

Let us assume that our errors make a normal distribution. Then the frequency of the occurrence of a particular error would

be given by the normal equation $y = y_0 e^{-c\frac{x^2}{2}}$. The probability of the occurrence of a particular error would be y/N. Hence, the probabilities representing the occurrence of the errors $x_1, x_2, x_3, \ldots, x_n$ would be given by the quantities

$$\frac{y_0 e^{-c\frac{x_1^2}{2}}}{N}, \frac{y_0 e^{-c\frac{x_2^2}{2}}}{N}, \frac{y_0 e^{-c\frac{x_3^2}{2}}}{N}, \ldots, \frac{y_0 e^{-c\frac{x_n^2}{2}}}{N}$$

Now it is a fundamental theorem in the study of probability that the probability of the simultaneous occurrence of several independent events is equal to the product of the probabilities of the several events, respectively. Hence in a normal distribution the probability that the errors x_1, x_2, x_3, . . . , x_n, will occur at the same time would be given by the product of the above quantities which represent the individual probabilities. If we denote the measure of this product probability by P, we shall have

$$(F) \qquad P = \frac{y_0 e^{-c\frac{x_1^2}{2}}}{N} \cdot \frac{y_0 e^{-c\frac{x_2^2}{2}}}{N} \cdot \frac{y_0 e^{-c\frac{x_3^2}{2}}}{N} \cdots \frac{y_0 e^{-c\frac{x_n^2}{2}}}{N}$$

We may, of course, multiply by adding the exponents and write

$$(G) \qquad P = \frac{y_0^n e^{-\frac{C}{2}(x_1^2 + x_2^2 + x_3^2 + \cdots + x_n^2)}}{N^n}$$

Placing the exponential factor in the denominator and at the same time changing the sign from minus to plus because of the change,

$$(H) \qquad P = \frac{y_0^n N^{-n}}{e^{+\frac{C}{2}(x_1^2 + x_2^2 + x_3^2 + \cdots + x_n^2)}}$$

Equation (H) shows that the value of P is a fraction whose value depends upon the sum of the squares of the errors. Since the value of the fraction is greatest when the denominator is least, the value of P will be greatest when the quantity within parentheses is least. That is, we must minimize the sum of the squares of the errors in order to obtain a maximum probability of the concurrence of these errors. From this standpoint, therefore, we have a partial explanation of the principle underlying the least-squares method used in many of our statistical developments.

Normal Probability Tables—Their Construction and Uses.— Many interesting properties may be pointed out through an analysis of the construction and uses of probabilities tables. These tables usually give ordinate values which represent the probabilities of the occurrence of corresponding deviate values and integral values (areas) which represent the probabilities of the occurrence of a deviate within a given range, *i.e.*, between any two particular ordinates. When the entire area under the curve is taken as 1, the area between any two designated ordinates is, therefore, the proportion of the total population falling within that range. Some tables give additional integral values which show the proportions of the distribution to the left and to the right of a particular ordinate.

We have seen that the equation of the normal curve of unit area (see page 286) is $y = \dfrac{1}{\sigma\sqrt{2\pi}}\, e^{-\frac{x^2}{2\sigma^2}}$, where x represents the deviation of a score from the mean of the distribution, σ the standard deviation, and y the ordinate which gives the probability of the occurrence of the deviate x. We have designated the quantity $(1/\sqrt{2\pi})e^{-\frac{x^2}{2\sigma^2}}$ by the letter z, and written

$$y = \frac{1}{\sigma}\, z \text{ [Eq. } (C)\text{, page 286]}$$

The values of z which correspond to different values of x/σ may be computed by direct substitution into the designated quantity above. For example, the value of z for the sigma unit $x/\sigma = 2$ could be found by simply evaluating the expression $(1/\sqrt{2\pi})e^{-\frac{(2)^2}{2}}$. The value of this expression, as can be verified by simple arithmetic processes, turns out to be 0.05399. If the reader will turn to Table XLIV, he will find this value of z appearing opposite the number 2.00 which appears in the x/σ column.

At this stage it may be well to point out that the z values which appear in the tables are to be taken as ordinate values only when the σ of the given distribution is 1. Otherwise, we must divide by the σ of the distribution under consideration in order to obtain the correct ordinate for a particular sigma unit value.

This fact is at once apparent from the form of Eq. (C). Hence, if we desired the probability of the occurrence of the sigma unit 2.00 in a distribution whose standard deviation is 5.00, we should have for the corresponding ordinate value

$$y = \frac{1}{\sigma}\, z = \frac{1}{5.00}\,(.05399) = .01080$$

This tells us that we should expect the occurrence of the sigma unit $x/\sigma = 2.00$ approximately once in every hundred random selections from our normal population.

In order to obtain the area under the normal curve between the mean ordinate and any other chosen ordinate, it is necessary to integrate the normal equation between the values of x/σ which correspond to these particular ordinates. Analytically this means that, if we let A represent the required area, our problem is to integrate the following expression:

$$(I) \qquad A = \int_0^{\frac{x}{\sigma}} \frac{1}{\sigma\sqrt{2\pi}}\, e^{-\frac{x^2}{2\sigma^2}}\, dx$$

where the upper limit refers to a definite sigma unit value.

In order to simplify matters, it is convenient to make the transformation $t = x/\sigma$ in Eq. (I). Our integral then becomes[1]

$$(J) \qquad A = \int_0^t \frac{1}{\sqrt{2\pi}}\, e^{-\frac{t^2}{2}}\, dt$$

There is no general formula for the value of this integral. For this reason, mathematicians have turned to convergent series in order to approximate to its value for different values of t. The process consists in the termwise integration of the series obtained by expanding the function $e^{-\frac{t^2}{2}}$ and of then calculating successive approximations of A for successive substitutions of t values. We shall not take the space to justify the validity of the process in this development, and we shall omit the detailed development of the series. The following convergent series may readily be derived and may be employed to compute areas under the normal curve between the mean ordinate (y axis) and any other ordinate.

$$(K) \quad A = \frac{1}{\sqrt{\pi}}\left[\left(\frac{t}{\sqrt{2}}\right) - \frac{1}{3\cdot 1!}\left(\frac{t}{\sqrt{2}}\right)^3 + \frac{1}{5\cdot 2!}\left(\frac{t}{\sqrt{2}}\right)^5 \right.$$
$$\left. - \frac{1}{7\cdot 3!}\left(\frac{t}{\sqrt{2}}\right)^7 + \cdots \right]$$

To calculate the area A from the mean up to the sigma unit $t = 2.00$, for example, we need only to substitute this value of t into the right-hand member of (K), using as many terms as are necessary to give the degree of accuracy desired. The student

---

[1] In making the change, we see that since $x/\sigma = t$, $x = \sigma t$, and thus $dx = \sigma\, dt$. This accounts for the disappearance of the σ in the denominator of the factor $\dfrac{1}{\sigma\sqrt{2\pi}}$.

may easily verify that the area for this value of t turns out to be 0.47725, approximately. This means that about 48 per cent of the total normal population falls within the range between the mean and two sigma units.

Because of the symmetry of the normal curve, the y axis divides the entire area into two equal parts. Therefore, when the total area is taken as 1, the proportion to the left of any

TABLE XXIII.—AREAS AND ORDINATES UNDER THE NORMAL CURVE IN TERMS OF ABSCISSAS

Abscissa $\left(\dfrac{x}{\sigma}\right)$, (t)	Area between mean ordinate and ordinate at $\dfrac{x}{\sigma}$	Area to left of ordinate at $\dfrac{x}{\sigma}$	Area to right of ordinate at $\dfrac{x}{\sigma}$	Area between ordinate at $-\dfrac{x}{\sigma}$ and $+\dfrac{x}{\sigma}$	Sum of areas to right of $+\dfrac{x}{\sigma}$ and to left of $-\dfrac{x}{\sigma}$	Ordinate (z)
0.0000	0.0000	0.5000	0.5000	0.0000	1.0000	0.3989
0.5000	0.1915	0.6915	0.3085	0.3829	0.6171	0.3521
0.6745	0.2500	0.7500	0.2500	0.5000	0.5000	0.3178
1.5000	0.4332	0.9332	0.0668	0.8664	0.1336	0.1295
2.0000	0.4772	0.9772	0.0228	0.9545	0.0455	0.0540
4.0000	0.5000	1.0000	0.0000	0.9999	0.0001	0.0001

ordinate on the right of the y axis may be obtained by adding 0.50000 to the value of A for that particular ordinate. If the ordinate in question lies to the left of the y axis, we must subtract the value of A from 0.50000 to obtain the left-hand portion of the area under the curve. On the other hand, if we desire the area to the right of an ordinate, we must subtract the value of A from 0.50000 for ordinates to the right of the y axis and add the value of A to 0.50000 for ordinates to the left of the same axis. The area between $-x/\sigma$ and $+x/\sigma$ (i.e., between ordinates equally spaced to the left and to the right of the mean) is twice the value of A. In any case, the proportions cut off by any particular ordinate or ordinates can be computed directly from the value of A. Table XXIII displays areas and corresponding ordinates for a few values of the abscissa x/σ.

All entries in the table have been computed on the basis of unit area. If, for example, $N = 1,000$, then 1,000 times the entries of areas gives the total frequencies for those columns. Thus for the case $x/\sigma = 2.00$ in a distribution of 1,000 scores, the probable frequency between the mean ordinate and the ordinate at two sigma units from the mean would be 1,000 times 0.47725, or 477.25. This tells us that we should expect approximately 477 cases out of 1,000 to fall within this range.

The reader will observe that one-fourth of the total area is included between the mean ordinate and the ordinate at 0.67449 sigma units from the mean; *i.e.*, where $x/\sigma = 0.67449$. Multiplying both members by σ, $x = 0.67449\sigma$, the value of a deviation which marks off one-fourth of the area—that fourth which lies on either side of the mean. Thus we see that half the total area lies between deviations which are at a distance of 0.67449σ from either side of the mean. We may conclude, therefore, that, if a deviation is chosen at random from a normal population, the chances are even that it will lie within this range. This range is commonly called the *probable error*. It is written

$$\text{P.E.} = 0.67449\sigma.$$

Graduation of Data to Normal Distribution.—The problem of graduating a given group of scores to a normal distribution properly belongs to the study of curve fitting. Nevertheless, it is well to consider the problem at this time in order to throw further light on the use and interpretation of normal probability tables. The task of adjusting a normal curve to a given distribution is one of passing a smooth curve through the upper extremities of theoretical ordinates (those taken from the tables) which are found to correspond to actual sigma values of the distribution at hand. It is usually advisable to make a list of those items which are necessary for purposes of computation before plotting the actual frequency polygon and superimposing the resulting theoretical curve. The graph itself gives us a visual impression of the goodness of fit; but, we are very often led to a more statistical test.[1]

The following data for observed frequencies are the scores obtained by 149 sophomores at Pennsylvania State College on the 1930 Carnegie Foundation Tests (Professional Education).

[1] See p. 417 for the χ^2 test.

TABLE XXIV.—SOPHOMORE SCORES ON THE PROFESSIONAL EDUCATION SECTION OF THE CARNEGIE FOUNDATION TESTS, 1930

Score intervals	Frequency	
319.5–339.5	3	
299.5–319.5	5	
279.5–299.5	8	$N = 149$
259.5–279.5	12	
239.5–259.5	19	
219.5–239.5	26	$M = 215.4$
199.5–219.5	22	
179.5–199.5	18	
159.5–179.5	14	$\sigma = 50.9$
139.5–159.5	6	
119.5–139.5	13	
99.5–119.5	3	

Our problem is first of all to determine theoretical normal curve frequencies for the intervals appearing in the table above. To do this, we must find the areas under the normal curve which correspond to these intervals and then multiply by 149. We simply find the area from the mean up to the upper boundary of the interval, and subtract the area which lies between the mean and the lower boundary of the same interval. In this way we find the theoretical frequencies for all the intervals.

Consider, for example, the interval (319.5–339.5). Since the mean is 215.4, the same interval in deviation form becomes (104.1–124.1). When we divide by the value of σ (50.9), the interval in sigma units becomes (2.04–2.43). From the normal probability tables (pages 485 to 487) we find that the area from the mean up to 2.43 sigma units is .493, and from the mean up to 2.04 sigma units is .480. Subtracting, we find the area included in the interval to be .013. We conclude that we may expect approximately 13 cases out of 1,000 cases to fall within the score interval (319.5–339.5). Since in our case $N = 149$, the predicted frequency would be, therefore, .013 · 149 = 1.94, or approximately 2. The reader will observe that actually 3 cases fell within this group.

We proceed in this manner to make a table of the graduation data for all the intervals. These data are displayed in Table XXV.

TABLE XXV.—NORMAL CURVE GRADUATION DATA FOR 149 SOPHOMORE SCORES ON THE CARNEGIE FOUNDATION TESTS, 1930

Interval boundaries	Deviation from mean	Deviation in σ units	Area up to σ unit	Portion of area between	Theoretical frequency	Actual frequency	Difference
339.5	+124.1	+2.43	.493				
				.013	2	3	−1
319.5	+104.1	+2.04	.480				
				.029	4	5	−1
299.5	+ 84.1	+1.65	.451				
				.055	8	8	0
279.5	+ 64.1	+1.26	.396				
				.091	13	12	+1
259.5	+ 44.1	+0.86	.305				
				.125	18	19	−1
239.5	+ 24.1	+0.47	.180				
				.149	22	26	−4
219.5	+ 4.1	+0.08	.031				
215.4	0.0	0.00	.000	.155	23	22	+1
199.5	− 15.9	−0.31	.124				
				.134	20	18	+2
179.5	− 35.9	−0.70	.258				
				.106	16	14	+2
159.5	− 55.9	−1.10	.364				
				.068	10	6	+4
139.5	− 75.9	−1.49	.432				
				.038	6	13	−7
119.5	− 95.9	−1.88	.470				
				.018	3	3	0
99.5	−115.9	−2.27	.488				

The area for the interval which included the mean

(199.5–219.5)

was obtained by adding the areas from the mean out to either extremity of the interval. The Difference column in the table may be used to make rapid adjustments in the frequency polygon and thus to give the points through which the smooth theoretical curve is to be drawn.

Figure 21 shows the frequency polygon of the sophomore scores together with the superimposed theoretical normal curve.

The Ordinates Method.—The normal curve of Fig. 21 was drawn through the points that represented the theoretical frequencies in each interval. Another very simple method of plotting the curve is to erect ordinates at given distances along the x axis and to pass the curve through the upper extremities of these ordinates.   Usually the practice is to start at the mean and erect an ordinate at each half sigma in each direction until

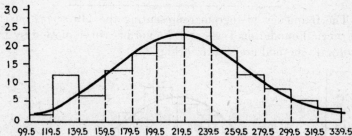

Fig. 21.—Normal-curve graduation of 149 sophomore scores on the Carnegie Tests, area method.

five or more ordinates are found on either side of the mean. With the frequency polygon already drawn on a scale that is marked off along the x axis for scores and on the y axis for frequencies, it is easy to determine graphically where the ordinates should be erected.   The method is simply that of graphing the equation of the normal curve, which we have seen (see page 286) may be written $y = \dfrac{N}{\sigma}\, z$.

In our problem $N = 149$, and in terms of intervals

$$\sigma = (50.9 \div 20) = 2.5$$

$N \div \sigma = 149 \div 2.5 = 59.6$.   The equation whose curve we wish to plot may thus be written $y = 59.6z$.   The value of z for each value taken along the x-axis may be calculated by logarithms from the equation $z = (1/\sqrt{2\pi})e^{-\frac{x^2}{2\sigma^2}}$ or more easily from our z table.[1]   The normal-curve ordinates at the mean,

[1] Appendix, Table XLIV.

±0.5σ, ±1.0σ ± 1.5σ, ±2.0σ, ±2.5σ, and ±3.0σ for our problem are as follows:

x/σ	z	$y = (59.6z)$
0	0.3989	23.77 (mean ordinate)
±0.5	0.3521	20.98
±1.0	0.2420	14.42
±1.5	0.1295	7.71
±2.0	0.0540	3.21
±2.5	0.0175	1.04
±3.0	0.0044	.26

The frequency histogram representing the 149 scores on the Carnegie Foundation Tests and the normal curve plotted by the ordinates method are shown in Fig. 22.

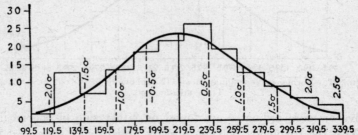

FIG. 22.—Normal curve graduation of 149 sophomore scores on the Carnegie Tests, ordinates method.

Goodness of Fit.—The use of chi square in testing goodness of fit of the normal curve is illustrated in Chap. XIV. Another test of normality developed recently involves the ratio of the mean deviation to the standard deviation.[1] Geary gives a table of average ratios to expect for different n's and also for the highest and lowest in 1 per cent and in 5 per cent of the samples. He also gives the standard error of these ratios which he calls ω_n. Concerning the use of this ratio as a test of normality Geary says:

From this investigation it appears very likely that, for quite small samples drawn at random from a normal universe with mean zero, the distribution of ω_n is fairly close to normal . . . The advantages of ω_n, regarded as a function of the original variables x, are as follows: like β_2 it

[1] GEARY, R. C., "The Ratio of the Mean Deviation to the Standard Deviation as a Test of Normality," *Biometrika*, Vol. 27, pp. 310–332 (1935).

assumes a characteristic value for infinite normal random samples; the values of its semi-invariants indicate that its distribution is far closer to normal, even for moderate samples, than that of β_2; and . . . its frequency distribution can be determined for all normal samples. Its principal disadvantage is that it is not symmetrical in the original variables . . . It would seem advisable to randomize the sample a few times and to calculate ω_n for each permutation. The mean or the median ω_n might then be taken as the representative value for the purpose of determining the probability of normality.

For the distribution of ω_n (A.D./σ) Geary employs the same technique as Student for t and Pearson for χ^2, viz., joint probability. He gives tables for the mean value to be expected, for σ_{ω_n}, and for the upper and lower 1 per cent and 5 per cent values. He holds that even for quite small samples from a normal distribution the distribution of ω_n will not be far from normal. The probability points of ω_n for the upper and lower 1 and 5 per cent levels, the mean of ω_n, and the standard deviation of ω_n are given in Table XXVI for different values of $N - 1$, labeled n.

TABLE XXVI.—THE 1 AND 5 PER CENT PROBABILITY POINTS OF ω_n

n	Upper 1%	Upper 5%	Lower 5%	Lower 1%	Mean of ω_n	Standard deviation of ω_n
5	.980	.954	.696	.626	.8385	.0786
10	.941	.911	.710	.656	.8180	.0613
15	.916	.891	.720	.677	.8113	.0516
20	.902	.879	.728	.691	.8079	.0454
25	.892	.870	.734	.701	.8059	.0410
30	.884	.864	.739	.709	.8046	.0376
35	.878	.859	.743	.715	.8036	.0350
40	.873	.855	.746	.720	.8029	.0328
45	.869	.851	.749	.725	.8023	.0310
50	.865	.849	.751	.728	.8019	.0295
75	.853	.839	.759	.741	.8005	.0242
100	.846	.834	.764	.748	.7999	.0210
500	.820	.814	.783	.776	.7983	.0095
1,000	.813	.809	.787	.782	.7981	.0067

For the data of Table XXIV $n = 148$, $\sigma = 50.9$, and
$$A.D. = 40.3.$$
$\omega_n = A.D./\sigma = 40.3 \div 50.9 = .7917.$ From Table XXVI we

see that this value is within the 5 per cent level for an n between 100 and 500 and is very close to the mean ω_n to be expected. On the basis of the Geary test we would conclude, therefore, that the sophomore scores on the Carnegie Foundation Tests are distributed normally. This agrees with the χ^2 test of goodness of fit discussed on page 418.

APPLICATIONS OF THE NORMAL CURVE CONCEPT

The normal curve is put to very many uses in educational and sociological research, some of which are discussed and illustrated at length in the elementary texts. To ask what use can be made of such a concept as that of normality of distribution is much like asking what use can be made of a lathe. A lathe is a tool which we can employ in making all sorts of products, according to our needs in the particular exigency; and the same is true of statistical formulas, including the normal curve function. Nevertheless we shall list a few of the types of uses to which the normal curve function has been applied, describing them here very briefly and recommending further reading in the sources, or in the more elementary texts, for students who wish to pursue the matter further.

1. To assign difficulty values to questions in a test. As questions become increasingly difficult a larger percentage of pupils fail them, the percentage increasing slowly at first, rapidly around the middle difficulties, and then slowly again at the upper extreme. Difficulty values are assigned in terms of the distance along the x axis from the mean or from some other zero point to the ordinate which divides the proportion that succeeded with the question from the proportion that failed it.[1]

2. To assign difficulty values to different scores on a test. The technique is essentially the same as that involved in the paragraph above, except that the ordinate is located by the proportion made up of those who earned a lower score than the one in question plus half those who earned the same score.[2]

3. To set standards for the distribution of grade marks. For this purpose the base line of a normal distribution is marked off into as many equal divisions as there are steps in the scale of

[1] Woody, Clifford, *Measurement of Some Achievements in Arithmetic*, Teachers College Bureau of Publications, Columbia University, 1916.

[2] McCall, W. A., *How to Measure in Education*, The Macmillan Company, 1922, p. 278.

grades and the area of each of these divisions is taken as norm for the percentage of individuals to receive the corresponding mark. Sometimes the base line is cut off at a range of five sigmas and sometimes a range of six sigmas.

4. To indicate the numbers of pupils to be expected in each division when desiring to divide pupils into ability groups of equal range of talent. The technique is the same as under 3.

5. To transmute marks distributed according to different standards of leniency. Suppose a teacher gives 20 per cent of his students A, 40 per cent B, 30 per cent C, 8 per cent D, and 2 per cent E. By use of formula (168a), a difficulty value for each of these grades and a comparison with the difficulty of corresponding grades by other teachers may be determined, and, if desired, all grades may be transmuted to the same standard. To make such computations is left as an exercise for the student.

6. To make scales for measuring the merit of handwriting, drawing, English composition, etc. For this purpose specimens of these objects are ranked into overlapping distributions and scale values determined from the mean of one of these distributions to the mean of the next. Thurstone has recently extended and improved upon this technique in making attitude scales. His essential addition consists in taking the σ of one of the distributions as standard and stating all steps in terms of this standard, thus securing more consistent units than by the older method.[1]

7. To make scales for measuring the mores of society, and to measure deviations from morality.[2]

References for Further Reading

PEARSON, KARL: "Historical Note on the Origin of the Normal Curve of Errors," *Biometrika*, Vol. 16, pp. 402–404.

ROMANOVSKY, V.: "Notes on the Moments of a Binomial $(p + q)^n$ about its Mean," *Biometrika*, Vol. 15, pp. 410–412.

[1] *J. Abn. and Soc. Psychol.*, Vol. 21, pp. 384–400; or *The Amer. Sociol.*, Vol. 31, pp. 529–554.

[2] PETERS, C. C., *Motion Pictures and Standards of Morality*, The Macmillan Company, 1933, Chaps. II-V. For an extended account of the uses of the normal curve in psychological and educational research see J. P. Guilford, *Psychometric Methods*, McGraw-Hill Book Company, Inc., 1936, Chaps. IV-IX. For a shorter account see H. E. Garrett, *Statistics for Students in Psychology and Education*, Longmans, Green & Company, rev. ed., 1937, Chap. VI.

CHAPTER XI

THE CORRELATION RATIO

CURVILINEAR CORRELATION

When we treated standard error of estimate (pages 112 to 117), we found that $\sigma_{est_y} = \sigma_y\sqrt{1 - r_{xy}^2}$. This standard error of estimate we saw to be the standard deviation of one of the columns of the correlation table, on the assumption that all the columns have the same standard deviation. We may denote it σ_c as well as σ_{est}. Using this notation, squaring, and proceeding with several other algebraic transformations,

$$\sigma_c^2 = \sigma_y^2(1 - r_{xy}^2) = \sigma_y^2 - \sigma_y^2 r_{xy}^2; \qquad \sigma_y^2 r_{xy}^2 = \sigma_y^2 - \sigma_c^2$$

$$r_{xy}^2 = \frac{\sigma_y^2 - \sigma_c^2}{\sigma_y^2} = 1 - \frac{\sigma_c^2}{\sigma_y^2}; \qquad r_{xy} = \sqrt{1 - \frac{\sigma_c^2}{\sigma_y^2}}$$

Thus an r could be computed in terms of the standard deviation of a column and the standard deviation of the whole distribution. The r is, thus, determined by the extent of the scatter of the columns in comparison with the extent of the scatter in the whole distribution. However, σ_c^2 must be calculated from the regression line as origin, and this cannot be done in advance of a knowledge of the r itself. But we can get a convenient measure of relationship by giving up the demand that σ_c be computed from measures taken as deviations from the regression line and by letting the measures from which it is computed be deviations *from the mean of the column*. The value of our correlation will not now be quite the same, so we must employ a new symbol for it.

$$\eta_{yx} = \sqrt{1 - \frac{\sigma_{c_m}^2}{\sigma_y^2}} \qquad \text{(Correlation ratio)} \quad (173)$$

This coefficient, eta, may include the case of *curvilinear correlation*. It gives us a measure of the extent to which the y scores

312

for each given x value are grouped compactly together and, consequently, indicates the degree to which some law is present in the relation between the x and the y factors, but the line of the means may become a nonrectilinear one. Hence we may not use η in the simple regression equation developed in connection with r, for that is an equation for a straight-line relation. The accompanying correlation tables, showing for pupils in two grades of the rural schools of Centre County, Pa., the relation of scores in the Otis Classification Test to pupils' ages, depict this sort of situation. It will be seen from the formula that η varies between 0 and 1. For, if there is no scatter of the columns at all, so that all y scores for a given x value come at exactly the same point showing complete determination of y values by x values, $\sigma_{c_m}^2 = 0$, the value under the radical becomes 1, and its square root is 1. If there is no law operative, so that scores in each column scatter as widely as the whole distribution does, $\sigma_{c_m}^2 = \sigma_y^2$, and we have under the radical $1 - 1 = 0$, so that $\eta = 0$. η can never be negative, since its only function is to show the degree of the presence of a law—and that degree can run only from none to complete. But η will always be exactly equal to r (in the case of complete rectilinearity) or greater than r—never less. This is because a standard deviation is always the least possible when its deviations are taken from the mean of its distribution, as they are in the case of η. Thus σ_c^2 taken from the regression line, which lies outside the mean of at least some of the columns except in the case of strictly rectilinear regression, is greater than $\sigma_{c_m}^2$. Hence less is subtracted from the 1 under the radical in the η formula, and, consequently, the η is greater than the corresponding r.

In practice the formula for η is usually put into a different form from that given above. To get it into the conventional form, we shall square it and carry it through a simplifying process.

$$\eta_{yx}^2 = 1 - \frac{\sigma_{c_m}^2}{\sigma_y^2} = \frac{\sigma_y^2 - \sigma_{c_m}^2}{\sigma_y^2}$$

The mean of a column lies at a distance of d, we shall say, from the mean of the whole distribution. If our measures are in deviation form, this d will equal, of course, $\Sigma y_c/n_c$, where n_o is the number of cases in the column in question. Then for any one column, taking our measures as deviations from the mean of the whole y distribution as said,

$$\sigma_{c_m}^2 = \frac{\Sigma y_c^2}{n_c} - \left(\frac{\Sigma y_c}{n_c}\right)^2$$

Summing for all the columns weighted for frequency and dividing by the sum of the frequencies,

$$\frac{\Sigma n_c \sigma_{c_m}^2}{N} = \frac{\Sigma(\Sigma y_c^2)}{N} - \frac{\Sigma n_c (\Sigma y_c / n_c)^2}{N}$$

If we make the assumption of homoscedasticity this becomes

$$\frac{N\sigma_{c_m}^2}{N} = \frac{\Sigma\Sigma y^2}{N} - \frac{\Sigma n_c M_c^2}{N}; \ \sigma_{c_m}^2 = \sigma_y^2 - \sigma_{m_c}^2; \ \sigma_y^2 - \sigma_{c_m}^2 = \sigma_{m_c}^2$$

Making in the η^2 formula above the substitution of the value just shown, we have

$$\eta_{yx}^2 = \frac{\sigma_{m_c}^2}{\sigma_y^2}; \ \eta_{yx} = \frac{\sigma_{m_c}}{\sigma_y} \quad \text{(Second form of the correlation ratio)} \quad (174)$$

Thus η equals the standard deviation of the means of the columns divided by the standard deviation of the entire distribution. The formula for the regression of x on y would obviously be $\eta_{xy} = \sigma_{m_c}/\sigma_x$, where, of course, in the former case the columns for which the standard deviation of means is taken are columns of y values for particular values of x, while in the latter case they are columns of x values for particular values of y.

The formula for η is frequently employed in just the form given. But we can put it into a more convenient shape and can pair it with a formula for r for the same data, by a little algebraic transformation.

The mean of any column is $\Sigma y_c / n_c$ where n_c is the frequency for that column. We wish to find the standard deviation of the set of means involved in all the columns. We shall employ the formula for σ^2 with zero as the assumed mean, which is

$$\sigma_x^2 = \frac{\Sigma f X^2}{N} - \left(\frac{\Sigma f X}{N}\right)^2$$

But instead of aggregating the moments as we go, we shall let them stand in the formula as they result from each of the separate columns. Our frequencies for the successive columns, 0, 1, 2,

3, . . . , we shall represent by $n_0, n_1, n_2, n_3, \ldots$ Our moments must, of course, be weighted by these frequencies. Our standard deviation squared for the means of the y columns will be, then,

$$\sigma^2_{m_c} = \frac{1}{N}\left[n_0\left(\frac{\Sigma y_0}{n_0}\right)^2 + n_1\left(\frac{\Sigma y_1}{n_1}\right)^2 + n_2\left(\frac{\Sigma y_2}{n_2}\right)^2 \right.$$
$$\left. + n_3\left(\frac{\Sigma y_3}{n_3}\right)^2 + \cdots\right] - \left(\frac{\Sigma y_N}{N}\right)^2$$

The N refers to the total population in contrast with the n's of the several columns which refer to the populations of their respective columns. We may now combine the n's with the quantities in parentheses and have

$$\sigma^2_{m_c} = \frac{1}{N}\left(\frac{\overline{\Sigma y_0^2}}{n_0} + \frac{\overline{\Sigma y_1^2}}{n_1} + \frac{\overline{\Sigma y_2^2}}{n_2} + \frac{\overline{\Sigma y_3^2}}{n_3} + \cdots\right) - \left(\frac{\overline{\Sigma y_N^2}}{N^2}\right)$$

The sigma of the whole set of y's, which we need in squared form for our denominator, is given by the familiar formula

$$\sigma^2_y = \frac{\Sigma y_N^2}{N} - \left(\frac{\Sigma y_N}{N}\right)^2$$

Substituting this value for σ^2_y and then multiplying both numerator and denominator by N^2, we have, for η^2,

$$\eta^2_{yx} = \frac{N\left(\dfrac{\overline{\Sigma y_0^2}}{n_0} + \dfrac{\overline{\Sigma y_1^2}}{n_1} + \dfrac{\overline{\Sigma y_2^2}}{n_2} + \dfrac{\overline{\Sigma y_3^2}}{n_3} + \cdots\right) - \overline{\Sigma y_N^2}}{N\Sigma y_N^2 - \overline{\Sigma y_N^2}}$$

$$\text{(Third formula for } \eta^2) \quad (175)$$

Note that this is η^2. Do not forget to extract the square root.

Now we can nicely pair a formula for r with this one by merely summing our xy values by columns and letting these partial sums stand in that form in the formula. We shall make zero our assumed mean in respect to both arrays; so our x values will be, successively, 0, 1, 2, 3, etc., up to one less than the number of columns. Of course, the formula would be essentially the same if we took some other assumed mean than zero, only then the partial sums would have the minus sign at the left of this assumed mean and the plus at the right. With these paired formulas we can easily get both η and r from essentially the same operations, only a few extra minutes being required to get either one when the other has been computed.   The following is the r formula:

$$r = \frac{N(\Sigma y_1 + 2\Sigma y_2 + 3\Sigma y_3 + 4\Sigma y_4 + \cdots) - \Sigma x_N \cdot \Sigma y_N}{\sqrt{(N\Sigma y_N^2 - \overline{\Sigma y_N^2})(N\Sigma x_N^2 - \overline{\Sigma x_N^2})}}$$

(Formula for r paired in structure with the eta formula)   (175a)

The P.E. of η is usually given as

$$\text{P.E.}_\eta = .6745 \frac{1 - \eta^2}{\sqrt{N}}$$

We shall now apply these two paired formulas to the computation of η and r for the data of Table XXVII and present similar data for another grade for comparison and as an exercise for the reader.   The data are scores on the Otis Classification Test

TABLE XXVII.—SCORES ON THE OTIS CLASSIFICATION TEST BY CHILDREN IN THE EIGHTH GRADE OF THE RURAL SCHOOLS OF CENTRE COUNTY, PA., DISTRIBUTED ACCORDING TO CHRONOLOGICAL AGE

Score	Chronological age; years-months							Totals	Y	fY	fY²
	10 to 10-11	11 to 11-11	12 to 12-11	13 to 13-11	14 to 14-11	15 to 15-11	16 to 16-11				
140–149		1						1	12	12	144
130–139				1	1	1		3	11	33	363
120–129			3	2	1	2		8	10	80	800
110–119			2		4			6	9	54	486
100–109		4	4	4	6	4		22	8	176	1,408
90– 99		2	3	8	8			21	7	147	1,029
80– 89		2	9	7	9	2		29	6	174	1,044
70– 79	2	4	4	13	14	9		46	5	230	1,150
60– 69		3	8	11	9	5	1	37	4	148	592
50– 59	1	1	4	6	19	9		40	3	120	360
40– 49	1	2	3	4	2	10	1	23	2	46	92
30– 39	1	1		2	1	2	2	9	1	9	9
20– 29					2	2		4	0	0	0
Totals..	5	20	40	58	76	46	4	249		1,229	7,477
ΣY_c	16	110	225	298	383	189	8	1,229			
$\overline{\Sigma Y_c^2}/n_c$	51	605	1,266	1,531	1,930	777	16				
X	0	1	2	3	4	5	6				
fX	0	20	80	174	304	230	24	832			
fX^2	0	20	160	522	1,216	1,150	144	3,212			

made by pupils in the rural schools of Centre County, Pa., in 1928 in the eighth grade and in the sixth grade. The scores are distributed according to the chronological ages of the pupils, and our problem is to find the correlation between the ages and scores within a single grade range.

The summation of the y moments by columns, Σy_c, is obtained in precisely the same manner as in the Pearson product-moment method of correlation described in Chap. IV. Here, as there, the sum of the y moments by columns equals the sum by rows, so that we have a check on the correctness of the work. That sum in this problem is 1,229. Applying our formula, we have

$$\eta_{yx}^2 = \frac{249(51 + 605 + 1,266 + 1,531 + 1,930 + 777 + 16) - 1,229^2}{249(7,477) - 1,229^2}$$

$$= .0772$$

Taking the square root, $\eta_{yx} = .277 \cdots$

$$r = \frac{249(110 + 2 \cdot 225 + 3 \cdot 298 + 4 \cdot 383 + 5 \cdot 189 + 6 \cdot 8) - 1,229 \cdot 832}{\sqrt{(249 \cdot 7,477 - 1,229^2)(249 \cdot 3,212 - 832^2)}}$$

$$= -.163$$

TABLE XXVIII.—SCORES ON THE OTIS CLASSIFICATION TEST BY CHILDREN IN THE SIXTH GRADE OF THE RURAL SCHOOLS OF CENTRE COUNTY, PA., DISTRIBUTED ACCORDING TO CHRONOLOGICAL AGE

Scores	Chronological age; years-months							Totals
	9 to 9-11	10 to 10-11	11 to 11-11	12 to 12-11	13 to 13-11	14 to 14-11	15 to 15-11	
110–119				1				1
100–109	1	1						2
90– 99			1	3				4
80– 89		3	3		2	1		9
70– 79		4	10	4	1			19
60– 69		4	13	7	1	1	1	27
50– 59	2	3	19	8	5	2	1	40
40– 49	3	8	15	8	8	2		44
30– 39	3	8	11	11	10	5	2	50
20– 29	4	3	7	14	6	4	1	39
10– 19		3	3	7	4	3		20
00– 09		1	2	1	1			5
Totals.........	13	38	84	64	38	18	5	260

It will be observed that the η is larger than the r, as we said above must be the case whenever they are not identical with each other. Also the η is positive, while here the r is negative. An η is always positive, since it indicates only the extent to which the columns are shortened in comparison with the total distribution and hence the extent of the operation of some law causing the y scores to be more or less definitely placed for given values of x. What that law is we can know only by a further examination of the trend, while r indicates both the extent of the law and the direction of the trend.

The probable error of our η is

$$\text{P.E.}_\eta = .6745 \frac{1 - .277^2}{\sqrt{249}} = .058$$

Since η is nearly five times its probable error, it is clear that a law is operating to place y scores in terms of x scores; i.e., there is a correlation between scores and chronological age within this eighth grade range.

Applying the same two formulas to Table XXVIII η turns out to be .222 and r to be $-.154$. The two grades show, therefore, very consistent results.

Hitherto the chief use made of η was to test rectilinearity of regression. The regression lines in Tables XXVII and XXVIII are both curved. Is that due merely to chance sampling or is there a significant departure from rectilinearity which may be expected to persist with successive sampling? The extent of departure of η from r is a function of the departure of the regression from rectilinearity. It has been customary to test the significance of this departure by applying Blakeman's test of significance of $(\eta^2 - r^2)$. In the previous edition of this book we explained that test and applied it to Tables XXVII and XXVIII. But we found it to give results which were not plausible. The inadequacy of the Blakeman test is now recognized, and we are dropping it from our treatment here. Instead, we recommend applying the χ^2 test of goodness of fit to test the significance of the departure of the actual regression from rectilinearity. Fisher[1] gives a value for χ^2 which, for the straight line

[1] FISHER, R. A., "The Goodness of Fit of Regression Formulae," *J. Roy. Statistical Soc.*, Vol. 85, Part IV, pp. 597–612 (1935). (The distribution is not quite the conventional one for χ^2, though close enough for large samples. For small samples Fisher gives a correction.)

as the theoretical value, reduces to

$$\chi^2 = (N - k) \frac{\eta^2 - r^2}{1 - \eta^2} \qquad \text{(χ^2 in terms of η^2 and r^2)} \qquad (176)$$

In this the N is the population of the sample and k is the number of columns. The result is interpreted in the manner explained on pages 410 to 419, with the aid of Table XLVII, page 498. The χ^2 table must be entered with $n = (k - 2)$ or $n' = (k - 1)$. The value of χ^2 calculated by this formula for Table XXVII is 13.26. Entering the table of χ^2 values with $n = (7 - 2)$, which is 5, we find that a χ^2 of 13 shows a P of .023379, and χ^2 of 14 shows a P of .015609. Linear interpolation between these for $\chi^2 = 13.26$ gives $P = .021359$. The probability is, therefore, a little more than .02 (two chances in a hundred) that a discrepancy as great as the one obtained in this problem might arise as a matter of chance fluctuation even though the true regression were rectilinear. That would leave the hypothesis that the regression might be rectilinear not wholly refuted, though rendered rather untenable. The fact, however, that a second sample shows a departure from rectilinearity in the same direction (both regression lines having the same general shape) further weakens the hypothesis that the true regression line might be rectilinear. The first sample alone gives a fairly significant (beyond 5 per cent), but not highly significant (1 per cent or less), difference from rectilinearity; but the two samples jointly give highly significant evidence of the curvilinearity of the regression.[1]

A CORRELATION RATIO WITHOUT BIAS

Unfortunately η is affected by the number of items in the several classes as well as by the inherent extent of correlation. For, as we saw on page 69, the variance of a class shrinks more and more, compared with its true population value, as the n decreases. In the numerator of the fraction in the formula,

$$(A) \qquad \eta^2 = 1 - \frac{\sigma_c^2}{\sigma_y^2}$$

the true population value would, on the average, be $n_c \sigma_c^2 / (n_c - 1)$, while that of the denominator would be $\dfrac{N}{N - 1} \sigma_y^2$. Because n_c

[1] On page 327 we give a better test for the goodness of fit of regression lines.

is not equal to N, the value of the fraction and, consequently, the value of η^2 will be affected by the population of the sample, or by the number of classes into which the total population is divided. In order to get a correlation ratio independent of this disturbance, Kelley[1] developed recently a new formula for the correlation ratio, which he designated ϵ.

If we employ population variances instead of sample variances, the estimates of the variances will not be altered by reason of smallness of populations in the columns, or in the whole y distribution, because our method of estimating population variances takes care of that. We learned on page 70 how to substitute for sample variance an estimate of the population variance: we need only divide our sum of squares by $(N - 1)$ instead of by N. Or, if we already have σ^2, s^2 (the estimate of the population variance) is merely $\dfrac{N}{N-1}\sigma^2$. So instead of σ_y^2 in the η formula we need only to use $\dfrac{N}{N-1}\sigma_y^2$. For the numerator we need the population variance of the σ_c^{2}'s. If our assumption of homoscedasticity were met perfectly, we could get that by merely taking $\dfrac{n_c}{n_c-1}\sigma_c^2$ where σ_c^2 is computed from any column. But we shall do better to estimate the population variance of the columns by taking a weighted average from all the columns. Letting $s_{c_i}^2$ stand for an estimate of the population variance of a particular column and letting n_{c_i} be the number of items in that column,

$$s_{c_i}^2 = \frac{n_{c_i}}{n_{c_i} - 1}\sigma_{c_i}^2$$

Clearing of fractions,

$$(n_{c_i} - 1)s_{c_i}^2 = n_{c_i}\sigma_{c_i}^2$$

Summing for all the columns,

$$\sum_1^k (n_{c_i} - 1)s_{c_i}^2 = \sum_1^k n_{c_i}\sigma_{c_i}^2$$

where k is the number of columns, n_{c_i} stands for the population of any column by which the $\sigma_{c_i}^2$'s are to be weighted, and the

[1] KELLEY, T. L., "An Unbiased Correlation Measure," *Proc. Nat. Acad. Sci.*, Vol. 21, pp. 554–559 (1935).

symbols above and below the Σ indicate the limits of summation. Assuming homoscedasticity for the purpose of estimating the population variance for the columns, but retaining on the right differing σ_c^2 values and weighting them for their population values, and dropping the j subscripts,

$$(\Sigma n_c - k)s_c^2 = \Sigma n_c\sigma_c^2; \text{ whence } s_c^2 = \frac{\Sigma n_c\sigma_c^2}{N-k}$$

Substituting these two estimates of the population variances in Eq. (A) and using ϵ^2 to designate the estimate of $\bar{\eta}^2$ (for we can never know $\bar{\eta}$, the true population ratio, but only estimate it),

$$\epsilon^2 = 1 - \frac{\dfrac{\Sigma n_c\sigma_c^2}{N-k}}{\dfrac{N\sigma_y^2}{N-1}} = 1 - \frac{\Sigma n_c\sigma_c^2(N-1)}{N\sigma_y^2(N-k)} \qquad (177)$$

(Correlation ratio without bias)

The elements of this formula can readily be computed from the squares of deviations from the means

$$\Sigma n_c\sigma_c^2 = \Sigma\Sigma(y_c - \bar{y}_c)^2; \; N\sigma_y^2 = \Sigma(y - \bar{y})^2$$

Or they can be computed from the scores by the following equivalent formulas:

$$\Sigma n_c\sigma_c^2 = \left(\Sigma y^2 - \Sigma \frac{\overline{\Sigma y_c}^2}{n_c}\right); \; N\sigma_y^2 = \left(\Sigma y^2 - \frac{\overline{\Sigma y}^2}{N}\right)$$

Or, if η^2 has already been computed, we may substitute it in formula (177) and get ϵ^2 in terms of η^2. Preserving the weightings of the variance of the columns for the differing populations of the columns,

$$\eta^2 = 1 - \frac{\Sigma n_c\sigma_c^2}{N\sigma_y^2}; \text{ whence } \frac{\Sigma n_c\sigma_c^2}{N\sigma_y^2} = 1 - \eta^2$$

and from the above $\epsilon^2 = 1 - \dfrac{\Sigma n_c\sigma_c^2}{N\sigma_y^2}\cdot\dfrac{N-1}{N-k}$,

$$\epsilon^2 = 1 - \frac{(N-1)}{(N-k)}(1-\eta^2) = \frac{(N-k)-(N-1)+(N-1)\eta^2}{N-k}$$

$$\epsilon^2 = \frac{(N-1)\eta^2-(k-1)}{N-k} \qquad (\epsilon^2 \text{ in terms of } \eta^2) \quad (178)$$

If we substitute zero for ϵ^2 in formula (178) we shall get a value for the average η^2 when the true η is zero. Calling this η_0^2,

$$\frac{(N-1)\eta_0^2 - (k-1)}{N-k} = 0; \quad (N-1)\eta_0^2 = (k-1)$$

$$\eta_0^2 = \frac{k-1}{N-1}; \quad \eta_0 = \sqrt{\frac{k-1}{N-1}} \qquad \begin{array}{l}\text{(The average value of } \eta \\ \text{when the true } \bar{\eta} \text{ is zero)}\end{array} \quad (179)$$

Since σ_c^2 is always less than σ_y^2 and since η_0 could extremely rarely be expected to be exactly zero, it is easy to see why η should tend to have a slight positive bias. Kelley's formula corrects for this.

Besides the constant positive bias in η, there is a second disturbing factor for which the ϵ technique corrects in part but for which a further correction is needed; i.e., the dependence of η upon the number of classes into which the x distribution is divided. One reason why η with a large number of categories differs from the value in the same situation with a smaller number is that with the larger number the populations in the several classes are lessened. If there were as many classes as the total number of items N, η would necessarily be unity; for with a single item in each column the variance of the column would be zero. But in the total population, which is hypothetically infinite in size, the variances would remain the same regardless of the narrowing of classes, because the populations in the classes would still be infinite. Thus to the extent to which ϵ overcomes the effect of smallness of populations in the classes, it corrects for differing numbers of categories. In the direction of fineness of grouping this constitutes the necessary correction. But in the direction of broad categories a disturbing factor still remains. If a category is broad enough to combine within it a number of elementary classes, the means of these several elementary classes will differ from the mean of the combined elementary classes to the extent to which there is present regression which differs from zero. Thus the variances of the broad classes will be somewhat too great as compared with the variances of the constituent elementary classes, and ϵ from broad categories will be somewhat too low. But a satisfactory correction for this is easily made. If it is assumed that, within each broad class, the regression is rectilinear and the slope is represented by $\pm \epsilon \frac{\sigma_y}{\sigma_x}$, exactly the same technique may be applied as that employed for correcting rectilinear correlation for broad categories, described on pages 393 to 399. This assumption is not strictly true, but it is the best simplifying assumption that can be made[1] and is correct to a good degree of approximation. On this assumption the correction involves merely dividing the obtained ϵ by the product of the r's between index values and variates in each of the arrays, which r's are tabled on page 398.

$$_c\epsilon = \frac{\epsilon}{r_{xx'}r_{yy'}} \qquad (\epsilon \text{ corrected for broad categories}) \qquad (180)$$

We shall now apply these two corrections to the η^2 computed for Table XXVII, page 316. First the correction for bias is as follows:

$$\epsilon^2 = \frac{(N-1)\eta^2 - (k-1)}{(N-k)} = \frac{(249-1)(.0772) - (7-1)}{(249-7)}$$
$$= .0544$$

$$\epsilon = .233$$

To correct for broad categories we must divide the ϵ obtained above by the product of the r's between index values and variates for each of the two distributions. These depend upon the number of categories and the assumed shape of the distributions. Both the distributions as to age and as to achievement are approximately normal, so we use the third column of r's in the table. For ages the number of categories is 7, and the corresponding r between index values and variates in the row for 7 categories is .970. In respect to achievement there are 13 categories, for which the tabled r is .991. Dividing by the product of these two r's, we have

$$_c\epsilon = \frac{.233}{(.970)(.991)} = .242$$

This corrected ϵ has a standard meaning, free from bias and independent of the size of the population of the sample and of the number of classes into which the sample is divided. In this form it is free from the objections on account of which

---

[1] This is the same assumption that is made by STUDENT in deriving a different formula for correcting η for broad categories. STUDENT, "Correction to Be Made to the Correlation Ratio for Grouping," *Biometrika*, Vol. 9, p. 317.

Fisher dismissed η as of "extremely limited" utility.[1] Thus corrected ϵ should have a wide and important usefulness in statistical research. We show below that it has all the merits of Fisher's *analysis of variance* technique and has, besides, a constructive meaning which makes it a positive rather than a merely negative utility.

In the article previously referred to, Prof. Kelley derives a formula for the standard error of ϵ^2 and of ϵ.

$$\sigma_{\epsilon^2} = \frac{1 - \epsilon^2}{\sqrt{N-1}} \left[\frac{2(k-1)}{N-k} + 4\epsilon^2 \right]^{\frac{1}{2}} \qquad \text{(Standard error of } \epsilon^2) \qquad (181)$$

which holds when $1/N$ is not small in comparison with $1/\sqrt{N}$.

$$\sigma_{\epsilon} = \frac{1 - \epsilon^2}{2\epsilon\sqrt{N-1}} \left[\frac{2(k-1)}{N-k} + 4\epsilon^2 \right]^{\frac{1}{2}} \qquad \text{(Standard error of } \epsilon) \qquad (182)$$

which is satisfactory if ϵ is not small.

The interpretation of the values obtained from the application of these formulas requires a knowledge of the form of the distribution of samples around any hypothetical true value of the statistic. At present we do not know that distribution (except as treated in our next paragraph). If the correlation is not very high and the population reasonably large, we may take the distribution to be normal, with little risk of appreciable distortion in our interpretation. We raise that question of distribution in our next paragraph. The reader may wish to compare the outcome from the technique of our next paragraph with what he would get from formula (181) on the assumption of a true value of zero for ϵ^2 and the use of the table of the normal distribution.

Testing the Null Hypothesis.—Frequently we wish to know whether any law at all is present or whether the ϵ we have from our sample might reasonably have arisen merely by chance fluctuation in sampling. For this purpose we need to know the distribution of ϵ^2 when the true correlation is zero. We have made tables for this distribution which are presented on pages 494–497 of this book. To test in this way the ϵ^2 of our illustration, we enter our table with $(k-1)$ equals 6, $(N-k)$ equals 242. We do not find there a row for 242, so we shall interpolate between

[1] FISHER, R. A., *Statistical Methods for Research Workers*, 7th ed., p. 264.

the rows 200 and 400. In row 200 and column 6 we find .032 for the 5 per cent point and .052 for the 1 per cent point. In row 400 the values are .016 and .027. Interpolation gives .029 and .047. The ϵ^2 in our illustration is .054, which is larger than even the one which stands at the 1 per cent point. This means that, if there were no law relating educational score to age within a single grade, we would get such a large ϵ^2 considerably less than 1 time in 100. The null hypothesis is, therefore, disproved; it is highly probable that there *is some* law relating educational achievement score and age within a single grade, and the extent of this law is expressed by a correlation ratio of .242. To determine what is the character of that law should be the next step in our research with these data. That step would be curve fitting, which we discuss in Chap. XV.

On a later page (337) we give data which are there employed to illustrate analysis of variance. Those same data can easily be worked up into ϵ^2, as follows:

$$\epsilon^2 = 1 - \frac{s_c^2}{s_y^2} = 1 - \frac{44,390}{154,420} = 1 - .287 = .713$$

Here $(k - 1)$ is 4 and $(N - k)$ is 25. Entering our table with these n's we find an ϵ^2 of .195 at the 5 per cent point and .305 at the 1 per cent point. Our obtained ϵ^2 is much greater than even the 1 per cent value, which means that, if there were no law present, so large a value would be obtained much less than 1 time in 100. This is entirely consistent with the showing by the technique of analysis of variance; as reference to page 338 will show. In fact, the test by the epsilon technique and the analysis of variance technique will always give precisely the same results. Thus we see there is a law relating breed of cattle to milk production and the extent of this law is expressed by the correlation ratio .845, the square root of ϵ^2. What the law is must be determined by comparing means and variabilities of production among the breeds with large samples and controlled conditions. Whether or not for this test ϵ^2 should be corrected for broad categories depends upon whether the classes are continuous and arbitrarily divided into classes or whether they may be more sensibly regarded as centering around point values. The former of our illustrations undoubtedly involves the former character, while the second is probably of the latter class.

THE PARTIAL CORRELATION RATIO

Any formula for partial η in terms of lower order correlations would either demand that we know and apply the equation of the regression curve, which would be too cumbersome to be practical, or that we make assumptions about this curve which would be too hazardous to risk in practice.[1] But a partial correlation ratio can be determined by selection. Suppose we have, in a large population, scores on general intelligence (x), high-school scholarship (z), and academic success in college (y), and we wish to know the correlation ratio between high-school scholarship and college success with the general intelligence factor held constant. We can sort our individuals into classes on the general intelligence (x) factor, then subsort these classes according to high-school scholarship (z). After both x and z are thus held constant, these subclasses will still have a certain variance due to factors other than x and z.

If we denote the weighted average y-variance of the subclasses by $\sigma_{s_c}^2$ and that of the x classes by σ_c^2, then by definition of the partial correlation ratio,

$$\eta_{yz \cdot x}^2 = 1 - \frac{\sigma_{s_c}^2}{\sigma_c^2} \qquad \text{(Partial } \eta^2, \, y \text{ on } z \text{ with } x \text{ held constant)} \qquad (183)$$

For partial epsilon this would be

$$\epsilon_{yz \cdot x}^2 = 1 - \frac{\Sigma n_{s_c} \sigma_{s_c}^2 (N - k)}{\Sigma n_c \sigma_c^2 (N - kp)} \qquad \text{(Partial } \epsilon^2, \, y \text{ on } z \text{ with } x \text{ held constant)} \qquad (184)$$

where k is the number of classes into which the population is sorted on x, and p is the number of classes into which each x class is subsorted. One could get a tentative idea of the extent of the partial correlation by determining the variance of one sample of

---

[1] L. Isserlis derived such a formula: "The Partial Correlation Ratio," *Biometrika*, Vol. 10, pp. 391–411. In spite of the title, the Isserlis formula is for multiple eta instead of for partial eta. But it can lead into the latter by substituting the value found for multiple eta [$H_{y(xz)}$] into the formula: $\eta_{yz \cdot x}^2 = (H_{y(xz)}^2 - \eta_{yz}^2)/(1 - \eta_{yz}^2)$. But the derivation assumes that the regression of y on x for z constant is rectilinear and also that of z on y is rectilinear for x constant. These are too hazardous assumptions for refined practice.

y scores from a single x class and then drawing from this a sub-sample for a single z value and computing the variance of this subclass. The partial correlation ratio would be, so far as this meager trial could suggest, the square root of the difference between these two variances divided by the variance of the x class. This would yield more valid results to the extent to which the average from a number of subclasses was employed rather than a single one; and, of course, for a good determination the values should be summed over the whole table. With the Hollerith machine equipment this should not be a very difficult process.

TESTING THE GOODNESS OF FIT OF ANY REGRESSION LINE

In terms of ϵ^2 we can easily make an "exact" test of the goodness of fit of any regression line. This parallels the χ^2 test on page 319 but is a more precise one and applies not only to a rectilinear regression but to regression lines of any shape. We said that, after having found by the correlation ratio technique that *some* law is present in our data, our next concern would be to investigate the nature of that law. One method of doing this is to seek the curve that best fits the trend. The technique of curve fitting is considered in Chap. XV. Having fitted a promising curve, we would next wish to test mathematically the goodness of the fit and hence the appropriateness of the type of curve fitted. Our formula for doing this is derived as follows:

Refer again to such a layout as that of Table XXVII, page 316. Conceive of a new set of derived values, y', each of which is the original value taken as a deviation from the point on the regression to which its column belongs. These derived values would make a new table of columns with a new set of means fluctuating about a line of zero slope. For this derived table we can have a new correlation ratio,

$$(B) \qquad \epsilon'^2 = 1 - \frac{s_c^2}{s_{y'}^2}$$

The variance of each new column will be the same as before, since there is no change except that a constant has been subtracted from all the scores, which does not affect the variance. But $s_{y'}^2$ will differ from s_y^2. We must find a value for $s_{y'}^2$. In a given column, if J_i is the value of the point on the regression line in terms of deviations from the whole y mean,

$$y_i = y_i' + J_i; \; y_i^2 = y_i'^2 + J_i^2 + 2y_i'J_i;$$

$$\frac{\Sigma y_i^2}{n_{c_i}} = \frac{\Sigma y_i'^2}{n_{c_i}} + \frac{\Sigma J_i^2}{n_{c_i}} + 2\frac{\Sigma y_i'J_i}{n_{c_i}}$$

Summing for all the columns weighted for their frequencies and dividing by the sum of the weights,

$$\frac{\Sigma y^2}{N} = \frac{\Sigma y'^2}{N} + \frac{\Sigma J^2}{N} + 2\frac{\Sigma\Sigma y_i'J_i}{N}$$

But, if the regression line is the best-fit one, the last term above will sum to zero over the whole sample, or substantially so. Therefore,

$$\sigma_y^2 = \sigma_{y'}^2 + \sigma_J^2. \quad \text{And, transposing, } \sigma_{y'}^2 = \sigma_y^2 - \sigma_J^2$$

Multiply through by $N/(N-1)$,

(C) $$s_{y'}^2 = s_y^2 - \frac{N}{N-1}\sigma_J^2$$

Now define a new term, R^2, so that $R^2 = \sigma_J^2/\sigma_y^2$, whence

$$\sigma_J^2 = R^2\sigma_y^2 = R^2\frac{N-1}{N}s_y^2.$$

Substituting in (C),

$$s_{y'}^2 = s_y^2 - R^2s_y^2 = s_y^2(1 - R^2)$$

Substitute this value in (B),

$$\epsilon'^2 = 1 - \frac{s_c^2}{s_y^2(1 - R^2)} = \left[\frac{1 - R^2}{1 - R^2} - \frac{s_c^2}{s_y^2(1 - R^2)}\right]$$

$$= \frac{1}{1 - R^2}\left(1 - R^2 - \frac{s_c^2}{s_y^2}\right)$$

$$= \frac{1}{1 - R^2}\left(-R^2 + 1 - \frac{s_c^2}{s_y^2}\right) = \frac{\epsilon^2 - R^2}{1 - R^2}$$

Therefore

$$\epsilon'^2 = \frac{\epsilon^2 - R^2}{1 - R^2} \tag{185}$$

If the fitted line is a rectilinear one, R is merely r, the coefficient of correlation. This follows directly from our showing on page 240 that the standard deviation of the points on the straight regression line equals $r\sigma_y$. For, by definition,

$$R^2 = \frac{\sigma_J^2}{\sigma_y^2} = \frac{r^2\sigma_y^2}{\sigma_y^2} = r^2$$

For other regression lines general formulas can easily be made; or the standard deviation of the points on the regression line can be computed directly by reason of knowledge of the frequency at each column and the ability to calculate the J_i value at each column from the equation of the fitted curve.

We may apply this technique to testing the rectilinearity of regression for the data in Table XXVII, employing the values of the statistics found earlier in this chapter.

$$\epsilon'^2 = \frac{\epsilon^2 - r^2}{1 - r^2} = \frac{.0544 - (-.163)^2}{1 - (-.163)^2} = .0286$$

ϵ'^2 has the same form of distribution as ϵ^2, so we use the same tables for interpreting it. The value cited on page 325 for this table for ϵ^2 when the true correlation is zero was .029 at the 5 per cent point and .047 at the 1 per cent point. So the obtained value for ϵ'^2 lies only a little distance below the 5 per cent point and the departure from rectilinearity is shown to be barely significant. This tallies with the other tests made earlier in this chapter.

When a parabola is fitted by the methods of Chap. XV, its equation turns out to be

$$Y = 4.1812 + 1.1091X - .2288X^2$$

The R^2 is found, by computation, to be .253. Therefore

$$\epsilon'^2 = \frac{\epsilon^2 - R^2}{1 - R^2} = \frac{.0544 - .0652}{1 - .0652} = -.0108$$

This is a low value, much below the 5 per cent point, .027. So the parabola gives an excellent fit. The ϵ'^2 is negative, which means that the deviations are actually less than they would be *on the average* if the true regression line were the one which we fitted. η^2 can never be negative, but ϵ^2 can be. If the true relation is zero, the ϵ^2's from samples must *average* zero, so that some samples must yield negative ϵ^2's.

Exercises

1. Compute η and ϵ for Table XXVIII, and determine the probability that there is a true correlation above zero; the probability that the regression is rectilinear.

2. Test the rectilinearity of regression in Table IX, page 100, by both the χ^2 and the ϵ'^2 tests.

3. Apply the correlation ratio technique to the exercises used in the next chapter and compare it with the analysis of variance technique.

4. With a large population of suitable scores from a study to which you have access, try computing a partial η and partial ϵ.

References for Further Study

EZEKIEL, MORDICAI: "The Determination of Curvilinear Regression Surfaces in the Presence of Other Variables," *J. Amer. Statistical Assoc.*, Vol. 21, pp. 310–320.

ISSERLIS, L.: "The Partial Correlation Ratio," *Biometrika*, Vol. 10, pp. 391–411.

KELLEY, T. L.: "An Unbiased Correlation Measure," *Proc. Nat. Acad. Sci.*, Vol. 21, pp. 554–559.

STUDENT: "Correction to Be Made to the Correlation Ratio for Grouping," *Biometrika*, Vol. 9, pp. 316–320.

WOO, T. L.: "Tests for Ascertaining the Significance of the Correlation Ratio," *Biometrika*, Vol. 21, pp. 1–66.

CHAPTER XII

ANALYSIS OF VARIANCE

ANALYSIS OF THE SAMPLE VARIANCE

At least to persons already familiar with rectilinear and curvilinear correlation, we believe that the most illuminating approach to the now popular analysis of variance is through these familiar concepts. We shall show first that, so long as we stay within the sample, analysis of variance is an extremely simple process. After we have shown this, we shall broaden the concept and lead by successive steps into some of its more complicated ramifications.

The reader is asked to refer again to a typical correlation chart, such as that on page 100. It will be observed that there remains some scatter in each y column even though all the individuals in the column have the same x value. In other words, when x is held constant, there still remains some variability in the y scores. But, when correlation is present, this variability is less than that for the whole distribution; put in terms of proportion it is σ_c^2/σ_y^2. Since this is the proportion of the variance (the σ^2) remaining when x is held constant, it may be considered the proportion of the variance in y attributable to the factors in y other than x. Conversely, the reduction in variance when x is held constant is the part of the variance attributable to the x factor. Put in terms of the proportion of the entire variance of y, this is

$$\frac{\sigma_y^2 - \sigma_c^2}{\sigma_y^2} = 1 - \frac{\sigma_c^2}{\sigma_y^2}$$

Now, as shown on page 117,

$$r = \sqrt{1 - \frac{\sigma_c^2}{\sigma_y^2}}; \text{ whence } r^2 = 1 - \frac{\sigma_c^2}{\sigma_y^2} = \frac{\sigma_y^2 - \sigma_c^2}{\sigma_y^2}$$

Thus the total variance may be divided into two portions of which the proportion attributable to the x factor (or rather, to what is common to x and y) is equal to r^2 and the proportion attributable to the other factors is $\sigma_c^2/\sigma_y^2 = 1 - r^2$. r^2 is sometimes called the *coefficient of determination;* hence the proportion of the total variance attributable to the factor that is correlated with y is the same as the coefficient of determination.

But in the above formula σ_c^2 was taken from the straight regression line as origin rather than from the means of the respective columns. That is not what is customarily done in computing a σ. If the reader will now refer to the correlation ratio, page 312 in our preceding chapter, he will find this limitation removed in the following formula for the correlation ratio:

$$\eta^2 = \frac{\sigma_y^2 - \sigma_c^2}{\sigma_y^2} = 1 - \frac{\sigma_c^2}{\sigma_y^2}$$

where σ_c^2 is computed from the means of the columns as origin. This is true for r^2 only when the regression is strictly rectilinear. Hence it is always true (assuming homoscedasticity) that the proportion of the variance attributable to the x factor is η^2 and the proportion to the other factors is σ_c^2/σ_y^2, which is also $1 - \eta^2$. In formula (174), page 314, it is shown that

$$\frac{\sigma_y^2 - \sigma_c^2}{\sigma_y^2} = \frac{\sigma_m^2}{\sigma_y^2}$$

Hence we may restate the above in the following form: The variance of y is separable into two parts; the proportion attributable to x is $\sigma_m^2/\sigma_y^2 = \eta^2$; the proportion attributable to factors other than x is $\sigma_c^2/\sigma_y^2 = 1 - \eta^2$.

Since these relations are fundamental in the problem of analysis of variance, we shall make another (independent) approach and arrive at the same conclusion. But we shall adopt a more conventional notation; instead of using a subscript m to denote a mean, we shall place a bar over the letter representing the array of which it is the mean. Thus, $\sigma_{\bar{y}}$ means the same as σ_{m_y}. We set up the following identity, for a single score:

$$(y - \bar{y}) = (y - \bar{y}_c) + (\bar{y}_c - \bar{y})$$

the barred y without a subscript referring to the mean of the whole y series while that with the subscript c stands for the mean of the column in which a particular y score is found. Squaring,

$$(y - \bar{y})^2 = (y - \bar{y}_c)^2 + (\bar{y}_c - \bar{y})^2 + 2(y - \bar{y}_c)(\bar{y}_c - \bar{y})$$

Now sum for all individuals, first by columns and then across columns for the entire table. Let k denote the number of columns and n_c the number of individuals in a column, the letters below and above the summation sign indicating the limits between which we sum.

$$\Sigma_1^N(y - \bar{y})^2 = \Sigma_1^k\Sigma_1^{n_{cj}}(y - \bar{y}_c)^2 + \Sigma_1^k\Sigma_1^{n_{cj}}(\bar{y}_c - \bar{y})^2$$
$$+ 2\Sigma_1^k\Sigma_1^{n_{cj}}(y - \bar{y}_c)(\bar{y}_c - \bar{y})$$

As long as we sum within columns, $(\bar{y}_c - \bar{y})^2$ will remain the same within the several columns. When we sum across the columns, we shall get

$$\Sigma_1^k n_{cj}(\bar{y}_c - \bar{y})^2$$

When we sum by columns in the cross-products term, $(\bar{y}_c - \bar{y})$ will remain a constant; but for each column $\Sigma(y - \bar{y}_c)$ will be zero, since the y's are taken as deviations from the mean of the column $\bar{y}_c$ as origin. Hence, in summing for the whole table, we have

(A) $\Sigma_1^N(y - \bar{y})^2 = \Sigma_1^k\Sigma_1^{n_{cj}}(y - \bar{y}_c)^2 + \Sigma_1^k n_{cj}(\bar{y}_c - \bar{y})^2$

By reason of the meaning of a sample variance, this can be written

$$N\sigma_y^2 = \Sigma n_{cj}\sigma_{c_j}^2 + \Sigma n_{cj}\sigma_{\bar{y}_c}^2$$

If, now, we assume homoscedasticity, we shall have

$$N\sigma_y^2 = \Sigma n_{cj}\sigma_c^2 + \Sigma n_{cj}\sigma_{\bar{y}_c}^2$$

But $\Sigma n_{cj} = N$, since the sum of populations by columns gives the entire population. Whence

$$N\sigma_y^2 = N\sigma_c^2 + N\sigma_{\bar{y}_c}^2$$

Dividing by N,

$$\sigma_y^2 = \sigma_c^2 + \sigma_{\bar{y}_c}^2; \text{ or } \frac{\sigma_c^2}{\sigma_y^2} + \frac{\sigma_{\bar{y}_c}^2}{\sigma_y^2} = 1$$

Thus again we are brought to the fact that the sample variance may be analyzed into two portions, one of which is the variance within the columns (or classes) and the other of which is the variance of the means of classes.

In this development we have carried the general case where the populations in the various classes may be different; hence our $\sigma^{2\prime}$s are weighted for the frequency of the several classes contributing to them. If we had chosen the special case of a symmetrical table, where all classes have the same frequency n, the derivation would have been much simpler.

ANALYSIS OF THE POPULATION VARIANCE

So long as we confine ourselves to analysis of the sample variance, analysis of variance is a very simple and straightforward process; it is merely another way of expressing what can be put as η^2 or as r^2. But R. A. Fisher, who introduced the technique, chooses to project the analysis into the population variance (see page 69) rather than keep to the sample variance. There is available a precise test of reliability on that plane. We shall now turn to that form.

We cannot carry the general case by the Fisher method; we must restrict the application in two respects: (1) We must (if we are to follow strictly the mathematical requirements) have always a symmetrical table—each class (column) containing the same n; and (2) we must limit the problem to the application of the null hypothesis, $i.e.$, we must assume a homogeneous population (no correlation) and test to see whether that hypothesis is tenable. We reenter our development above at (A). But since the n is to be the same in each column, this will take the following simple form:

$$\Sigma_1^N (y - \bar{y})^2 = \Sigma_1^k \Sigma_1^n (y - \bar{y}_c)^2 + n \Sigma_1^k (\bar{y}_c - \bar{y})^2$$

where n is the number in a class (the number of rows) and k is the number of classes (of columns). We may estimate a population variance from the first sum of squares by dividing by $(N - 1)$, and from the second by dividing by $(N - k)$, as shown on page 321. From $\Sigma(\bar{y}_c - \bar{y})^2$ we can estimate the variance of the *means* of the infinite supply of random samples which make up the population by dividing by $(k - 1)$. But remember that, if we are dealing with *random samples*, of the same size n, $\sigma_m^2 = \tilde{\sigma}^2/n$, where $\tilde{\sigma}^2$ is the true population variance. So, clearing of fractions, $\tilde{\sigma}^2 = n\sigma_m^2$. Hence the last term, $n\Sigma(\bar{y}_c - \bar{y})^2$, can be made to estimate the population variance by dividing by $(k - 1)$. Thus we have three estimates of the population variance as follows, derived from the sums of squares and the degrees of freedom standing below them:

$$s_1^2 \qquad\qquad s_2^2 \qquad\qquad s_3^2$$

$$\frac{\Sigma(y - \bar{y})^2}{N - 1} \qquad \frac{\Sigma\Sigma(y - \bar{y}_c)^2}{N - k} \qquad \frac{n\Sigma(\bar{y}_c - \bar{y})^2}{k - 1}$$

But we may no longer carry the equality sign between the first and the sum of the two others, because they have been divided by different values. Each, now, estimates a population variance.

The first one estimates the variance of the measures including all factors. The second estimates a variance for a hypothetical population in which the x factor is held constant but the other factors in y are allowed to vary. The third estimates a meaningful population variance if the assumption of no correlation is completely fulfilled. For $\tilde{\sigma}^2 = n\sigma_m^2$ only if the samples from which σ_m^2 is taken are completely random ones, of the same size, and drawn according to the laws of chance upon a whole homogeneous population. It is these two assumptions—homogeneous population and samples of equal size—that limit the analysis of variance technique to the null hypothesis and to tables with columns all of the same n. In practice, adjustment is made for unequal columns, but that is a rough adjustment without strict mathematical warrant.

THE TEST OF SIGNIFICANCE

Now even if the classes (the columns) in our table differed from one another and from the whole distribution only by chance, these three estimates of the population variance would differ somewhat merely by reason of fluctuation in sampling. But to the extent to which there is present some law which brings it about that the classes differ materially in mean score, to that extent the population variance estimated from the means of classes will be large in comparison with that estimated from within the classes themselves. When the difference is small, chance fluctuation can plausibly explain it; but when the difference becomes great, it cannot be plausibly attributed to chance. The formula developed by Fisher for testing the divergence of these estimates of the population variance does not, however, involve subtracting the variances but rather dividing one by another. This is a more sensitive and precise way of measuring divergence than subtraction would be.

The test assumes the null hypothesis; if the classes were really all alike—"belonged to the same homogeneous population"—what would be the probability of getting in a sample so great a divergence as the one we have in hand in our sample? The answer involves a derivation that is merely an extension of the ones for Student's t and for Pearson's χ^2. We show something of it in Chap. XIV. If *independent* samples are drawn from an infinite homogeneous parent population, these samples will differ in variance. The chance of obtaining a given sample can be stated in terms of probability, and the probability of obtaining simultaneously any two or more samples is the product of the probabilities of obtaining them separately. By stating mathematically the probability of obtaining two variances simultaneously and then integrating, it is possible to determine the probability of obtaining two variances which diverge from each other by a given amount even though both samples arise from the same parent population. The process is inherently simple and straightforward, but the necessity of successively integrating e functions involves some mathematical dodges and makes the arithmetic laborious. For this reason it is not feasible to determine at each application the probability that two variances as divergent as the ones in hand might have arisen by chance from the same parent population. So Fisher has tabled these probabilities for certain values. They must be tabled in terms of the size of the two samples as well as the extent of divergence between the estimated variances. Fisher tabled these in terms of a function he calls z, which is $\dfrac{1}{2} \log_e \dfrac{s_1^2}{s_2^2}$, and also equals

$$(\log_e s_1 - \log_e s_2) = \tfrac{1}{2}(\log_e s_1^2 - \log_e s_2^2).$$

But Snedecor tabled s_1^2/s_2^2, which he designated F, because that is the function obtained directly from the calculations and thus saves looking up log values. Many people believe Snedecor's table is the most convenient in use.[1] s_1^2 is always to be taken as the larger of the two variances. A fundamental condition of the

---

[1] We do not include in this volume tables of F or of z, because we believe that the research workers for whom we are writing should usually employ the ϵ technique described in our preceding chapter. The ϵ technique tells all that analysis of variance tells and more. We give tables for the distribution of ϵ^2. Those who wish to use the F and z tables can find them in other books.

test of significance is that the two estimates be independent. This makes it necessary to compare the variance estimated from the means with that estimated from the classes, since the other pairs of variances are correlated. Other comparisons can be made by adjusting for the element of correlation.

EXAMPLES OF ANALYSIS OF VARIANCE

We shall now give a simple example of analysis of variance. Table XXIX displays the number of pounds of milk given in a month by six cows of each of five breeds as taken from the records at Pennsylvania State College. The problem is to determine

TABLE XXIX.—NUMBER OF POUNDS OF MILK GIVEN BY SIX COWS OF EACH OF FIVE BREEDS IN 1 MONTH AT PENNSYLVANIA STATE COLLEGE

Cow No.	Breeds				
	Holstein	Jersey	Guernsey	Ayrshire	Brown Swiss
1	1,562	914	926	1,080	1,237
2	1,897	920	700	1,231	1,246
3	1,559	1,147	831	1,347	1,058
4	1,594	712	989	999	1,112
5	1,535	702	819	1,375	1,013
6	2,498	727	904	1,009	1,095
Totals.........	10,645	5,122	5,169	7,041	6,761

$\Sigma\Sigma y$ for whole table, 34,738

$\Sigma\Sigma y^2$ for whole table, 44,702,480

$$n\Sigma(\bar{y}_c - \bar{y})^2 = \frac{k\Sigma\overline{\Sigma y_c}^2 - \overline{\Sigma\Sigma y}^2}{kn} = \frac{(5)(261,556,272) - 34738^2}{(5)(6)} = 3,368,424$$

$$\Sigma\Sigma(y - \bar{y}_c)^2 = \frac{n\Sigma\Sigma y^2 - \Sigma\overline{\Sigma y_c}^2}{n} = \frac{6,658,608}{6} = 1,109,768$$

$$\Sigma(y - \bar{y})^2 = \frac{N\Sigma\Sigma y^2 - \overline{\Sigma\Sigma y}^2}{N} = \frac{30(44,702,480) - 34,738^2}{30} = 4,478,192$$

$$s_m^2 = \frac{n\Sigma(\bar{y}_c - \bar{y})^2}{k - 1} = \frac{3,368,424}{5 - 1} = 842,106$$

$$s_c^2 = \frac{\Sigma\Sigma(y - \bar{y}_c)^2}{N - k} = \frac{1,109,768}{30 - 5} = 44,390$$

$$s_y^2 = \frac{\Sigma(y - \bar{y})^2}{N - 1} = \frac{4,478,192}{30 - 1} = 154,420$$

(Note that $n\Sigma(\bar{y}_c - \bar{y})^2 + \Sigma\Sigma(y - \bar{y}_c)^2 = \Sigma(y - \bar{y})^2$. This serves as a check on the arithmetic.)

whether chance fluctuation of sampling alone could explain the observed differences among the breeds while in reality all the breeds are alike in milk production (belong to the same homogeneous population) or whether this null hypothesis is untenable. If one has available a calculating machine, it is most convenient to obtain the needed sums of squares by the formulas given at the foot of the table, which are algebraic equivalents of the basic formulas. Making the calculations indicated, we get the following as our three estimates of the population variance:

From means of columns, 842,106.
From within columns, 44,390.
From the total distribution, 154,420.

Dividing the estimate from means by that from within columns to get F, we have

$$F = \frac{s_m^2}{s_c^2} = \frac{842,106}{44,390} = 18.99$$

In order to see what the probability is of obtaining so great an F merely by chance fluctuation, we enter Snedecor's table with the n_1 for means equal to $(k - 1)$, which is 4, and the n_2 for classes equal to $(N - k)$, which is 25. In the column for $n_1 = 4$ and the row for $n_2 = 25$, we find 2.76 for the 5 per cent value and 4.18 for the 1 per cent. Our obtained F, 18.99, is much beyond even the 1 per cent value. This means that, if there were no true difference between the breeds in milk production, we would obtain so great a difference in variances much less than 1 time in 100. The difference in breeds is, therefore, highly significant and the null hypothesis, that the breeds might not differ, is refuted.

We may show how this technique can be extended into educational problems by the following examples. Dressel obtained the

Source	Degrees of freedom	Sum of squares	Mean square
Between means of high schools............	14	19.51	1.393
Within high schools.....................	795	492.79	0.6197
Total.................................	809	512.30	0.6333

$$F = \frac{1.393}{0.6197} = 2.25$$

following data on the college grades of 810 students coming from 15 different high schools. The problem was to ascertain whether different high schools differ significantly in the degree to which their graduates succeed in making good college grades.

We do not find in Snedecor's table an entry for 809 and 14 degrees of freedom, but the F for 1,000 and 14 degrees of freedom is 1.70 for the 5 per cent point and 2.09 for the 1 per cent point while for 400 and 14 degrees of freedom the entry is 1.72 for 5 per cent and 2.12 for 1 per cent. So our obtained 2.25 is beyond the one to be expected in even 1 per cent of the samples on the basis of chance fluctuation. So the differences of means of high schools cannot be reasonably attributed to chance; the high schools differ significantly in respect to the success of their graduates in college. If Snedecor's table of F is not available and the worker wishes to look up the significance from Fisher's z table, he must obtain

$$z = \tfrac{1}{2} \log_e F$$

which in this application is $\tfrac{1}{2} \log_e 2.25 = 0.40546$. If a table of natural logarithms is not available, z can be obtained from a table of common logarithms as follows:

$$z = \tfrac{1}{2}(2.302585 \log_{10} F) = 1.151294 \log_{10} F$$

which the reader will find by verification to be for this application also 0.40546. Fisher's z table will then give interpretations entirely consistent with Snedecor's F table for the same number of degrees of freedom.

So high schools are found to be significantly different in respect to the success of their students in college. But intrinsically the relation is low; the significance is high because the population is large. We can get a measure of the strength of the relation by computing ϵ^2, as explained in our previous chapter. This is very easily done from the above data. It involves merely dividing the population variance estimated from "within high schools" by that estimated from the total, then subtracting the quotient from 1.00.

$$\epsilon^2 = 1 - \frac{0.6197}{0.6333} = .0214; \epsilon = \sqrt{.0214} = .144$$

If we have computed ϵ^2 instead of F, we can make the significance test by referring to our Table XLVII, page 497. Here, for $N - k = 1,000$ and $k - 1 = 14$, the ϵ^2 at the 5 per cent point is .010 and that at 1 per cent is .015, while for $N - k = 400$ and $k - 1 = 14$ the 5 per cent value is .024 and the 1 per cent .036. This tells precisely the same story regarding significance that the F test or the z test tells: the ϵ^2 could not reasonably be attributed to chance fluctuation of sampling. Because ϵ^2 shows the strength of the relation as well as its significance and since the test of significance of ϵ^2 gives outcomes identical with those for F or z, we publish only the table for ϵ^2 and not those for F and z.

As another example we shall use some data a part of which is from a study by Thorndike and a part hypothetical because the necessary details are lacking in Thorndike's report. A test of mental ability was administered to 4,540 subjects who had taken different combinations of courses in high school, making nine different curricular groups. The problem was to determine whether the several curricula differed in the effectiveness of their training as measured by this test.

Source	Degrees of free-dom	Sum of squares	Mean square
Between means of curricular groups........	8	38,517	4,815
Within curricular groups................	4,531	14,544,510	3,210
Total.................................	4,539	14,583,027	3,213

$$F = 1.50$$

For 8 and 1,000 degrees of freedom an F of 1.89 stands at the 5 per cent level and 2.43 at the 1 per cent level, while for 8 degrees and infinity the 5 per cent point is 1.88 and the 1 per cent is 2.41. So our F of 1.5 would arise by chance fluctuation more than 5 times in 100. There is, therefore, little promise in the hypothesis that the several curricula differ in training value. Nine curricula of these types which do not differ in training value in the infinite population could reasonably often give as large differences in a sample of our size as the ones we have in hand.

The reader may wish to try the ϵ test on this problem as an exercise.

ANALYSIS OF VARIANCE INTO MORE THAN TWO PARTS

We may set up the following identity, for one individual's score:

$$(y - \bar{y}) = (\bar{y}_c - \bar{y}) + (\bar{y}_r - \bar{y}) + (y - \bar{y}_c - \bar{y}_r + \bar{y})$$

The $\bar{y}_c$ stands for the mean of a column and the $\bar{y}_r$ for the mean of a row. The identity involves merely adding certain values to the quantity at the right and then subtracting them, so as to balance the equation. If, now, we square and sum for all individuals in the sample, we shall get the sum of the squares of the four quantities in the several parentheses plus a series of cross products. But the cross products all vanish, because the total of the sums from them is zero. We are thus left with the following expression (into which we have inserted an extra parenthesis for later reference).

$$(B) \quad \Sigma_1^N(y - \bar{y})^2 = \Sigma_1^k\Sigma_1^n(\bar{y}_c - \bar{y})^2 + \Sigma_1^k\Sigma_1^n(\bar{y}_r - \bar{y})^2$$
$$+ \Sigma_1^k\Sigma_1^n[(y - \bar{y}_c) - (\bar{y}_r - \bar{y})]^2$$

The first two terms at the right of the equality sign are the sums of squares "between classes," like the ones we met above; only, we have both the sums of squares of means of columns and those of means of rows. The term in brackets is a residual remaining in the total variance beyond the two sums of squares from means of columns and of rows. We have already shown that population variances can be estimated from $\Sigma\Sigma(\bar{y}_c - \bar{y})^2$ and $\Sigma\Sigma(\bar{y}_r - \bar{y})^2$ by dividing by the appropriate number of degrees of freedom, *viz.*, one less than the number of columns and one less than the number of rows, respectively. It can also be shown that a further estimate of the population variance can be made by dividing the residual by the appropriate number of degrees of freedom, which Irwin[1] proves to be in this case $(k - 1)(n - 1)$. Thus we have

Between columns, $\Sigma\Sigma(\bar{y}_c - \bar{y})^2$, $(k - 1)$ degrees of freedom.
Between rows, $\Sigma\Sigma(\bar{y}_r - \bar{y})^2$, $(n - 1)$ degrees of freedom.
Residual, $\Sigma\Sigma(y - \bar{y}_c - y_r + \bar{y})^2$, $(k - 1)(n - 1)$ degrees of freedom.

[1] IRWIN, J. O., "Mathematical Theorems Involving Analysis of Variance," *J. Roy. Statistical Soc.*, Vol. 94, p. 290.

When grouped in one way, as shown in (B), the entries in the brackets give, as close examination will show, the within-the-class sum of squares when the deviations are themselves taken as deviations from the means of the rows; and, when grouped in another way, the sum of squares within the other class as deviations from the means of columns. By taking the deviations in the columns, thus, from the means of the rows, the effect of the gross differences in rows is removed, and we have the residual variance in columns with the row factor held constant. If the population variance estimated from the residual is then compared with the population variance estimated from the means of columns, by the methods previously discussed in this chapter, evidence can be obtained regarding the departure of the column variation from chance with the row factor held constant. If the columns are independent of one another, as in our example where the Jerseys and the others were selected entirely at random regarding the Holsteins, the outcomes from this method will contain no new information; the significance will be the same except for random variation. If the entries in the columns (families) are matched in some manner, as by putting on the same row cows equally far along in gestation, the significance may be affected considerably. If, even with matching, there is no intercorrelation except zero among the columns, the significance will be unchanged. But, if there is positive intercorrelation, the residual will be decreased and the significance of the differences between families thereby increased. If there is negative intercorrelation, the matched group arrangement will yield a larger residual variance and a lower reliability than the random one.

We shall illustrate this in the table below. The table was adapted from data given by Snedecor on the influence of certain

TABLE XXX.—YIELD OF POTATOES UNDER DIFFERENT FERTILIZERS

	1	2	3	4	5	Total
1	C344	B428	A423	E317	D323	1,835
2	D367	A430	E398	C387	B447	2,029
3	B317	C389	D425	A389	E449	1,969
4	E303	D393	C404	B347	A234	1,681
5	A291	E423	B412	D432	C386	1,944
Total.....	1,622	2,063	2,062	1,872	1,839	9,458

fertilizers on the yield of potatoes. The table contains several features of which we wish to make use later and which we ignore here. One of these features is the prefacing of each entry by a letter; ignore that for the present. Nor is it necessary for our present purpose that the arrangement have the same number of rows as columns. It could, for our present purpose, be a five by six, or any other rectangular arrangement. Our only present requirement is that the items in a row belong together as a class—as the same side of a field, pigs of the same age, or teachers employed in the same city.

The outlay in Table XXX represents a field divided into five strips (rows) and subdivided into 25 blocks by strips in the perpendicular direction. Let us say that the rows represent north-south divisions of the field into strips which may differ in fertility, and the columns represent the east-west orientation. The numerical entries represent the average number of bushels per acre in the blocks. Our first concern is to find whether the field is homogeneous in productiveness. Test first for east-west homogeneity, then for north-south homogeneity. This is done just as in our previous example. We have the following:

Source	Sum of squares	Degrees of freedom	Mean
Total	73,657	$(N - 1) = 24$	3,069
Between columns	26,850	$(k - 1) = 4$	6,712
Residual	46,807	$(N - k) = 20$	2,340

$$F = \frac{6,712}{2,340} = 2.87. \quad P = 5 \text{ per cent}$$

For north-south (rows) as follows:

Source	Sums of squares	Degrees of freedom	Mean
Total	73,657	24	3,069
Between rows	15,034	4	3,758
Residual	58,623	20	2,931

$$F = \frac{3,758}{2,931} = 1.28. \quad P > 5 \text{ per cent} \ (P \text{ is greater than 5 per cent})$$

By this test the field appears to differ somewhat in productivity as we go from east to west; the F for columns is exactly at the

5 per cent level, meaning that, if in the true population they did not differ, we would have obtained so great a divergence between our estimates of variance only 5 times in 100. But in the north-south direction heterogeneity is not established, since the F stands much below even the 5 per cent level and means that we would get so large a discrepancy considerably more than 5 times in 100 merely by chance fluctuation.

But now we shall apply the technique discussed in the paragraph preceding the table; we shall hold rows constant in productivity and test the columns for homogeneity. Then we shall hold columns constant and test the rows for homogeneity.

In the above procedure the sum of squares in our residual was the total sum minus that for "between columns" while we were testing columns, and this same total minus that "between rows" when we were testing rows. But here the residual sum of squares will be, as inspection of Eq. (B) shows, the total less the sum of the squares between means of columns *and* that between means of rows. That is, the residual is

$$73,657 - (26,850 + 15,034) = 31,773.$$

This residual is the same for testing both rows and columns and is always most easily obtained by subtraction from the total. The degrees of freedom for this residual are now only $(k - 1)(n - 1) = (4)(4) = 16$, so that the mean is 1,986. So we have for columns

$$F = \frac{6,712}{1,986} = 3.38. \quad 1 < P < 5 \text{ per cent} \qquad \text{(P is greater than 1 and less than 5 per cent)}$$

For rows,

$$F = \frac{3,758}{1,986} = 1.89. \quad P > 5 \text{ per cent}$$

Evidence of lack of homogeneity in the patches is increased by this added element of control, in respect both to rows and to columns. In the case of the columns it reaches a point which gives fairly conclusive evidence that the strips differ in productivity.

THE LATIN SQUARE

We now introduce a third element of control, for which the letters preceding the yields entered in Table XXX were employed. The letters stand for different fertilizer treatments. Each of five fertilizers, represented by the letters A, B, C, D, E, respectively, was used in five blocks scattered through the field. The particular layout of the field now becomes important to us. We observe that each replication of a fertilizer treatment occurs in a different row and a different column, one replication in each row and one in each column. This necessitates that the layout be square, a k by k table with k experiments each replicated k times. This arrangement is called the *Latin square*.

We want now to test whether or not the fertilizers designated A, B, C, D, E, respectively, affected the yield of potatoes differently when the productivity of the 25 blocks is equated in respect to both rows and columns. We want to get a residual sum of squares as the "experimental error" that will be freed from the systematic contribution of differences in fertilizers. That suggests that we equate these scores by subtracting (algebraically) from each fertilizer score the difference between the mean of the class to which it belongs and the grand mean. This is another way of describing a process exactly similar to the one to which we resorted on page 341 when we were providing for the analysis of variance into three parts. Hence in the residual we subtract from the expression on page 341 such a differential and, to balance the equation, also add it. Calling the mean of a fertilizer class $\bar{y}_f$, we have

$$(y - \bar{y}) = (\bar{y}_c - \bar{y}) + (\bar{y}_r - \bar{y}) + (\bar{y}_f - \bar{y}) + \{(y - \bar{y}_c) - [(\bar{y}_r - \bar{y}) + (\bar{y}_f - \bar{y})]\}$$

If, now, we square and sum, all cross products will sum to zero *if the fertilizer treatments are so arranged that one replication occurs in each column and one in each row*, as happens in the Latin square. In other random arrangements they may approximately sum to zero but there is no mathematical assurance that they will do so. Thus we have left

$$\Sigma(y - \bar{y})^2 = \Sigma(\bar{y}_c - \bar{y})^2 + \Sigma(\bar{y}_r - \bar{y})^2 + \Sigma(\bar{y}_f - \bar{y})^2 + \Sigma(y - \bar{y}_c - \bar{y}_r + \bar{y} - \bar{y}_f + \bar{y})^2$$

To the two sets of sums of squares between classes we add a further one, that of the means of fertilizer classes. The residual now is reduced and is best obtained by subtraction from the total. If the conditions named above have been fulfilled, a population variance can be estimated from the new residual by dividing the sum of squares by the appropriate number of degrees of freedom. The number of degrees of freedom is $k - 1$ less than before, where k is the number of replications of the experimental factor.[1] In this case the degrees of freedom are $16 - 4 = 12$. Summing by classes the scattered scores for fertilizer treatments we get the following:

	Sum	Mean
A	1,767	353.4
B	1,951	390.2
C	1,910	382.0
D	1,940	388.0
E	1,890	378.0

The sums of squares between rows and between columns we had before. We can easily calculate the sum of squares of the means of the fertilizer groups from the data given just above. We get the new residual sum of squares by subtraction from the total. Bringing all these together we have the following:

Source	Sum of squares	Degrees of freedom	Mean
Total	73,657	24	3,069
Between columns	26,850	4	6,712
Between rows	15,034	4	3,758
Between fertilizer classes	4,347	4	1,087
Residual	27,426	12	2,285

In order to test for reliability, we now divide each population variance estimated from between classes (*i.e.*, from means of classes) by the one estimated from the residual and have the following:
For columns

$$F = \frac{6,712}{2,285} = 2.94. \quad P > 5 \text{ per cent}$$

For rows

$$F = \frac{3,758}{2,285} = 1.64. \quad P > 5 \text{ per cent}$$

[1] FISHER, R. A., *Statistical Methods for Research Workers*, 7th ed., p. 276.

For interpreting F, the table must be entered with 4 and 12 degrees of freedom.

For fertilizers the mean from between classes is actually less than that from within the classes. This indicates that the fluctuation from class to class is less than that which would ordinarily come from chance sampling. So the fertilizers evidently have no differential effect that this experiment determines —unless it should exert some influence to make the average of the classes alike without simultaneously making the individuals within classes alike, which is extremely improbable. It is, therefore, highly improbable that there is a real effect rather than a chance one. But we shall look up its probability anyway in the F table. We must always divide the larger by the smaller variance, since the distribution would be of the same shape for negative deviations as for positive.

$$F = \frac{2{,}285}{1{,}087} = 2.10. \quad \text{P} > 5 \text{ per cent}$$

For 12 and 4 degrees of freedom an F of 5.91 stands at the 5 per cent point. So an F of 2.10 could easily come about by chance.

It is possible to arrange a Latin square so as to admit still a further factor. Then each cell will contain a score according to one classification designated by a Latin letter and the same score according to another classification represented by a Greek letter, so that each cell entry will be prefaced by two letters. This is called the Greco-Latin square. The arrangement must be such that each Latin letter appears once in each row and in each column, each Greek letter once in each row and each column, and each Latin letter once with each Greek letter. This permits the analysis of variance into four parts besides the residual (error). The mathematical derivation of its formula would follow along the same lines as the one we gave for the Latin square. The number of Greco-Latin squares that can be set up is narrowly limited; out of all the possible Latin squares only a small fraction can be arranged as Greco-Latin squares. The interested reader may pursue this further in Fisher's *Design of Experiments*, pages 90 to 93.

The analysis of variance into three parts (between rows, between columns, and residual) is not limited to the Latin square, though it is limited to a rectangular table in which rows consist

of scores matched on one basis and columns consist of scores
matched on another basis. The analysis into further factors
(without subclasses) is limited to the Latin square or to some
other equally effective method of randomizing the plots. It is
clear that such an experimental design as the Latin square fits
agricultural research especially well. A field is likely to differ in
fertility even in closely proximate positions. The division of the
field into blocks so placed as to sample all parts of the field in a
systematic way is an excellent scheme for making probable
equally favorable conditions for all the experimental factors.
Sometimes it may be useful in other types of research (see Exercise 4, page 359). But research workers in education, psychology, and sociology, for whom chiefly we are writing, are
likely to find fulfillment of its peculiar replication requirements
cumbersome and impractical. We shall later have something
to say about borrowing research techniques which were designed
for one type of problem and trying to fit them into another.

ANALYSIS WITH SUBCLASSES

Further complexity is introduced into analysis of variance
when each class is divided into subclasses and certain comparisons
are made involving the subclasses. This is really only an
aggregation of elemental problems which, taken singly, are
precisely the same as the ones we discussed above. It is a
case of "wheels within wheels." We think it best, at least for
novices and probably for all workers, to attack these phases one
by one instead of driving them all abreast.[1] Always one should
realize that his problem consists in facing an aggregate of classes
which may differ more or less in respect to the position of their
means, and his question is whether these means differ more than
the variability within the classes would justify on the basis of
chance. Sometimes there will be a set of subclasses viewed
within a larger class which itself is only a part of the whole;
sometimes there will be a number of such sets of subclasses
averaged together. But always the investigator should approach
his problem by putting a certain question to it—a certain
hypothesis—and manipulating his data in such manner as to
give him the answer to that particular question. Each question

[1] A good example of such step by step analysis will be found in L. H. C.
Tippett, *The Methods of Statistics*, Williams and Norgate, 2d ed., 1937, pp.
218–226.

will demand bringing together certain classes and comparing them in certain ways. If he keeps his eye clearly on the means he is examining for fluctuation and the classes of which they are the means, he will have no difficulty with such issues as what sums of squares are required or what are the numbers of degrees of freedom.

DEGREES OF FREEDOM

In order to remove some of the sense of magic which, for the layman, centers about this concept of degrees of freedom appropriate for estimating a population variance, we shall show Fisher's derivation for the case involving the estimate from "within classes."[1] It can be shown that the distribution of estimates of variance from samples is such that the probability that an estimate will fall in the range ds_p^2 is

$$C_p \sigma^{-(n_p-1)} (s_p^2)^{\frac{n_p-3}{2}} e^{-\frac{n_p s_p^2}{2\sigma^2}} d(s_p^2)$$

where n_p is the population of the array in the sample and C_p is a quantity depending only on n_p. Since the columns of a correlation table (or the classes in any analysis of variance setup) are assumed to be independent, the probability that all the observed values of s_p^2 will fall in assigned ranges is the product of all such probabilities for all the k columns or classes. The optimum estimate of σ is the value of σ which will make the joint probability a maximum. In order to find this value, we differentiate the function with respect to σ, equate the derivative to zero, and solve for σ (see pages 10 to 15 if necessary). We shall do that with the expression here made up of the products from the columns. But first we shall take logs, then differentiate. Remember that the log of a product is a sum of logs. Let P be the joint probability. Then

$$\log P = \Sigma(\log C_p) - [\Sigma(n_p - 1)] \log \sigma \\ + \Sigma(n_p - 3) \log s_p - \tfrac{1}{2}(\Sigma n_p s_p^2)\sigma^{-2} + \Sigma \log d(s_p^2)$$

The reason no log appears in the next to the last term is, of course, because it would be $\log_e e$, which equals 1. Taking

[1] FISHER, R. A., "The Goodness of Fit of Regression Formulae," *J. Roy. Statistical Soc.*, Vol. 85, pp. 599–600 (1922).

derivatives with respect to σ (see page 22 if necessary), we have

$$\frac{dP/d\sigma}{\sigma} = -[\Sigma(n_p - 1)]\frac{1}{\sigma} + [\Sigma n_p s_p^2]\frac{1}{\sigma^3}$$

Equating this derivative to zero and solving, we get

$$[\Sigma(n_p - 1)]\sigma^2 = \Sigma n_p s_p^2$$

so that the value of σ^2 which will make P a maximum, which we shall designate $\hat{\sigma}^2$, is

$$\hat{\sigma}^2 = \frac{\Sigma n_p s_p^2}{\Sigma(n_p - 1)}$$

But $\Sigma(n_p - 1) = \Sigma n_p - \Sigma 1 = N - k$ and $s_p^2 = \Sigma(y - \bar{y}_p)^2/n_p$; whence

$$\hat{\sigma}^2 = \frac{\Sigma\Sigma(y - \bar{y}_p)^2}{N - k}$$

where the double summation is over all the cells in all the columns.

Since k is the number of classes (columns), it is clear that the number of degrees of freedom when estimating the population variance from within classes will be the total N of the sample utilized less the number of classes. If the classes themselves all have the same n', then $(N - k) = (kn' - k) = k(n' - 1)$. That the number of degrees of freedom for the total is $(N - 1)$ was shown very simply on page 70. In the case of means (between classes) the divisor is $(k - 1)$, which involves again the same principle as the $(N - 1)$ for which we have just cited the reason. Irwin has shown that the case of analysis of variance into more than two parts reduces algebraically to the same basis. Determination of the number of degrees of freedom in regression and in other applications follows equally logically with the proper adaptation for the type of distribution involved. The reader has, of course, noticed that the degrees of freedom are additive, which fact follows from some complication of the algebraic expression $(N - k) + (k - 1) = (N - 1)$. We have also shown that, because the cross products vanish, the sums of squares are additive and each sum of squares corresponds to the appropriate degrees of freedom. But we believe that workers will perform their analyses much more safely and intelligently if, instead of depending upon this mechanical principle, they

will, as said above, get their eye on the classes they are comparing
—with the variation of the means of these classes and the variability within the classes—and picture to themselves what
they are doing, in the more fundamental sense discussed in this
paragraph.

FURTHER RAMIFICATIONS OF ANALYSIS OF VARIANCE

The conventional treatment of analysis of variance includes,
besides a much fuller account of analysis with subclasses, schemes
for adjusting for classes of unequal populations, for interpolating
scores, for correcting for covariance, for "confounding" replications, etc. It is beyond the scope and purpose of this book
to pursue these topics. The interested reader can find them
treated in such books as Snedecor's *Statistical Method*, Tippett's
The Methods of Statistics, Rider's *Introduction to Modern Statistical Methods*, Fisher's *Statistical Methods for Research Workers*,
and Fisher's *Design of Experiments*.

THE SPECIAL CASE OF TWO CLASSES

Analysis of variance may be applied, with interesting results,
to the special case of two arrays. This, the reader will observe,
involves the question whether the means of the two classes differ
significantly and is, therefore, the familiar case of the significance
of the difference between two means, assuming the null hypothesis
which we treated on pages 177–179. This, according to the
technique explained there, is expressed by the relation

$$(C) \qquad t = \frac{\bar{x}_1 - \bar{x}_2}{s\sqrt{(1/n_1) + (1/n_2)}}$$

where s is the population variance estimated from the two arrays
jointly. In terms of analysis of variance we have

(D) Between classes, $N_1(\bar{x}_1 - \bar{x})^2 + N_2(\bar{x}_2 - \bar{x})^2$ with $(k - 1)$
     $= (2 - 1) = 1$ degree of freedom

(E) Within classes, $\Sigma(x_1 - \bar{x}_1)^2 + \Sigma(x_2 - \bar{x}_2)^2$ with $(N_1 + N_2 - 2)$ degrees of freedom

Now the mean, $\bar{x}$, is

$$\bar{x} = \frac{N_1\bar{x}_1 + N_2\bar{x}_2}{N_1 + N_2}$$

Substituting this in (D) and simplifying,

$$N_1 \left(\bar{x}_1 - \frac{N_1\bar{x}_1 + N_2\bar{x}_2}{N_1 + N_2} \right)^2 + N_2 \left(\bar{x}_2 - \frac{N_1\bar{x}_1 + N_2\bar{x}_2}{N_1 + N_2} \right)^2$$

$$= N_1 \left(\frac{N_1\bar{x}_1 + N_2\bar{x}_1 - N_1\bar{x}_1 - N_2\bar{x}_2}{N_1 + N_2} \right)^2$$

$$+ N_2 \left(\frac{N_1\bar{x}_2 + N_2\bar{x}_2 - N_1\bar{x}_1 - N_2\bar{x}_2}{N_1 + N_2} \right)^2$$

$$= N_1 N_2^2 \frac{(\bar{x}_1 - \bar{x}_2)^2}{(N_1 + N_2)^2} + N_1^2 N_2 \frac{(\bar{x}_2 - \bar{x}_1)^2}{(N_1 + N_2)^2}$$

$$= \frac{(N_1 + N_2)N_1 N_2 (\bar{x}_1 - \bar{x}_2)^2}{(N_1 + N_2)^2} = \frac{N_1 N_2}{(N_1 + N_2)} (\bar{x}_1 - \bar{x}_2)^2$$

$$(F) \qquad\qquad = \frac{(\bar{x}_1 - \bar{x}_2)^2}{(1/N_1) + (1/N_2)}$$

Now Eq. (F) divided by its number of degrees of freedom (which is 1) gives s^2 as estimated from between classes, and Eq. (E) divided by its number of degrees of freedom (which is $N_1 + N_2 - 2$) gives s^2 as estimated from within classes. Whence

$$(G) \qquad\qquad F = \frac{(\bar{x}_1 - \bar{x}_2)^2}{s_c^2 \left(\dfrac{1}{N_1} + \dfrac{1}{N_2} \right)}$$

The s_c^2 is calculated in the same manner as shown on page 178. So comparison of (C) and (G) will show that F is precisely t^2. We can test the significance either by looking in the F or z tables for testing the relation of estimates of variance or by looking in the t table for means. We must enter the F table or the z table with $n_1 = 1$ and $n_2 = N - 2$. If the N's are even reasonably large, we may use the normal-curve tables for t. Otherwise we enter the special table for Student's distribution with $n = (N_1 + N_2 - 2)$.

Thus analysis of variance can be employed to test the significance of the difference between two means; it will give exactly the same result as the conventional difference of means technique when the null hypothesis is assumed—as, indeed, it must if both methods are correct and mathematics continues to be consistent.

There has begun to be some use of this technique in educational research.[1] But we can see no advantage whatever in it. The

[1] See Bond, Eva, "Reading and Ninth Grade Achievement," *Teach. Coll. Contrib. Educ.* No. 756, 1938.

analysis of variance technique gives no added information whatever over the difference of means technique; its arithmetic outcomes are precisely the same. On the other hand, it suffers from the fact that the tables of z and of F are much less complete for this case than are the tables for t. It suffers particularly from the fact that its relations are less clear to the layman, hence making its appeal as magic. Of course, it is by its nature limited to confirming or refuting the null hypothesis and cannot work into the more general case represented by formulas (90) and (95), to say nothing of all the other more positive techniques of classical statistics. The fact that analysis of variance technique can be extended to cover the case of two classes is of academic interest in showing that the analysis of variance technique is general. But the fact that it *can* be used in this application is no reason why it *should* be used when more effective alternative techniques are available.

THE RELATION OF ANALYSIS OF VARIANCE TO ϵ

In our preceding chapter we explained and extended a statistic recently developed by Kelley—the unbiased correlation ratio which he named ϵ. Epsilon involves much the same calculations as analysis of variance. The F and the z tests employed with analysis of variance do not directly indicate the *strength* of the relation that is present, but only its reliability. Analysis of variance, that is, tells only the negative side of the story, limiting itself to confirming or refuting the null hypothesis. Epsilon, on the other hand, shows in language with a uniform meaning what is the strength of the relation that is present and at the same time permits an "exact" test of its reliability. There is a functional relation between ϵ and F, as follows:[1]

$$F = \frac{(N - k)\epsilon^2 + (k - 1)}{(k - 1)(1 - \epsilon^2)}$$

where k is the number of classes and N is the whole population of the sample. Whereas ϵ is the same for a given strength of relation regardless of the size of the sample or the number of classes into which it is divided, F varies with the size of the sample and the number of classes for a given strength of relation, as inspection of the above formula shows. Epsilon has a meaning

[1] See pp. 421–422.

as uniform as that of r, with which, in fact, it becomes identical if the regression of classes along an ordered axis is rectilinear.

The relation of ϵ to analysis of variance is most obvious when the analysis of variance is into two parts—between classes and within classes, which is the usual form. But it obtains in the same manner when variance is analyzed into more than two parts, as discussed on pages 341 to 344. For this further analysis merely adjusts the scores so as to free the variation in the residual from additional controlling factors, whereupon the residual scatter normally becomes less. By definition of the squared correlation ratio it is merely 1 minus the residual variance from the means of classes divided by the total variance; and ϵ can just as properly turn on a corrected residual variance as F can.

But in this application we cannot compute ϵ in terms of the within-class variance over the total variance; we must, instead, compute it in terms of between classes (*i.e.*, means of classes) and within classes (*i.e.*, the residual). But in the case of columns of equal n's (which must always obtain where variance is to be analyzed into more than two parts), this is sufficiently easily done. Straightforward algebraic manipulation of the fundamental equations gives us for this case

$$\epsilon^2 = \frac{N\sigma_m^2 - (k-1)s_c^2}{N\sigma_m^2 + (df)s_c^2}$$

where (df) is the number of degrees of freedom *appropriate to the residual*. The σ_m^2 here is the variance of the means of classes *in the sample* and is very different from the population variance estimated from the means. But s_c^2 is the population estimate from the squares within classes, obtained by dividing the sum of squares by the degrees of freedom in the customary manner. We can, however, put both of these variances in terms of populations estimates if we wish. Letting s_m^2 be the population variance estimated from the means in the customary manner [*i.e.*, by dividing $n\Sigma(\bar{y}_c - \bar{y})^2$ by $k - 1$], we have

$$\epsilon^2 = \frac{(k-1)s_m^2 - (k-1)s_c^2}{(k-1)s_m^2 + (df)s_c^2} \tag{186}$$

Redoing by the epsilon technique the problem of the relation of columns to productivity in potatoes with rows and variety held constant (pages 345 to 348), we have

$$\epsilon^2 = \frac{4(6,712) - 4(2,285)}{4(6,712) + 12(2,285)} = .326$$

In our table an ϵ^2 of .361 stands at the 5 per cent point for 4 and 12 degrees of freedom, so that the chances of obtaining an ϵ^2 of .326 in this sample merely by chance are somewhat greater than 5 in 100, which agrees with the determination by the F technique.

An illuminating outcome will follow by treating by the epsilon technique the case of varieties in that same problem.

$$\epsilon^2 = \frac{4(1,087) - 4(2,285)}{4(6,712) + 12(2,285)} = -.088$$

The ϵ^2 is negative. While no negative η^2 can result from a sample, negative ϵ^2's can arise by chance fluctuation from a true correlation of zero, or near zero. They arise only by chance, so that there is no use in looking up the reliability. The distribution of ϵ^2 is not symmetrical and our table does not give negative ϵ^2's. But the negative values parallel roughly the positive ones. The .088 is far below the .361 which stands at the 5 per cent point for 4 and 12 degrees of freedom. Our finding by this technique agrees, therefore, with what we obtained by the F test in analysis of variance. The ϵ^2 will be negative whenever the population variance estimated from means of classes is less than that estimated from the residual.

Partial epsilon, discussed on page 326, parallels analysis of variance with subclasses.

Prior to Kelley's derivation of epsilon and our table of its distribution, the correlation ratio was of rather limited service. For the interpretation of eta was somewhat dependent upon the size of the population and the number of classes into which it was divided. Furthermore, there was available no "exact" test of the significance of η. But ϵ is entirely free from these limitations. It has a completely uniform and standardized meaning, and our table for its distribution is exact.[1] In fact the ϵ test

[1] The term *exact distribution* is a technical term introduced into statistics by Fisher to mean that, in dividing the deviation of a statistic from a hypothetical value to get t, cognizance is taken of the fact that the divisor is not the true population variability but an estimate of it. For small samples

of reliability gives *precisely* the same results as the F test of analysis of variance for a given problem. The fact that ϵ has a uniform positive meaning in addition to its ability to make an exact test of the null hypothesis should give it a useful place in statistics.

It is true that, traditionally, η and ϵ have usually been thought of as belonging to those situations in which the classes could be quantitatively ordered on the x axis, though this has not been uniformly the case. But it is to be noted that there is nothing in either the η or the ϵ formula that depends upon the x placement; the correlation ratio is wholly independent of such serial ordering. It is only if we wished to follow up the calculation of the correlation ratio by curve fitting that we would be interested in the serial ordering of the classes. Such added purpose is wholly independent of the ϵ itself. Moreover, analysis of variance, also, would be wholly meaningless if the classes did not belong to a common quantitative series which could, hypothetically, be quantitatively ordered. When, that is, one analyzes the variance of a number of breeds of cattle with reference to milk production, it is on the assumption that there is some x factor of which the different breeds have different amounts by reason of which the mean amount of milk produced differs from breed to breed. Apart from such x factor there could be no basis for comparison at all, any more than there could be a basis for comparing hoes with ideals. If it is true that analysis of variance must presuppose the hypothetical possibility of quantitatively ordering its classes but need not stress the actual ordering and that ϵ likewise permits such ordering but is not dependent upon it, there is no fundamental difference between the ϵ technique and the analysis of variance technique in the types of situations to which they apply.

After the ϵ technique has shown the presence of *some* law and the extent of its strength, the next step is to study the nature

---

this estimate is likely to be poor and the resulting distribution is more leptokurtic than the normal one. As the sample increases in size the estimate improves, so that s approaches $\bar{\sigma}$ and the exact distribution approaches the normal. While theoretically differing anywhere short of infinity, the differences between the two distributions become negligible when N reaches a moderately good size.

of that law. This will probably take the form of trying to fit to the data several types of curves (see Chap. XV) and testing the goodness of their fit by ϵ'^2. Or it may take the form of comparing means and other statistics (such as variability, skewness, etc.) between the classes taken in pairs and of testing the significance of the differences by such techniques as are described in Chap. VI.

THE PLACE OF ANALYSIS OF VARIANCE IN RESEARCH

Analysis of variance belongs as a first step in a major research where one wishes to make a rough preliminary test of his hypothesis in advance of going to the expense of the elaborate setup needed for a thorough investigation. An agricultural research worker, for example, has the hypothesis that different varieties of wheat may, in a given locality, yield sufficiently different amounts of crops to justify adopting one of them rather than others. His first step may be to make a comparison of all of them simultaneously, with rather small samples, randomized in some effective manner as in a Latin square.[1] If he finds that, in this trial, the varieties differ no more than chance would explain, he abandons his hypothesis; or at least he gives it a second preliminary trial. But, if his hypothesis is confirmed and he finds that the varieties do differ significantly on the average (for analysis of variance always lumps its classes into an average), he is ready to proceed with the positive aspect of his research. He will then set up his experiment, or series of experiments, with a single variable and a large sample, will undertake to determine which variety yields more than which and by how much of a differential, etc. Or an investigator in Education gets the hunch that teacher personality may influence the degree of introversion-extroversion of pupils. His first step may be to draw small samples of pupils from a half dozen teachers in a half dozen different cities, administer to them a test of introversion-extroversion, and by the analysis of variance technique

---

[1] Of course, when he actually sets up his preliminary study, he formally puts the hypothesis the other way around: he tries the null hypothesis that *there may be no difference*. But a research worker is ordinarily led into a problem by a positively conceived hypothesis rather than a negatively conceived one.

see whether there is any plausibility in his hunch.   If there is, he will then proceed to the positive type of investigation, measuring the amount of differences and making tests of the probable limits of these amounts, correlating extroversion effects with certain measurable characteristics of teachers, etc.   In this preliminary exploratory stage analysis of variance, with its limitation to refuting or confirming the null hypothesis, its adaptation to small samples, and its ability to test simultaneously a number of variations in the experimental factor, may serve the purpose very well.   It is especially useful in agricultural research, where the expense of securing large samples under experimental conditions is very great.   But for the positive side of the research the investigator will need the standard procedures of classical statistics, such as correlation, curve fitting, and contrast of correlated matched groups.   Constructive research is just ready to begin where analysis of variance leaves off.   In the field of educational research we are now finding some investigators who make a showing of their findings in terms of analysis of variance when the size and character of their sample would permit them to make the positive rather than the merely negative presentation.   Sometimes we find them, after making the positive showing, also making a showing in terms of analysis of variance.   That is precisely parallel to the behavior of an engineer who would first successfully construct his bridge and thereafter conduct an elaborate argument to prove that it would *probably be possible* to construct such a bridge.   It is always pedantic to try to make forced use of statistical devices borrowed from another field when they only poorly fit.   Statistical procedures are *tools* to be drawn upon only as needed for definite and well-understood purposes, and those tools are best which are not only most natural for the worker but also most readily understood by the reader to whom the findings of the research are to be addressed.   The great historical contributions to statistics did not come about by the intention of the author to make a statistical formula; on the contrary, they were inventions devised for interpreting certain baffling research problems with which the investigator was confronted in some concrete setting.   It is such natural emergence of procedures from the needs of the situation, rather than the imitative use of statistics, that should be the ideal toward which we work.

WHEN A HYPOTHESIS IS REFUTED

Since analysis of variance has for its purpose the dismissal of hypotheses that fail to meet the test of statistical significance, it is fitting to say a word about when a hypothesis has been refuted. There is danger that research workers may interpret too literally and mechanically the preliminary evidence afforded by the technique as to when a hypothesis should be abandoned. If the F falls below the 5 per cent point, this means that there are more than 5 chances in 100 that accidents of fluctuation might account for one's finding and that he must not be at all sure of any real differences among his classes. But, conversely, it means that there are, maybe, 85 or 90 chances in 100 (8 or 10 to 1) that there *are* real differences which a better controlled study would reveal; and he might be quite unjustified in hastily giving up his hypothesis without further investigation. It is an error of one form to overreadily accept the conclusiveness of our findings; but it is an error of a second form to suppose that a hypothesis has been fully refuted when it has merely been brought below the level of certainty.

Exercises

1. H. L. Smith and M. T. Eaton give the data on the effect of drill in fundamental combinations upon ability to add eight digit exercises as shown in the table on page 360. No drill preceded test 1. Successive tests followed at intervals of one week with drill on the number combinations intervening. Thus the drill was cumulative throughout the period within which the drill was given.
Does the analysis of variance show significant differences in means among the four tests: (a) when variance is analyzed into two parts? (b) When variance is analyzed into three parts, taking cognizance of the fact that the columns are positively intercorrelated? Speculate upon the meaning of the different outcomes you get by these two different procedures.
2. Compute and interpret ϵ for this table.
3. Would r be an appropriate statistic in the above problem? Would curve fitting? What is the relation among r, ϵ, and curve fitting?
4. A sociologist wishes to make a preliminary test of his hypothesis that nationalities in urban communities differ in respect to the time they allow to elapse before taking out their first naturalization papers. He suspects that the city in which they live and also the ecological zone within the city may be factors. With hypothetical figures (or real ones if you can get them) set up a Latin square to test this hypothesis. Lay off five cities as columns and, as rows, use zones between concentric circles centering about the downtown business district. How do you fit in the nationalities?

Subject	No. of columns added correctly			
	Test 1	Test 2	Test 3	Test 4
1	11	15	20	17
2	40	39	37	40
3	38	38	35	40
4	35	40	39	39
5	22	29	37	34
6	32	36	39	34
7	23	24	23	26
8	23	24	20	30
9	10	16	18	17
10	23	29	30	28
11	25	28	27	31
12	18	19	22	24
13	22	27	34	33
14	14	17	17	17
15	21	30	29	29
16	20	25	31	30
17	34	33	36	37
18	38	38	40	37
19	31	39	38	40
20	26	24	29	27
21	23	28	26	31
22	26	31	26	30
23	24	25	28	26
Means..	25.2	28.4	29.2	30.3

References for Further Study

FISHER, R. A.: *Statistical Methods for Research Workers*, Oliver and Boyd, 7th ed., 1938. (Slightly revised editions of this book have been published at intervals of about 2 years since 1924. It is the parent book in this field, but difficult to read.)

————: *The Design of Experiments*, Oliver and Boyd, Edinburgh, 1935. (A small book devoted to an exposition of how to set up experiments, primarily in agricultural research.)

IRWIN, J. O.: "Mathematical Theorems Involved in the Analysis of Variance," *J. Roy. Statistical Soc.*, Vol. 94, pp. 284–300.

RIDER, PAUL R.: *An Introduction to Modern Statistical Methods*, John Wiley & Sons, Inc., 1939. (Makes some attempt to give mathematical derivations, but they are not very complete.)

SNEDECOR, G. W.: *Statistical Methods*, George Banta Publishing Company. (The most complete popularized account of analysis of variance and of the other phases of Fisher's statistics. Written chiefly for research workers in agriculture.   Indispensable to workers in that field and useful to others.   It makes little attempt to show the mathematical foundations for the formulas, confining itself to an explanation of their use for persons of little statistical training.)

TIPPETT, L. H. C.: *The Methods of Statistics*, Williams and Norgate, 2d ed., 1937.   (The clearest available explanation of analysis of variance with some attention to its mathematical foundations.   In our opinion the best single book undertaking to popularize the Fisher statistics for persons of a moderate amount of statistical training.   The book contains no tables.)

CHAPTER XIII

FURTHER METHODS OF CORRELATION

In Chap. IV we treated the Pearson product-moment correlation technique and the Spearman ranks method, which latter is just a special algebraic adaptation of the product-moment formula. The Pearson product-moment formula is the best one to use where it can be applied. But many situations arise in which it would be desirable to employ a correlation technique in which this formula is, for one reason or another, not applicable. In this chapter we shall set forth several alternative procedures, each adapted to some particular type of situation.

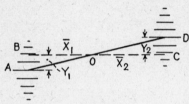

Fig. 23.

BISERIAL CORRELATION

We sometimes have our data given in the form of two mutually exclusive categories in respect to one factor and in quantitative scores in respect to the other factor. It is not difficult to develop a formula for the coefficient of correlation between the two factors under these conditions. In Table XXXI we display such measures from a study by Sones on the relation of size of family to the tendency of children to leave school before the age of eighteen. In column 2 is given the distribution of 200 children who remained in school according to the size of the families to which they belong, in column 3 is given a corresponding distribution for 100 children who had left school, while in column 4 the totals are shown. We want the coefficient of correlation between size of family and tendency of the children to leave school. We shall lay off our situation graphically on the accompanying chart. AD is the straight line passing through the means of the two arrays. The slope of line AD is the regression coefficient and, when multiplied by the ratio of the σ's of the two factors, becomes the coefficient of correlation. Letting y_2

362

stand for DC, y_1 for AB, $\bar{x}_2$ for OC, $\bar{x}_1$ for OB, and b for the slope of the line of the means, we have

$$b_{yx} = \frac{y_2}{\bar{x}_2} = \frac{y_1}{\bar{x}_1} = \frac{y_2 + y_1}{\bar{x}_2 + \bar{x}_1}$$

This last term on the right comes from application of "alterna-

TABLE XXXI.—DISTRIBUTION OF CHILDREN WHO REMAINED IN SCHOOL AND OF CHILDREN WHO LEFT SCHOOL BEFORE EIGHTEEN YEARS OF AGE, ACCORDING TO SIZE OF FAMILIES[1]

(1)	(2)	(3)	(4)
No. children in family	Remained in school	Left school	Total
12	2		2
11	4	3	7
10	4	2	6
9	4	8	12
8	20	3	23
7	10	17	27
6	24	12	36
5	18	18	36
4	30	10	40
3	34	12	46
2	34	10	44
1	16	5	21
Means...........	4.57	5.31	4.82

[1] SONES, ELWOOD, "A Study of One Hundred Boys and Girls, Sixteen to Eighteen Years of Age, Who Have Left School and a Similar Group Remaining in School," master's thesis at Pennsylvania State College, 1933.

tion" and "composition" (recall elementary algebra or geometry). Now since r equals b multiplied by the σ ratio,

$$r_{xy} = b_{yx} \frac{\sigma_x}{\sigma_y} = \frac{y_2 + y_1}{\bar{x}_2 + \bar{x}_1} \cdot \frac{\sigma_x}{\sigma_y}$$

The $(y_2 + y_1)$ is the total distance between the means of the two distributions, hence $(M_{y_2} - M_{y_1})$. The $(\bar{x}_2 + \bar{x}_1)$ is the distance between the means of the two parts into which the distribution of pupils in respect to persistence in school is divided. We may reasonably assume that, in respect to disposition to remain in school, pupils make a normal distribution, and we have already learned that the mean of the tail of a normal distribution from the mean of the whole distribution is z/p, where z is the height of the ordinate of a normal distribution of unit area and unit standard deviation at the point of truncation and p is the proportion of the whole distribution in the tail (see page 289). Therefore, $\bar{x}_2$ equals z/p, and $\bar{x}_1$ equals z/q, so that

$$(\bar{x}_1 + \bar{x}_2) = \left(\frac{z}{p} + \frac{z}{q}\right) = \frac{(zq + zp)}{pq} = \frac{(p + q)z}{pq}$$

But $(p + q)$ is the whole area of the distribution and, since we are dealing in terms of proportion, is 1. Substituting 1 for $(p + q)$, $(\bar{x}_1 + \bar{x}_2) = z/pq$.

$\sigma_x = 1$, since we assumed in calculating the z of the numerator that the x factor makes a normal distribution of unit area and of unit standard deviation. The standard deviation of the y factor can readily be found; it is the standard deviation of the scores constituting the sum of the two partial y distributions (here shown in column 4) and is to be computed

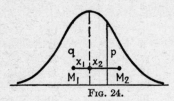

FIG. 24.

in the customary manner. If the grouping is very coarse, Sheppard's correction should be made in the computation of this sigma. We are now ready to substitute in the r_{xy} formula above the several equivalents just found, and we have

$$r_{xy} = \frac{(M_{v_2} - M_{v_1})pq}{z\sigma_y} \qquad \text{(Biserial coefficient of correlation)} \quad (187)$$

Let us now apply this formula to Sones' data as displayed in Table XXXI. M_{v_2} equals 5.31 and M_{v_1} is 4.57. The proportion leaving school, p, is .33 while the proportion remaining is $(1 - .33)$ or .67. The standard deviation of the distribution in column 4 is 2.57 and the z shown in our table (page 482) for a tail of .33 is 0.3635. Substituting these values in the formula, we have

$$r = \frac{(5.31 - 4.57)(.333)(.667)}{(2.57)(0.3635)} = .176$$

Soper[1] gives as an approximate value of the standard error of biserial r, provided q is not less than .05, the following:

$$\sigma_r = \frac{\left(\dfrac{\sqrt{pq}}{z} - r^2\right)}{\sqrt{N}}$$ (Standard error of biserial r)   (188)

The probable error would, of course, be .6745 times the standard error.

The assumptions involved in the biserial r formula should be carefully noted. No assumptions whatever are made about the shape of the distribution in which the quantitative scores are found. But the assumption is definitely involved that this distribution is not mutilated in such fashion as to change its standard deviation as' compared with what it would be in a random sample of the total population drawn upon. Normality is assumed in the distribution in which the dichotomy occurs. It is also assumed that the whole sample distribution is present and that the two tails fit together into a whole normal distribution. In using the formula, there is great temptation to draw upon the upper and lower extreme tails and omit individuals from the middle of the distribution. If, for example, one is attempting to study by this technique the correlation between professional training and teacher success, it would not do to select 100 of the best teachers (constituting, say, the uppermost 20 per cent of the whole teaching population) and the 100 poorest, for that would chop out the middle of the distribution and give r's much too high. A method for dealing with such widespread dichotomies is given later in this chapter.

The biserial r is really a very promising technique for research in education and in the psychological and social sciences. The following are illustrations of a few types of situations in which it could be advantageously employed:

1. Having athletes divided into successful and unsuccessful and having measurements in a number of traits possibly related to athletic success, find the correlation of each of these traits with success.

2. Having teachers similarly divided, find the correlation of a number of factors with teacher success.

[1] SOPER, *Biometrika*, Vol. X, p. 390.

3. Having a large sample of motion pictures divided into "good" and "poor" (or perhaps "above average" and "below average") from the standpoint of excellence in the technique of dramatic art and knowing the financial returns from each of the pictures of the sample, determine the correlation between excellence in dramatic art and financial success.

4. Having measures of certain temperamental traits for a sample of divorced women and for a corresponding sample of women who are not divorced, ascertain the coefficient of correlation between each of these temperamental traits and the tendency to be divorced.

Evidently large numbers of such problems could be formulated in various areas of research.

TETRACHORIC CORRELATION

A second type of situation is where we have our data in both variables merely in the form of the number of individuals, or the proportion of individuals, in each of two categories. Thus we may have a total population of teachers divided into "successful" and "unsuccessful" (meaning above or below a certain dividing point in respect to success) and have information that a of the former have taken courses in pedagogy beyond 6 hr. and b of them have not, while of the latter c have had such courses

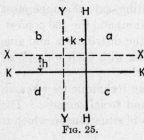

Fig. 25.

beyond the 6 hr. and d have not. We wish to find what correlation exists between success in teaching and the taking of courses in pedagogy. We lay our data off in the form of a fourfold table, as indicated in Fig. 25. The dichotomic lines are KK and HH, while the means of the distributions lie at XX and YY, respectively. In order to make our case general, we are not assuming that the dichotomies are equal but are allowing the dichotomic lines to lie at distances h and k, respectively, from the means.

As a foundation for approaching our problem, we must get an equation for the correlation surface where both of the two correlated arrays are assumed to be normal distributions. If z' is the frequency of y scores at any particular value of x, then, according to our formula for the normal curve given on page 286,

(A)
$$z' = \frac{N}{\sigma_x\sqrt{2\pi}} e^{-\frac{x^2}{2\sigma^2_x}}$$

These y scores constitute a column which itself may be assumed to make a normal distribution with its mean on the regression line (assumption of rectilinearity of regression). The frequency of any y score in this column, when the y is measured from the mean of the column as origin, is

(B)
$$z'' = \frac{N_c}{\sigma_{y_c}\sqrt{2\pi}} e^{-\frac{y^2_c}{2\sigma^2_{y_c}}}$$

where the N_c is the number of individuals in the column and the σ_{y_c} is the standard deviation of the column. We learned (page 113) that the standard deviation of a column in a correlation surface is $\sqrt{1 - r^2}$ times the standard deviation of the entire y distribution. The measurements of y_c are taken, as said above, as deviations from the regression line. This point on the regression line for this column is $r(\sigma_y/\sigma_x)x$ distant from the mean of the whole y distribution. Therefore, in the case of any score, $y_c = \left(y - r\frac{\sigma_y}{\sigma_x}x\right)$. Making this substitution for the y_c and $\sigma_y\sqrt{1 - r^2}$ for σ_{y_c}, we have

(C)
$$z'' = \frac{N_c}{\sigma_y\sqrt{2\pi}\sqrt{1 - r^2}} e^{-\frac{\left(y - r\frac{\sigma_y}{\sigma_x}x\right)^2}{2\sigma^2_y(1 - r^2)}}$$

Equation (A) represents the number of individuals out of a total population of N that are to be expected in a given column of a normal distribution. Hence the proportion of chances a given individual has of being in that column is the value given on the right of the equation divided by N, which would be the same expression with 1 as its numerator instead of N. Such fraction represents the, probability that a given item will be in that column, and hence that it will have this particular x value. Similarly the expression at the right of Eq. (C) with 1 instead of N_c as its numerator represents the probability that, if a given item is in the column, it is in a given cell in that column—has a given y value. Therefore the probability of an item being in a given cell—having a particular xy value—is the product of these two probabilities, and the number of items that fulfill these two conditions is N times the fraction representing the joint probability. So we have, as the frequency of items in any given cell,

$$(D) \qquad F_{xy} = \frac{N}{2\pi\sigma_x\sigma_y\sqrt{1-r^2}} e^{-\left[\frac{x^2}{2\sigma_x^2} + \frac{y^2 - 2rxy\frac{\sigma_y}{\sigma_x} + r^2\frac{\sigma^2_y}{\sigma^2_x}x^2}{2\sigma^2_y(1-r^2)}\right]}$$

The exponent of the e will simplify, by straightforward algebraic manipulation, and yield the following form:

$$F_{xy} = \frac{N}{2\pi\sigma_x\sigma_y\sqrt{1-r^2}} e^{-\left[\frac{1}{2(1-r^2)}\right]\left[\frac{x^2}{\sigma^2_x} + \frac{y^2}{\sigma^2_y} - 2r\frac{xy}{\sigma_x\sigma_y}\right]} \qquad (189)$$

(Frequency in a single cell, nor-
mal correlation surface for two
variables)

Suppose, now, we have our correlation surface divided into four quadrants, as depicted in the chart at the opening of this section, a, b, c, and d representing the numbers of individuals in the several quadrants. Then $(a + b + c + d)$ would obviously equal N. Equation (189) gives us the number of individuals within a cell of a given x value and simultaneously of a given y value. If we can sum for all the cells by quadrants, we shall have the frequencies constituting the entire population. Thus integrating from $x = k$ to $x = $ infinity and from $y = h$ to $y = $ infinity, we shall get the population in quadrant a as our integral (for double integration see page 38). Correspondingly integrating from $x = k$ to $x = -\infty$ and from $y = h$ to $y = -\infty$, we get d. Similarly we could integrate in the other quadrants to get b and c, while the sum of these integrals would yield the total population N. In this integral the only unknown term would be r, and we could solve the resulting equation for r.

But this is an extremely difficult integration to perform, and we shall not attempt here to follow it through. In a long article, Karl Pearson[1] has performed the integration and has arrived at the following result:

---

[1] PEARSON, KARL, "On the Correlation of Characters Not Quantitatively Measurable," Trans. Roy. Soc. (London), Series A, Vol. 195, pp. 1–47, especially pp. 1–7.

$$\frac{2\pi(ad - bc)}{N^2}\, e^{\frac{1}{2}(h^2+k^2)} = r + r^2\, \frac{hk}{2} + r^3\, \frac{(h^2 - 1)(k^2 - 1)}{6}$$

$$+ \frac{r^4}{24}\, hk(h^2 - 3(k^2 - 3)) + \frac{r^5}{120}\, (h^4 - 6h^2 + 3)(k^4 - 6k^2 + 3)$$

$$+ \frac{r^6}{720}\, hk(h^4 - 10h^2 + 15)(k^4 - 10k^2 + 15)$$

$$+ \frac{r^7}{5,040}\, (h^6 - 15h^4 + 45h^2 - 15)(k^6 - 15k^4 + 45k^2 - 15)$$

$$+ \frac{r^8}{40,320}\, hk(h^6 - 21h^4 + 105h^2 - 105)(k^6 - 21k^4 + 105k^2$$

$$- 105) + \text{etc.}$$

(Formula for tetrachoric correlation, dichotomic lines at k/σ_x and h/σ_y from the respective means)   (190)

The k and the h here are measured in terms of σ_x and σ_y, so that their values can be looked up in our table, page 481; they are simply the values given in the x/σ_x column for q representing the proportion of cases on either side of the dichotomic line for each of the two correlated distributions. So r is the only unknown term in the equation. In solving the equation logarithms must, of course, be used to find the value of the expression on the left,[1] and an approximation method must be employed on the right, as we shall illustrate shortly.

Such a formula is really too complicated to be of much service in routine statistical work. We can simplify it by placing upon the situation certain restrictions. One of these is to place the dichotomic lines at the means (or at the medians, which is the same thing in the normal distributions we are obliged to assume). Then h and k will both equal zero, the e will have zero as its exponent and hence become equal to 1, certain terms will entirely disappear, and the previously complicated formula will simplify to

$$\frac{2\pi(ad - bc)}{N^2} = r + \frac{r^3}{6} + \frac{9r^5}{120} + \frac{225r^7}{5,040} + \cdots$$

[1] Or the expression on the left of the equation may be put into simpler form as follows:

$$\frac{2\pi(ad - bc)}{N^2}\, e^{\frac{1}{2}(h^2+k^2)} = \frac{(ad - bc)}{N^2\left(\frac{1}{\sqrt{2\pi}}\, e^{-\frac{1}{2}h^2}\right)\left(\frac{1}{\sqrt{2\pi}}\, e^{-\frac{1}{2}k^2}\right)} = \frac{(ad - bc)}{N^2 zz'}$$

The z's have here the conventional meaning, and their values may be looked up in our tables from the q's of the two distributions.

The right-hand member of this equation can be found in a list of trigonometric series as the arcsine of r; *i.e.*, it is equal to an angle of which the sine is r, the angle being measured in radians. It is likely to be found in such list in the form

$$\sin^{-1} r = r + \frac{1}{2} \cdot \frac{r^3}{3} + \frac{1}{2} \cdot \frac{3}{4} \cdot \frac{r^5}{5} + \frac{1}{2} \cdot \frac{3}{4} \cdot \frac{5}{6} \cdot \frac{r^7}{7} + \cdots$$

Therefore, by reason of the meaning of arcsine,

$$r = \sin 2\pi \frac{(ad - bc)}{N^2} \qquad \text{(Formula for tetrachoric } r \text{ when the dichotomic lines are at the means)} \qquad (191)$$

The π here is 180 deg. and N is $(a + b + c + d)$.

As another scheme for simplification that does not compel equal dichotomies, Pearson, in the same article, develops certain empirical formulas that give approximately correct r's, the mean error in 15 trials being less than 4 per cent. The simplest of these is the following:

$$r = \sin \frac{\pi}{2} \frac{\sqrt{ad} - \sqrt{bc}}{\sqrt{ad} + \sqrt{bc}} \qquad \text{(One formula for tetrachoric } r, \text{ dichotomic lines not necessarily at the means)} \qquad (192)$$

By taking advantage of the fact that the sine of an angle equals the cosine of (90 deg. minus the angle), we can put this formula into a little simpler shape. Remember that, since $\pi = 180$ deg., 90 deg. $= \pi/2$. Making this substitution,

$$r = \cos \left(\frac{\pi}{2} - \frac{\pi}{2} \cdot \frac{\sqrt{ad} - \sqrt{bc}}{\sqrt{ad} + \sqrt{bc}} \right)$$

Combining within the parentheses,

$$r = \cos \left(\pi \frac{\sqrt{bc}}{\sqrt{ad} + \sqrt{bc}} \right) \qquad \text{(Second formula for tetrachoric } r, \text{ no restriction on position of dichotomic lines)} \qquad (193)$$

It is necessary to recognize the assumptions involved in the development of the formulas for tetrachoric r. These are the following: homoscedasticity, rectilinearity of regression, normal distributions in both of the distributions as wholes, normal distributions in the individual columns, and continuous rather than widespread dichotomies.

The formula for the P.E. of tetrachoric r as given by Pearson in the original article here drawn upon is very complicated and laborious to apply, especially for the general case. We shall give it below, without proof, and then follow through some approximations Pearson proposes by way of simplifying it.

$$\text{P.E.}_r = \frac{0.6745}{\chi_0\sqrt{N}}\left[\frac{(a+d)(c+b)}{4N^2} + \psi_2^2\frac{(a+c)(d+b)}{N^2}\right.$$

$$+ \psi_1^2\frac{(a+b)(d+c)}{N^2} + 2\psi_1\psi_2\frac{ad-bc}{N^2} - \psi_2\frac{ab-cd}{N^2}$$

$$\left. - \psi_1\frac{ac-bd}{N^2}\right]^{\frac{1}{2}} \begin{array}{l}\text{(General formula for the probable}\\ \text{error of tetrachoric } r)\end{array} \quad (194)$$

where

$$\psi_1 = \frac{1}{\sqrt{2\pi}}\int_0^{\beta_1} e^{-\frac{x^2}{2}}\,dx; \psi_2 = \frac{1}{\sqrt{2\pi}}\int_0^{\beta_2} e^{-\frac{y^2}{2}}\,dy$$

$$\beta_1 = \frac{k-rh}{\sqrt{1-r^2}}; \beta_2 = \frac{h-rk}{\sqrt{1-r^2}}$$

and

$$\chi_0 = \frac{1}{2\pi}\cdot\frac{1}{\sqrt{1-r^2}}\,e^{-\frac{1}{2}\cdot\frac{1}{1-r^2}(h^2+k^2-2rhk)}$$

Under certain conditions this formula greatly simplifies. If h and k are both zero, $\beta_1 = \beta_2 = \psi_1 = \psi_2 = 0$. Then everything within the brackets will disappear except the first term, and the χ_0 will be equal to $1/(2\pi\sqrt{1-r^2})$, so that we shall have

$$\text{P.E.}_r = \frac{0.6745(2\pi\sqrt{1-r^2})}{\sqrt{N}}\left[\frac{(a+d)(c+b)}{4N^2}\right]^{\frac{1}{2}} \quad (195)$$

(Probable error of tetrachoric r when the dichotomic lines are at the means in both arrays)

It can be shown by a process of algebraic and trigonometric transformations which we shall not reproduce here that, assuming $a = d$ and $b = c$ as would be the case when the dichotomic lines are at the means,

$$\frac{(a+d)(c+b)}{4N^2} = \left[1 - \left(\frac{\sin^{-1} r}{90°}\right)^2\right]\frac{1}{16}$$

Making that substitution in the formula above and changing the 2π to $\pi/2$ in order to compensate for the 4 placed as a multiplier with the quantity for which substitution is being made, we have as an equivalent formula,

$$P.E._r = \frac{0.6745}{\sqrt{N}}\frac{\pi}{2}\sqrt{1-r^2}\sqrt{1-\left(\frac{\sin^{-1}r}{90°}\right)^2} \qquad (196)$$

(Alternative formula for the P.E. of tetrachoric r when the dichotomic
lines are at the means)

If r equals zero but h and k have any values, then substitution
in the general formula will show that

$$P.E._r = \frac{0.6745}{z_h z_k \sqrt{N}}\sqrt{\frac{(a+b)(a+c)(d+b)(d+c)}{N^4}} \qquad (197)$$

(Probable error of tetrachoric r when the true r is zero)

$$= \frac{0.6745}{z_h z_k \sqrt{N}}\sqrt{p_h q_h p_k q_k}$$

For the important task of testing the null hypothesis, formula
(197) is the one to use. This gives the basis for an answer
to the question whether we might have obtained the r we have
in hand by chance fluctuation in sampling when the true r is
zero. This is the most frequent use we have for the standard
error of r. Finally, if both h and k are zero and r is zero, substitution in the general formula gives us

$$P.E._r = \frac{0.6745\pi}{2\sqrt{N}} \qquad \text{(198)}$$

(Probable error of a tetrachoric r of zero
when the dichotomic lines are at the
means in both arrays)

Unable to find a way of simplifying the general formula,
Pearson resorted to the empirical scheme of combining the
formulas for the three special cases, multiplying together formulas
(196) and (197) and dividing by formula (198).[1] This gave
him an approximate formula which he found upon trial to give
P.E.'s differing from the true ones at most by one or two units
in the third decimal place. This formula, as the reader can
easily verify, is as follows:

$$P.E._r = \frac{0.6745}{z_h z_k \sqrt{N}}$$
$$\sqrt{\frac{(1-r^2)(a+b)(a+c)(d+b)(d+c)}{N^4}\left[1-\left(\frac{\sin^{-1}r}{90°}\right)^2\right]}$$
$$= \frac{0.6745}{z_h z_k \sqrt{N}}\sqrt{(1-r^2)p_h q_h p_k q_k\left[1-\left(\frac{\sin^{-1}r}{90°}\right)^2\right]} \qquad (199)$$

(Approximate general formula for the probable error of tetrachoric r)

[1] PEARSON, *Biometrika*, Vol. 9, pp. 23, 24.

The z's here have the customary meaning—the height of the ordinates of a normal distribution of unit area and unit standard deviation at the points of truncation by their respective dichotomic lines. The values of these can be found in our tables. The $\sin^{-1} r$ is the arcsine of r; *i.e.*, the angle of which r is the sine. Probable errors of tetrachoric r's are of the same order of magnitude as those of product moment r's of corresponding size and population, although the former are perhaps 40 or 50 per cent higher.

As an illustration, we shall now compute the tetrachoric r for the hypothetical data given at the opening of this section about the relation of teacher success to the taking of courses in pedagogy. Let us say that of 135 successful teachers 80 have had courses in pedagogy beyond 6 hr. and 55 have not, while of 90 unsuccessful ones 20 have had such courses and 70 have not. We shall first employ the complete formula, (190), in order to illustrate its operation and to ascertain how much the results from it differ in this problem from those obtained from the short formula. As

55	80
b	a
d	c
70	20

Fig. 26.

a first step we drop all terms containing r beyond the second power. Using on the left the form given in the footnote, page 369.

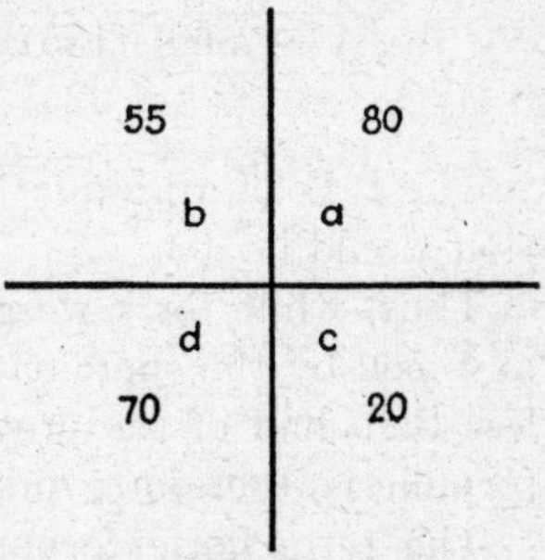

$$\frac{(5,600 - 1,100)}{(225^2)(.395)(.386)} = r + r^2 \frac{(.253)(.141)}{2}$$
$$.582 = r + .0178r^2$$

Completing the square and solving this equation for r gives, as a first approximation, $r = .577$.

Inspection of the signs of the additional terms on the right of the equation constituting the complete formula leads to the conclusion that this value for r is somewhat too high. Let us try .550, substituting this in all the terms on the right side of the equation. If the .550 is the correct value, we shall get on the right side of the equation .5823 to equal the same quantity on the left. But we get .5856, which is too much. Let us try for r .548. This gives us on the right .5832, which is still a trifle too high. Try .547. This yields on the right .5820.

This has now passed below the value on the left but by only a trifling amount. The true r, correct to the third decimal place, is therefore .547. On pages 501 to 504 we give tables to facilitate these calculations.

Let us next apply to the same data the cosin π formula.

$$r = \cos \frac{\sqrt{bc}}{\sqrt{ad} + \sqrt{bc}} \pi = \cos \frac{\sqrt{1,100}}{\sqrt{5,600} + \sqrt{1,100}} 180°$$
$$= \cos 55°17' = .569$$

The probable error of this r by formula (199) is

$$P.E._r = \frac{0.6745}{(.395)(.386)\sqrt{225}}$$
$$\sqrt{\frac{(1 - .569^2)(135)(100)(125)(90)}{225^4} \left[1 - \left(\frac{34.72°}{90°}\right)^2 \right]} = .054$$

The P.E. of a product moment r of the same size and population would be .03.

Thus, while for r we get the value .547 by the long formula and .569 by the short one, a difference of .022, that difference is less than half of the probable error. The result from the short formula is, therefore, quite good enough.

The tetrachoric formulas are especially valuable in case of characters not measurable in definite quantitative ways but in which we can make broad distinctions—such as between persons who have left school and those who have not left, persons who have been retained on a job and those who have been discharged, persons who are above average and those who are below average in success, etc. Nevertheless the formulas can be applied to quantitatively measurable factors by making dichotomies at the medians or at any other fixed points, regardless of whether those points correspond in the two arrays. But in this case the worker must not be surprised to find an r computed by the tetrachoric formula to differ appreciably from the one he would get from the same sample by the product-moment method. The differences between r's computed for the same sample by these two methods may be as great as r's from different samples by either one of the methods, or nearly as much. This is partly because the assumptions involved in the tetrachoric method may not have been fulfilled, and partly because of chance arrangements within the quadrants which affect the product moment r

but not the tetrachoric one. Apart from the question of non-fulfillment of the assumptions, it is when the population is relatively small that the tetrachoric r is likely to differ most widely from the product-moment one.

TETRACHORIC r FROM WIDESPREAD CLASSES

When working with the correlation methods discussed in the two preceding sections, it is not always convenient to deal with the *whole* distribution divided into two parts; it is often much more convenient to deal with widespread classes. If, for example, we wish to find the correlation between pedagogical training and efficiency in teaching, it is the most economical and tempting procedure to take a sampling of the best teachers and a sampling of the poorest ones rather than to consider all. But none of our conventional correlation formulas apply to such a situation; they all demand the presence of full distributions. For years the authors have experienced the almost desperate need in research for such a formula, which would give correlation coefficients of the same meaning and value as the product moment r's and yet permit operation only with the extreme tails of one of the distri-

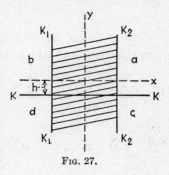

FIG. 27.

butions. To meet this need we have developed the following formulas.

For tetrachoric correlation from widespread classes we have a situation like that represented in the accompanying diagram, our individuals located in quadrants but an open gap between lines $K_1 K_1$ and $K_2 K_2$. We may integrate for the correlation surface from k_2 to infinity and from h to infinity to get a. This integral will not differ at all from what it would be if the whole surface were present, because the integration is from the dividing line outward and not across the vacant middle. When put in terms of proportion of the entire population by dividing by N, this integral will be

$$(E) \qquad \frac{a}{N} = \frac{1}{2\pi} \int_{k_2}^{\infty} \int_{h}^{\infty} e^{-\frac{1}{2}(x^2+y^2)} \, dx \, dy + z_{k_2} z_h S$$

Since the e under the double integral sign has as exponent the sum of two terms, it may be separated into the product of two integrals, so that Eq. (E) may be written as follows:

$$(F) \quad \frac{a}{N} = \left[\frac{1}{\sqrt{2\pi}} \int_{k_2}^{\infty} e^{-\frac{x^2}{2}} \, dx \right] \left[\frac{1}{\sqrt{2\pi}} \int_{h}^{\infty} e^{-\frac{y^2}{2}} \, dy \right] + z_{k_2} z_h S$$

Now examination will show that the first of these integrals is the summation of the z's (and, consequently, of the probabilities) in the x distribution from k_2 to infinity and hence the tail of the x distribution from k_2 to infinity, which we shall call p_{k_2}. The second integral is, similarly, the tail of the y distribution, which we shall call p_h. Making these substitutions, and making some algebraic transformations, we have

$$(G) \qquad \frac{a}{N} = p_{k_2} p_h + z_{k_2} z_h S; \; \frac{(a/N) - p_{k_2} p_h}{z_{k_2} z_h} = S$$

The S is the slowly converging series given at the right in formula (190) and which we here restate in abridged form.

$$\frac{a - N p_k p_h}{N z_k z_h} = r + r^2 \frac{hk}{2} + r^3 \frac{(h^2 - 1)(k^2 - 1)}{6}$$
$$+ r^4 \frac{hk(h^2 - 3)(k^2 - 3)}{24} + \cdots$$

The N of this formula we are likely not to know except by implication. But we do know the number of individuals in the four quadrants so far as the remaining tails include them, and we must know the proportion of the whole population included in each tail. We may, therefore, put N in terms of these directly known elements as follows:

$$(a + c) = p_{k_2} N; \; (b + d) = p_{k_1} N; \text{ so } (a + b + c + d)$$
$$= N(p_{k_2} + p_{k_1})$$

Therefore,

$$N = \frac{a + b + c + d}{p_{k_2} + p_{k_1}}$$

Making this substitution in formula (G) and letting

$$(a + b + c + d) = n$$

instead of N which stands for the whole population of the unmutilated distribution, we have

$$\frac{a(p_{k_2} + p_{k_1}) - np_{k_2}p_h}{nz_{k_2}z_h} = S \qquad (200)$$

Similarly integrating for d from $x = k_1$ to $x = -\infty$ and from $y = h$ to $y = -\infty$, we have

$$\frac{d(p_{k_1} + p_{k_2}) - np_{k_1}q_h}{nz_{k_1}z_h} = S_1 \qquad (201)$$

The q_h at the right is used in the ordinary sense: it is $(1 - p)$. Note that cognizance must be taken of the sign of h and of k, so that S of formula (200) does not have the same value as S_1 of formula (201). It is advisable to take two determinations of r, one from formula (200) and one from formula (201), and accept as the true value of r the geometric mean of the two. However, if the assumptions of the development have been fully met, the two values will be identical.

Suppose, now, that the two tails of the x distribution are equal and that the dichotomy in the y distribution is at the mean. Then k_1 will equal k_2, h will be zero, p_h will be $\frac{1}{2}$, z_h will be $1/\sqrt{2\pi}$, and S and S_1 will be identical in value. We may then advantageously combine formulas (200) and (201) and have

$$\sqrt{\left(\frac{2ap_k\sqrt{2\pi}}{nz_k} - \frac{p_k\sqrt{2\pi}}{2z_k}\right)\left(\frac{2dp_k\sqrt{2\pi}}{nz_k} - \frac{p_k\sqrt{2\pi}}{2z_k}\right)} = S'$$

$$(H) \qquad \frac{p_k\sqrt{2\pi}}{z_k}\sqrt{\left(\frac{2a}{n} - \frac{1}{2}\right)\left(\frac{2d}{n} - \frac{1}{2}\right)} = S'$$

If our assumptions have been fully met that the tails are equal and the dichotomic line dividing the y distribution is at the mean, a would equal d and b would equal c. But, for reasons of unequal sampling at the two ends, if for no others, this will seldom be precisely the case in empirical samples. Let us, therefore, take $\sqrt{ad}$ for each a and d, $2\sqrt{bc}$ for $(b + c)$, and $2\sqrt{ad}$ for $(a + d)$. Then we would have

$$\frac{p_k\sqrt{2\pi}}{z_k}\left[\frac{2\sqrt{ad} - \frac{1}{2}(a + d + b + c)}{a + d + b + c}\right] = S'$$

$$\frac{p_k\sqrt{2\pi}}{z_k}\left[\frac{2\sqrt{ad} - \sqrt{ad} - \sqrt{bc}}{2\sqrt{ad} + 2\sqrt{bc}}\right] = S'$$

$$(I) \qquad \frac{p_k\sqrt{2\pi}}{2z_k} \cdot \frac{\sqrt{ad} - \sqrt{bc}}{\sqrt{ad} + \sqrt{bc}} = S'$$

We shall now substitute the value of S' for the special condition where the dichotomy is at the mean of the y distribution, and hence where $h = 0$, and have the following formula:

$$\frac{p\sqrt{2\pi}}{2z_k} \cdot \frac{\sqrt{ad} - \sqrt{bc}}{\sqrt{ad} + \sqrt{bc}} = r - \frac{r^3}{6}(k^2 - 1)$$

$$+ \frac{r^5}{40}(k^4 - 6k^2 + 3) - \frac{r^7}{336}(k^6 - 15k^4 + 45k^2 - 15)$$

$$+ \frac{r^9}{3,456}(k^8 - 28k^6 + 210k^4 - 420k^2 + 105)$$

$$- \frac{r^{11}}{42,240}(k^{10} - 45k^8 + 630k^6 - 3,150k^4 + 4,725k^2 - 945)$$

$$+ \frac{r^{13}}{599,040}(k^{12} - 66k^{10} + 1,485k^8 - 13,860k^6 + 51,975k^4$$

$$- 62,370k^2 + 10,395) - \frac{r^{15}}{9,676,800}(k^{14} - 91k^{12} + 3,003k^{10}$$

$$- 45,045k^8 + 315,315k^6 - 945,945k^4 + 945,945k^2 - 135,135)$$

$$+ \frac{r^{17}}{175,472,640}(k^{16} - 120k^{14} + 5,460k^{12} - 120,120k^{10}$$

$$+ 1,351,350k^8 - 7,567,560k^6 + 18,918,900k^4 - 16,216,200k^2$$

$$+ 2,027,025) - \cdots \quad \begin{matrix}\text{(Tetrachoric coefficient of correlation}\\ \text{when one series is divided at the}\\ \text{mean and only symmetrical tails} \quad (202)\\ \text{remain from the other distribution,}\\ \text{the entries being in frequencies)}\end{matrix}$$

The series continues infinitely. We have given it at this length to indicate its behavior as terms are added, but seldom will the practical worker have occasion to use more than the first three terms on the right. In fact we shall give below a scheme that requires the practical worker to use only the first power of r and permits him then to ascertain the value for the whole formula from our tables. Obviously the series will converge rapidly for low r's, but for high r's it converges extremely slowly. In order to get reasonable convergence for r's of .95 to .99, several times as many terms must be employed as we have given. In making our tables in the Appendix we were obliged to carry the formula to the hundredth power of r in order to handle the high r's.

The k is found in the table for any proportion we wish to retain in each of the tails, this proportion being the p of our formula. The k is the distance from the mean of a normal distribution of unit area and unit standard deviation to the ordinate that cuts off the required tail, and it is labeled x in the terminology of our tables. If a tail of 15.87 per cent (practically 16 per cent) is employed, k will equal 1, and hence the second term on the right of the equation will vanish leaving the first power of r and powers beginning with 5. Unless r is rather high, these powers of r of 5 or greater may safely be neglected.

Although we shall offer below a short-cut method, we shall illustrate the operation of this formula for the sake of making the principle clear. Out of a total student body of 1,257 members[1] 156 of approximately the best 16 per cent in scholarship had accomplishment quotients above the average, while 54 had AQ's below average. On the contrary, of the poorest approximately 16 per cent in scholarship 31 had AQ's above average and 184 below. In this instance, contrary to what would ordinarily be the case, we know the precise percentage in the tails, because we measured the whole population for another purpose; it is 16.9 per cent. But extremely small errors are involved in the resulting r from slight discrepancies in estimating the percentage in the tails under conditions where that percentage cannot be precisely measured. The k for 16.9 per cent is 0.9581, which is so nearly 1 that no appreciable error would be involved in taking it as 1 for the sake of simplifying the arithmetic. For the first approximation we shall use only the first power of r.

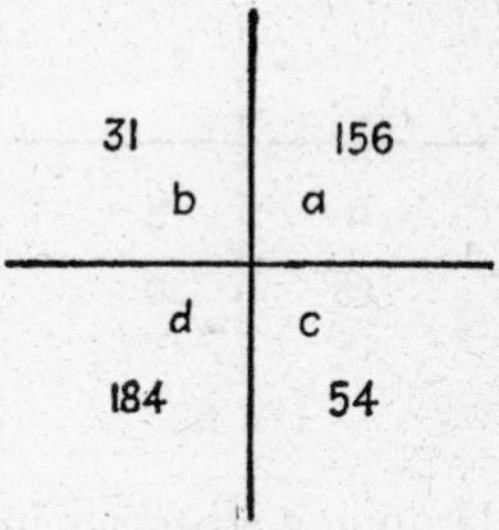

31	156
b	a
d	c
184	54

FIG. 28.

$$r = \frac{.169\sqrt{2\pi}(\sqrt{184 \cdot 156} - \sqrt{54 \cdot 31})}{2(0.252)(\sqrt{184 \cdot 156} + \sqrt{54 \cdot 31})} = .513$$

This is the value of the quantity on the left side of our equation, formula (202). The total value on the right must exactly balance this when we take account of all the terms. In order to compensate for the additional terms, we would need to carry on a process of approximation precisely similar to that illustrated on page 373. But, when we try substituting .514 for r in the first five terms of the equation on the right, we obtain for the

[1] PETERS, C. C., "A Method for Computing Accomplishment Quotients on the High School and College Levels," *J. Educ. Res.*, Vol. 14, pp. 99–111.

value of this member of the equation .5138, while substituting .513 gives us .5128; so that .513 is the closest we can get with three decimal places, and our first r required no correction. The Pearson product moment r, computed from the whole population, is .511, which is in remarkably close agreement with that given by our formula.

We have employed here a problem resulting in a rather low r, hence the series converged rapidly, so that we obtained a precise determination by using only the first few terms. But unfortunately the series converges very slowly for high values of r, so that it may be necessary to substitute in the formula through so many terms as to become impractical. We have, therefore, provided tables (pages 505 to 507) for reading values of the r's for the completed formula from those obtained by solving the equation for only the first power of r. The use of these makes wholly unnecessary the method of successive approximations just illustrated and makes the computation of any r an extremely simple process. Suppose, for example, we have the fourfold layout indicated on the right, the p for each tail being 12 per cent.

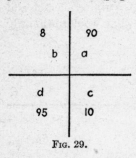

Fig. 29.

Dropping all terms in r except the first, we have

$$r' = \frac{.12\sqrt{2\pi}(\sqrt{90 \cdot 95} - \sqrt{8 \cdot 10})}{2(.20)(\sqrt{90 \cdot 95} + \sqrt{8 \cdot 10})} = .6192$$

Entering Table L with $p = 12$ per cent and following down this column, we find .6185 as the nearest value. Interpolating, we get as the corresponding true r, correct to 3 places, .651. For r's below .25 no correction is needed; unless extremely high accuracy is required, the value obtained from solving for only the first power may be taken as the true r. But for r's above .50 or .60 (depending much upon the percentage in the tail) the correction is important, and the more so as the r's approach unity.

Two Pennsylvania State College graduate students made empirical tests of this tetrachoric formula. C. E. Amos made 78 determinations of the tetrachoric r's in accordance with the conditions of the formula, and of the corresponding product moment r's, with populations of from 128 to 802.   The average deviation of the tetrachoric r's from the product-moment ones was about 7 per cent.   The most extreme divergence was five product-moment P.E.'s; but prevailingly the deviations stayed within one P.E.   R. W. Jacks tried departures from the conditions of the y dichotomy at the mean and from equality of proportions in the tails and nevertheless used the formula that assumes these conditions in order to see how far we may depart from the assumptions and yet get satisfactory results.   He took as p the geometric mean of the two p's and as the z the geometric mean of the two involved in his data.   Out of 87 determinations, he found no substantially greater error than that by Amos when imposing the conditions assumed in the development.   We may, therefore, depart somewhat from the assumptions of our development and yet have substantially correct results.   Our formula would then be

$$\frac{\sqrt{2\pi}\sqrt{p_1 p_2}}{2\sqrt{z_{k_1} z_{k_2}}} \cdot \frac{\sqrt{ad} - \sqrt{bc}}{\sqrt{ad} + \sqrt{bc}} = S' \tag{203}$$

where S' is the value given at the right of the equality sign in formula (202).

But if the dichotomy in the y distribution differs more than moderately from the mean and reasonably accurate results are required, it is best to use formulas (200) and (201) rather than (203).   In that case the formula must be solved for two quadrants by the method of approximation illustrated on page 379.   But in order to lessen the labor of such calculations, we have set up values for the quantities in parentheses for all tails from 5 per cent to 40 per cent and up to the 25th power of r.   These tables are found in the Appendix, pages 501 to 504.   Suppose in some particular problem p_{k_1} is 25 per cent and p_h is 33 per cent. The tables need make no distinction between p_h and p_k.   We look in the table for the coefficient as determined by the p_k and at another place in the table for the coefficient as determined by p_h. In the case of our illustration these would run as follows:

$$r + (0.4770)(0.3111)r^2 + (-0.2225)(-0.3292)r^3$$
$$+ (-0.3504)(-0.2520)r^4$$

But one must carefully observe that if either the h or the k is negative, the sign of its part of the coefficient is reversed as compared with the signs in the table in all even powers of r but not in the odd powers. If the h and the k in the quadrant with which we are operating lie in the same direction from their respective means, the sign of the combination is plus; otherwise it is minus. But a little experience will show that the r must reach at least .16 before carrying the r's beyond the first power will affect the third decimal place and beyond .20 before the second decimal place will be affected. When the r reaches .80 or .90, the equation must be solved through a considerable number of terms.

P.E. OF TETRACHORIC r FROM WIDESPREAD CLASSES

We have not yet developed a satisfactory general formula for the probable error of tetrachoric r from widespread classes, but we submit tentatively the following one. It is for r', the value when all but first powers of r are dropped from formula (202). But r' may be regarded as $r(1 - j)$, where $(1 - j)$ is the value obtained by dividing the series at the right by r. Thus, since r is a function of r', the P.E. of the latter is a proper basis for inferring the P.E. of the former.

Since we assume the dichotomy of the y distribution to be at the mean and only symmetrical tails remaining in the x distribution, we can put formula (202) into the following form:

$$r' = (\alpha - \beta) \frac{p\sqrt{2\pi}}{2z_k}$$

where $\alpha = (a + d)/n$ and $\beta = (b + c)/n$, the n being the number of individuals in the two tails combined. Then

$$\delta r' = \delta(\alpha - \beta) \frac{p\sqrt{2\pi}}{2z_k}$$

The $\frac{p\sqrt{2\pi}}{2z_k}$ is a constant. Let m represent it. Then

$$\delta r' = m\delta(\alpha - \beta)$$

Squaring, summing, and dividing by the number of samples,

$$\frac{\Sigma \overline{\delta r'}^2}{S} = m^2 \left(\frac{\Sigma \overline{\delta \alpha}^2}{S} + \frac{\Sigma \overline{\delta \beta}^2}{S} - 2 \frac{\Sigma \overline{\delta \alpha} \ \overline{\delta \beta}}{S} \right)$$

Therefore,

$$\sigma_{r'}^2 = m^2(\sigma^2{}_\alpha + \sigma^2{}_\beta - 2r_{\alpha\beta}\sigma_\alpha\sigma_\beta)$$

It is obvious that $r_{\alpha\beta} = -1$, for the population remaining in the tails is divided into only those two parts, so that as the one increases the other must decrease. Therefore

$$\sigma_{r'}^2 = m^2(\sigma^2{}_\alpha + \sigma^2{}_\beta + 2\sigma_\alpha\sigma_\beta)$$

But $(\alpha + \beta) = 1$. Applying, therefore, the formula for the standard error of a proportion: $\sigma_\alpha = \sqrt{\alpha\beta/n}$. Similarly $\sigma_\beta = \sqrt{\alpha\beta/n}$. Thus, since σ_α is found to be equal to σ_β, we have, by substituting in our last $\sigma_{r'}^2$ formula above, $\sigma_{r'}^2 = 4m^2\sigma^2{}_\alpha$. Replacing m with its equivalent and taking the square root,

$$(J) \qquad \sigma_{r'} = \frac{p\sqrt{2\pi}}{z_k} \sqrt{\frac{\alpha\beta}{n}}$$

We may now replace α and β with their values in numbers of individuals, and, by substituting these in (J), we have

$$\sigma_{r'} = \frac{p\sqrt{2\pi}}{z_k\sqrt{n}} \sqrt{\frac{(a+d)(b+c)}{n^2}} \quad \text{(Probable error of tetrachoric } r' \text{ from widespread classes)} \quad (204)$$

$$\text{P.E.}_{r'} = \frac{0.6745p\sqrt{2\pi}}{z_k\sqrt{n}} \sqrt{\frac{(a+d)(b+c)}{n^2}}$$

By some algebraic manipulation based on the fact that $(\alpha + \beta)$ equals 1, we can put formula (204) also into the following form, equivalent to (204) except to the extent to which the assumption of symmetry in the tails and division of the y distribution at the mean is violated:

$$\text{P.E.}_{r'} = \frac{0.6745}{z_k\sqrt{n}} \sqrt{\frac{\pi p^2}{2} - r'^2 z_k^2} \qquad (204a)$$

By formula (204) the P.E. of the r' of .513 computed on page 379 would be

$$\text{P.E.}_{r'} = \frac{.169\sqrt{2\pi}\,0.6745}{0.252\sqrt{425}} \sqrt{\frac{(156+184)(31+54)}{425^2}} = .022$$

By formula (204a) this P.E. would be

$$\text{P.E.}_{r'} = \frac{0.6745}{0.252\sqrt{425}} \sqrt{\frac{.169^2\pi}{2} - .513^2\,0.252^2} = .021$$

The above are formulas for the P.E. of r'. But r is a function of r', so that we may find the P.E.$_r$ directly from P.E.$_{r'}$. We may symbolize the procedure in the following formula:

$$\text{P.E.}_r = \tfrac{1}{2}[f(r' + \text{P.E.}_{r'}) - f(r' - \text{P.E.}_{r'})] \qquad (205)$$

In verbal directions this means that we look up in our tables in the Appendix the r corresponding to (r' plus its P.E.) and again the r corresponding to (r' minus its P.E.) and take for P.E.$_r$ half the difference between these two. For any multiple a of one P.E. we would need to take $1/2a$ times the difference between the r function of ($r' + a \cdot \text{P.E.}_{r'}$) and of ($r' - a \cdot \text{P.E.}_{r'}$).

In the case of an r' as low as the one of .513 of our illustrative problem there will be a negligible difference between P.E.$_r$ and P.E.$_{r'}$. But we shall make the translation anyway for the sake of illustrating the procedure.

The r corresponding to an r' of (.513 + .022) for a tail of .169 is .535, while that for (.513 − .022) is .491. Therefore

$$\text{P.E.}_r = \tfrac{1}{2}(.535 - .491) = .022$$

BISERIAL r FROM WIDESPREAD CLASSES

We shall now develop a formula for biserial r from widespread classes to match the one just presented for tetrachoric correlation. There are many situations in which such formula may be extremely useful in educational and sociological research; for example, where we wish to investigate the relation of teaching success to certain measured personality traits, or of attendance at movies to conduct outcomes, or of marital success to certain measurable factors, where we can have distributions of scores on the factors we wish to correlate with our criterion but where it is feasible to investigate in detail only those extremes of the whole population which are outstandingly "high" in the criterion trait and those which are outstandingly "low."

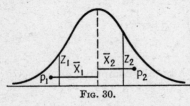

Fig. 30.

Referring to the diagram, let p_1 be the proportion in one of the tails and p_2 the proportion in the other tail. Then, using the same graphical relations as those employed at the opening of this chapter,

$$b = \frac{y_1}{\bar{x}_1} = \frac{y_2}{\bar{x}_2} = \frac{y_1 + y_2}{\bar{x}_1 + \bar{x}_2} = \frac{M_2 - M_1}{(z_1/p_1) + (z_2/p_2)} = \frac{(M_2 - M_1)p_1 p_2}{p_2 z_1 + p_1 z_2}$$

$$r = b\frac{\sigma_x}{\sigma_y} = \frac{(M_2 - M_1)p_1 p_2}{p_2 z_1 + p_1 z_2}\frac{1}{\sigma_y} = \frac{(M_2 - M_1)p_1 p_2}{\sigma_y (p_2 z_1 + p_1 z_2)} \qquad (206)$$

(Biserial coefficient of correlation from widespread classes)

If the two tails are equal, as will often be the case, this formula reduces to

$$r = \frac{(M_2 - M_1)p}{2z\sigma_y} \qquad \text{(Biserial coefficient of correlation from widespread classes in case of symmetrical tails)} \qquad (207)$$

The only awkwardness involved in the use of this formula is connected with σ_y. This must be the standard deviation of the whole y distribution, unmutilated by chopping out the middle of the x distribution. This σ may be calculated from a sample of the whole population, or it may be inferred theoretically from the remaining portions. The sample may be reasonably small compared with the whole population from which the tails are taken, since the standard error of a standard deviation is relatively low and since slight changes in the sigma do not greatly affect biserial r. For those situations in which it is not practicable to obtain this σ from the whole population, or from a sample of the whole population, we developed a formula for inferring it from the remaining tails. The complete derivation is given in the previous edition of this book. The proof is somewhat lengthy, and for that reason we omit it here, referring the interested reader to pages 279 to 282 of the lithoprinted edition. The formula which eventuates is

$$\sigma_y = \left\{ \frac{\Sigma Y_1{}^2 + \Sigma Y_2{}^2 + \frac{1}{4}(n_1 + n_2)\left[M_1 + M_2 + b\left(\frac{z_1}{p_1} - \frac{z_2}{p_2}\right)\right]^2}{(n_1 + n_2)} \right.$$

$$\left. - \frac{n_1 M_1 + n_2 M_2}{n_1 + n_2}\left[M_1 + M_2 + b\left(\frac{z_1}{p_1} - \frac{z_2}{p_2}\right) - \frac{b^2}{(p_1 + p_2)}(z_2 x_2 - z_1 x_1)\right]\right\}^{\frac{1}{2}}$$

(The standard deviation of a total distribution taken from tails remaining after mutilation when the moments are in score form)   (208)

where Y_1 is a *score* in the lower tail of the distribution and M_1 is the mean of the scores in that tail, while z and x have the customary meanings in a normal distribution of unit area and unit standard deviation. Note that the x's in formula (208) are unbarred and refer to the distances from the mean of the whole distribution to the points of truncation.

In solving a practical problem, we must first find the b for our particular problem, for which the value, as indicated on page 385 is

$$b = \frac{(M_2 - M_1)p_1p_2}{p_2z_1 + p_1z_2}$$

Then, armed with this information of the value of b, we determine the value of σ_y by the use of formula (208) or one of its variants. Finally we use formula (206) to find biserial r. The r will merely be the b divided by σ_y. Remember that x_1 will customarily have in its own right the minus sign, which will be offset by the minus in the term $-x_1z_1$ of Eq. (208) and similar expressions above. Thus, if neither tail is greater than 50 per cent, both final xz products will be positive. Unless the worker watches his step he may get confused on this point.

Besides normality in the total distribution of the population in both variables, this formula assumes sharp truncation of the tails. Such sharp truncation is possible if we have actual measurements in the criterion factor. But sometimes we must merely estimate whether or not individuals belong in the categories with which we are working, in which case the reliability of the r is lowered. This is merely because of the unreliability of measurement in the criterion factor and affects our problem in the same manner as unreliability of measurement always affects correlation.

We shall now use as a practical example of this procedure the same study employed in our section on tetrachoric correlation —correlation between grade-point averages and accomplishment quotients for 1,257 college students. We shall display the mutilated correlation table shown on page 387, all that middle section of students who made grade-point averages between 1.00 and 1.99 being eliminated from consideration.

Working with these data with intervals as units above the mid-point of interval .30–.39 as assumed mean instead of with raw scores, we find for the 294 students (23.4 per cent) who had made grade-point averages of 2.00 or better a mean of 7.846 and ΣY_2^2 of 19,365, while the 215 students (17.1 per cent) who had made grade-point averages below 1.00 had average AQ's of 4.340 and

TABLE XXXII.—ACCOMPLISHMENT QUOTIENTS OF "GOOD" AND "POOR" COLLEGE STUDENTS

AQ	Average grade points	
	fY_1 Below 1.00	fY_2 2.00 and above
2.00–2.09		2
1.90–1.99		
1.80–1.89		2
1.70–1.79		3
1.60–1.69		3
1.50–1.59	1	7
1.40–1.49	1	9
1.30–1.39		23
1.20–1.29	3	34
1.10–1.19	8	67
1.00–1.09	18	70
0.90–0.99	8	50
0.80–0.89	50	21
0.70–0.79	59	3
0.60–0.69	37	
0.50–0.59	21	
0.40–0.49	6	
0.30–0.39	3	
Totals........	215	294

ΣY_1^2 of 4,807. Our first task is to find b and then σ_y from these data.

$$b = \frac{(M_2 - M_1)p_1 p_2}{p_2 z_1 + p_1 z_2} = \frac{(7.846 - 4.340)(.171)(.234)}{(.234)(0.2540) + (.171)(0.3066)} = 1.254$$

$$\sigma_y = \left[\frac{4,807 + 19,365 + \dfrac{509}{4}\left[7.846 + 4.340 + 1.254 \left(\dfrac{0.2540}{.171} - \dfrac{0.3066}{.234} \right) \right]^2}{509} \right.$$

$$- \frac{(215)(4.340) + (294)(7.846)}{509}\left\{ 4.340 + 7.846 \right.$$

$$\left. + 1.254 \left(\frac{.2540}{.171} - \frac{.3066}{.234} \right) \right\}$$

$$\left. - \frac{1.254^2}{.171 + .234}\left[(0.2540)(0.9502) + (0.3066)(0.7257) \right] \right]^{\frac{1}{2}} = 2.283$$

$$r_{xy} = \frac{b_{yz}}{\sigma_y} = \frac{1.254}{2.283} = .549$$

In this case we happen to know the mean, the standard deviation, and the r as computed from the whole population, and we went the roundabout way of inferring these merely for the sake of illustrating the procedure one would need to follow if he were not fortunate enough to know the σ. The correct σ is 2.301 (in intervals) instead of the 2.283 we obtained by inference, and the correct r is .533 when corrected for broad categories as compared with our .549. Inspection of the complete correlation chart reveals that the regression is slightly curvilinear and this violation of the assumptions back of the formulas threw us off a little. But the discrepancy is less than one standard error, and this is no greater than could be expected from r's computed from different samples. In fact it must be expected that the extremes of distributions will differ in relation to their own distributions as wholes in somewhat the same manner as the regression lines of successive samples differ from one another, so that r's computed from widespread classes may be expected to diverge from corresponding ones computed by the product-moment method to a degree comparable with the fluctuation of r's by either method from sample to sample. But the average of the r's from a number of samples may be expected to be the same by both types of method, and in any one sample the chances are just as good of approaching the true r closely by the methods of these last few sections as by the product-moment method—or perhaps a little better since the P.E.'s of the former r's are smaller for the same number of actually utilized individuals.

Formula (208), where we must infer both the mean of the distribution and its standard deviation from a few fragments, requires considerable penciling, as the reader had probably noticed to his horror. Of course, no one in his senses would use that method if his data permitted him to compute a regular Pearson product moment r. But the labor of penciling in the application of this formula is trifling compared with that which might be involved in testing, or otherwise investigating, the great middle bulk of the distribution.

The foregoing example was intended to show how to infer the standard deviation when it is unknown and then to compute the biserial r. Following is a typical example of the many potential uses of this formula in practical research. In it the σ of the whole population is known. After presenting it, we shall derive formulas for the standard error of this type of r. In order to test the validity of the Bernreuter Personality Inventory, Krupa[1] gave to 450 freshmen at Pennsylvania State College a verbal description of a neurotic person and a verbal description of a stable person (in addition to similar treatment of other traits). He asked these freshmen to write the names of freshmen of their acquaintance who were much like the persons therein described. Twenty-one subjects were named as neurotic three or more times, and 39 as stable. All the freshmen had previously marked the Bernreuter Personality Inventory. Thus Krupa had the distribution of the neuroticism scores for the 4.66 per cent of his subjects who most impressed their fellow students as neurotic, and also the distribution of these B1N scores for the 8.67 per cent who impressed their fellow students as most stable; and he knew the standard deviation of these B1N scores for the whole 450 students. That the neuroticism mean of the scores for the former group was higher than that for the latter showed *some* validity in the Bernreuter inventory. To put the extent of that validity into standard correlation language, Krupa applied formula (206) as follows:

$$r = \frac{(M_2 - M_1)p_1p_2}{(p_1z_2 + p_2z_1)\sigma_y}$$
$$= \frac{(68.19 - 31.00)(.0867)(.0466)}{[(.0466)(0.1578) + (.0867)(0.0977)]30.06} = .316$$

We need, now, a standard error for this r. The standard error when the true r is zero will serve a useful purpose, because it will enable us to test whether fluctuations of sampling could be expected ever to yield so large an r as the one obtained if the true r were zero. The derivation is easy. The formula for r can be expressed in two parts as follows:

$$r_{\text{bis}} = \frac{p_1p_2}{(p_1z_2 + p_2z_1)\sigma_y} \cdot (M_2 - M_1)$$

Except for a very slight sampling fluctuation of σ_y which we shall ignore, the first of these parts is a constant in a universe of samples from a certain population, so that the standard error is

[1] Unpublished master's thesis at Pennsylvania State College, 1939.

merely this constant times the standard error of the difference between means assuming the null hypothesis. This [formula (101), page 178] is

$$\sigma_{M_2 - M_1} = \tilde{\sigma}\sqrt{\frac{1}{n_2} + \frac{1}{n_1}} = \tilde{\sigma}\sqrt{\frac{n_1 + n_2}{n_1 n_2}} = \tilde{\sigma}\sqrt{\frac{p_1 N + p_2 N}{p_1 p_2 N^2}}$$
$$= \tilde{\sigma}\sqrt{\frac{p_1 + p_2}{p_1 p_2 N}}$$

The $\tilde{\sigma}$ is that of either class in the tails of the distribution. But, since the correlation is assumed to be zero and hence the slope of the regression line is zero, this σ will be the same for both tails and the same for all columns in the complete correlation table, and hence the same as the $\tilde{\sigma}_y$ of the whole distribution. Taking the product of the two parts and taking account of the relation between σ and $\tilde{\sigma}$, we have the following:

$$\sigma_{r_{bis}} = \frac{\sqrt{p_1 p_2}}{(p_1 z_2 + p_2 z_1)\sqrt{N - 1}}\sqrt{(p_1 + p_2)} \tag{209}$$

(The standard error of biserial r
from widespread classes when
the true r is zero)

Substituting in this formula the values from Krupa's study, the standard error of his r is

$$\frac{\sqrt{(.0867)(.0466)}}{(.0466)(0.1578) + (.0867)(0.0977)\sqrt{450 - 1}}\sqrt{.0867 + .0466}$$
$$= .069$$

The obtained r is 4.6 times its standard error; so the probability that it could have arisen by chance fluctuation when the true r is zero is extremely slight.

For many purposes, including the one typified here, we need also the *general* formula for the standard error of this r. Both its derivation and its application are more complicated. It follows along the same general lines, but we cannot assume that the sigmas are equal as we could in the case above. The necessary standard deviations can be put in terms of known parameters and then put through a series of algebraic transformations, resulting in the following:[1]

[1] When the two tails come together so as to make a continuous distribution, our formula (209) reduces to Soper's, (188), where the true r of zero is

$$\sigma_{r_{\text{bis}}} =$$

$$\frac{\sqrt{p_1 p_2}}{(p_1 z_2 + p_2 z_1)\sqrt{N}}\sqrt{(p_1 + p_2) - r^2\left(\frac{p_2 z_1^2}{p_1^2} + \frac{p_1 z_2^2}{p_2^2} + \frac{p_2 x_1 z_1}{p_1} - \frac{p_1 x_2 z_2}{p_2}\right)}$$

(General formula for the standard error
of biserial r from widespread classes)   (209a)

For Krupa's problem this works out as follows:

$$\frac{\sqrt{(.0867)(.0466)}}{[(.0466)(0.1578) + (.0867)(0.0977)]\sqrt{450}}\left[(.0466 + .0867) \right.$$

$$- .316^2 \left[\frac{(.0867)(0.0977)^2}{(.0466)^2} + \frac{(.0466)(0.1578)^2}{(.0867)^2} \right.$$

$$\left. \left. - \frac{(.0867)(1.6781)(0.0977)}{(.0466)} - \frac{(.0466)(1.3616)(0.1578)}{(.0867)} \right] \right]^{\frac{1}{2}} = .066$$

Since at this point r's do not distribute themselves *normally* about a true value, the type of interpretation employed on pages 135 to 139 is not strictly applicable; but its use does not distort the meaning too much for practical purposes. Employing that type of interpretation here, the odds are about two to one that the true validity correlation coefficient in relation to this kind of criterion lies somewhere between .316 minus .066 and .316 plus .066; *i.e.*, between .250 and .382.

It is worth noting that the standard error of a product moment r with the same actually employed population (*i.e.*, 60) would be .116, which is nearly twice as high as the .066 of our biserial r from widespread classes; and that of a biserial r with a continuous population of size 60 divided at the middle would be .149. This suggests the economy of working with widespread classes where feasible.

MEAN-SQUARE CONTINGENCY CORRELATION

Another form of correlation which has been used to some extent is one based on χ^2. On pages 414 to 418 we show how to compute χ^2 from a contingency table. Our interest there is in

substituted in his. For a continuous distribution, formula (209a) gives results very close to Soper's but does not reduce algebraically to his. That is because both Soper's formula and ours make certain assumptions and approximations, though not the same ones. Because of the space required for the printing of the complete derivation of our formula, we cannot publish it here. The derivation is given in an article by the senior author (Peters) in *Psychometrika* for August, 1941.

determining whether chance fluctuations alone could explain the relations which appear to exist in the table; *i.e.*, to test the null hypothesis. But a positive measure of correlation can be based on these same calculations, getting a measure which is designated by C and called the *mean-square contingency correlation:*

$$C = \sqrt{\frac{\chi^2}{\chi^2 + N}} \qquad \text{(Mean-square contingency coefficient)} \qquad (210)$$

This measure of correlation is particularly fitting for materials which do not lend themselves to arrangement in categories that can be certainly said to be quantitatively ordered, or where the distances between the intervals are not susceptible of definite quantification. C varies between 0 and 1. But it does not, in itself, indicate the sign or the character of the regression. This must be determined by inspection. Karl Pearson showed that, if the items are capable of interpretation as a quantitatively ordered series, if the distributions are normal, and if the regression is rectilinear, C becomes identical with r as the number of categories is indefinitely increased. But, since these assumptions are usually so far from fulfillment and since C is fairly laborious to compute compared with other forms of correlation, we do not regard it as a particularly useful form. Tetrachoric r, or the form we shall discuss later in this chapter, will ordinarily serve the same purpose better.

On pages 415 and 416 some data by Burgess and Cottrell on marriage adjustment in relation to level of education are used to illustrate application of the χ^2 technique. We shall here draw upon the explanation and the calculation of χ^2 which is given there. For this problem $\chi^2 = 36.9$, and N is 513. Hence

$$C = \sqrt{\frac{\chi^2}{N + \chi^2}} = \sqrt{\frac{36.9}{36.9 + 513}} = .25$$

The formula which Pearson gives for the standard error of C is somewhat laborious to apply, and we are not explaining it here. The interested reader will find it in Kelley's *Statistical Method*, page 369.

The maximum size of C is limited by the number of categories into which the distributions are divided. It can easily be shown[1]

[1] See the lithoprinted edition of this book, p. 288.

that the maximum value C can have when computed from a square contingency table with t rows and t columns is

$$\sqrt{\frac{t-1}{t}}$$

Thus, even though we know the correlation is perfect, our formula cannot give us a higher correlation than $\sqrt{(t-1)/t}$, which is .866 in the case of a 4-category table. Even in a table with 15 categories in each array the maximum correlation can be shown, by substituting 15 for t, to be only .966. In our next section we shall show how to correct for this, at least in part.

CORRECTING COEFFICIENTS OF CORRELATION
FOR BROAD CATEGORIES

The coefficient of mean-square contingency is not the only coefficient of correlation that is left too low when computed from a table with broad intervals. The same thing is true of all correlations. It is true of every product moment r calculated from a correlation chart as compared with the r calculated from the paired scores. A correction is really called for in every r calculated from a correlation table where the scores are grouped in intervals wider than one unit, and it is imperatively called for whenever the number of categories is at all small—say below ten. We shall, therefore, attack in general terms the problem of correcting a coefficient of correlation for broad categories, then return to the application of the technique to the C of the above section.

We shall first treat the case in which our classes are taken as centered about the *means* of their respective intervals; then afterward we shall take up the case, familiar to us in customary correlation work like that discussed in our Chap. IV, in which the items within an interval are regarded as centered about the mid-point of the interval.

Let the unprimed letters stand for values centered around the means of their intervals while the primed letters stand for the variates themselves. Then r_{xy} is the correlation in terms of intervals, while $r_{x'y'}$ is the correlation when all the variates are taken at their actual values. We want to find $r_{x'y'}$ in terms of r_{xy}. We shall employ in simple form the technique of partial correlation treated in a preceding chapter. On page **243** the reader will find the formula

$$r_{01\cdot2} = \frac{r_{01} - r_{02}r_{12}}{\sqrt{1 - r_{12}^2}\sqrt{1 - r_{02}^2}}$$

We shall let the 0 be x, the 1 be y, and the 2 be x'. Then

$$r_{xy\cdot x'} = \frac{r_{xy} - r_{xx'}r_{yx'}}{\sqrt{1 - r_{yx'}^2}\sqrt{1 - r_{xx'}^2}}$$

The $r_{xy\cdot x'}$ is the correlation between x and y with the x' variates held constant. But, if the x' values are held constant, the x's would be constant, since the x's are the means of the x''s by intervals. Because any variable correlated with a constant gives a zero correlation, $r_{xy\cdot x'}$ equals zero. So we have

$$\frac{r_{xy} - r_{xx'}r_{yx'}}{\sqrt{1 - r_{yx'}^2}\sqrt{1 - r_{xx'}^2}} = 0$$

Multiplying through by $(\sqrt{1 - r_{yx'}^2}\sqrt{1 - r_{xx'}^2})$, we get

$$r_{xy} - r_{xx'}r_{yx'} = 0$$

and transposing,

$$r_{xy} = r_{xx'}r_{yx'}$$

We should like to be rid of the $r_{yx'}$, so we shall try another partial correlation.

$$r_{x'y\cdot y'} = \frac{r_{x'y} - r_{x'y'}r_{yy'}}{\sqrt{1 - r_{yy'}^2}\sqrt{1 - r_{x'y'}^2}}$$

This partial r is the correlation between the y's and the x''s with y' held constant. But if the y' is constant, the y must be constant for the same reason as given under the x's. So our partial correlation would again be equal to zero. Setting the fraction on the right equal to zero, clearing of fractions, and transposing as above, $r_{x'y} = r_{x'y'}r_{yy'}$.

We shall now substitute this value for $r_{x'y}$ in the equation second above where we said we wished to get rid of it. After making this substitution, we have,

$$r_{xy} = r_{xx'}r_{x'y'}r_{yy'}$$

What we started out to find was the correlation between the variates taken at their true values in terms of the correlation when the values were taken as centered about the means of intervals. That is, we want a value for $r_{x'y'}$. We can easily solve for it the equation just given, getting

$$r_{x'y'} = \frac{r_{xy}}{r_{xx'}r_{yy'}} \qquad \begin{array}{l}\text{(Formula for correcting an } r \text{ for broad} \\ \text{categories when calculated in terms} \\ \text{of means of intervals)}\end{array} \qquad (211)$$

The correlation between the variates is, therefore, the correlation in terms of means divided by the product of the r's between means and variates in each of the two arrays.

But the catch is that, except in cases where we can draw upon ready-made tables, we are not likely to know the coefficient of correlation between means and variates within each of the distributions. We must meet this difficulty by next getting a formula for the r's between the means and the variates of a distribution.

If we assume rectilinearity of regression between means and variates, the value of a variate computed from the mean of its interval is, as we learned when we studied the simple regression equation in deviation form, $\bar{x}' = r_{xx'} \frac{\sigma_{x'}}{\sigma_x} x$. But the $\bar{x}'$ is the one that lies on the regression line, and, assuming rectilinearity of regression as said above, it is at the mean of its column. Therefore $\bar{x}'$ is the same as x, which is by notation the value of the mean. Dividing through therefore by this value, we get $r_{xx'} = (\sigma_x/\sigma_{x'})$. In a precisely similar manner it can be shown that

$$r_{yy'} = \frac{\sigma_y}{\sigma_{y'}} \qquad \begin{array}{l}\text{(Formula for the coefficient of correlation between} \\ \text{means and variates within a distribution)}\end{array} \qquad (212)$$

If now we substitute these values for the r's in formula (211), we get another formula for correcting for broad categories that is simpler for many applications.

$$r_{x'y'} = \frac{r_{xy}}{(\sigma_y/\sigma_{y'}) \cdot (\sigma_x/\sigma_{x'})} = \frac{r_{xy}\sigma_{x'}\sigma_{y'}}{\sigma_x\sigma_y} \qquad \begin{array}{l}\text{(Equivalent formula} \\ \text{for } r \text{ corrected for} \\ \text{broad categories in} \\ \text{case computed in} \\ \text{terms of means of} \\ \text{intervals)}\end{array} \qquad (213)$$

If we are working with distributions of unit area and unit standard deviation (as we are when we deal with proportions in the several intervals and apply x and z values from our tables pages 481 to 484) and if we assume normality of distribution as it is assumed in those tables, both the $\sigma_{x'}$ and the $\sigma_{y'}$ will be 1, by definition. Then our formula will simplify to

$$r_{x'y'} = \frac{r_{xy}}{\sigma_x \sigma_y} = \frac{\Sigma xy}{N \sigma_x^2 \sigma_y^2}$$

(Formula for r corrected for broad categories in case of measures centered about means of intervals and a normal distribution of unit area and unit standard deviation) (213a)

This does not apply to the correction of r's computed from such correlation tables as we dealt with in Chap. IV and as we employ in most product-moment work, because there the items are taken to be centered about the mid-points of the intervals (called *index values*) rather than about the means of intervals. A reasonably satisfactory correction can be made for this case, but not so neatly as for the case of means.

Let x_i be the deviation of the mid-point score value of an interval in the x array, and let x be a score in deviation form. Let y_i and y have similar meanings in the other array; and let c_x be the difference between an x and the corresponding index value and c_y have a corresponding meaning in the other array. Then

$$r_{x'y'} = \frac{\Sigma(x_i + c_x)(y_i + c_y)}{N \sigma_{(x_i + c_x)} \sigma_{(y_i + c_y)}} = \frac{\Sigma x_i y_i + \Sigma x_i c_y + \Sigma y_i c_x + \Sigma c_x c_y}{N \sigma_{(x_i + c_x)} \sigma_{(y_i + c_y)}}$$

Some c_x's will be positive and some negative. If there were nearly perfect correlation, not only would the c_x's fall in the same interval as their corresponding paired y values but would also tend to fall on the same side of the mid-point of the interval to which they belonged in the other array; thus there would tend to be an excess of like-signed $x_i c_y$ values. But that would happen only in extremely high correlations. Under all other conditions they would fall largely at random on either side of the mid-point and thus have random plus or minus signs; or they might even fall into other intervals in the y array from the corresponding one in the x array. Hence, over the whole distribution the $y_i c_x$ products would tend to sum to zero. The same thing would be true of the $x_i c_y$ products and the $c_x c_y$ products. Hence for an approximation which holds well for all except extremely high r's, the numerator needs no correction. The σ's in the denominator are standard deviations of distributions in terms of index values, and their correction calls merely for Sheppard's correction, treated on pages 84 to 89. Therefore, we have

$$r_{x'y'} = \frac{\Sigma xy}{N\sqrt{\sigma_x^2 - (1/12)}\sqrt{\sigma_y^2 - (1/12)}}$$

$$= r_{xy}\frac{\sigma_x\sigma_y}{\sqrt{\sigma_x^2 - (1/12)}\sqrt{\sigma_y^2 - (1/12)}} \quad \begin{array}{l}\text{(}r\text{ corrected for broad}\\ \text{categories in the case}\\ \text{of index values)}\end{array} \quad (214)$$

Thus we can either incorporate the needed correction in the original computations by making Sheppard's correction in the standard deviations or we can correct an r computed from broad categories by dividing it by the product of the two ratios

$$\frac{\sqrt{\sigma_x^2 - (1/12)}}{\sigma_x} \quad \frac{\sqrt{\sigma_y^2 - (1/12)}}{\sigma_y}$$

where the σ's are the ones computed in terms of index values. It is these ratios which are tabled as the fourth and fifth columns in Table XXXIII, page 398. This formula is extremely important, since it fits the situation in which we customarily compute coefficients of correlation. It is so easy to make Sheppard's correction (merely subtract one-twelfth before taking the square root, or such modifications of this as are explained on page 73) that it would be a good practice to make it in all correlations computed from correlation tables. Certainly it is imperative to make it if the number of intervals is as few as 5 or 6 and better to do it with anything less than 12 or 14.

One more case of interest is the special one where we may assume a rectangular distribution. As shown on page 107, the standard deviation of the means of a rectangle is $\sqrt{(k^2 - 1)/12}$, where k is the length of the rectangle,[1] while the standard deviation of the variables in a rectangular distribution (which is the same as one in which the number of subdivisions is indefinitely large) is $\sqrt{k^2/12}$. Using, then, for $r_{x'x}$ the standard deviation of the means over the standard deviation of the variates, we have

$$r_{x'x} = \sqrt{\frac{k^2 - 1}{k^2}} \quad \begin{array}{l}\text{(Correlation of variates with either}\\ \text{means or index values in a rec-}\\ \text{tangular distribution)}\end{array} \quad (215)$$

[1] Kelley (*Statistical Method*, p. 267) gives as the standard deviation of a rectangle $\sqrt{\dfrac{k(k-1)}{12}}$. But this is incorrect, and his table of values of r's on p. 268 (of *Statistical Methods*) is also incorrect as far as the column for rectangular distributions is concerned.

In correcting r for broad categories where rectangular distributions are involved, we substitute this value for one or both of the r's between means and variates called for by formula (211).

If the width of intervals differs for different parts of the distribution, we must actually compute the σ of the means or of the index values. But, if the intervals are either known to be equal or may be assumed to be equally spaced and if we assume a certain known type of distribution, then the r's may be tabled once for all. Thereafter, knowing the number of categories into which the distributions are divided, it is only necessary to refer to such a table to obtain the r's required for the denominator of the fraction in formula (211). We shall give such table below. Because sometimes the number of categories is the same

TABLE XXXIII.—COEFFICIENTS OF CORRELATION BETWEEN VARIATES AND MEANS OR INDEX VALUES

No. of categories	Between means and variates, normal distribution		Between index values and variates, normal distribution		Between either means or index values, rectangular distribution	
	$r_{xx'}$	$r^2_{xx'}$	$r_{xx'}$	$r^2_{xx'}$	$r_{xx'}$	$r^2_{xx'}$
2	.798	.637	.816	.667	.866	.750
3	.859	.738	.859	.737	.943	.889
4	.915	.837	.916	.839	.968	.938
5	.943	.890	.943	.891	.980	.960
6	.959	.921	.960	.923	.986	.972
7	.970	.940	.970	.941	.990	.980
8	.976	.953	.977	.955	.992	.984
9	.981	.963	.982	.964	.993	.987
10	.985	.969	.985	.970	.995	.990
11	.987	.974	.988	.976	.996	.992
12	.989	.979	.990	.980	.996	.993
13	.991	.982	.991	.983	.997	.994
14	.992	.984	.992	.985	.997	.995
15	.993	.986	.994	.987	.998	.996

in both distributions and sometimes different, we shall give both r and r^2, the r^2 being needed in the former case and the product of two different r's in the latter. The r's for means were computed by formula (212), using a range of six sigmas along the base line. Those for index values were computed by formula

(214), and those for rectangular distributions by formula (215). The reader will note with interest, and perhaps surprise, the extremely close parallelism between the r's for means and variates and those for index values and variates.

We shall now return to the correction for broad categories of the C we computed for the Burgess and Cottrell data. An examination of the correlation table on page 415 reveals a very peculiar distribution. Certainly it is not a normal distribution, and neither is it rectangular. It is somewhat triangular in shape. Since we have no ready-made formula for correction in the case of triangular distributions, we would not be far amiss by viewing it as approximately the same shape as one-half of a normal distribution. If the regression between means and variates in a normal distribution is rectilinear, as we have been assuming, the slope of the regression line will be the same for the lower half as for the whole distribution. We shall therefore do well enough by using the correction for a normal distribution, provided we treat the number of categories as eight rather than four. Referring to the table for the r between means and variates in case of eight categories, we have

$$r = \frac{.25}{.953} = .262$$

If we had treated the distribution as rectangular, with four divisions, our result would not be very different; we should have been required to divide the .25 by .938 and should have obtained .266.

QUANTITATIVE VARIATES, UNEQUALLY SPACED INTERVALS

The type of situation to which we next wish to apply a correlation technique is one in which we may plausibly think of the variates as quantitative in nature but in which we have insufficient reason to believe the intervals into which the distributions are divided are of uniform length. In addition the number of categories is likely to be rather small, so that correction for broad categories is needed. As a concrete illustration of this type of problem we shall use part of an investigation by Fred F. Lininger on the relation of milk drinking to various types of physical and mental growth. The correlation table below shows on the X axis three categories for amount of milk consumed while on the Y axis are laid off amounts of gain in weight during the school year. The study was conducted in the public schools of Philadelphia.

TABLE XXXIV.—EXTENT OF CONSUMPTION OF MILK IN RELATION TO GAIN IN WEIGHT

Gain in weight, lb.	No milk	Milk at home only	Milk at home and school	Total	Per-cent-age	Location of mean
	f	f	f	f		
Over 6	9	69	62	140	8.8	+1.815
4–6	64	242	227	533	33.1	+0.698
1–3	153	364	281	798	49.6	−0.474
0–0.99	29	48	25	102	6.3	−1.637
Loss..........	13	16	6	35	2.2	−2.386
Totals........	268	739	601	1,608		
Percentage.....	16.7	46.0	37.4			
Mean..........	−1.498	−0.280	+1.013			

We cannot consider the distance from the central point of "no milk" to "milk at home only" one step and that from "milk at home only" to "milk at home and school" another step of the same length. We do not know at all the relative lengths of these steps. In order to get some quantitative index for these distances, we must make some assumption about the nature of our distributions. It does not seem unreasonable to assume a normal distribution of children in respect to the amount of milk consumed by them. Since in this distribution we know the proportion of cases in each of the three categories, we can find the distance of the mean of each of the sectors from the mean of the distribution as a whole by a method discussed under our treatment of the normal curve, page 290. If the distance from the mean of the sector to the mean of the whole distribution be designated as x, the height of the bounding ordinate at the left of the sector by z_1, and the height of the bounding ordinate at the right of the sector by z_2, then

$$x = \frac{z_1 - z_2}{\text{area}}$$

In the sector on "milk at home and school" $z_1 = 0.3789$ as given in the table, page 481, for a q of .374. Here z_2 is zero, because this sector extends to the upper end of the distribution. Hence

$$x_1 = \frac{0.3789 - 0}{.374} = 1.013$$

For the middle sector $z_1 = 0.2502$, as shown in the table for a q of .167, and $z_2 = 0.3789$ as before. Hence the mean of this middle sector lies at a distance from the mean of the whole distribution

$$x_2 = \frac{0.2502 - 0.3789}{.460} = -0.280$$

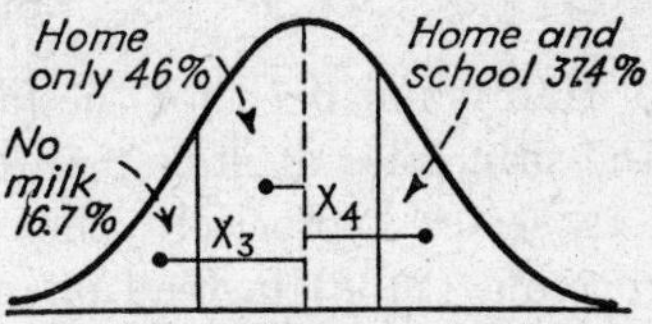

Fig. 31.

In a similar manner the other x value, and all the y values are found.

We now compute the coefficient of correlation in precisely the same manner as a Pearson r for any other correlation table. The procedure does not differ at all from that described in Chap. IV. As the result we get

$$r = \frac{\Sigma xy}{N\sigma_x\sigma_y} = \frac{217.08}{1608(.890)(.923)} = .164$$

But this r stands in considerable need of correction for broad categories, especially in respect to the x variable where there are only three categories. To make this correction, we need to divide the obtained r by the product of the r's between means and variates as indicated in formula (212)—for we have been working with our data centered about means of intervals rather than about index values. We shall forego looking in our table of these r values, page 398, because the intervals may not be sufficiently equally spaced. According to formula (212):

$$r_{xx'} = \frac{\sigma_x}{\sigma_{x'}} \text{ and } r_{yy'} = \frac{\sigma_y}{\sigma_{y'}}$$

We have already computed σ_x and σ_y; they are the standard deviations of the means obtained in connection with our solution above. Since we have assumed a normal distribution and are working with proportions with the aid of our integral tables, the standard deviation of the variates will be 1 in each of the distributions—for our table upon which we drew for x and z values is based on the assumption of unit area and unit standard deviation.   Therefore

$$r_{xx'} = \frac{\sigma_x}{1} = \sigma_x = .890; \text{ and } r_{yy'} = \frac{\sigma_y}{1} = \sigma_y = .923$$

Our corrected r then becomes

$$_cr = \frac{.164}{(.890)(.923)} = .200$$

Had it not been for the fact that we wished to illustrate fully the principles at stake, we could have saved several steps, and yet secured precisely the same result, by applying directly formula (213*a*) instead of proceeding by way of formulas (211) and (212).

If we had assumed our intervals equal in span and had obtained our values from Table XXXIII for the r's between means and variates, we would have had

$$_cr = \frac{.614}{(.859)(.943)} = .202$$

But this closeness of approximation is somewhat accidental; unless the intervals are actually spaced equally, we would not always come as near the correct value by using the table.

Exercises

1. By dividing the students in Table IV into those "high" in general intelligence (score 100 or above) and those "low" in this function (below 100), compute a biserial r between intelligence-test standings and grade-point averages.   Compare this with the Pearson product moment r.   Compute the P.E. of the product moment r and compare it with the P.E. of the biserial r.

2. By dividing both distributions at some convenient point, compute tetrachoric r for the same two factors as in Exercise 1, and compare with the two r's computed in Exercise 1.   Compute the P.E. of this r.

3. Compute this r from broad categories; *i.e.*, group the intelligence scores into, say, four intervals and grade-point averages into five, determine r, and correct it for broad categories.

4. Compute an r for the Burgess and Cottrell data on page 415 by the methods described on pages 391 to 393.

5. Out of a total population of 475 college seniors, 71 were selected by a guess who test as most outstanding in social leadership and another 69 as least effective in social leadership.   Of the high ones 27 had taken more than six credit hours of history and 44 had taken 6 hr. or less, whereas of the low ones 14 had taken more than 6 hr. and 55 less.   Compute the coefficient of correlation between amount of history taken and effectiveness in social leadership.   Of these same students 26 of the high and 34 of the low had taken more than 6 hr. of physical science while 45 of the high and 35 of the low had taken less.   Compute a similar r between extent of study of physical science and leadership.

References for Further Reading

EZEKIEL, MORDICAI: "The Determination of Curvilinear Regression Surfaces in the Presence of Other Variables," *J. Amer. Statistical Assoc.*, Vol. 21, pp. 310–320.

HARRIS, J. A., and A. E. TROLOAR: "On a Limitation in the Applicability of the Contingency Coefficient," *J. Amer. Statistical Assoc.*, Vol. 22, pp. 460–473; Vol. 24, pp. 367–375.

KELLEY, T. L.: *Statistical Method*, The Macmillan Company, 1923, pp. 196–278.

PEARSON, EGON S.: "The Probable Error of a Class Index Correlation," *Biometrika*, Vol. 14, pp. 261–280.

RANDO, T.: "Standard Error of the Mean Square Contingency," *Biometrika*, Vol. 21, pp. 376–428.

SOPER, H. E.: "The Probable Error of the Bi-serial Expression for the Coefficient of Correlation," *Biometrika*, Vol. 14, pp. 261–280.

SYMONDS, PERCIVAL M.: "Comparison of Statistical Measures of Overlapping, with Charts for Estimating the Value of Bi-serial r," *J. Educ. Psychol.*, Vol. 21, pp. 586–596.

CHAPTER XIV

CHI SQUARE

THE NATURE OF χ^2

In recent years a great deal of attention has been given the χ^2 test developed by Pearson.[1] The situations to which this test may be applied are of the type where we have both theoretical and observed measures and wish to know whether differences between these measures can reasonably be regarded as chance variations. Provided the true variance within each class can be known or estimated, the χ^2 technique can be applied to a number of different types of problem to measure the probability of getting a given divergence in a sample from corresponding theoretical values in the parent population. One use is the testing of fit of a normal curve to the sample population; and it can be applied to all forms of curve fitting where we can know the distribution of the classes to the means of which we are attempting to fit the curve. Another important application is to test for association between variates in a contingency table.

In general, if x is a value in the form of a deviation from the mean of the whole population of its class and, in the infinite population, the variates are normally distributed, then χ^2 is defined by the relation

$$\chi^2 = \frac{\Sigma x^2}{\tilde{\sigma}_x^2}$$

where $\tilde{\sigma}_x^2$ is the true population variance of the class. The x may be a single measure, or it may be the mean of a sample, or a proportion, or any other statistic normally distributed. It is evident that χ^2 is related to s^2, the variance of the set of n statistics; for, if the deviations are taken from the population mean of each class and are summed through the set, $\Sigma x^2 = ns^2$.

---

[1] PEARSON, KARL, "On the Criterion that a Given System of Deviations . . . Can Be Reasonably Supposed to Have Arisen from Random Sampling," *Phil. Mag. (London)*, Vol. 50, pp. 157–175 (1900).

Hence, if the $\tilde{\sigma}_x^2$ is the same for all the classes of which χ^2 is made up,

$$\chi^2 = \frac{\Sigma x^2}{\tilde{\sigma}_x^2} = \frac{ns^2}{\tilde{\sigma}_x^2}$$

In this chapter our interest is in the distribution of χ^2 from samples. $\tilde{\sigma}_x^2$ will always be the same for a given population. But if the null hypothesis is assumed (that each class is a random sample from the same homogeneous population), s^2 is an unbiased estimate of $\tilde{\sigma}^2$. Therefore, the ratio $s^2/\tilde{\sigma}_x^2$ will sometimes be less than 1 and sometimes greater; as the sample is increased in size, s^2 will approach $\tilde{\sigma}_x^2$, and χ^2 will approach n. For certain purposes which will appear later, we need to know the shape of the χ distribution and its area between certain ordinates. It may be said at once that this distribution is *not* that of the normal curve, except in one special case.

Suppose, now we consider our x's one at a time. Then each χ^2 will be merely $x^2/\tilde{\sigma}_x^2$. The probability of getting a χ^2 of any particular value will be the same as the probability of getting an $x^2/\tilde{\sigma}_x^2$ of that same value. If we write z_1^2 to denote this value of $x^2/\tilde{\sigma}_x^2$, the probability that a value z_1 will lie within an elemental range dz_1 would be merely

$$df = \frac{1}{\sqrt{2\pi}} e^{-\frac{z_1^2}{2}} dz_1$$

The probability of getting a χ *as great as, or greater than,* a given value would be the integral of the (normal) distribution function, *viz.*,

$$P = \int_{z_1}^{\infty} \frac{1}{\sqrt{2\pi}} e^{-\frac{z_1^2}{2}} dz_1$$

the value of which can be found in the normal probability tables.

Let us now deal with the probability of getting two given independent values of χ simultaneously. That probability is the product of the two probabilities of getting them separately. Hence the probability that these two variates will occur conjointly within the same cell (elemental area) $dz_1 dz_2$ becomes

$$df = \left(\frac{1}{\sqrt{2\pi}} e^{-\frac{z_1^2}{2}} dz_1\right)\left(\frac{1}{\sqrt{2\pi}} e^{-\frac{z_2^2}{2}} dz_2\right) = \left(\frac{1}{\sqrt{2\pi}}\right)^2 e^{-\frac{1}{2}(z_1^2 + z_2^2)} dz_1 dz_2$$

and the probability of getting simultaneously, in an infinite supply of samples, values as great as, or greater than, these two would be

$$(A) \qquad P = \int_{z_1}^{\infty} \int_{z_2}^{\infty} \left(\frac{1}{\sqrt{2\pi}} \right)^2 e^{-\frac{1}{2}(z_1^2 + z_2^2)} dz_1 dz_2$$

If we write $\chi^2 = z_1^2 + z_2^2$ and concern ourselves with the problem of calculating this probability, we are confronted with the fact that the value of χ^2 may be the same although z_1 and z_2

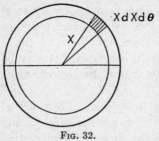

FIG. 32.

may vary from sample to sample. We have here the equation of a circle, center at the origin, with a radius equal to χ, so that the elemental area representing the joint probability may be in any position on an elemental circular region of χ as a radius. In order to state this fact more exactly and to evaluate the double integral, it is convenient to resort to polar coordinates (Fig. 32).

The elemental area $dz_1 dz_2$ becomes[1] in polar coordinates $\chi \, d\chi \, d\theta$. Substituting χ^2 for $z_1^2 + z_2^2$ and $\chi \, d\chi \, d\theta$ for $dz_1 dz_2$ above, we have

$$df = \left(\frac{1}{\sqrt{2\pi}} \right)^2 e^{-\frac{1}{2}\chi^2} \chi \, d\chi \, d\theta$$

If we denote by df the total probability of the occurrence of χ within the circular region, we must integrate the above expression with respect to θ from 0 to 2π. Integrating with respect to θ, noting that $\left(\frac{1}{\sqrt{2\pi}} \right) \chi e^{-\frac{1}{2}\chi^2} d\chi$ remains constant,

$$df = \left(\frac{1}{\sqrt{2\pi}} \right)^2 \chi e^{-\frac{1}{2}\chi^2} d\chi \left[\theta \right]_0^{2\pi}$$

or,

$$(B) \qquad df = \left(\frac{1}{\sqrt{2\pi}} \right)^2 \chi e^{-\frac{\chi^2}{2}} d\chi (2\pi) = \chi e^{-\frac{\chi^2}{2}} d\chi$$

[1] See KENNEY, J. F., *Mathematics of Statistics*, Part II, p. 37, for a simple statement of the reason for this.

The probability of obtaining a value of χ as great as or greater than a given χ_1 would be expressed by

$$P = \int_{\chi_1}^{\infty} \chi e^{-\frac{\chi^2}{2}} d\chi$$

This last integral is of the form $e^v dv$ (see page 24) and may be integrated directly. Performing this integration, we have

$$P = \left[-e^{-\frac{\chi^2}{2}} \right]_{\chi_1}^{\infty}$$

or,

(C) $$P = e^{-\frac{\chi_1^2}{2}}$$

For a given value of χ *obtained from two independent values of x,* we could calculate P from this formula. Thus if $\chi_1 = 1$, we would obtain, upon substituting in formula (C),

$$P = e^{-\frac{(1)^2}{2}} = \frac{1}{\sqrt{e}} = \frac{1}{\sqrt{2.718}} = .6065$$

This tells us that the chances are slightly more than 60 in 100 that we would obtain at random a value of χ as great as, or greater than, 1 when the value of χ^2 is made up of the sum of the squares of two *independent* variates.

If we are concerned with the probability of the simultaneous occurrence of three independent values of x, we would have a triple integral corresponding to (A); or for n values, we would have an n-fold integral.

Formula (B) expresses the χ distribution function in the case of *two* independent variates—the two independent quantities, distributed normally about zero, that make up χ^2. It will be noticed that the exponent of χ in this same formula is 1—one less than the number of independent variates. If we were to go through a similar process for *three* independent variates z_1, z_2, z_3, we would arrive at the formula

$$df = k\chi^2 e^{-\frac{1}{2}\chi^2} d\chi$$

in which k is a constant, and the exponent of the χ factor is 2. In this situation χ may be interpreted as the radius of a sphere, and the elemental region as a spherical shell of thickness $d\chi$.

When the number of independent variates exceeds three, it becomes impossible to visualize the meaning of the probability of χ within an elemental region, and we say that we are dealing with the geometry of hyperspace. The mathematics, although more complicated, is carried out in a manner analogous to that which we have already developed above, and we are able to obtain the general formula for the distribution of χ. When χ^2 is defined by the equation

$$\chi^2 = z_1^2 + z_2^2 + z_3^2 + \cdots z_n^2$$

the element for the distribution of χ becomes

$$(D) \qquad\qquad df = k\chi^{n-1}e^{-\frac{\chi^2}{2}}d\chi$$

in which k is a constant determined mathematically to be

$$\frac{1}{\dfrac{n-2}{2}!2^{\frac{n-2}{2}}}$$

Notice again that the exponent of χ is $(n-1)$—one less than the number of *independent variates* that went to make up the quantity χ^2. Formula (D) is the χ distribution equation, corresponding in concept to the normal probability equation. One difference that should be pointed out is that the χ equation is a function of n as well as of χ, whereas the normal equation is a function of x alone. This is because the normal probability function is a special form of the χ function resulting when $n = 1$, as may be seen by putting $n = 1$ in formula (D).

Suppose, now, in a two-variable problem our operation were so restricted that $(x_1 + x_2)$ would need to sum to a fixed amount. Then when we had the probability of getting either x_1 or x_2, that of getting the remaining one would be exactly the same. There would be only one degree of freedom instead of two. If there were n values, but so limited that they had to sum to a fixed amount, then the probability of getting a certain value for the set of n would be exactly the same as the probability of getting the appropriate value for the $(n - 1)$ independent ones. There would be, *i.e.*, $(n - 1)$ degrees of freedom from which the probability would be determined. Thus, for every restriction that brings it about that a remaining term is determined when the

others are known, the number of degrees of freedom is reduced
by 1. So the multiplicity of the integral is not n, the total
number of terms, but $(n - a)$ where a is the number determined
when the others are given.

Thus in principle it would be simple enough to determine what
is the probability of getting a χ value as great as or greater than a
given value; we would need only to integrate the product normal
probability function as many times successively as we have
degrees of freedom from the several indicated limits to infinity.
But in practice this would be an impossibly arduous task and
would be wholly impractical as a procedure. By resorting to
generalized polar coordinates the evaluation becomes a perfectly
straightforward task and may be carried out by integrating
successively by parts, care being taken to consider separately the
cases when n is even and when n is odd. Since the task is long
and tedious we shall leave it to the ambitious student as an exercise and simply write down the resulting formulas.

When n is even, the expression for the probability of obtaining
by random sampling a value of χ equal to or exceeding a given
value is found to be

$$P = e^{-\frac{\chi^2}{2}}\left[1 + \left(\frac{1}{2}\chi^2\right) + \frac{1}{2!}\left(\frac{1}{2}\chi^2\right)^2 + \cdots \right.$$
$$\left. + \frac{1}{[(n-2)/2]!}\left(\frac{1}{2}\chi^2\right)^{\frac{n-2}{2}}\right] \quad (216)$$

When n is odd,

$$P = \sqrt{\frac{2}{\pi}}\int_\chi^\infty e^{-\frac{\chi^2}{2}}d\chi + \sqrt{\frac{2}{\pi}}e^{-\frac{\chi^2}{2}}\left[\chi + \frac{1}{3}\chi^3 + \frac{1}{3\cdot5}\chi^5 + \cdots \right.$$
$$\left. + \frac{1}{3\cdot5\cdots(n-2)}\chi^{n-2}\right] \quad (217)$$

As soon as χ is known either Eq. (216) or (217) can be evaluated
after substitution and the value of P discovered. Even this is
too complicated to use in practice, so Elderton, working with
Pearson, tabled its values. Since the distribution is different
for different n's, the values are given not only for different χ^2's
but also for different n's. We give Elderton's table on pages 498
to 500. Later Fisher also tabled the χ^2 values in a different
form; and still later Kelley and others also did so.

THE COMPUTATION AND USE OF χ^2

Now that we have given the χ distribution and have shown how the formulas for P are obtained, we proceed to show how the value of χ^2 is found in practice and how the χ^2 test may be applied. We saw that the probability of obtaining together values of z_1 and z_2 within the cell $dz_1 dz_2$ is expressed by the quantity $\left(\dfrac{1}{\sqrt{2\pi}}\right)^2 e^{-\frac{1}{2}(z_1^2 + z_2^2)} dz_1 dz_2$ when the two variates are assumed to be distributed normally about zero and are uncorrelated. In the more general case where z_1 and z_2 may be correlated, the product function would be, as shown on page 368, the following:

$$ dz = z_0 e^{-\frac{1}{2}\left[\frac{1}{1-r_{12}^2}\left(\frac{x_1^2}{\sigma_1^2} + \frac{x_2^2}{\sigma_2^2} - 2r_{12}\frac{x_1 x_2}{\sigma_1 \sigma_2}\right)\right]} dx_1 dx_2 $$

For the generalized case (n large and correlation present) Pearson gives the formula

$$ z = z_0 e^{-\frac{1}{2}\left(\sum \frac{\Delta_{pp}}{\Delta}\frac{x_p^2}{\sigma_p^2} + 2\sum \frac{\Delta_{pq}}{\Delta}\frac{x_p}{\sigma_q}\frac{x_q}{\sigma_q}\right)} \tag{218} $$

in which z_0 is a constant and the expression in parentheses involves the summation of terms containing correlation determinants and the n variates and standard deviations, the first term to be summed for all values of p from 1 to n, and the second for all pairs of values of p and q in which p is less than q. Pearson defines the quantity within parentheses to be χ^2 and proceeds to show in his mathematical development that for the type of application most frequently made of χ^2, this complicated quantity can be expressed in terms of weighted squared deviations between theoretical and observed frequencies. The proof is so complicated that we do not deem it advisable to include it here. The formula for χ^2 in terms of theoretical and observed frequencies is

$$ \chi^2 = \sum \frac{(f_o - f_t)^2}{f_t} \qquad \text{(Chi square for goodness of fit of observed to theoretical frequencies)} \tag{219} $$

in which f_o and f_t are the observed and theoretical frequencies, respectively, in each group, and the summation extends over all groups.

In practice we have only to compute χ^2 from formula (219), to make certain of the *number of independent variates* (degrees of freedom) that contributed to its value, and to determine from tables the probability of getting a value as large or larger on the basis of random sampling. Let us now consider a dice-throwing experiment in order to make more concrete the meaning of P by using a very simple illustration.

The authors threw 12 dice in a group 14 times and recorded the number of aces appearing in each throwing. Assuming the dice to be balanced perfectly, we should expect theoretically two aces to appear at each throwing; but, of course, this perfect record was not obtained because of the influence of chance or other factors. There were differences between observed frequencies and those to be expected theoretically; and the question arose as to whether these differences were so great as to lead us to believe that the dice were biased. The actual number of aces appearing among the 12 dice at each throwing (f_o), the theoretical number expected (f_t), the deviations between observed and theoretical frequencies $(f_o - f_t)$, these deviations squared $(f_o - f_t)^2$, and the weighted squared deviations $(f_o - f_t)^2/f_t$ are shown in Table XXXV.

TABLE XXXV.—NUMBER OF ACES APPEARING AMONG 12 DICE IN 14 THROWINGS

No. of aces appearing at each throw (f_o)	Theoretical No. of aces expected at each throw (f_t)	Deviations between theoretical and observed $(f_o - f_t)$	Deviations squared $(f_o - f_t)^2$	Squared deviations weighted $\dfrac{(f_o - f_t)^2}{f_t}$
1	2	−1	1	$\frac{1}{2}$
3	2	1	1	$\frac{1}{2}$
2	2	0	0	0
3	2	1	1	$\frac{1}{2}$
1	2	−1	1	$\frac{1}{2}$
4	2	2	4	2
2	2	0	0	0
4	2	2	4	2
1	2	−1	1	$\frac{1}{2}$
0	2	−2	4	2
3	2	1	1	$\frac{1}{2}$
2	2	0	0	0
3	2	1	1	$\frac{1}{2}$
1	2	−1	1	$\frac{1}{2}$
30	28	2		$\chi^2 = 10$

The value of χ^2 is seen to be 10, made up from the 14 *independent variates* or deviations. Entering the tables with a $\chi^2 = 10$ and $n = 14$ (14 is the number of independent variates or degrees of freedom), we find that $P = .762$. This means that we should expect to find a value of χ^2 equal to or greater than 10 in more than 76 out of 100 cases on the basis of chance, and this probability is so large that we do not have reason to believe that the dice were biased.

Degrees of Freedom.—At this point it might be well to make further mention of the meaning of *degrees of freedom* or *number of independent variates*. In the dice-throwing experiment the number of aces appearing in any of the 14 groups was *independent* of the frequency in any of the other groups. Hence we must take $n = 14$ when entering the tables to find P. In the examples that are to follow, we shall see that the number of independent variates or degrees of freedom is not necessarily the same as the number of groups used in the computation of χ^2. If, for example, we had ten groupings of deviations between observed and theoretical frequencies and *the total number of frequencies was the same in each sample*, there would be only *nine* independent variates or degrees of freedom since the tenth group contribution could be found by subtracting the total of nine groups from the grand total.

How many degrees of freedom obtain in a given application of χ^2 depends upon what sort of universe of samples one has in mind. If, in a contingency table, one is asking his question about the sampling fluctuation in that set of samples in which the marginal totals remain the same sample after sample, there are $(k - 1)(r - 1)$ degrees of freedom, where k is the number of columns and r is the number of rows, because the necessity of constant totals for each row and for each column restricts the fluctuation in each column to $(k - 1)$ cells and in each row to $(r - 1)$ cells. It was upon this interpretation that Fisher fastened in his epoch-making article.[1] It was only that limitation which made exact mathematical treatment possible, since Pearson's original development hinged upon known theoretical values, which could only be afforded in a sampling scheme if the marginal totals remained the same for the whole supply of

[1] FISHER, R. A., "On the Interpretation of χ^2 from Contingency Tables," *J. Royal Statistical Society*, Vol. 85, pp. 87–94 (1922).

samples and hence was the same as that of the population
sampled. But one may, and in most practical research would,
wish to ask his question about the sampling fluctuation in *all*
random samples of the same N, not only in that small portion
of samples in which the marginal totals remain constant. In
our illustration of Table XXXVII, for example, the normal
expectation is that neither the relative numbers taking graduate
work, college, etc., nor the numbers in the various categories of
marriage adjustment would remain the same in successive samples, but that these marginal totals would fluctuate from sample
to sample as well as the frequencies in the several cells, the total
population of the whole sample alone being fixed. Here it
would be only the nth cell that could be filled in from a priori
knowledge, and the number of degrees of freedom would be
$(n' - 1)$ instead of $(k - 1)(r - 1)$. In a relatively recent
article Karl Pearson[1] has shown very clearly and convincingly
that the number of degrees of freedom for this interpretation is
$(n' - 1)$, even though the theoretical values are estimated from
the sample. He presents conclusive experimental evidence
that the χ'^2's thus obtained have very closely the same mean
and very nearly the same standard deviation as the χ^2's obtained
from known theoretical values and that the correlation between
χ'^2 and χ^2 in a number of trials is very high—from .93 to .99.
Thus the number of degrees of freedom must depend upon one's
meaning: if he is talking about the general case in which the
samples may vary in every respect except N, the number of
degrees of freedom is $(n' - 1)$, where N is the total population
and n' is the total number of cells; if he is talking about the
special case in which the marginal totals are to remain constant
through all the samples, the number of degrees of freedom is
$(k - 1)(r - 1)$. In most statistical work this distinction has
been ignored; workers have followed for all purposes Fisher's
lead in using $(k - 1)(r - 1)$ indiscriminatingly. Since that is
now the established custom, we shall follow it here in our illustrations in order to avoid confusion. But careful workers should
make and apply the indicated distinction. In the article referred
to, Pearson shows that the same principle applies in fitting an
empirical distribution to the normal curve. If one fits a curve

[1] PEARSON, KARL, "Experimental Discussion of the (χ^2, p) Test for Goodness of Fit," *Biometrika*, Vol. 24, pp. 351–381 (1932).

by using the mean and the standard deviation as well as the N, the number of degrees of freedom is $(n' - 3)$ if he is talking about a succession of samples of N, *all of which have the same mean and the same standard deviation* as the initial one. If he is not imposing that restriction and instead is talking about the general case where only N remains constant, the number of degrees of freedom is $(n' - 1)$ regardless of the fact that two additional statistics of the sample were employed in the fitting. This latter procedure is the one now most frequently followed in American practice, though a few workers have used the former.

EXAMPLES OF THE χ^2 TEST APPLIED TO CONTINGENCY TABLES

Table XXXVI gives by nationalities the number of foreign-born males twenty-one years of age or over who have been naturalized in a certain district, together with the theoretical number to be expected in terms of percentages of the total number naturalized.

TABLE XXXVI.—NUMBER OF FOREIGN-BORN MALES TWENTY-ONE YEARS OF AGE OR OVER, NATURALIZED

	Italians	Russians	Polish	Others	Total
Number naturalized.......	161	82	20	32	295
Theoretical number........	(183)	(58)	(26)	(28)	(295)
Total number in district....	366	116	52	54	588

The numbers in parentheses were obtained by taking percentages of the total number naturalized for each nationality group. $(\frac{366}{588})(295)$ gives 183, the number of Italians expected to be naturalized in the district on the basis of nationality representation. $(\frac{116}{588})(295)$ gives 58, the number expected for the Russian group. In a similar fashion the other theoretical frequencies in parentheses were obtained.

In order to compute the value of χ^2, we must use the formula $\chi^2 = \Sigma(f_o - f_t)^2/f_t$. The data for this purpose are as follows:

$(f_o - f_t)$	-22	24	-6	4	χ^2
$(f_o - f_t)^2$	484	576	36	16	
$\dfrac{(f_o - f_t)^2}{f_t}$	2.64	9.93	1.38	.57	14.52

$$n = 3$$

We have, therefore, that $\chi^2 = 14.52$. Since the frequency for the group marked Others can be obtained by subtracting the total for the three other nationality groups, we have here only *three independent variates* or *degrees of* freedom. Entering the chi-square probability tables with $n = 3$ and $\chi^2 = 14.52$, we obtain by interpolation between 14 and 15, $P = .002$. This probability is too small to conclude that the differences among the nationality groups in the proportion naturalized can be explained as having arisen from errors of random sampling. We conclude, therefore, that there are other factors operating to account for the differences.

Another example might be to test whether there is association between marriage adjustment and the amount of education possessed by the individual. Table XXXVII displays the observed frequencies of marriage-adjustment scores for 513 husbands according to education.[1]

TABLE XXXVII.—DISTRIBUTION OF MARRIAGE-ADJUSTMENT SCORES AT DIFFERENT EDUCATIONAL LEVELS[1]

Education	Marriage-adjustment score in relation to husbands' education				Totals
	Very low	Low	High	Very high	
Graduate work..........	4 (11.9)	9 (17.8)	38 (29.8)	54 (45.5)	105
College................	20 (23.1)	31 (34.6)	55 (57.9)	99 (89.4)	205
High school............	23 (17.2)	37 (25.8)	41 (42.9)	51 (66.1)	152
Grades only............	11 (5.8)	10 (8.6)	11 (14.4)	19 (22.2)	51
Totals................	58	87	145	223	513

[1] Adapted from Burgess and Cottrell.

Of the 513 husbands tested 105 had engaged in graduate work; and of these 4 received "very low" marriage-adjustment scores, 9 "low," etc. The theoretical number to be expected in each cell is given in parentheses. For example, (11.9) is the theoretical frequency of "very low" scores for husbands having had graduate work. The theoretical frequencies for each cell are obtained by first computing the probability for each cell and then multiplying by the total number. Since there are 105 scores in the first row,

[1] BURGESS, ERNEST W., and COTTRELL, LEONARD S., JR., "The Prediction of Adjustment in Marriage," *Amer. Sociol. Rev.*, October, 1936, p. 748.

we take as the probability of obtaining a score in that row $\frac{105}{513}$. The probability that a score will lie in the first column is taken as $\frac{58}{513}$. The probability that a score will lie in the first row and the first column—the upper left-hand cell—will then be the product of these probabilities or $(\frac{105}{513})(\frac{58}{513})$. To obtain the number of frequencies to be expected in that cell, we must multiply the probability by the total number 513. We have $(\frac{105}{513})(\frac{58}{513})(513) = (11.9)$. The other theoretical frequencies in parentheses are found in a similar manner.

Let us now determine χ^2 for the contingency table dealing with the relationship of marriage-adjustment scores and husbands' education. Here there are four columns (Very low, Low, High, and Very high) and four rows (Graduate work, College, High school, and Grades only). Since from the marginal totals we are able to compute the fourth row or column, knowing the three others, we have $(4 - 1)(4 - 1) = (3)(3) = 9$ degrees of freedom, if we are making the customary interpretation that the marginal totals remain fixed.

The theoretical frequencies for each cell have already been calculated and are found in parentheses in Table XXXVII. We now display in Table XXXVIII the deviations between theoretical and actual frequencies and the weighted squared deviations for each cell.

TABLE XXXVIII.—DEVIATIONS BETWEEN THEORETICAL AND OBSERVED FREQUENCIES $|f_o - f_t|$ AND WEIGHTED SQUARED DEVIATIONS $\frac{(f_o - f_t)^2}{f_t}$ FOR THE CONTINGENCY TABLE XXXVII

Education	Marriage-adjustment scores in relation to husbands' education				Totals
	Very low	Low	High	Very high	
Graduate work	7.9 (5.3)	8.8 (4.3)	8.2 (2.5)	8.5 (1.7)	(13.8)
College	3.1 (0.4)	3.6 (0.3)	2.9 (0.1)	9.6 (1.0)	(1.8)
High school	5.8 (1.9)	11.2 (4.8)	1.9 (0.1)	15.1 (4.3)	(11.1)
Grades only	5.2 4.6)	1.4 (0.2)	3.4 (0.8)	3.2 (4.6)	(10.2)
Totals	(12.2)	(9.6)	(3.5)	(11.6)	(36.9)

The numbers given in parentheses are the squared deviations divided by the theoretical frequencies for the cells. In the upper left-hand cell, for example, we have

$$(f_o - f_t) = 4 - 11.9 = -7.9$$

the deviation, and $(f_o - f_t)^2/f_t = (-7.9)^2/11.9 = (5.3)$, the weighted squared deviation. The other numbers in parentheses are computed in the same way. The number (36.9) appearing in the lower right-hand corner of the table is the sum of all the squared deviations weighted for the theoretical frequencies and is, therefore, our value of χ^2. We enter the tables with $\chi^2 = 36.9$ and $n = 9$ and find that $P = .000142$. This value of P is so small that we cannot attribute the differences to errors in sampling, but must believe there is an association between marriage adjustment and husbands' education.

Let us now apply the χ^2 test to the normal-curve graduation data for the 149 sophomore scores on the Carnegie Foundation Tests, 1930, found in Table XXV. The differences between the theoretical curve and the histogram shown in Fig. 21 reveal that in some intervals the curve calls for greater frequency and in other intervals less frequency than actually exists in our data. The question naturally arises as to what extent the superimposed curve truly represents the data in question. The χ^2 test works very well in testing goodness of fit; for, if the probability is so large that we may obtain on the basis of chance a value of χ^2 as large as, or larger than, the one in hand, we may reasonably conclude that the fit is a good one. On the other hand, if the probability is small, we are unable to account for the difference on the basis of chance fluctuation and must conclude that the curve is not representative of our data.

The chi-square technique is not sound unless the numbers in the cells are reasonably large.[1] For this reason it is customarily advised that cells with small frequencies be combined. Since the upper 3 and the lower 3 intervals of Table XXIV contain ten or fewer theoretical frequencies, we have lumped these extreme tails into 2 intervals, making 8 intervals for our data instead of 12. The theoretical frequencies of the intervals are determined in terms of the normal-curve function and the N of this sample, as shown on page 418. The parameters in terms of which this sample is fitted to the normal curve are $N = 149$, mean $= 215.4$, and $\sigma = 50.9$.

[1] See KENNEY, *op. cit.*, p. 170, for a simple statement of the reason for this.

TABLE XXXIX.—THE COMPUTATION OF χ^2 FOR THE NORMAL-CURVE
GRADUATION OF TABLE XXIV

Interval	Frequencies		$(f_o - f_t)$	$(f_o - f_t)^2$	$\dfrac{(f_o - f_t)^2}{f_t}$
	f_o	f_t			
279.5–339.5	16	14	2	4	.29
259.5–279.5	12	14	−2	4	.29
239.5–259.5	19	19	0	0	.00
219.5–239.5	26	23	3	9	.39
199.5–219.5	22	24	−2	4	.17
179.5–199.5	18	20	−2	4	.20
159.5–179.5	14	16	−2	4	.25
99.5–159.5	22	19	3	9	.47
Totals.............	149	149	0.00	..	$\chi^2 = 2.06$

The χ^2 is 2.06. We next wish to know the probability that
so large a χ^2 could arise from this type of situation merely on
the basis of chance fluctuation. With what number of degrees
of freedom shall we enter the table? The same dual interpretation is possible here as in the case of contingency tables, discussed
on page 412. If we mean how frequently would chance fluctuation give rise to a χ^2 as large as 2.06 in a sample of 149 scores when
only the size of the sample remains constant, the number of
degrees of freedom is $(n' - 1) = (8 - 1) = 7$. Entering Table
XLVIII with $n = 7$ and interpolating between $\chi^2 = 2$ and
$\chi^2 = 3$, we get $P = .95$. If we mean to ask about the P for that
universe of samples which continues to have, sample after sample,
the same mean and the same σ as the initial one as well as the
same N, the degrees of freedom are $(n' - 3) = (8 - 3) = 5$.
For this the P is .84. Both of these indicate a very good fit.
The former means that, even if the function were distributed
perfectly normally in the whole population, as great departure
as we obtained or greater would occur in samples 95 times in 100.
The latter means that, even in that more restricted sampling
in which the mean and the standard deviation as well as the size
of the sample remain constant, so great a discrepancy would occur
by chance 84 times in 100. We may, therefore, feel no hesitancy
in believing that the distribution would be normal except for
chance fluctuation. In fact, the fit is unnaturally good; the
most likely P for a true fit is about .50.

χ^2 VALUES OUTSIDE THE RANGE OF OUR TABLE

Our table, following Elderton, extends from $n = 2$ to $n = 29$. For $n = 1$, χ is distributed as half of a normal distribution, as shown on the opening pages of this chapter. So, for $n = 1$, look in our normal distribution table, pages 485 to 487, under $\chi = x/\sigma_x$ and obtain the percentage in the tail of the distribution, then multiply this by 2. For example, $\chi^2 = 4$; $\chi = 2$; in the table for $x/\sigma_x = 2$, $q = (.50 - .4772) = .0228$;

$$P = (2)(.0228) = .0456$$

This is the P corresponding to $\chi^2 = 4$.

For applications where n exceeds 29, Fisher has proposed that we assume that $\sqrt{2\chi^2}$ may be treated as a normal deviate about $\sqrt{2n - 1}$ as mean.[1] Example: $\chi^2 = 50$; $n = 41$; $\sqrt{82 - 1} = 9$. $\sqrt{2\chi^2} = 10$. $t = 10 - 9 = 1$. Looking in our table for

$$\frac{x}{\sigma_x} = 1$$

we find that $P = (.50 - .3413) = .1587$.

RELATIONS AMONG χ^2, F, AND z

Recall, from our opening paragraphs, that

(E) $$\chi^2 = \frac{\Sigma x^2}{\sigma_x^2} = \frac{ns^2}{\sigma_x^2}$$

i.e., the denominator must contain the true population variance. But sometimes this cannot be known and must be estimated. Then the probability of a given value for the fraction as a whole is a resultant of the probabilities of getting independently the two sample values of numerator and denominator instead of that of the numerator alone. The fact that now both numerator and denominator are sample estimates changes the shape of the distribution from that of a Pearson type III curve to a type VI curve.[2] For the ratio of the two sample variances Fisher uses

---

[1] By differentiating Eq. (D) with respect to χ, equating the derivative to zero, and solving, we find the modal value of $\sqrt{2\chi^2}$ to be $\sqrt{2n - 2}$. Because the distribution is skew, the modal value would differ somewhat from the mean value.

[2] FISHER, R. A., "The Goodness of Fit of Regression Formulae, and the

e^{2z} and Snedecor uses F, so that

$$(F) \qquad\qquad e^{2z} = F = \frac{s_1^2}{s_2^2}$$

The distribution of z or of F is found by using the product probability principle. From Eq. (E), $s_1^2 = \chi_1^2\bar{\sigma}^2/n_1$, and $s_2^2 = \chi_2^2\bar{\sigma}^2/n_2$. Then $F = (n_2\chi_1^2)/(n_1\chi_2^2)$, or $\chi_1^2 = (n_1/n_2)\chi_2^2 F$. Now using the general χ^2 distribution, we are able to write down the simultaneous distribution of χ_1^2 and χ_2^2. After writing down this complicated product function, we substitute for χ_1^2, the value $(n_1/n_2)\chi_2^2 F$, integrate for the whole range, and finally obtain the distribution

$$df = 2\frac{[(n_1 + n_2 - 2)/2]!}{\dfrac{n_1-2}{2}!\,\dfrac{n_2-2}{2}!}\, n_1^{\frac{n_1}{2}} n_2^{\frac{n_2}{2}} \frac{e^{n_1 z}dz}{(n_1 e^{2z} + n_2)^{\frac{n_1+n_2}{2}}}$$

The probability integral for the distribution of z or of F yields very complicated expressions which must be evaluated for different values of n_1 and n_2. Tables for z for the 5 per cent and the 1 per cent points of the distribution were made by Fisher for $n_1 = 1, 2, 3, 4, 5, 6, 8, 12, 24$, and ∞; and for n_2 values from 1 to 30, together with 60 and ∞. Snedecor made corresponding tables for the distribution of F.

STUDENT'S t

Student's t is defined by the relation

$$(G) \qquad\qquad t = \frac{x}{s_x}$$

where x is a deviation of a statistic from the true value in any application in which the x's may be assumed to be normally distributed and s_x is an estimate of the standard deviation of the x's made from the sample. But, from (E),

$$s_x = \frac{\chi\bar{\sigma}}{\sqrt{n}}, \text{ whence } t = \frac{x}{\chi\bar{\sigma}/\sqrt{n}} = \frac{x\sqrt{n}}{\bar{\sigma}}\cdot\frac{1}{\chi}$$

Since $\bar{\sigma}$ and $\sqrt{n}$ are constants, the distribution of t is found by first writing down the simultaneous distribution for x (normal) and for χ (as defined above), as is done in the case of the z distribution, substituting for x in terms of t, and performing the proper integration. The distribution turns out to be

$$(H) \qquad df = \frac{\dfrac{n-1}{2}\,!}{\dfrac{n-2}{2}\,!\,\sqrt{\pi n}}\left(1 + \frac{t^2}{n}\right)^{-\frac{1}{2}(n+1)} dt$$

The definition of t in Eq. (G) is more general than that with which Student himself dealt. He dealt with only the case of the mean divided by an estimate of its standard error. But Eq. (G) assumes that the distribution is general for the whole class of statistics in which deviations from the true value make a normal distribution, and Fisher has proved that this is true. The distribution of t is applicable "to all cases which can be reduced to a comparison of the deviation of a normal variate with an independently distributed estimate of its standard deviation, derived from the sums of squares of homogeneous normal deviations, either from the true mean of the distribution or from the means of samples."[1] We give tables for the probability integral of t on pages 173 and 488.

ϵ^2 IN TERMS OF F

In Chap. XI we made use of the distribution of ϵ^2 when the true η^2 is zero and cited a table we had constructed for this purpose. We shall here derive the formula upon which that table was built.

On page 333 we showed that in the sample

$$\sigma_y^2 = \sigma_c^2 + \sigma_{\bar{y}_c}^2$$

Substituting population estimates for sample values

$$\frac{N-1}{N}\,s_y^2 = \frac{N-k}{N}\,s_c^2 + \frac{k-1}{kn}\,s_m^2$$

where s_m^2 is the estimate of the population variance from the means of classes. Dividing through by $s_c^2(N-1)/N$, and remembering that $kn = N$,

$$\frac{s_y^2}{s_c^2} = \frac{N-k}{N-1} + \frac{k-1}{N-1}\cdot\frac{s_m^2}{s_c^2}$$

[1] *Metron*, Vol. 5, p. 94.

But in the case where all variances are assumed to be estimates of the same homogeneous population variance (*i.e.*, where the null hypothesis is being tested), $s_m^2/s_c^2 = F$. Therefore

$$(I) \qquad \frac{s_y^2}{s_c^2} = \frac{N-k}{N-1} + \frac{k-1}{N-1}F$$

Now, by definition, $\epsilon^2 = 1 - s_c^2/s_y^2$. Hence, by algebraic manipulation and then substitution in (I),

$$\epsilon^2 = 1 - \frac{s_c^2}{s_y^2} \cdot \frac{s_c^2}{s_c^2} = 1 - \epsilon^2;$$

$$\frac{s_y^2}{s_c^2} = \frac{1}{1-\epsilon^2}; \frac{1}{1-\epsilon^2} = \frac{N-k}{N-1} + \frac{k-1}{N-1}F$$

Multiply through by $(1 - \epsilon^2)(N - 1)$, transpose, and solve for ϵ^2,

$$(N - 1) = (N - k) - (N - k)\epsilon^2 + (k - 1)F - (k - 1)F\epsilon^2$$
$$(N - k)\epsilon^2 + (k - 1)F\epsilon^2 = (k - 1)F - (N - 1) + (N - k)$$
$$= (k - 1)F - (k - 1)$$
$$\epsilon^2 = \frac{(k - 1)F - (k - 1)}{(k - 1)F + (N - k)} \qquad (220)$$

We constructed our table of the distribution of ϵ^2 by substituting for the values of F at the 1 per cent and the 5 per cent positions at the various N and k levels. This is Table XLVII, pages 494 to 497.

A RECENT APPROACH TO SAMPLING DISTRIBUTIONS

The whole matter of sampling distributions will probably be given reorientation in terms of some recent developments which bring all the issues we discussed in this chapter together into very simple perspective. Huntington[1] has recently shown how to write in general terms the distribution of the quotient between two independent statistics when we know the sampling distribution of each of them. Suppose x is a variable distributed in accordance with a probability law $\int_{-\infty}^{+\infty} f_1(x)dx = 1$, and y is a variable distributed in accordance with the probability law $\int_0^\infty f_2(y)dy = 1$, x and y being independently distributed. Then

[1] HUNTINGTON, E. V., "Frequency Distributions of Product and Quotient," *Ann. Mathematical Statistics*, Vol. 10, pp. 195–198 (1939).

the quotient $w = x/y$ will be distributed according to the law $\int_{-\infty}^{+\infty} Q(w)dw = 1$, where

$$Q(w) = \int_0^\infty f_1(wy)f_2(y)y\ dy$$

This integral may be evaluated as soon as we are able to insert the values from the distributions of the separate statistics, x and y. There are three cases as follows:

1. Where x has a gamma distribution and y is a constant. This is χ^2, developed by Karl Pearson in 1900.

2. Where x has a normal distribution and y has a gamma distribution. This is t, developed by Student in 1908 but previously discovered by at least two other mathematicians.

3. Where both x and y have gamma distributions. This is Fisher's z or Snedecor's F, developed by R. A. Fisher about 1924.

We know the distributions of x and y for all these cases, provided the samples are independent random ones drawn from variables normally distributed in the parent population. Historically the sampling distributions of x and y were derived by use of hyperspace geometry, by the technique of generalized polar coordinates, and the presence of certain expressions like "degrees of freedom" comes over from this geometric approach. But Dunham Jackson[1] has recently shown how to derive these equations by purely analytic (algebraic) methods. This recent work by analytic methods makes possible simplification and unification of the concepts and processes involved in the topics of this chapter in a manner that is in marked contrast with the intricacies and the difficulties involved in their historical development. But it is beyond the scope of this volume to follow through these derivations.

Exercises

1. Put together into a single contingency table the data given on page 83 regarding conformity by taxi drivers and chauffeurs, and apply the χ^2 technique to determine whether or not these differ significantly. Since χ^2 cannot work with percentages, take each population to be 1,000, and reduce entries to numbers.

2. For the exercises in this chapter where the number of degrees of freedom was taken as $(k-1)(r-1)$ use instead $(n'-1)$ and compare. Compare

[1] JACKSON, DUNHAM, "Mathematical Principles in the Theory of Small Samples," *Amer. Mathematical Monthly*, Vol. 42, pp. 344–364 (1935).

for plausibility the two interpretations appropriate to the different degrees of freedom.

3. In the *Journal of Educational Psychology*, Vol. 30, page 119, Wood and Davis give the following distributions of scores in acquisition and retention for a certain unit of work. The first row gives the score values and the last two rows give the frequencies for these scores in acquisition and in retention.

Score	7	9	11	13	15	17	19	21	23	25	27	Total
Frequency acquisition	4	3	4	11	8	20	11	10	7	10	5	93
Frequency retention	3	3	11	16	10	19	12	9	7	3	1	94

a. Wood and Davis apply the chi-square technique to this in order to determine whether there is any true difference between retention and acquisition, *taking the obtained acquisition frequencies as the "expected" (theoretical) ones and the retention frequencies as the obtained ones.* Perform this operation. What would need to be assumed about the constancy of the acquisition scores in successive samples when that method is used? How reasonable is that assumption?

b. Work the problem to find χ^2 by the regular method of a contingency table. What are now the assumptions? How reasonable are they?

References for Further Reading

DEMING, W. E.: "The Chi-square Test and Curve Fitting," *J. Amer. Statistical Soc.*, Vol. 29, pp. 372–382 (1934).

FISHER, R. A.: "On the Interpretation of Chi-square from Contingency Tables," *J. Roy. Statistical Soc.*, Vol. 85, pp. 87–94 (1922).

———: "The Goodness of Fit of Regression Formulae," *J. Roy. Statistical Soc.*, Vol. 85, pp. 597–612 (1922).

———: "The Mathematical Distribution Used in Common Tests of Significance," *Econometrika*, Vol. 3, pp. 353–367 (1935).

KENNEY, JOHN F.: *Mathematics of Statistics*, D. Van Nostrand Company, Inc., 1939, Part II, Chap. 8.

PEARSON, KARL: "On the Criterion that a Given System of Deviations . . . Can Be Reasonably Supposed to Have Arisen from Random Sampling," *Phil. Mag. (London)*, Vol. 50, pp. 157ff. (1900).

———: "On the Chi-square Test of Goodness of Fit," *Biometrika*, Vol. 14, pp. 186–191 (1923).

———: "Experimental Discussion of the Chi-square Test of Goodness of Fit," *Biometrika*, Vol. 24, pp. 351–373 (1932).

———: "On a New Method of Determining Goodness of Fit," *Biometrika*, Vol. 26, pp. 425–442.

CHAPTER XV

CURVE FITTING

THE PROBLEM

In many statistical applications one is required to find a smooth curve that is well adapted to indicate the general trend of the relationship between varying quantities. All with which he has to work is a number of plotted points obtained through measurement or testing, which points indicate the operation of some law of behavior with respect to these variables. The choice of the type of curve that would best represent any trend depends, of course, upon how we define the term *best* and upon the apparent adaptability of the curve to the data at hand.

The extent to which the equation of a particular curve is descriptive of variation is limited by errors of sampling and insufficiency of data. Whenever experiment shows that some law of behavior is being obeyed, we must first assume, therefore, that it is expressible to a certain degree of approximation in a mathematical formula. We are then at liberty to set up a definition of *best fit*, and to proceed to derive the equation of the curve which best indicates the trend of our data. This task is known as *curve fitting*.

TYPES OF CURVES

There is a great number of curves which different distributions seem to follow. Experience has shown, however, that the vast majority of data tend to follow a few types with remarkable frequency. The straight line, the parabola, the exponential curves of growth and decay, the Gompertz curve, the normal-probability curve, and the normal ogive are among those most frequently encountered. Their equations are given herewith:

(A) $y = mx + b$ (straight line)
(B) $y = ax^2 + bx + c$ (parabola)
(C) $y = be^{+ax}$ (organic growth)
(D) $y = be^{-ax}$ (organic decay)

$$(E) \quad y = \frac{1}{\sigma\sqrt{2\pi}} \int_{-a}^{+a} e^{-\frac{x^2}{2\sigma^2}} dx \qquad \text{(normal ogive curve)}$$

$$(F) \quad y = ki^{r'} \qquad \text{(Gompertz curve)}$$

$$(G) \quad y = \frac{1}{\sigma\sqrt{2\pi}} e^{-\frac{x^2}{2\sigma^2}} \qquad \text{(normal-probability curve)}$$

Other equations of the second degree and higher, further trigonometric equations, parabolas of the nth degree, and many others are perhaps equally important. We shall, however, limit our treatment to those listed above and to a cursory account of the Pearson system of curves. The methods of curve fitting employed here are applicable to many other curves as well.

METHODS OF CURVE FITTING

There are several ways in which the fitting of curves may be accomplished. If the plotted points reveal a straight-line trend, we may simply place a thin, transparent ruler, or a cord, over them and adjust it in a way we consider best. This method, known as the *graphical method*, requires experience and good judgment. It should be used in situations where only moderate accuracy is required.

For straight-line fitting, the method of averages is usually superior to the graphical method. The points are considered in two groups, and an average point is taken for each group. The problem is then simply that of finding the equation of the straight line which passes through these two points. This method should not be attempted unless there is an unquestionable straight-line trend, and the points are evenly scattered throughout. A disadvantage of the method of averages is that it does not lead to a unique equation, since the groupings are entirely arbitrary. It is, however, an easy method and may be used where rapid calculations are required.

Probably the most important method of curve fitting is that of least squares. The principle of least squares states that the curve of a given type which best fits a given set of points is one in which the constants of the equation are so chosen as to make the sum of the squares of the errors a minimum. These errors are the amounts by which the actual ordinates of the points fail to agree with the ordinates of points on the curve. Thus, if y be the ordinate of one of the plotted points, and $\bar{y}$ be the ordinate of a corresponding point on the theoretical curve, we are to make $\Sigma(y - \bar{y})^2$ a minimum. The usual methods of the differential calculus are employed for this purpose and, as we shall see later, lead to a set of equations known as *normal equations*. By solving these normal equations, we find the values of the constants appearing in the type equation which we assumed to indicate the trend of the points. The method of least squares is general and may be applied to a variety of curves. We shall illustrate the least-squares method in the following examples.

FITTING A STRAIGHT LINE

Consider the following values of x and y:

x	0	3	6	9	12	15	18	21	24	27	30
y	5	9	16	24	26	35	39	46	47	56	63

When these values are plotted on graph paper (Fig. 33), it appears at once that there is a general straight-line relationship between the two varying quantities. Our problem is to deter-
mine the equation of the line
which best expresses this relationship, *i.e.*, the equation of
the line of best fit.

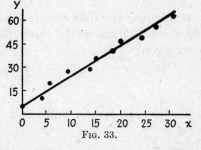

FIG. 33.

For convenience let us label
the 11 paired items given above
as (x_1, y_1), (x_2, y_2), (x_3, y_3), etc.
Some of these points will fall
above the line we seek, and some will fall below it. In other words, some of the errors will be positive, and some will be negative. But since we are to make the sum of the *squares* of the errors a minimum, we need not be concerned with the negative signs. Since the ordinate value of any point on the line is expressed by the straight-line equation $\bar{y} = ax + b$, these errors—differences between the actual and the theoretical ordinate values—may be written as follows:

$$y_1 - \bar{y}_1 = y_1 - (ax_1 + b)$$
$$y_2 - \bar{y}_2 = y_2 - (ax_2 + b)$$
$$y_3 - \bar{y}_3 = y_3 - (ax_3 + b)$$
etc.

According to the least-squares principle we must minimize $\Sigma(y_i - \bar{y}_i)^2$, where the summation is to extend from 1 to the number of plotted points. In this summation we may replace $\bar{y}$ by its equal $(ax + b)$. Then the quantity to be made a minimum becomes $\Sigma[y - (ax + b)]^2$, in which the summation is to extend over the total number of points.

We learn in the differential calculus that in order to make the above quantity a minimum or a maximum, we must have both the derivative with respect to a and that with respect to b equal to zero. We need, therefore, only to form these derivatives, equate them to zero, and solve the resulting equations for a and b[1]. Squaring the quantity within brackets, we obtain

$$\Sigma(y^2 + a^2x^2 + b^2 - 2axy - 2yb + 2abx)$$

Summing termwise and removing from under the summation symbol the a and the b which are independent of the summation, this expression becomes

$$\Sigma y^2 + a^2\Sigma x^2 + nb^2 - 2a\Sigma xy - 2b\Sigma y + 2ab\Sigma x$$

Performing the differentiation with respect to a and then with respect to b and at the same time equating the results to zero, we have,[2]

$$2a\Sigma x^2 - 2\Sigma xy + 2b\Sigma x = 0$$
$$2a\Sigma x - 2\Sigma y + 2nb = 0$$

Transposing certain terms and dividing each equation through by 2,

(H) $$a\Sigma x^2 + b\Sigma x = \Sigma xy$$
$$a\Sigma x + bn = \Sigma y$$

In Eq. (H) all the summations are known quantities. We have, therefore, two simultaneous equations in the unknowns a and b. Solving the simultaneous equations by the usual methods, we find

$$a = \frac{n\Sigma xy - \Sigma x \cdot \Sigma y}{n\Sigma x^2 - (\Sigma x)^2} \tag{221}$$

[1] It may be shown by further mathematical treatment that in the present instance the condition for a minimum, and not a maximum, is satisfied.

[2] Observe that when differentiation is performed with respect to a particular letter, the others are treated as constants.

$$b = \frac{\Sigma x^2 \cdot \Sigma y - \Sigma x \cdot \Sigma xy}{n \Sigma x^2 - (\Sigma x)^2} \qquad (221a)$$

Equations (221) and (221a) are general formulas which may always be used in finding the constants a and b. It is obvious that the method is perfectly general and holds for any number of plotted points. All that the worker need do is to compute the indicated sums and substitute into these formulas.

The reader will note the similarity between the form of the expression for a and that of the coefficient of correlation r, (page 99). It can be seen that if the variabilities in the case of an r are made equal (*i.e.*, if $\sigma_x = \sigma_y$), the formula for r reduces to the formula for a. This tells us that a coefficient of correlation is the slope of the line of best fit when the variabilities are made equal.

For the example with which we began this development, the sums which extend over the 11 items are as follows:

$$\Sigma xy = 7{,}374; \ \Sigma x = 165; \ \Sigma y = 366; \ \Sigma x^2 = 3{,}465; \ (n = 11)$$

Substituting into Eqs. (221) and (221a) and performing the indicated arithmetical operations, we find $a = 1.90$; $b = 4.73$.

The equation of the line of best fit, obtained by the method of least squares, is, therefore,

$$y = 1.90x + 4.73$$

THE PARABOLA

If the plotted points indicate a parabolic trend, we may find by the least-squares method the equation of the parabola of best fit. Consider, for example, the following 12 values of x and y.

x	0	1	2	3	4	5	6	7	8	9	10	11
y	25	12	15	5	8	7	3	18	10	20	25	50

These points when plotted (see Fig. 34) reveal an unmistakably parabolic trend. Let us assume, therefore, that the desired curve is of the form $y = ax^2 + bx + c$. The constants a, b, and c are to be determined from the data by the method of least squares.

As in the case of the straight line, we shall develop the formulas for the general case and then arrive at particular values by substitution.

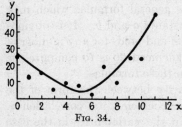

FIG. 34.

Our problem is to minimize $\Sigma(y_i - \bar{y}_i)^2$ where y_i stands for the ordinate of any of the actual points, and $\bar{y}_i$ the theoretical ordinate. But since we are assuming that the theoretical value of $\bar{y}$ is given by the expression $\bar{y} = ax^2 + bx + c$, we may say that we must minimize $\Sigma[y - (ax^2 + bx + c)]^2$.

$$\Sigma(y - ax^2 - bx - c)^2 = \Sigma y^2 + \Sigma a^2 x^4 + \Sigma b^2 x^2 + \Sigma c^2$$
$$- 2\Sigma yax^2 - 2\Sigma ybx - 2\Sigma yc$$
$$+ 2\Sigma acx^2 + 2\Sigma bcx + 2\Sigma abx^3$$

Differentiating in turn with respect to a, b, and c and setting the derivatives equal to zero, we obtain

(I)
$$2\Sigma ax^4 - 2\Sigma yx^2 + 2\Sigma bx^3 + 2\Sigma cx^2 = 0$$
$$2\Sigma bx^2 - 2\Sigma yx + 2\Sigma ax^3 + 2\Sigma cx = 0$$
$$2\Sigma c - 2\Sigma y + 2\Sigma ax^2 + 2\Sigma bx = 0$$

We may take the constants a, b, and c outside the summation symbols. Furthermore, $\Sigma c = nc$. Making these changes, dividing through each equation by 2, and at the same time rearranging the terms by transposition, Eqs. (I) may be written

(J)
$$a\Sigma x^4 + b\Sigma x^3 + c\Sigma x^2 = \Sigma x^2 y$$
$$a\Sigma x^3 + b\Sigma x^2 + c\Sigma x = \Sigma xy$$
$$a\Sigma x^2 + b\Sigma x + nc = \Sigma y$$

Equations (J) are the normal equations for the parabola of best fit. We need only to compute the summations for the data of our problem and then solve the resulting equations for a, b, and c. The sums for the data given above are as follows:

$\Sigma x^4 = 39{,}974 \qquad \Sigma x^3 = 4{,}356 \qquad \Sigma x^2 = 506 \qquad \Sigma x = 66$

$\Sigma y = 198 \qquad \Sigma xy = 1{,}328 \qquad \Sigma x^2 y = 12{,}220 \ (n = 12)$

Our normal equations are, therefore,

$$39{,}974a + 4{,}356b + 506c = 12{,}220$$
$$4{,}356a + 506b + 66c = 1{,}328$$
$$506a + 66b + 12c = 198$$

Upon solving these equations by the ordinary methods of elimination, we find $a = 0.94$, $b = -8.66$, $c = 24.44$. Hence, the equation of the parabola of best fit is

$$y = 0.94x^2 - 8.66x + 24.44$$

We have seen that in the cases of the straight line and the parabola the task of obtaining the equation of the curve of best fit by the method of least squares is a direct one of minimizing errors—differences between actual and theoretical scores. The process leads to sets of normal equations which involve certain summations as the coefficients of the unknown parameters of the selected theoretical curve. Since the method is general and the results are unique, Eqs. (221) and (221a) may be regarded as formulas for straight-line fitting, and Eqs. (J) may be taken as the set of equations which yield the parabolic coefficients.

CURVES OF GROWTH AND DECAY

The problem of fitting curves of growth to a given set of data, is, in general, more complicated than that of fitting straight lines or parabolas. Especially complicated is the situation in which there is a tendency toward saturation or maturity in the later stages of the development of the growth factors.

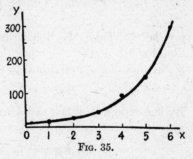

FIG. 35.

In the case of organic growth under ideal conditions, where the increments of growth are continuously accumulating, we may simplify our task by first transforming the assumed equation into another form and then working with this latter form. We simply take the logarithm of each member of the assumed equation. This puts the growth curve in the form of a straight line. Consider, for example, the following seven values of x and y.

x	0	1	2	3	4	5	6
y	10	15	20	40	90	150	300

These data reveal a trend of growth of a certain nature (Fig. 35). There appears no tendency toward saturation or maturity as we proceed with increasing values of the time factor x. We may assume, therefore, that the variation in growth can well be approximated by Eq. (C), $y = be^{+ax}$. The mathematical justification for this conclusion rests, as we shall see later, upon the straight-line trend of the log values obtained by taking the logarithm of the y values of the above list. We shall rewrite our list of paired values and include these log y values.

x	0	1	2	3	4	5	6
y	10	15	20	40	90	150	300
log y	1.00	1.18	1.30	1.60	1.95	2.18	2.48

The log y values are plotted against the x values in Fig. 36. Here we observe a straight-line trend of log values. Now let us study the nature of our assumed type equation. We have

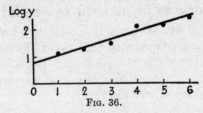

Fig. 36.

$y = be^{+ax}$. Take the logarithm (base 10) of each member; then $\log y = \log be^{+ax}$. Since the log of a product equals the sum of the logs of the individual factors, we may write

$$\log y = \log e^{+ax} + \log b$$

By the exponential law of logarithms, the first term on the right may be written $ax \log e$. Hence, our equation becomes

$$\log y = ax \log e + \log b$$

Now log e (base 10) equals 0.4343. Therefore,

$$\log y = 0.4343ax + \log b$$

This equation is a straight-line form if we let $Y = \log y$,

$$A = 0.4343a,$$

$B = \log b$. That is, our equation is of the form $Y = Ax + B$. Moreover, our problem has been reduced to that of finding the straight line of best fit for our data when expressed in terms of log units which vary with the original x units. In addition, we have justified the selection of the type (C) curve to fit the data.

To complete the problem, we have only to make use of the formulas (221) and (221a)—using Y (log y) in place of the y appearing therein. The summations required are as follows:

$$\Sigma xY = 42.14, \ \Sigma x^2 = 91, \ \Sigma Y = 11.69, \ \Sigma x = 21, \ n = 7$$

Substituting these values into Eqs. (221) and (221a), we find

$$A = \frac{7(42.14) - (21)(11.69)}{7(91) - (21)^2} = 0.25$$

$$B = \frac{(91)(11.69) - (21)(42.14)}{7(91) - (21)^2} = 0.91$$

One form of the equation of best fit is, therefore,

$$Y = 0.25x + 0.91$$

or, log $y = 0.25x + 0.91$. This latter form may be expressed in exponential form in either one of two ways. Since log y is taken to the base 10, we may write as a consequence of the definition of a logarithm, $y = 10^{0.25x+0.91}$. Rearrange the right-hand member by the law of exponents for multiplication.

$$y = 10^{0.25x} \cdot 10^{0.91}$$

Now it is easily verified that $10^{0.91} = 8.1$. Hence,

(K) $$y = 8.1 \cdot 10^{0.25x}$$

Equation (K) is satisfactory as a final working form of the equation which best fits the data of our last list. The reader will observe that in place of e raised to the variable power, we have during the process changed to the number 10. This, of course, is not necessary; it may readily be put again in terms of e, as follows:

Let $10^{0.25x} = e^{cx}$, in which we wish to determine the value of c. Take logarithms (base 10) of both sides.

$$\log 10^{0.25x} = \log e^{cx}$$

Since the log of a quantity to an exponent equals the exponent times the log of the quantity,

$$0.25x \log 10 = cx \log e$$

Now make use of the facts that log 10 (base 10) = 1, and that log e (base 10) = 0.4343. Then $0.25x = 0.4343cx$.

Divide through by $0.4343x$. $c = 0.57$.   Hence

$$10^{0.25x} = e^{0.57x}$$

Substitute into (K), and we obtain

(L) $y = 8.1e^{0.57x}$

Equations (K) and (L) are entirely equivalent. Either of them may be regarded as that equation which is expressive of the growth variation indicated by the data with which we are working. A curve of this type is known as a curve of organic growth. It is frequently encountered whenever the conditions are nearly ideal and whenever there is no tendency toward saturation or maturity during the time measurements are being made.

Equation (D), in which the exponent is negative, is known as the curve of organic decay. It may be regarded as a growth curve in which the increments are continuously falling off as the variable x increases. A graph of a theoretical curve is given in Fig. 37. The method of fitting the curve of organic decay

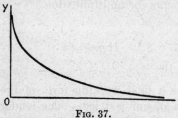

FIG. 37.

is the same as that of fitting the curve of organic growth. In either case the worker should be reasonably certain that his assumed curve is representative of the data at hand. The test of selection lies in taking logarithms of the y scores (growth measurements). If these log values, when plotted against the x scores (units of time), indicate a straight-line trend, the assumed curve may be considered predictive of the growth of the factor under consideration.

The problem of growth curves in general has received considerable attention in recent years. Many empirical formulas have been developed, and many theories concerning the nature of growth have been developed. Pearl has shown that the curve of population growth (an S shaped logistic curve) is applicable to many forms of growth.[1] He has also given evidence that the

[1] PEARL, RAYMOND, *The Biology of Populati n Growth*, Alfred A. Knopf, Inc., 1925; also *Studies in Human Biology*, Williams & Wilkins Company, 1924, Part IV.

same generalized curve deals excellently with unsymmetrical as well as with symmetrical growth.[1] Bass-Becking defines growth in terms of cell growth. In certain forms of development he finds growth best expressed as the differential quotient of cell volume increase and time interval. He has pointed out the interesting fact that whenever small cells grow at the same rate as large cells, a normal distribution of cells reappears after a finite number of growth periods and cell-division periods. This indicates the applicability of the normal ogive curve (the curve obtained by summing the ordinates of a normal curve) in certain situations. Peters believes that the curve of growth in ideational learning may be the ogive.[2] He gives both theoretical and empirical reasons for his hypothesis. L. L. Thurstone has found that the hyperbola seems best to fit the norms of 40 tests, and claims this type to be the curve of learning.[3] As Peters has pointed out, the hyperbolic trend is due to the fact that the material used by Thurstone involves only the upper levels of growth and consequently does not take into account the possible influence of the early learning increments upon the theoretical S shape.

THE NORMAL OGIVE CURVE

Type (E), which is shown at the beginning of this chapter, is the mathematical expression of the theoretical normal ogive. As the equation indicates, it is the curve resulting from integrating the normal-curve function. Empirically, this amounts to summating the ordinate values (z scores) of the normal distribution of data we have at hand. Figure 38 shows the normal ogive in relation to average scores from the Peters General Information Test.

THE GOMPERTZ CURVE

Perhaps one of the curves most applicable in biological and psychological research is the well-known Gompertz curve.[4]

---

[1] PEARL, R., and L. J. REED, "Skew Growth Curves," *Proc. Nat. Acad. Sci.*, Vol. 11, pp. 16–22 (1925).

[2] PETERS, C. C., *Foundations of Educational Sociology*, rev. ed., 1930, The Macmillan Company, pp. 452–456.

[3] THURSTONE, L. L., "The Learning Curve Equation," *Psychological Monographs*, Vol. 26, No. 3 (1919, No. 114).

[4] GOMPERTZ, B., "On the Nature of the Function Expressive of Human

S. A. Courtis has begun with this formula as a basis, type (F), and has attempted to show a certain universality underlying all biological growth.[1] A feature of the work of Courtis consists in transforming the formula developed by Gompertz into a straight-line form by twice taking logarithms of each member of the original equation. He has shown that under standard conditions log log values of the percentages of development are directly proportional to the times in which changes in development occur. This means that the relationship between time and log log values may be represented by a straight line. In other words, the percentage of development increases to equal powers of itself in equal periods of time.

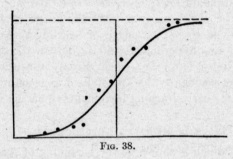

FIG. 38.

In order that the reader may become acquainted with the growth measurement methods of Courtis, we shall give a brief discussion of the mathematical theory underlying his work and follow this with an illustration.[2]

The equation of the Gompertz curve is

(M) $$y = ki^{r^t}$$

in which y represents measure of growth at the time t, k the value at maturity, i the initial development, and r the rate of growth. If we take k to be 1 and write our equation

(N) $$y = i^{r^t}$$

Mortality, and on a New Mode of Determining the Value of Life Contingencies," *Trans. Roy. Soc. (London)*, Vol. 115, pp. 513–585, 1825.

[1] COURTIS, S. A., *The Measurement of Growth*, Brumfield and Brumfield, 1932.

[2] For a full treatment of the mathematical properties of the Gompertz curve, see S. A. COURTIS, *op. cit.*

our growth is expressed in terms of percentage of development. Equation (N) is known as the *simplex growth curve.* Its fitting to growth data depends upon the following development:

Take the logarithm of each member of (N).

(O) $$\log y = r^t \log i$$

Take the logarithm of each member of (O).

(P) $$\log \log y = t \log r + \log \log i$$

Equation (P) is the equation of a straight line,

(Q) $$Y = At + B$$

in which

(R) $$Y = \log \log y; \; A = \log r; \; B = \log \log i$$

It is evident from the foregoing discussion that if the log log values of a given set of percentages of development indicate a straight-line trend, our problem is simply that of finding the constants A and B, and then returning to the original Gompertz curve (M). A is the slope of the line of the log log values, and B is the initial log log value, *i.e.*, the value when $t = 0$.

The two constants, A and B, may be found by the method of least squares whenever a fairly full set of values is at hand, *i.e.*, whenever we know the log logs of the percentages of development for units of time from incipiency to maturity. However, since we are assuming that the percentages of development increase in equal powers in equal periods of time, we may take A as the mean increase in the log logs from time interval to time interval over a known range of time. The initial point B may usually be determined from the display of the data. This latter method of finding A and B is most conveniently employed whenever but two or three points on the growth curve are reliably known and we wish to interpolate for the others, a problem of predicting the percentages of development for the entire growth period on the basis of a few known percentages, rather than of obtaining the formula expressive of the nature of growth of the organism[1] when measurements have been taken throughout its entire existence.

Let us now apply our methods to the fitting of the data listed below. The data are percentages of boys passing No. 20,

[1] The word *organism* is here used in the group sense. It is the totality of elements which compose the distribution of the growth data.

Fingers, of the Binet Test.[1] These percentages are distributed according to the chronological ages of the boys, and our problem is to find the equation of the curve which expresses the growth in their ability to pass the test.

PERCENTAGES OF BOYS PASSING THE BINET TEST, No. 20, FINGERS, AT DIFFERENT AGE LEVELS

Age in years	3.5	4.5	5.5	6.5	7.5	8.5	9.5	10.5
Per cent passing	0.0	28.4	62.5	86.0	95.3	98.6	99.3	100.0

Before going further we must make sure that we understand how to use log logs. Let us see how these values are found. Log 28.4 per cent = log .284 = (9.45332 − 10) (from tables). This may be written log .284 = −.54668. Now the log of a negative number does not exist. We, therefore, define the log of this negative quantity to be the log of the product of this quantity and −1. This amounts to disregarding the minus sign appearing before .54668.   Hence

$$\log \log .284 = \log .54668 = (9.73773 - 10)$$

(from tables). That is, log log .284 = −26227. The following may be taken as a working form when finding the log logs of decimals:

$$\log .625 = (9.79588 - 10) = -.20412$$
$$\log \log .625 = \log .20412 = (9.30988 - 10) = -.69012$$

The reader should prove that he understands the process of using log logs by obtaining −1.18376, −1.67965, −2.21325, and −2.51570 as the log logs of .860, .953, .986, and .993, respectively.

Now let us examine the log logs of the limits of our range of percentage values. We have log .000 = − ∞. Therefore, log log .000 = log ∞ = ∞. Also, we have log 1.000 = .00000. Hence, log log 1.000 = log .00000 = − ∞. This tells us that we are unable actually to reach the true points of initial development and maturity through the mathematical machinery of the Gompertz curve. We may, however, make our errors in these respects as small as we wish if our measurements are so fine that we may approach the limits of the percentage range sufficiently far. It is for these theoretical reasons that we must be content

[1] BURT, C., *Mental and Scholastic Tests*, P. S. King & Son, Ltd., London, 1922.

with an arbitrary point of incipiency, and consider maturity as 100 per cent development as measured by some natural standard.

We are now in a position to return to the illustration of percentage of boys passing the Binet test, just quoted. Choose as our starting point the age 4.5 years. This is the first year (or period in our time scale) that any growth has been recorded. At this point we may consider t equal to zero, and label the remaining periods 1, 2, 3, etc. The log logs corresponding to these time units are given above and are plotted in Fig. 39.

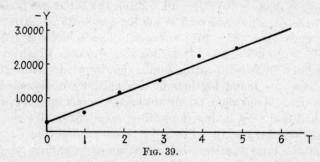

Fig. 39.

It is evident from the graph that the relationship between time units and log log percentage values is linear in trend. We may find the equation of the line which best expresses this relationship by the least-squares method. To do this, we have merely to apply formulas (221) and (221a) of this chapter in order to compute the required constants A and B. Observing that we are using t instead of x and Y instead of y, we have as formulas

$$A = \frac{n\Sigma tY - \Sigma t\Sigma Y}{n\Sigma t^2 - (\Sigma t)^2}, \quad B = \frac{\Sigma t^2\Sigma Y - \Sigma t\Sigma tY}{n\Sigma t^2 - (\Sigma t)^2}$$

The necessary sums to be substituted into these formulas are, of course, obtained from our log log data on page 438. They are (as may readily be verified) as follows:

$$\Sigma tY = -29.52809, \ \Sigma t = 15.00, \ \Sigma Y = -8.5475$$
$$\Sigma t^2 = 55.00, \ n = 6$$

When these values are substituted into the above formulas and simplifications are made, we find that $A = -.4666$, and $B = -.2575$.

Therefore, the equation of our growth curve expressed in log logs is

$$(S) \qquad\qquad Y = -.4666t - .2575$$

To get back to the original form of the Gompertz curve (N), we must now return to Eq. (R), the point at which our departure to the straight-line form began. We have, from these equations and the results just obtained, that $A = \log r = -.4666$.

Hence, to obtain r, we must find the antilog from the tables, as follows: $-.4666 = 9.5334 - 10$. From the tables we find that $r = .342$. Again, we have $B = \log \log i = -.2575$. To obtain i, we must then twice take antilogs. This is done as follows: $-.2575 = 9.7425 - 10$. Thus $\log i = -.5529$, which is the antilog of $9.7425 - 10$ with a minus sign inserted. (Remember that when we found log logs of decimals, we disregarded the minus sign. Thus when taking antilogs, we must insert it again.) We shall find i by taking the antilog of $-.5529$. We see that $-.5529 = 9.4471 - 10$. From the tables we find that $i = .28$.

Now the type equation that we assumed to express best the growth in the ability of boys to pass the Binet test is $y = i^{r^t}$. Hence, our final equation becomes upon substituting the values of r and i,

$$(T) \qquad\qquad y = .28^{.342^t}$$

Equation (T) is the curve of growth which best fits the data about growth of boys in passing the Binet fingers test. It may be looked upon as a formula for estimating percentages of development of boys in their ability to pass No. 20, Fingers, of the Binet Test. In practice, however, it may be found more convenient to substitute values of t into Eq. (S) and then convert these into percentage values by twice taking antilogs.

Courtis' methods of measuring growth should have wide application in the field of education as well as in many other branches of science. He has developed tables of *isochrons* which are the percentages of total time to reach maturation that correspond to percentages of development.[1] The construction of these tables necessitated, of course, the selection of an arbitrary range of log log values; *i.e.*, it was necessary to fix upon points of initial

[1] These tables may be obtained from the *Courtis Standard Tests*, 1807 E. Grand Boulevard, Detroit, Mich.

development and maturity. These limitations do not, however, seriously affect the practical values of the isochronic system in many growth situations, for it has been found that a wide variety of growth data agrees very closely in these respects. They do, however, limit theoretical generalizations concerning the nature of all biologic growth. In addition, it will be remembered that the Gompertz formula is expressive of the nature of growth when, and only when, the log log values of the percentages of development are linear in trend. If these log log values obey some other law, then it follows that the growth involved obeys some other law.[1]

In view of the minor limitations cited above, the Gompertz curve can well be employed in many growth situations. If the reader is unfamiliar with the use of logarithms, he may, of course, resort to the isochronic tables for ease of computations. The writers believe that for the beginner, at least, a fuller understanding of the basic principles underlying the study of growth curves will result from a clearer view of the mathematics involved.

TESTING GOODNESS OF FIT

Provided the variates can be grouped into classes so that some estimate may be made of the population variance of the constituent classes, a mathematical test of goodness of fit of our curves can be made. As shown on page 328, the formula is

$$\epsilon'^2 = \frac{\epsilon^2 - R^2}{1 - R^2}$$

where R^2 is the variance of the values computed for the regression line—when frequencies are considered—divided by the total variance. The reader should refer to our earlier treatment and make this test for such tables as our Tables XXVII and XXVIII.

THE PEARSONIAN SYSTEM OF CURVES

A set of frequency curves representing a wide variety of statistical distributions has been developed by Pearson.[2] The equa-

---

[1] There is, of course, no limit to the variation of curves that may give rise to different log log curves.

[2] PEARSON, KARL: "Mathematical Contributions to the Theory of Evolution," *Trans. Roy. Soc. (London)*, Series *A*, Vol. 186, pp. 343–414 (1895);

tions of these curves are found by integrating a certain differential equation having much support in the theory of probability and satisfying certain geometrical properties characteristic of unimodal frequency distributions. They are useful in fitting many symmetrical, skewed, J shaped, and other trends of data, and even include the normal curve as a special case.

The differential equation giving rise to the Pearsonian system of curves is

$$(U) \qquad \frac{dy}{dt} = \frac{(m - t)y}{a + bt + ct^2}$$

in which m, a, b, and c are constants, and $t = x/\sigma$.

In fitting a Pearsonian curve to a given set of data, the procedure for determining the constants is to express them in terms of moments of the system, substituting for these moments those calculated from the data. The values thus found determine the particular differential equation to be integrated to obtain the equation of the curve to be fitted to the data at hand. Kenney lists formulas for m, a, b, and c, all of which are given in terms of moments.[1]

After the form of the differential equation has been found, integration yields the equation of the type of curve to be fitted to the given data. The constant resulting from integration may then be found by using the fact that the area under the curve is N, the total frequency of the distribution. The equation thus arrived at is that of the curve fitted to the data at hand.

We shall now examine a few types of curves of the Pearsonian system, indicating the form of the differential equations giving rise to these types and pointing out how one might proceed to use the equations in curve fitting.

Type VII.—Suppose a given set of data yields the information that the quantities m, b, and c equal zero and that the constant a equals unity. Then the differential Eq. (U) becomes

$$(V) \qquad \frac{dy}{dt} = -ty$$

"Supplement to a Memoir on Skew Variation," Vol. 197, pp. 443–456 (1901); "Second Supplement to a Memoir on Skew Variation," Vol. 216, pp. 429–457 (1916).

[1] KENNEY, JOHN F., *Mathematics of Statistics*, D. Van Nostrand Company, Inc., 1939, Part II, p. 48.

Integrating, we find

$$y = Ae^{-\frac{t^2}{2}}$$

in which A is a constant to be determined from the data. We recognize this equation to be that of the normal curve and have seen elsewhere that $A = N/\sqrt{2\pi}$. The normal curve is known as the type VII curve of the Pearsonian system.

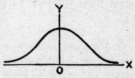

FIG. 40.—Type VII curve.

Type III.—If the moments of our data are such that c equals zero and m, a, and b are not equal to zero, (U) becomes

$$(W) \qquad \frac{dy}{dt} = \frac{(m - t)y}{a + bt}$$

Integration yields an equation of the form

$$y = A(K + t)^{K^2-1}e^{-Kt}$$

in which A is a constant to be determined from the condition that the area under the curve equals N, and K is found from the moments.

In the special case $K^2 = 1$, type III takes the form Type X,

$$y = Ae^{\pm t}$$

which is also known as *Laplace's first frequency curve*.

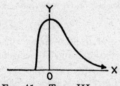
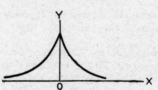

FIG. 41.—Type III curve. FIG. 42.—Type X curve.

The determination of the constants in the Pearsonian frequency curves is generally very laborious, involving the computation of the first four moments and the area under the curve. Examples of the representation of actual frequency distributions by several types may be found in *A First Course in Statistics* by D. C. Jones, and a rather complete account of all the curves in the Pearson system has been set forth by C. C. Craig. Figures of 12-types resulting from different values of the constants are shown in H. L. Rietz's "Mathematical Statistics" (*Carus Monograph*), Chap. III.

For further discussions of the Pearson system of curves the student is referred to Pearson[1] and Elderton.[2]

Exercises

1. Fit a second degree parabola to the data of Table XXVIII, page 317, by the method of least squares, and test the goodness of fit. How do your results compare with those we give on page 329?

2. Fit a third degree parabola to the data of Table XXVIII, page 316, and test the goodness of fit. What other types of curves might fit these data better?

References for Further Study

CRAIG, C. C.: "A New Exposition and Chart for the Pearson System of Frequency Curves," *Ann. Mathematical Statistics*, Vol. 7, No. 1, pp. 16–28.

EDGEWORTH, F. Y.: "On the Representation of Statistical Frequency by a Curve," *J. Roy. Statistical Soc.*, Vol. 70, 1907.

ELDERTON, W. P.: *Frequency Curves and Correlation*, 3d ed., Cambridge University Press, 1938.

GOMPERTZ, BENJAMIN: "On the Nature of the Function Expressive of the Law of Human Mortality, and a New Mode of Determining the Value of Life Contingencies," *Trans. Roy. Soc. (London)*, Vol. 115, 1825, pp. 513–583.

JONES, D. C.: *A First Course in Statistics*, George Bell & Sons, Ltd., 1921, pp. 178–248.

PEARSON, KARL: "On the Curves Which Are Most Suitable for Describing the Frequency of Random Samples of a Population," *Biometrika*, Vol. 5.

WHITTAKER, E. T., and G. ROBINSON: *Calculus of Observations*, D. Van Nostrand Company, Inc., 1924.

[1] PEARSON, KARL, *Tables for Statisticians and Biometricians*, 1924; "On the Systematic Fitting of Curves to Observations and Measurements," *Biometrika*, Vol. 1, pp. 265*ff.*; Vol. 2, pp. 1–23.

[2] ELDERTON, W. P., *Frequency Curves and Correlation*, 3d ed., Cambridge University Press, 1938.

CHAPTER XVI

THE TECHNIQUE OF CONTROLLED EXPERIMENTATION

To experiment is to control the behavior of animate or inanimate objects while we observe outcomes. Thus the physicist has a ball roll down an inclined plane which he adjusts in a manner to suit his purposes while he systematically observes the velocity or the distance traversed by the moving object, the agriculturalist treats soils in some predetermined way while he takes measured stock of the effects produced by the factors he is manipulating, or the chemist brings about certain changes in temperature and determines results. In essentially the same manner an educationalist applies to groups of pupils two or more different methods of teaching and objectively ascertains the relative degrees of success from each in contributing toward the attainment of certain specified objectives, or the economist-statesman tries municipal ownership of utilities in certain cities and measures success over against the success of such utilities under private ownership in similar cities. But, while it is characteristic of experimentation in the strict sense to have *purposive manipulation* of the factors involved in the experiment so as to make them contribute with maximum clearness and economy toward the answers to the specific questions we want answered, it is sometimes feasible to find in nature ongoings that so nearly conform to what we want that we may utilize them without further manipulation. Here selection may replace control. Such avoidance of the necessity for artificial manipulation is particularly convenient to a social scientist. The physicist, the chemist, the agriculturalist are permitted to operate on their materials at will—to lathe down a cylinder until it suits a particular purpose, to heat a solution to any required temperature, to treat the soil in any manner desired; but a sociologist studying adult societies is not at such liberty to manipulate groups of people for the sole purpose of his experiment. Neither does the economist nor the political scientist have such privilege except, perhaps, on rare occasions. The educationalist dealing with school children is able within limits to set up his environment to suit the needs of his research, but even he can often control his factors only in part and sometimes not at all. Under such limitations the sociologist may seek two sets of people who happen to differ from each other in the particular respect he wishes to investigate while being alike in all other essential ways and may use this contrast as a setting in which to study the effect of the differentiating factor. In the same manner the economist, the political scientist, the educationalist, or even the biologist, may take advantage of contrasts that the normal progress of events rather than his own manipulation has set up. Or the research worker may reconstruct such contrasts from records, thus having a sort of retroactive experiment. Comparisons which depend thus upon selection rather than upon control proceed under a heavy handicap, but they involve the same fundamental principles and call for the same statistical techniques as true experiments. We shall, therefore, have them in mind as well as controlled experiments in our discussion throughout this chapter.

In this chapter we are concerned chiefly with experiments involving growths of the sort in which students of education and the social and biological sciences are interested—growths not only in biological organism but in ideals, in skills, in informations, in folkways, as well. Where growths are normally in progress, an experimental factor can have only the effect of changing the rate of growth. In consequence, we must always measure the outcome in our experimental group against a control situation. When an experiment has been conducted without such control we do not know how much of the growth to attribute to the factor under special study and how much to other factors. Normally this control situation consists of a parallel group of individuals, or a parallel plot of ground, or what not, precisely like the experimental one in all pertinent factors except the experimental one. For the sake of maximum contrast it is best to have this differential factor present in as large degree as possible in the experimental group or plot and absent from the control situation; but, if that is not feasible, the two situations may differ by having the experimental factor present in large degree in the one situation and in small degree in the other.

It seems scarcely necessary for us to say here that care must be exercised to keep all other conditions constant in the two situations except the one experimental factor; this is the law of the single variable, so fundamental to all scientific experimentation. But to say that the variable must be *single* is not to say that it must be *atomistic*—that it must be simple in the sense that it cannot be analyzed into components. Many absurd blunders have been made in educational experimentation, at least, by overworking the principle of a single variable in the sense of a simple variable. In many of the experiments on homogeneous grouping of pupils, for example, effort was made to keep the type of instruction the same on both sides, the same textbooks and the same subject matter—to have, in short, all procedures exactly alike except that instructional groups were of small range of talent in the experimental groups and of great range in the control groups. But the whole purpose of homogeneous grouping, as employed normally in school, is to permit differentiation of instructional materials and procedures and adaptation of them to the differing levels of ability. When this part of the technique of dealing with homogeneous groups was discarded what was left was a mere abstraction having nothing to do with real educational alternatives. In useful experimenting we must set one practical *Gestalt* against another practical *Gestalt;* we must contrast one teaching procedure together with all the characteristics that normally accompany it with another procedure accompanied by all buttressing elements that would normally be used with it; or we must make an experimental contrast between one economic system together with all the ethical and legal and other drives that go with it to make it successful and another economic system accompanied also by the buttressing conditions essential to its integrity. In situations like this it is true, as the Gestalt psychologists have been pointing out, that the whole is more than the sum of its parts. In addition to the choice between major alternatives it is proper, of course, to make experimental comparison among specific variations within any one of the alternatives in order to find the effect of each constituent element and the optimum combination of these constituents. But, however the variable is defined that is to be our experimental factor, it must be "single" in the sense that it must constitute the only essential difference between our two situations.

MATCHING GROUPS

One of the most important factors to keep equal between the two sides is capacity to respond to the stimulus in which the experimental factor consists. In the case of learning experiments, that means capacity to learn materials in question on the part of the individuals who constitute the groups. Doubtless in experiments in sociology, in biology, in agriculture, and in other fields the capacity to respond lies also in constituent parts of the groups or of the plots experimented upon, but we shall direct our illustrations chiefly to the sort of situation typified by a learning experiment. In order that two groups may be optimally matched the *mean* learning ability should be the same in both groups and also the *distribution* of abilities should be of the same shape. It is possible to achieve this by manipulating the membership of the groups until the mean scores for capacity to learn are the same on both sides, and the standard deviations, and perhaps the indices of skewness and kurtosis, are alike. This is a perfectly legitimate way. But these ends can usually be achieved much more surely and easily by matching individuals in pairs. We have on our list, let us say, a student, A, in the experimental group with a certain learning score, and we seek for him a mate, A', in the control group who has the same score for capacity to improve. Then we take in the experimental group a second person, B, and seek a mate, B'. Thus we continue making pairs until we have constructed all that the personnel of our two groups permits. For a reason which we shall discuss later it is desirable to select and to list these in descending order of learning ability, as indicated by the matching scores. When groups are matched by this individual-pair method, it is automatically provided that the means of the capacity scores shall be the same for the two groups and that the shape of both distributions of abilities shall be alike. We shall soon see, too, that a number of collateral advantages accrue in the interpretations of our results. We need not insist upon precisely the same scores for the mates, because our measuring instruments are so far from perfectly valid that we cannot take seriously discrepancies of a few points. Differences as great as 5 or

10 per cent of the range are not too much, provided they are so balanced between the two sides as to keep the means practically the same. It is usually necessary to drop some members from one or both sides because they cannot be matched, but the number should seldom exceed 10 or 12 per cent unless the groups as originally constituted differ markedly in average ability. These unmatched individuals may remain with their groups, but none of their scores are to be counted in the bookkeeping of the experiment.. Insistence upon too great precision in matching is likely to reduce the number of pairs so as to lower reliability unnecessarily, while too crude matching results in groups that do not sufficiently closely parallel each other in the distribution of abilities.   If one group is much larger than the other, it would be feasible to have several mates in the large group for each member of the small group, but the same number of mates for each individual.[1]

On what criterion shall we match our groups? Any criterion is good that is likely to correlate highly with improvement in the function under experimental study; if scores on a criterion do not correlate well above zero with improvement in the function studied, that criterion is useless for purposes of matching. Scores on an intelligence test are frequently used as a basis for matching in educational experiments. Intelligence test scores correlate only fairly highly with most of the growths with which we are concerned and, in consequence, do only moderately well. But in many situations we have nothing better. Usually scores of previous academic achievement are more highly predictive of success, especially in the same field, than intelligence test scores are; hence they make a better basis for matching. For some types of experiments the social-economic status of the home makes a valuable basis for matching. We can get a safer basis for matching by combining several criteria than from a single one.   The ideal procedure is to pair simultaneously on all of these criteria, particularly if they are such as to correlate low with one another but each promising a rather high correlation with improvement in the trait studied.   Also pairs are much harder to make than on a single criterion, unless the number of individuals to be drawn upon is very large.   We are therefore often

[1] A method of achieving the effect of matching groups without loss of population is discussed later in this chapter, p. 463,

forced to the policy of taking an average of the scores from several factors. If these are highly intercorrelated, this averaging of several gives us a more *reliable* measure of capacity just as a longer single test would do; but if the intercorrelations are low, this averaging becomes abortive, since it makes toward equal composite scores for all the individuals.

We suggest the following alternatives in regard to matching:

1. If the function to be learned is new to the individuals, so that no measures of previous attainment are feasible, and if no other measures that are known to correlate more highly with the function are in sight, match on the basis of one or more intelligence tests.

2. If the persons are somewhat along on the curve of learning, match on the basis of good objective measures of present status in the function to be experimented upon. Use at least some of the same tests, or forms of the same tests, that are to be employed at the end of the experiment. We suggest this for several reasons: (*a*) attainment to date is likely to be highly predictive of learning ability in the trait considered; (*b*) matching on the basis of initial attainment places the two mates at about the same position on the learning curve, and position on the learning curve at the beginning of the race has much to do with the prospect of improvement; and (*c*) matching on initial scores with which final scores are to be compared is fairly likely to place together mates who have experienced similarly signed errors of measurement, particularly if a second criterion is also employed as suggested below.

3. A better basis than any measure of present attainment alone is a combination of some measure of present attainment, particularly a measure of initial status in the function under investigation, and a measure of prospective speed of progress— intelligence quotient or educational quotient. These two measures should not be averaged but should be used as simultaneous bases.

4. If more criteria are to be employed in matching, we suggest that they be combined into not more than two or three different types by averaging and that these few different types be used as simultaneous bases for matching.

When averaging scores it must be remembered that elements in a battery get a weighting in proportion to their variabilities.

If, therefore, we intend that the factors shall all have equal weight, we must put their scores into forms which have equal variabilities. This may be accomplished in several ways:

1. The scores in each test except one may be multiplied by some index that will make all variabilities approximately the same. If, for example, we accept A as the basis of one, all scores in test B must be multiplied by σ_A/σ_B in order to give factor B the same weight in the battery as A has. A corresponding thing is true of each of the other tests in the combination. If we wish to give multiple weight m to factor S, we can do so by multiplying the scores of test S by $m\sigma_A/\sigma_S$ instead of σ_A/σ_S.

2. We may reduce all scores to z form by dividing the deviation of each from the mean of the scores in that function for both groups combined by the standard deviation of these combined groups (see page 80). Besides being comparable for all sorts of measurements, such "standard scores" have some other advantages.

3. We may reduce all sets of scores to a distribution with a standard mean and a standard variability. This amounts merely to a modification of method 2.

MEASUREMENT OF OUTCOMES

Having matched the groups for apparent capacity to respond to the experimental factor and having kept all the factors except the experimental one constant while time elapsed for the spread of the two groups in growth, our next task becomes the measurement of progress. The least amount of measurement admissible is a test of achievement at the end of the experiment. If, however, conditions permit, it is highly desirable to have measurements of progress from time to time within the course of the experiment, so that we may be able to compare the two growth curves at several points instead of merely at the end. It is, too, highly desirable to have one or more delayed measurements in order to ascertain how well the differential advantage persists.

It is particularly desirable that the measurements be thorough. If the tests employed have low reliabilities, on account of shortness or other limitation, the obtained differences are smaller than the true ones. Equally unfortunate is the practice of measuring for only a few, or even only a single one, of the traits potentially affected by the experimental factor. When one has gone to the trouble to match groups and to maintain a differential in treatment of these groups, it is too bad to stop with less than the most nearly complete answer to our question that the situation would be able to make. Ideally we should measure with respect to every type of outcome that might hypothetically be affected by the experimental factor. Gates[1] gave a good example of comprehensive measurement when, in one of his experiments, he measured differences in seventeen different traits.

Later in this chapter we shall return to the discussion of the importance of thorough and valid measurements.

In all careful experimentation the measure employed for contrasting the central tendencies of the groups is the mean, not the median. Medians have lower reliabilities than means. Sometimes differences are taken in terms of proportion, e.g., the proportion of pupils elected to student offices from each of the groups, or the proportion making honor grades. We may also wish to compare the variabilities, since one of the methods may make for evenness of attainment on the part of the members of the group while the other may make for differences among individuals. Furthermore, we may desire to measure certain outcomes in terms of coefficients of correlation; particularly we may wish to know which sort of treatment brings attainments that correlate most highly with the measure of learning ability that constituted the basis for matching. We may desire, too, to know what proportion of individuals exceeded their mates by each method, and whether those who exceeded their mates in the experimental group were at the high levels of "intelligence" or at the low levels, or scattered at random through the distribution.

RELIABILITY OF DIFFERENCES

Having found differences, our next task is to consider their importance. Are they large enough to claim much attention? There are several ways in which we can play up our differences so as to give to ourselves and to others some rather concrete notion of their degree of importance.

1. We may put them in terms of percentage. We may say that the control group gained an excess of 0.43 points over the

[1] GATES, A. I., "A Modern Systematic versus an Opportunistic Method of Teaching," *Teach. Coll. Rec.*, Vol. 27, pp. 679-700.

experimental group which is 5.3 per cent of the size of the mean of the latter group; or that the gain by the control group was 118 per cent of that of the experimental group.

2. We may put the difference in terms of the period of time normally required for making as much progress. Thus we may say that the mean of the experimental group exceeded that of the control group by an amount equal to 3 months of educational age, or by half as much as the normal gain between the freshman and the senior year in a typical liberal arts college.

3. We may put the difference in terms of standard measures. This we do by dividing the difference between the means by the standard deviation of the scores *of the two groups combined*. To put the difference thus in terms of standard deviations is to give to it a meaning that is the same for all sorts of measurements and all sorts of situations and is a highly desirable practice.

4. We may show how far our obtained difference is from a chance one, and, consequently, what degree of assurance we may have that it will not turn in the opposite direction with further sampling. This is the matter of reliability and is dependent upon the size of the groups as well as upon the size of the difference. Since it does not turn upon the absolute size of the difference but upon a combination of this and the size of the population, it does not belong in the same category as the preceding three. Indeed a good interpretation of a difference (especially between means) should include both one of the previous three showings and this one on reliability in addition.

In our chapter on Reliability of Differences we gave the necessary formulas for the computation of these reliabilities. We shall here merely apply some of them to a typical experiment. We choose for this purpose part of a small experiment by John A. Cooper (Pennsylvania State master's thesis on "The Relation of Participation in College Athletics to Academic Success as Measured by Objective Tests"). The data we wish to use are set forth in Table XL. The students were matched on intelligence test scores and attainment was measured by the Carnegie Foundation Test for College Seniors. The differences by pairs of matched students are given in the column farthest to the right.

The mean of the athletes' score is 507, that of the nonathletes 530, and the difference 23. This last quantity tallies, as it

TABLE XL.—COMPARATIVE SCORES OF MATCHED ATHLETES AND
NONATHLETES ON THE CARNEGIE ACHIEVEMENT TESTS AT
PENNSYLVANIA STATE COLLEGE, 1928

Athlete			Nonathletes			
Student	Intelligence score	Achievement core	Student	Intelligence score	Achievement score	Difference
D	81	529	C	81	426	+103
F	79	410	P	79	332	+ 78
M	91	583	N	91	797	−214
P	96	380	F	94	486	−106
R	90	580	H	89	656	− 76
S	115	589	R	109	514	+ 75
V	73	539	C	73	489	+ 50
C	116	824	B	124	751	+ 73
M	98	506	H	98	538	− 32
M	105	832	F	105	455	+377
W	95	595	A	95	799	−204
B	95	592	R	93	564	+ 28
F	99	286	B	102	599	−313
A	92	397	P	92	638	−241
B	96	350	P	96	588	−238
M	87	582	H	87	491	+ 91
R	97	544	H	97	630	− 86
S	64	345	M	64	526	−181
J	89	542	S	89	545	− 3
P	90	592	M	90	590	+ 2
S	61	535	N	63	466	+ 69
E	75	389	W	75	372	+ 17
M	119	857	K	115	584	+273
E	111	571	B	111	537	+ 34
K	88	555	F	88	541	+ 14
M	95	511	G	97	477	+ 34
D	76	484	F	76	382	+102
T	67	408	M	71	537	−129
R	85	523	H	84	284	+239
S	89	387	G	59	343	+ 44
G	89	381	G	89	870	−489
G	89	356	A	87	467	−111
C	63	362	S	62	417	− 55
E	81	375	E	84	544	−169
M	75	569	K	72	420	+149
W	77	394	M	77	424	− 30
Means	88.5	507	..	87.5	530	− 23
Sigmas	....	135	..	14.9	130.44	166.25

Intelligence score call factor 1; athletic-achievement score, 2; and nonathletic achievement score, 3. $r_{12} = .564$, $r_{13} = .492$, $r_{23} = .215$.

must, with the sum of the differences by pairs (last column) divided by N. By formula (95), the standard error of this difference is

$$\sigma_{m_1 - m_2} = \frac{\sigma_{d's}}{\sqrt{N}} = \frac{166.25}{\sqrt{36}} = 27.7$$

The ratio of the difference to its standard error is

$$t = \frac{23}{27.7} = 0.83$$

This is far short of the conventionally demanded ratio of 3. But as we pointed out earlier, there is no magic in a ratio that reaches exactly 3, although it is true that near this point the odds against reversal begin to mount extremely rapidly with increasing ratios. On pages 169 to 170 we explained the method of interpreting such ratio of the difference to its standard error. Reference to the table of integrals of the normal curve shows that, if the true difference were zero, we would expect to obtain a difference as much as 0.83 standard errors above zero in 0.203 of the trials while we would expect the opposite in .797 of the trials. The chances are, therefore, 3.9 to 1 that the true difference is in favor of the nonathletes.

Are athletes more variable in attainment than nonathletes? The standard deviation of the scores of the former is 135 while that of the latter is 130 a difference of 5. Is that a reliable difference? The reliability formula required here is (104)

$$\sigma_{\sigma_2 - \sigma_3} = \sqrt{\sigma_{\sigma_2}^2 + \sigma_{\sigma_3}^2 - 2r_{23}^2 \sigma_{\sigma_2}\sigma_{\sigma_3}}$$
$$= \sqrt{\frac{\sigma_2^2 + \sigma_3^2 - 2r_{23}^2 \sigma_2 \sigma_3}{2N}}$$

The r here is .215 which when squared gives .04. To use this r here will really make only an insignificant difference, but we shall do it anyway in order to illustrate the principle. Then

$$\sigma_{\sigma_2 - \sigma_3} = \sqrt{\frac{135^2 + 130^2 - (2)(.04)(135)(130)}{72}} = 21.8$$

Dividing the difference by its standard error, we get

$$t = \frac{5}{21.8} = 0.23$$

This is too small a ratio to give any appreciable assurance that further sampling will not show the true difference to lie on the opposite side. The odds are only 1.5 to 1 that the true difference lies in the indicated direction.

We have made here the "large sample" type of interpretation, which is appropriate for an N of 36. This form of interpretation assumes that $\sigma_2 - \sigma_3$ is distributed normally. As a matter of fact, the distribution of standard deviations from samples is not normal and neither, in consequence, is that of the difference between standard deviations. But they approach normality as N increases, and, with $N = 25$ or more, the error in taking them to be normal is small and is not very great even with an N as low as ten.[1] But for an "exact" interpretation in small samples the probability of getting in a sample a divergence between σ's as great as the one in hand must be determined from the distribution of s_1/s_2 in the manner discussed on pages 335 to 337. The probability of getting a given divergence as measured by this *ratio* is the same as the probability of getting the same divergence in the form of a *difference* between these same sample values, because it is the probability of getting simultaneously sample values as far apart as these or farther when the true difference is zero.

Do the attainments of athletes correlate more highly with "intelligence" than those of nonathletes? In order to determine this, we must compute the r's between intelligence test scores and achievement test scores for both the athletic and nonathletic group. For the athletes this r is .564 and for the nonathletes it is .492. There is a difference of .072. Formula (107) would be the correct one to use. But in practice we usually ignore the r between the r's unless very precise results are required with a population large enough to justify such attempts at precision. In view of the low correlations in our problem, and the smallness of our population, we shall use formula (109) which is not only sufficient for our purpose here but will usually be sufficient when comparing the r's in controlled experimentation.

$$\sigma_{r_{12}-r_{13}} = \sqrt{\sigma_{r_{12}}^2 + \sigma_{r_{13}}^2} = \sqrt{.0191 + .0210} = .20$$

The ratio of the difference between the r's to the standard error

[1] See PEARSON, KARL, *Biometrika*, Vol. 10, p. 529; or DEMING and BIRGE, "Theory of Statistical Errors," *Rev. Modern Phys.*, Vol. 6, p. 129.

of that difference is .36, which is again too low to have satisfactory statistical significance.

The difference between the means is 0.18 standard deviations. In spite of the fact that the difference between the means is slightly in favor of the nonathletes, only seventeen of the nonathletes exceeded their mates in achievement score while nineteen athletes excelled. These advantages are scattered so miscellaneously over the range as not to suggest any relation between intelligence and the effect of athletic participation upon scholarship. This experiment shows slight if any difference in academic attainments between athletes and nonathletes at the college level. If there are real differences, our number of subjects is too small to demonstrate them. A little later we shall discuss the question of number of cases required to show decisive results where there are true differences but very small ones.

The example treated above employed measurements of only end differences. Table XLI gives data from an experiment in which measurement is in terms of gains. It is from a Pennsylvania State College master's thesis by Boyd M. Beagle on the effect of technical analysis in the teaching of appreciation of poetry. The experimental group is the one for which technical analysis had a place in the teaching between the time of taking initial measurements and the time of final measurement, while from the teaching of the control group such analysis was absent. Our formula for reliability in such application is (97), given on page 168. It is left for the reader to apply, as are also the other desirable interpretations.

The most carefully controlled experimentation involves well-matched groups. But sometimes experimenting is done with random groups. This was especially true of the early experiments, but sometimes occurs at present. A notable recent example is *An Experimental Study of the Educational Influences of the Typewriter in the Elementary School Classroom* by Ben D. Wood and Frank N. Freeman. When the number of individuals or groups compared is very large, random selection is fairly likely to bring about near equality in learning ability between the two sides. But even in the Wood-Freeman experiment, involving nearly 15,000 pupils, differences between the groups in scores of aptitude were sometimes appreciable, as were also differences in the average quality of the teachers on the two

TABLE XLI.—Scores in Judging Poetry by an Experimental and a Control Group—Abbott-Trabue Test

P.N.	Experimental group			Control group			D.G.
	I.S.	E.S.	G.	I.S.	E.S.	G.	
1	6	7	1	4	4	0	1
2	3	6	3	7	6	−1	4
3	5	7	2	7	7	0	2
4	5	5	0	8	7	−1	1
5	6	4	−2	6	5	−1	−1
6	8	9	1	7	5	−2	3
7	5	7	2	2	5	3	−1
8	3	5	2	6	5	−1	3
9	3	6	3	7	8	1	2
10	3	6	3	6	6	0	3
11	1	9	8	3	4	1	7
12	4	2	−2	3	9	6	−8
13	6	7	1	5	3	−2	3
14	6	5	−1	4	4	0	−1
15	3	6	3	5	3	−2	5
16	4	7	3	3	9	6	−3
17	2	2	0	4	5	1	−1
18	5	7	2	4	3	−1	3
19	5	4	−1	3	1	−2	1
20	4	6	2	6	6	0	2
21	6	8	2	6	8	2	0
22	3	4	1	2	5	3	−2
23	6	5	−1	3	3	0	−1
24	2	5	3	5	3	−2	5
25	0	2	2	1	3	2	0
26	3	3	0	5	8	3	−3
27	1	3	2	2	4	2	0
28	6	6	0	4	4	0	0
29	2	4	2	3	6	3	−1
30	6	6	0	4	5	1	−1
31	1	2	1	4	7	3	−2
32	5	6	1	5	4	−1	2

P.N. = pair number.
E.S. = end score.
D.G. = difference in gains.
I.S. = initial score.
G. = gains.

sides. A very much smaller number of subjects carefully
matched would give more decisive and less ambiguous results
than a larger number only loosely matched.

When random rather than matched groups are employed, the
r in the third term of the reliability formulas is to be regarded
as zero, so that the third term drops out.   For difference between
means, the formula then becomes

$$\sigma_{m_1-m_2} = \sqrt{\sigma_{m_1}^2 + \sigma_{m_2}^2}$$

This formula is frequently employed even when the contrasted
groups have been matched.   Then the obtained standard error
of the difference is higher than it should be, and the indicated
reliability is too low.   It may be worth while to ask how much
too low.   If the correlation were perfect and the two standard
deviations were equal, the $(-2r\sigma_{m_1}\sigma_{m_2})$ would completely offset
the $(\sigma_{m_1}^2 + \sigma_{m_2}^2)$, so that the resulting standard error would be
zero.   If the $r = .50$, the residuum under the radical would
be half as great as if the r were not considered and hence the
standard error, $\sqrt{.50}$ or $.70$ as large.   If the r were only $.20$,
the standard error would be $\sqrt{.80} = .89$ as much.   So, when
the r is large, consideration of it makes a vast difference, particularly in view of the fact that the odds increase much more rapidly
than the standard error decreases; but, when the r is small, the
effect of its consideration is negligible.

If the r belongs and has not been used, it may be of interest
when evaluating an experiment to speculate on the amount of
error involved.   The amount of correlation to be expected
between the end scores may be inferred from the r between the
matching factor and the end scores, which is sometimes given
and more often can be roughly guessed.   If the two end arrays
are uncorrelated except through the matching factor, the partial
r with the matching factor held constant will be zero.   Thus, if
the subscript 1 refers to the matching factor and 2 and 3 to the
two arrays of end scores,

$$r_{23.1} = \frac{r_{23} - r_{12}r_{13}}{\sqrt{1 - r_{12}^2}\sqrt{1 - r_{13}^2}} = 0$$

Clearing of fractions and solving,

$$r_{23} - r_{12}r_{13} = 0 \tag{222}$$
$$r_{23} = r_{12}r_{13}$$

Thus the cross correlation can be expected to be the product of the r's between the matching scores and the scores in each of the end arrays. If the two r's between matching and final scores are equal, the r between the arrays of end scores is the square of the r between end scores and matching scores. If subjects are matched on intelligence test scores and achievement is measured in terms of school grades, a correlation of from about .30 to .50 may be expected between matching scores and achievement so that the cross correlation may be expected to run from .09 to .25. If matching is done on an objective achievement test closely related to the final one, an r of .70 or .80 may be expected between matching and achievement arrays and an r between the two arrays of end scores of .49 to .64.

A trial of this formula on Cooper's data, Table XL, gives

$$r_{23} = (.564)(.492) = .277$$

The correlation obtained by computation is .215. In so small a population the assumptions are not fulfilled sufficiently well to give more than a reasonable approximation to the correct r.

ON CORRELATIONS WHERE GAINS ARE MEASURED

If measurement is made in terms of gains between initial and final status, the r's between the gains by the two groups must be expected to be very low except where the subjects are near the beginning of the growth curve in the function under study at the time the investigation begins. That is because, as the curve flattens out, gains correlate much less with initial scores than end scores do, so that, when squared, these r's suggest practically a zero correlation between the two arrays of gains. An increase in standard deviation between initial scores and final ones suggests a positive correlation between gains and initial status, while the absence of an increase or an actual decrease in the standard deviation suggests a zero or a negative correlation. The chief factor in making toward such low or negative correlations between gains and initial status is unreliability in the tests used for measuring gains. We have been able to show (although we shall not here consume the necessary space to give the derivation) that a negative correlation between gains and initial status in the same function in which the gains are measured is attributable to unreliability in the measuring instrument and that this correlation has the following magnitude:

$$r_{x_1 g_u} = -\sqrt{\tfrac{1}{2}(1 - r_{12})} \tag{223}$$

where x_1 is an initial score in the function, r_{12} is the reliability coefficient of the test, and g_u is that part of a gain between first and second testing that is due solely to the unreliability of the testing instrument. If the matching is not on initial status in the function in which gains are to be measured but on some outside criterion instead (say a general intelligence test, which we shall label with the subscript 0), and it is desired to know the r between gains due to unreliability and this matching factor, we can show that

$$r_{0 g_u} = -r_{01}\sqrt{\tfrac{1}{2}(1 - r_{12})} \tag{224}$$

It is because the positive r between truly measured gains and truly measured initial status only partly offsets this negative correlation due to unreliability in the measuring instruments that the r between gains and the matching factor so often proves to be zero or slightly negative. This argument also shows that, where results are to be measured in terms of gains, matching is much less important than where comparisons are in terms of only end scores.

Sometimes the occasion arises to infer what the r would be between some experimental factor (x_a) and true gains in another function. For example, we take initial and final measures of academic achievement and thus obtain fallibly measured gains (g). We compute the r between these fallibly measured gains and the extent of participation in extracurricular activities. We wish to infer what the r would be with the disturbing effect of the unreliability removed. We need, therefore, the r between gains and ECA with the gains due to the unreliability of the test held constant. Our regular formula for partial correlation is

$$r_{x_a g \cdot g_u} = \frac{r_{x_a g} - r_{x_a g_u} r_{g g_u}}{\sqrt{1 - r_{x_a g_u}^2}\,\sqrt{1 - r_{g g_u}^2}}, \; r_{g g_u} \neq 1 \tag{225}$$

The $r_{x_a g}$ we can compute from our data.

$r_{g g_u}$ can be shown to equal $(2\sigma_{x_1}/\sigma_g)\sqrt{\tfrac{1}{2}(1 - r_{12})}$ \hfill (225a)

$r_{x_a g_u}$ can be shown to equal $-r_{x_a x_1}\sqrt{\tfrac{1}{2}(1 - r_{12})}$ \hfill (225b)

We calculate these several r's and substitute them in our partial correlation formula.

COMBINING SEVERAL TRIALS

Sometimes we may wish to combine into a single showing the results from a number of trials in an experiment. We then need the difference between a sum of means by the experimental group and sum by the control group. If individuals have been paired, the standard error of such difference is simply the standard deviation of the column representing the differences between corresponding sums of scores by the paired individuals when this standard deviation has been divided by the square root of the number of pairs. That is, we make the same combination of scores of individuals as we intend to make of means, take the standard deviation of the resulting array, and divide this by $\sqrt{N}$. This involves formula (98). If subjects are not paired individually and yet groups are matched, so that an element of correlation is present, the formula for the standard error is easily derived by anyone for any combination he needs as follows:

$$
\begin{aligned}
\sigma^2_{(m_1+m_2+m_3+\ldots)-(m_4+m_5+m_6+\ldots)} \\
= \frac{\Sigma(m_1 + m_2 + m_3 + \cdots - m_4 - m_5 - m_6 \cdots)^2}{S} \\
= \frac{\Sigma m_1^2}{S} + \frac{\Sigma m_2^2}{S} + \frac{\Sigma m_3^2}{S} + \cdots \\
+ \frac{\Sigma m_4^2}{S} + \frac{\Sigma m_5^2}{S} + \frac{\Sigma m_6^2}{S} + \cdots \\
+ \frac{2\Sigma m_1 m_2}{S} + \frac{2\Sigma m_1 m_3}{S} + \cdots \\
- \frac{2\Sigma m_1 m_4}{S} - \frac{2\Sigma m_1 m_5}{S} - \cdots \\
+ \frac{2\Sigma m_4 m_5}{S} + \frac{2\Sigma m_4 m_6}{S} + \cdots \\
= \sigma^2_{m_1} + \sigma^2_{m_2} + \sigma^2_{m_3} + \cdots + \sigma^2_{m_4} + \sigma^2_{m_5} + \sigma^2_{m_6} \\
+ \cdots + 2r_{12}\sigma_{m_1}\sigma_{m_2} + 2r_{13}\sigma_{m_1}\sigma_{m_3} + \cdots \\
- 2r_{14}\sigma_{m_1}\sigma_{m_4} \cdots \\
+ 2r_{45}\sigma_{m_4}\sigma_{m_5} \cdots
\end{aligned}
$$

(Continue with all corresponding possible combinations) (226)

If the groups are random ones instead of matched ones, all r's are zero and only the terms of the form $\sigma^2_{m_i}$ remain. But it should be remembered that only closely similar units are to be thus additively combined.

A REGRESSION TECHNIQUE FOR MATCHING GROUPS

We can employ a regression technique for the hypothetical matching of groups, which obviates the necessity of having precisely matched pairs. In our control group we determine the regression of end scores upon the matching scores. Then we predict for each member of the experimental group the end score he would be expected to make on the basis of his learning ability as indicated by his matching score. If the mean of the obtained scores is significantly greater than that of the "expected" scores, the experimental factor is indicated as having a differential potency in contributing to growth.[1] We shall apply this technique to Cooper's experiment reported on page 454. We need the ordinary rectilinear regression equation and need to make predictions by the method explained on pages 110 to 112. Letting X_1 be the intelligence test scores for the nonathletes and X_3 their final scores, letting X_3' be a predicted score rather than an obtained one, and employing the numerical values of the statistics as computed from Tables XL and XLII,

$$X_3' = r \frac{\sigma_3}{\sigma_1}(X_1) + \left(M_{x_3} - r \frac{\sigma_3}{\sigma_1} M_{x_1} \right)$$

$$= .492 \frac{130.44}{14.9} X_1 + \left(530 - .492 \frac{130.44}{14.9} 87.5 \right)$$

We now apply this regression equation to predicting what should be the final score for each member of the experimental group in case the experimental factor had no differential effect. To do this we merely enter in succession as Y_1 the intelligence test scores of the members of the experimental group. Rewriting the equation in terms of Y_j' with the complex expressions evaluated, we have

$$Y_2' = 4.307 Y_1 + 153.12$$

The first athlete in the table has an intelligence test score of 81. Substituting this for Y_1 in the regression equation, we predict

---

[1] This is similar to Fisher's covariance technique. Obviously it can be applied to agricultural or sociological or to other data with suitable control factors and the substitution of the appropriate outcomes for "growth."

for him a score of 501.99. He actually made a score of 529, so that for him $Y_2 - Y_2' = +27.01$. The predicted scores, attained scores, and differences for the 36 individuals are entered in Table XLII.

The mean difference of the predicted scores from the attained scores is -27.47, so that the athletes had lower scores on the achievement test than nonathletes of corresponding intelligence. In order to test whether or not this is a significant difference, we need to know the standard error of this mean difference. We shall take first the case where the experimental group and the control group have the same N and where the two groups are perfectly equated.

Let y be an obtained end score in the experimental group (instead of y_2, for the moment), and let y' be a predicted one; similarly, let x_3' be a predicted final score for the control group. Let us take both $\bar{y}$ and $\bar{y}'$ as deviations of sample means from the means of the whole of their respective populations. Then

$$\sigma_{\bar{y}-\bar{y}'}^2 = \sigma_{\bar{y}}^2 + \sigma_{\bar{y}'}^2 - 2r_{\overline{yy'}}\sigma_{\bar{y}}\sigma_{\bar{y}'}$$

But, in each sample, the mean of the predicted y' scores is the same as the mean of the x_3' scores (which also equals the mean of the x_3 scores), since they were predicted from initial scores perfectly equated with the corresponding x_1 scores. Hence, making this substitution,

$$\sigma_{\bar{y}-\bar{y}'}^2 = \sigma_{\bar{y}}^2 + \sigma_{\bar{x}_3}^2 - 2r_{\bar{x}_3\bar{y}}\sigma_{\bar{x}_3}\sigma_{\bar{y}}$$

$$= \frac{\tilde{\sigma}_{\bar{y}}^2}{N} + \frac{\tilde{\sigma}_{\bar{x}_3}^2}{N} - 2r_{x_3y}\frac{\tilde{\sigma}_{\bar{x}_3}\tilde{\sigma}_{\bar{y}}}{N}$$

(A) $\qquad = \dfrac{\tilde{\sigma}_{\bar{x}_3}^2(1 - r_{x_1x_3}^2)}{N} + \left[\dfrac{\tilde{\sigma}_{\bar{x}_3}^2 r_{x_1x_3}^2}{N} + \dfrac{\tilde{\sigma}_{\bar{y}}^2}{N} - 2r_{x_3y}\dfrac{\tilde{\sigma}_{\bar{x}_3}\tilde{\sigma}_{\bar{y}}}{N}\right]$

Again, in the sample,

$$\sigma_{y-y'}^2 = \sigma_y^2 + \sigma_{y'}^2 - 2r_{yy'}\sigma_y\sigma_{y'}$$

Now $r_{yy'} = r_{y_1y_2}$, because each y' is the corresponding y_1 multiplied by a constant, b. $\sigma_{y'}$ is the standard deviation of the scores predicted as lying on the regression line, and (page 240) we showed that this equals $r\sigma_y$. However, since the y's are predicted from the x regression line, $\sigma_{y'} = r_{x_1x_3}\sigma_{x_3}$. Making these substitutions, we have

$$\sigma_{y-y'}^2 = \sigma_y^2 + \sigma_{x_3}^2 r_{x_1 x_3}^2 - 2r_{y_1 y_3} r_{x_1 x_3} \sigma_y \sigma_{x_3}$$

But we showed on page 459 that, assuming no correlation except through the matching factor,

$$r_{x_1 x_3} r_{y_1 y_3} = r_{x_3 y_3}$$

Substituting this and dividing by $(N - 1)$,

(B) $$\frac{\sigma_{y-y'}^2}{N-1} = \frac{\sigma_y^2}{N-1} + \frac{\sigma_{x_3}^2 r_{x_1 x_3}^2}{N-1} - 2r_{x_3 y} \frac{\sigma_{x_3} \sigma_y}{N-1}$$

But, allowing for the fact that the σ's in (A) are the population variances and those in (B) are the sample variances, this quantity is the same as the quantity in brackets in (A). We can simplify (A) by substituting (B) into it. We also adjust the term outside the brackets to the sample value by dividing by $(N - 1)$ instead of by N. We then have

$$\sigma_{\bar{y}-\bar{y}'}^2 = \frac{\sigma_{x_3}^2 (1 - r_{x_1 x_3}^2)}{N-1} + \frac{\sigma_{y-y'}^2}{N-1} \qquad \text{(227)}$$

(Sampling variance of the difference between the means of predicted and obtained scores, when experimental and control groups are perfectly equated)

That is for the case of perfectly equated groups. We need a more general formula. Since we are using population variances, our formula need not be affected by differing N's for the experimental and the control groups. But if the *mean* of the matching scores of the experimental group differs from that of the control group, we need an adjustment for that difference. In that case $\sigma_{x_3}^2$ cannot, for the purpose of substitution for $N\sigma_{\bar{y}'}^2$, be taken from the mean of its own array but, instead, from that mean plus $b(\bar{x}_1 - \bar{y}_1)$, where b is the regression coefficient. The variance of this further factor must be added to the variance due to the other factors (since it is independent of the others). This will give us, for our general case, where the subscripts i and f stand for the equating scores and the achievement scores, respectively,

$$\sigma_{\bar{y}-\bar{y}'} = \sqrt{\frac{\sigma_{x_f}^2(1 - r_{x_i x_f}^2)}{N_x - 1} + \frac{\sigma_{y-y'}^2}{N_y - 1} + \frac{(\bar{x}_i - \bar{y}_i)^2 \sigma_{x_f}^2 (1 - r_{x_i x_f}^2)}{(N_x - 1)\sigma_{x_i}^2}}$$

(General formula for the standard error of the difference between means of predicted and obtained scores in an experimental comparison for one matching factor) (228)

TABLE XLII.—PREDICTED SCORES IN COMPARISON WITH ATTAINED SCORES, COOPER'S EXPERIMENT

Student	Intelligence score	Predicted score	Attained score	Difference
D	81	501.99	529	+ 27.01
F	79	493.37	410	− 83.37
M	91	545.06	583	+ 37.94
P	96	566.59	380	−186.59
R	90	540.75	580	+ 39.25
S	115	648.43	589	− 59.43
V	73	467.53	539	+ 71.47
C	116	652.73	824	+171.27
M	98	575.21	506	− 69.21
M	105	605.36	832	+226.64
W	95	562.28	595	+ 32.72
B	95	562.28	592	+ 29.72
F	99	579.51	286	−293.51
A	92	549.36	397	−152.36
B	96	566.59	350	−216.59
M	87	527.83	582	+ 54.17
R	97	570.90	544	− 26.90
S	64	428.77	345	− 83.77
J	89	536.44	542	+ 5.56
P	90	540.75	592	+ 51.25
S	61	415.85	535	+119.15
E	75	476.15	389	− 87.15
M	119	665.65	857	+191.35
E	111	631.20	571	− 60.20
K	88	532.14	555	+ 22.86
M	95	562.29	511	− 51.29
D	76	480.45	484	+ 3.55
T	67	441.69	408	− 33.69
R	85	519.21	523	+ 3.79
S	89	536.44	387	−149.44
G	89	536.44	381	−155.44
G	89	536.44	356	−180.44
C	63	424.46	362	− 62.46
E	81	501.99	375	−126.99
M	75	476.15	569	+ 92.85
W	77	484.76	394	− 90.76
Mean	88.5	534.53	507.06	− 27.47
Standard deviation	....	......	135	117.08

Applying this formula to Cooper's data, we get

$$\sigma_{\bar{y}-\bar{y}'}$$

$$= \sqrt{\frac{(130.44)^2(1 - .492^2)}{36 - 1} + \frac{117.08^2}{36 - 1} + \frac{(1)^2(130.44)^2(1 - .492^2)}{(36 - 1)(14.9)^2}}$$

$$= 27.6. \quad t = \frac{27.47}{27.6} = 1.00$$

On page 455 the standard error computed by the customary method was found to be 27.7, a result in remarkably close agreement with the one found here.   But the difference between means by that method was only 23 instead of our present 27.47. That discrepancy is due to the fact that the two groups were not perfectly equated; the athletes (experimental group) had a mean intelligence test score one point higher than the control group, and that one point difference in matching score carried the expectation of an extra achievement score of just about four points.   Although for all practical purposes the two procedures tell the same story, the regression technique was really more accurate than the conventional matched-group technique because it showed what would be the expected difference if the groups were perfectly matched, as well as the reliability of that difference.   Of course, in practice we would not employ the regression technique where we had the groups already matched, but we used it here on that type of problem in order that we might make comparisons between the methods.

For equating on a combination of several factors, y's should be predicted by the partial regression equation (see Chap. VIII). Everything will behave in the same manner as with single matching except that the multiple correlation coefficient $R^2_{x_f}(i_1, i_2, \ldots, i_k)$ will replace $r^2_{x_i x_f}$ in the first term under the standard-error radical and the third term under the radical will become

$$\frac{\sigma^2_{x_f}[1 - R^2_{x_f(i_1, i_2, \ldots, i_k)}]}{N_x - 1} \sum \frac{(\bar{x}_{i_j} - \bar{y}_{i_j})^2}{\sigma^2_{i_f} \cdot i_1 i_2 i_3 \cdots (-i_j) \cdots i_k}$$

where $\bar{x}_{i_j}$ is the mean of any one of the matching factors in the control group and $\bar{y}_{i_j}$ is the mean of the corresponding matching array for the experimental group, the task calling for the summation of all the differences between such matching means squared and divided by the partial variance of its own x_i array.

For the number of matching variables indicated on the left, the partial sigma values required for the denominator are given at the right. Beyond four matching factors (if desirable to use more than four, which is doubtful), the worker should resort to the Doolittle method to compute multiple R for

$$\sigma^2_{i_j \cdot i_1 i_2 i_3 \cdots i_k} = \sigma^2_{i_j}[1 - R^2_{i_j(i_1 i_2 i_3 \cdots i_k)}]$$

For simplicity we shall write 1, 2, 3, etc., for $i_1 i_2 \ldots i_k$.

No. of
Variables

2    $\sigma^2_{1\cdot2} = \sigma^2_1(1 - r^2_{12}); \sigma^2_{2\cdot1} = \sigma^2_2(1 - r^2_{12})$

3    $\sigma^2_{1\cdot23} = \sigma^2_1(1 - r^2_{13})(1 - r^2_{12\cdot3})$

      $\sigma^2_{2\cdot13} = \sigma^2_2(1 - r^2_{23})(1 - r^2_{12\cdot3})$

      $\sigma^2_{3\cdot12} = \sigma^2_3(1 - r^2_{23})(1 - r^2_{13\cdot2})$

4    $\sigma^2_{1\cdot234} = \sigma^2_1(1 - r^2_{12})(1 - r^2_{13\cdot2})(1 - r^2_{14\cdot23})$

      $\sigma^2_{2\cdot134} = \sigma^2_2(1 - r^2_{23})(1 - r^2_{24\cdot3})(1 - r^2_{12\cdot34})$

      $\sigma^2_{3\cdot124} = \sigma^2_3(1 - r^2_{23})(1 - r^2_{34\cdot2})(1 - r^2_{13\cdot24})$

      $\sigma^2_{4\cdot123} = \sigma^2_4(1 - r^2_{34})(1 - r^2_{24\cdot3})(1 - r^2_{14\cdot23})$

The formulas for the required partial r's can be found on pages 243 to 244 of this volume.

This third term in the standard-error formula is the most tedious of all the parts of the work, and yet it makes a trivial difference in the value obtained if the groups are reasonably close together in the means of the matching elements. If the groups are not far from equal in equating scores and no great exactness is required, this third term of the standard-error formula might be dropped; the worker, then, should remember that the obtained standard error is a trifle smaller than the correct one.

The above formulas are based on large sample theory. If, because the sample is small, the t is to be interpreted in terms of Student's distribution, each $(N - 1)$ in the denominator should be replaced by $(N - k - 1)$, where k is the number of matching factors. Then use Table XII or XLV and XLVI instead of the table for the normal distribution, entering the table with

$$(N_x + N_y - k - 2)$$

degrees of freedom.

It will be observed that this technique involves matching each experimental subject with a *hypothetical* one in the control group who stands on the same point on the x axis, then comparing his final score with that of the *mean* of a hypothetical *class* of controls who had the same matching score as his. In the matched-group technique we equate the actual scores of paired subjects and compare the actual end scores of the same two.

We applied the regression technique to Cooper's experiment for the sake of comparison of methods. Ordinarily we would not apply it to that problem because the groups were already satisfactorily matched by pairs. The regression technique is particularly useful where the subjects cannot be paired without too much sacrifice in size of population. The two groups need not be exactly equated for means on the matching factor, but to the extent to which the control group lies on a different level from the experimental group on the matching criterion, to that extent we make a hazardous assumption of rectilinearity of regression beyond the range of the control group scores. There is no need that control and experimental groups have the same number of subjects. Each group should be as large as available populations permit, although there would be loss rather than gain by including subjects who were clearly abnormal from the standpoint of any of the conditions of the experiment.

INCREASED RELIABILITY FROM REPLICATION OF EXPERIMENTS

We shall now return to a further consideration of the relation of the size of our sample to the reliability of our differences. We have had abundant occasion to see that the standard error of a difference varies inversely as the square root of the number of subjects. When true differences are small, as they often are, it is not possible to establish them reliably with such small groups of subjects as we may have at our command. Let us get this fact before us more vividly in terms of a formula for the number of subjects needed to give a standard error of a predetermined size when the true difference is believed to be a given amount. Let D stand for the true difference and t be the ratio of a difference to its standard error upon which we intend to insist.

$$ t = \frac{D}{\sigma_{\text{diff}}} = \frac{D}{\sqrt{(\sigma_1^2 + \sigma_2^2 - 2r\sigma_1\sigma_2)/N}} $$

Let us assume that the two σ's are equal. Then, squaring and rearranging the N,

$$t^2 = \frac{ND^2}{2\sigma^2(1-r)}$$
$$N = \frac{2t^2\sigma^2(1-r)}{D^2} \tag{229}$$

From a series of experiments[1] the authors concluded that the true difference to be expected from a certain kind of moral instruction in school is about 0.4 of a standard deviation. Taking this standard deviation to be substantially the same as the one of our formula (the latter can be made the same by computing it from the two distributions combined instead of from one of them) and ignoring the element of correlation, the number of pairs of pupils indicated to yield a ratio of 3 would be

$$N = \frac{(2)(3^2)\sigma^2}{0.4^2\sigma^2} = 113$$

This is the number required to give a ratio as high as 3 in half the trials. If we demand a ratio of 3 in as many as five-sixths of the trials, we must substitute 4 for t instead of 3, and our required number is 200.

Since it is often impracticable to have as large experimental groups as those suggested above and since many situations involve differences that are important even though small, our dependence must frequently be placed upon the reliability of a set of replicated experiments. When the outcomes of a number of experiments point in the same direction, the reliability of the set is much greater than that of any one taken alone and much greater, too, than the average of the reliabilities of the several samples. We are, therefore, led to the consideration of the reliability of a set of experiments.

It is a fundamental principle of the mathematics of chance that if the probability of the occurrence of an event is p under one condition and q under another condition, it is pq for the two conditions combined. Suppose, then, the probability is 7 in 100 that a given difference would have been obtained if the true difference were zero or less in one experiment and 12 in a 100

[1] See *Journal of Educational Sociology*, December, 1933, the whole of which number is devoted to these experiments.

that a given other difference would have been obtained if the true one were zero or below, the two experiments being entirely independent of each other. On the above mentioned principle the probability is only $(.07)$ $(.12) = .0084$ that such differences would have been obtained both times in the two independent trials if the true difference were zero or below. This same principle would hold for any combination of additional probabilities where always the same type of event occurred; *i.e.*, where always the difference turned out on the same side. Thus the odds are very great that the true difference lies on the indicated side when it continues in successive samples to be found consistently on that side, even though the odds indicated at any one trial are not high.

When the odds are low at the first few trials, it is extremely unlikely that the differences will continue to fall consistently on the same side. If they do so, that fact suggests unusual (but not impossible) deviation from the laws of chance or else something erroneous about the calculation of the probabilities. When the odds are low in the individual samples, it is to be expected that some advantages will fall on one side of zero and some on the other. Even in such case, however, the reliability of a set of samples is greater than the average from the samples taken singly. In order to put this fact in better perspective, we shall develop some statistical formulas expressing the relations involved, not so much with the purpose of actually applying them to calculate joint probability but rather as a general basis for the interpretation of the effect of replicating (repeating) an experiment.

We assume an experimental factor running through all the trials equally potent to separate the contrasted groups in all trials, except for the effect of chance errors of sampling. Let n_1, n_2, n_3, . . . be the number of pairs of individuals in the several experiments. Similarly let D_1, D_2, D_3, . . . be the differences between means in samples, and let t_1, t_2, t_3, . . . be the ratios of the several differences to their standard errors. Then

$$(C) \qquad t_1 = \frac{D_1}{\sigma_{D_1}}$$

$$(D) \qquad \sigma_{D_1} = \frac{\sigma_{d_1}}{\sqrt{n_1}}$$

where σ_{d_1} is the standard deviation of the array of paired differences in experiment 1. Furthermore, $D_1 = M_{d_1}$, whence

$$(E) \qquad\qquad D_1 = \frac{\Sigma d_1}{n_1}$$

Thus, substituting (D) and (E) in (C),

$$(F) \qquad\qquad t_1 = \frac{\Sigma d_1 \sqrt{n_1}}{n_1 \sigma_{d_1}}$$

$$= \frac{\Sigma d_1}{\sigma_{d_1} \sqrt{n_1}}$$

and, multiplying through by $\sqrt{n_1}$, $t\sqrt{n_1} = \Sigma d_1/\sigma_{d_1}$.

Thus we have the paired differences in "standard (z) scores" taken from zero as origin. If now we use the symbol z for these scores and sum for all the experiments, we have $\Sigma\Sigma z_d = \Sigma t \sqrt{n}$, it being thus indicated that each t is to be weighted by the square root of its corresponding n. If we assume that these deviations divided by the standard deviations of their respective series are sufficiently similar to permit averaging them without distortion of meaning, the difference between the means of the summed experimental and control groups will be the same as the mean of all the paired differences; viz.,

$$(G) \qquad\qquad D_t = \frac{\Sigma\Sigma z_d}{\Sigma n} = \frac{\Sigma t \sqrt{n}}{\Sigma n}$$

The t for this set of combined z scores will be, by analogy with (F),

$$t_t = \frac{\Sigma t \sqrt{n} \cdot \sqrt{\Sigma n}}{\sigma_{z_{d_t}} \Sigma n} \qquad\qquad (230)$$

where now the $\sigma_{z_{d_t}}$ is the standard deviation of the whole consolidated population of paired differences. If the $z_{d's}$ were taken as deviations from the true mean instead of from zero and if the z scores were standard scores from the total population instead of from the subgroups, this $\sigma_{z_{d_t}}$ would be 1, which is always the value of the standard deviation of a set of z scores. This latter condition need not worry us, since the sigma of a standard-error formula is properly that of the total population of samples rather than that of a single sample. The former condition operates only to add a constant to all scores, which does not affect the variability. Thus the standard deviation is substantially 1, and (230) simplifies to

$$(H) \qquad\qquad t_t = \frac{\Sigma t \sqrt{n}}{\sqrt{\Sigma n}}$$

This would lend itself to calculation if we had the several ratios and the several populations. If we may assume substantially equal populations in the several samples, our formula further simplifies as follows:

$$t_t = \frac{\Sigma t}{\Sigma n} \cdot \frac{\sqrt{\Sigma n} \cdot \sqrt{n}}{1} = \frac{\Sigma t}{an} \cdot \sqrt{n}\sqrt{n}\sqrt{a} = M_t\sqrt{a} \qquad (230a)$$

Thus, if the samples are assumed to be equal in size of population and equally potent in contributing to a validly measured difference, the ratio between the total mean difference and its standard error may be taken to be substantially the square root of the number of samples times the mean ratio. Thus from 25 determinations the standard-error ratio may be expected to be five times as great as the average ratio from a single determination.

The formulas of this section, just as those of the following sections, are not offered as useful formulas for actually making a quantitative computation of the correct statistic; the assumptions which must be made are too precarious to make that safe, except as a rough estimate. The argument is intended merely to stress the fact that the reliability of a set of experiments with differences prevailingly in the same direction is much higher than that of the average single trial. But it must be noted that this applies only where the populations of the several experiments are independent of one another; it does not apply with full force to the case where the same pupils are remeasured, but only where there are added chance samples of the total population regarding which the generalization is to be stated.

One of the authors[1] has shown elsewhere that summing together subtests, as when the experimenter gives a test at the end of each of a number of units in the course of the experiment and then sums the scores into totals in addition to making separate

[1] PETERS, C. C., "Increasing Reliability in Controlled Experiments," *J. Educ. Psychol.*, Vol. 30, pp. 143–150.

showings, also increases the reliability of the experiment. Apart from the question of fatigue, the same effect would be achieved by very extensive tests at the close of the experiment. If the *paired differences* in a matched-group experiment correlate zero among the subtests, which is rather likely to be the case, the following formula indicates the manner in which t may be expected to respond to summing together a comparable tests as compared with the t from a single test:

$$t_s = t_i \sqrt{a} \tag{231}$$

where t_s is the ratio of the difference to its standard error for the summed scores, t_i is that of a single test, and a is the number of tests. This indicates tremendous gains in reliability from extensive testing.

VALID MEASUREMENTS

The previous section was directed against the practice of using short and meager tests for measuring outcomes of experimentation and small populations. In this section we shall show the influence of validity of measurement in separating the means. Unfortunately it often happens in experimentation that commercial tests are employed to measure outcomes because they have prestige or because they are readily available, when they are not very closely related to the difference the experimental factor could be expected to make. That is, they may be valid for other purposes but not particularly valid for measuring the outcomes of the particular experiment in question. We shall show that the difference between measured outcomes in experimental and control groups is likely to be attenuated by reason of this lack of validity in the testing instrument.

Let c stand for the elements which a test measures that are affected by the experimental factor, let b stand for other identifiable elements validly measured as some kind of performance but not a performance affected by the experimental factor, and let e be chance factors caught in the measures. The test is, then, valid for its purpose to the extent to which it measures only the c factors. Each individual's score will be made up of $c + b + e$ factors. The difference between the means will be little affected by the b or the e factors, since they will tend to average about the same on the experimental and the control sides. But the variability will be affected by the b and the e factors as well as by the c factors; it will be increased by reason of them.

If the test were perfectly valid, the difference, measured in standard scores, would be D/σ_c, while with an invalid test it is $D/\sigma_{(c+b+e)}$. This latter is $\sigma_c/\sigma_{(c+b+e)}$ times as great as the former. But $\sigma_c/\sigma_{(c+b+e)} = r_{c(c+b+e)}$, which is the validity coefficient of the test—the correlation between its scores and perfectly valid scores of the same function. The proof of that is as follows: Consider our measures of c, b, and e to be in the form of deviations from the means of their respective arrays. Then

$$ r_{c(c+b+e)} = \frac{\Sigma c^2 + \Sigma cb + \Sigma ce}{N\sigma_c\sigma_{(c+b+e)}} $$

But, since b and e are uncorrelated with c, Σcb and Σce equal zero. Taking the N with the Σc^2 of the numerator, we have

$$ r_{c(c+b+e)} = \frac{\sigma_c^2}{\sigma_c\sigma_{(c+b+e)}} = \frac{\sigma_c}{\sigma_{(c+b+e)}} $$

If D_t represents the difference when validly measured and D the difference obtained by the somewhat invalid test, we have, from the last sentence preceding the proof, $D = rD_t$, or $D_t = D/r$. Thus the difference would be separated if validly measured to an amount equal to the obtained difference divided by the validity coefficient of the test for measuring the particular function differentiating between the experimental and the control processes, when we are talking in terms of standard scores. This will operate to raise the standard-error ratio since the σ of the denominator, which has been decreased by elimination of the irrelevant elements from the test, is the one which appears in the standard-error formula.

The validity coefficient we are talking about here has nothing to do with the validity coefficients often published by test makers, which are correlations with scores from other trusted tests measuring presumably the same function. We mean by the validity coefficient the coefficient of correlation between scores containing no factors other than relevant ones and corresponding scores containing some such factors—an r that could have, under ordinary testing conditions, only a theoretical meaning but about which it is, nevertheless, illuminating to speculate.

Of course, in practice we could not ordinarily make this correction quantitatively, because we do not know the validity coefficient of the test for the purpose in hand. But this argument shows the danger involved in employing testing instruments in experimentation which have little pertinency to the experimental factor and do little justice to it, then taking seriously the small and unreliable differences thus obtained. This very often happens in practice. It is not improbable that tests are sometimes employed for measuring outcomes in experimentation which are padded out by 90 per cent of irrelevant elements while failing to include another 90 per cent of the outcomes actually influenced by the experimental factor. Under these conditions the real difference would be ten times as great (in standard terms) as the obtained one.

A SIGNIFICANT RATIO

Finally, we must again protest the magic that is involved, chiefly for laymen in statistics, in a ratio of just 3 between a difference and its standard error. This is completely arbitrary. Several other equally arbitrary ratios have been suggested. Fisher proposes 2, while McCall has obtained wide use of 2.78. All these ratios, except perhaps Fisher's, are higher than are usually attainable in experiments in education and the social sciences. If one looks through the experimental literature in these fields, he will find that by these standards the vast majority of experiments turn out to show differences that are "not statistically significant." That would be harmless enough if such outcome were not so frequently misinterpreted. It is often taken to mean that the two procedures are equal in value while the experiment may indicate odds of 10 to 1, or 100 to 1, or even 500 to 1 that one is superior to the other. Under such circumstances the evidence does not mean that the procedures are probably of equal effectiveness but only that *it has not yet been conclusively proved* that *A* is better than *B*. We should like to bet on the stock market with the odds 100 to 1 in our favor, or even 5 to 1; and in the same spirit we are willing to consider with more favor than we accord its rival a procedure that an experiment indicates to be superior by odds of much less than the 740 to 1 that a ratio of 3 indicates, while we await more conclusive evidence.

In order to make this objection somewhat more tangible, we might tentatively suggest another particular ratio—if we could feel guaranteed that it, too, would not be taken as magic. If the reader will examine the shape of a normal curve, he will find a place where the curve bends to a maximum degree in thinning out the distribution into a long tail. This point, as one can easily determine by placing the third derivative of the normal-curve function equal to zero and solving for x, is $\sqrt{3}$ sigmas from the mean; that is, 1.73σ. We suggest that this might be taken as a standard for provisional acceptance of the findings of an experiment, and we propose that it might be named the *working ratio*. This point of maximum deflection is the place where the tail begins most radically to thin and hence where the odds begin to increase extremely rapidly with added x distances. Of course, that does not really make it any less arbitrary as a standard; but that ratio represents odds of 23 to 1, and those would seem to be high enough to gamble on while we seek more conclusive evidence.

Exercises

1. Work up Beagle's experiment (page 458) in a number of ways. Of course, the population here is too small to justify elaborate statistical manipulation, but the data are presented because the scores are so small as to involve a minimum of penciling, and they will do well enough for practice.

   a. Find the difference between the means of gains for the two groups and the reliability of that difference.

   b. These groups were matched on general intelligence test scores. Although these scores are not given here, the pairs are ranked in descending order on the basis of them. Compute ρ between this general intelligence criterion and initial scores in appreciation of literature. On the basis of this finding criticize the use of general intelligence test scores as a matching basis in this experiment.

   c. Compare the groups on the basis of merely end scores. Does this comparison tell the same story as that told by gains? Which tells the safer story?

   d. In which group do final scores correlate more highly with initial scores? What is the importance of that, if any?

   e. How do gains correlate with initial scores? With the matching element? Compare with formulas (223) and (224), page 461.

   f. What correlation is there between gains in the experimental and in the control group? Compare with page 459.

   g. Try the difference method of correlation on Exercise *e* [formula (44), page 101], and compare its findings and its convenience with the usual product formula.

h. Compare the variability of gains in the experimental group with that in the control group, and interpret results.

i. The Abbott-Trabue test has rather low reliability for this age level. What effect has that on the findings? You have from these exercises information on the reliability of this measure for these groups. Find it.

2. Examine the write-ups of experiments in doctors' and masters' theses, and in journals, and compare their techniques with the recommendations of this chapter.

3. If you wish to do Exercise 2 more systematically, make a score card for experimental technique, and with it systematically evaluate the techniques employed in a wide sampling of experiments in education, psychology, and the social sciences.

References for Further Study

JOHNSON, P., and J. NEYMAN: "Tests of Certain Linear Hypotheses and Their Application to Source Educational Problems," *Statistical Research Memoirs*, University of London, Vol. I, pp. 57–95.

KIMBALL, B. F.: "Comparison of Scores of Two Populations under Equalization of Scores of a Second Attribute," *J. Educ. Psychol.*, Vol. 28, pp. 135–143.

RULON, P. J., and C. W. CROON: "Procedure for Balancing Parallel Groups," *J. Educ. Psychol.*, Vol. 24, pp. 585–590.

SHEN, EUGENE: "A Generalized Formula for Testing the Significance of Experimental Treatments," *The Harvard Ed. Rev.*, Vol. 10, pp. 70–74.

THOMSON, GODFREY H.: "A Formula to Correct for the Effect of Errors of Measurement on the Correlation of Initial Values with Gains," *J. Exper. Psychol.*, Vol. 7, pp. 321–324.

THORNDIKE, E. L.: "The Influence of Chance Imperfections of Measurement upon the Relation of Initial Scores to Gain or Loss," *J. Exper. Psychol.*, Vol. 7, pp. 225–232.

APPENDIX
TABLES XLIII TO LI

TABLE XLIII.—NORMAL PROBABILITY INTEGRAL ORIENTED IN TERMS OF q

q	x/σ_x	z	q	x/σ_x	z	q	x/σ_x	z
.500	0.0000	.3989	.450	0.1257	.3958	.400	0.2533	.3863
.499	0.0025	.3989	.449	0.1282	.3957	.399	0.2559	.3861
.498	0.0050	.3989	.448	0.1307	.3955	.398	0.2585	.3858
.497	0.0075	.3989	.447	0.1332	.3954	.397	0.2611	.3856
.496	0.0100	.3989	.446	0.1358	.3953	.396	0.2637	.3853
.495	0.0125	.3989	.445	0.1383	.3951	.395	0.2663	.3850
.494	0.0150	.3989	.444	0.1408	.3950	.394	0.2689	.3848
.493	0.0175	.3989	.443	0.1434	.3949	.393	0.2715	.3845
.492	0.0201	.3989	.442	0.1459	.3947	.392	0.2741	.3842
.491	0.0226	.3988	.441	0.1484	.3946	.391	0.2767	.3840
.490	0.0251	.3988	.440	0.1510	.3944	.390	0.2793	.3837
.489	0.0276	.3988	.439	0.1535	.3943	.389	0.2819	.3834
.488	0.0301	.3988	.438	0.1560	.3941	.388	0.2845	.3831
.487	0.0326	.3987	.437	0.1586	.3940	.387	0.2871	.3828
.486	0.0351	.3987	.436	0.1611	.3938	.386	0.2898	.3825
.485	0.0376	.3987	.435	0.1637	.3936	.385	0.2924	.3823
.484	0.0401	.3986	.434	0.1662	.3935	.384	0.2950	.3820
.483	0.0426	.3986	.433	0.1687	.3933	.383	0.2976	.3817
.482	0.0451	.3985	.432	0.1713	.3931	.382	0.3002	.3814
.481	0.0476	.3985	.431	0.1738	.3930	.381	0.3029	.3811
.480	0.0502	.3984	.430	0.1764	.3928	.380	0.3055	.3808
.479	0.0527	.3984	.429	0.1789	.3926	.379	0.3081	.3804
.478	0.0552	.3983	.428	0.1815	.3924	.378	0.3107	.3801
.477	0.0577	.3983	.427	0.1840	.3922	.377	0.3134	.3798
.476	0.0602	.3982	.426	0.1866	.3921	.376	0.3160	.3795
.475	0.0627	.3982	.425	0.1891	.3919	.375	0.3186	.3792
.474	0.0652	.3981	.424	0.1917	.3917	.374	0.3213	.3789
.473	0.0677	.3980	.423	0.1942	.3915	.373	0.3239	.3786
.472	0.0702	.3980	.422	0.1968	.3913	.372	0.3266	.3782
.471	0.0728	.3979	.421	0.1993	.3911	.371	0.3292	.3779
.470	0.0753	.3978	.420	0.2019	.3909	.370	0.3319	.3776
.469	0.0778	.3977	.419	0.2045	.3907	.369	0.3345	.3772
.468	0.0803	.3977	.418	0.2070	.3905	.368	0.3372	.3769
.467	0.0828	.3976	.417	0.2096	.3903	.367	0.3398	.3766
.466	0.0853	.3975	.416	0.2121	.3901	.366	0.3425	3762
.465	0.0878	.3974	.415	0.2147	.3899	.365	0.3451	.3759
.464	0.0904	.3973	.414	0.2173	.3896	.364	0.3478	.3755
.463	0.0929	.3972	.413	0.2198	.3894	.363	0.3505	.3752
.462	0.0954	.3971	.412	0.2224	.3892	.362	0.3531	.3748
.461	0.0979	.3970	.411	0.2250	.3890	.361	0.3558	.3745
.460	0.1004	.3969	.410	0.2275	.3887	.360	0.3585	.3741
.459	0.1030	.3968	.409	0.2301	.3885	.359	0.3611	.3738
.458	0.1055	.3967	.408	0.2327	.3883	.358	0.3638	.3734
.457	0.1080	.3966	.407	0.2353	.3881	.357	0.3665	.3730
.456	0.1105	.3965	.406	0.2378	.3878	.356	0.3692	.3727
.455	0.1130	.3964	.405	0.2404	.3876	.355	0.3719	.3723
.454	0.1156	.3963	.404	0.2430	.3873	.354	0.3745	.3719
.453	0.1181	.3962	.403	0.2456	.3871	.353	0.3772	.3715
.452	0.1206	.3961	.402	0.2482	.3868	.352	0.3799	.3712
.451	0.1231	.3959	.401	0.2508	.3866	.351	0.3826	.3708

TABLE XLIII.—NORMAL PROBABILITY INTEGRAL ORIENTED IN TERMS OF q.
(Continued)

q	x/σ_x	z	q	x/σ_x	z	q	x/σ_x	z
.350	0.3853	.3704	.300	0.5244	.3477	.250	0.6745	.3178
.349	0.3880	.3700	.299	0.5273	.3472	.249	0.6776	.3171
.348	0.3907	.3696	.298	0.5302	.3466	.248	0.6808	.3164
.347	0.3934	.3692	.297	0.5330	.3461	.247	0.6840	.3157
.346	0.3961	.3688	.296	0.5359	.3456	.246	0.6871	.3151
.345	0.3989	.3684	.295	0.5388	.3450	.245	0.6903	.3144
.344	0.4016	.3680	.294	0.5417	.3445	.244	0.6935	.3137
.343	0.4043	.3676	.293	0.5446	.3440	.243	0.6967	.3130
.342	0.4070	.3672	.292	0.5476	.3434	.242	0.6999	.3123
.341	0.4097	.3668	.291	0.5505	.3429	.241	0.7031	.3116
.340	0.4125	.3664	.290	0.5534	.3423	.240	0.7063	.3109
.339	0.4152	.3660	.289	0.5563	.3417	.239	0.7095	.3102
.338	0.4179	.3656	.288	0.5592	.3412	.238	0.7128	.3095
.337	0.4207	.3652	.287	0.5622	.3406	.237	0.7160	.3087
.336	0.4234	.3647	.286	0.5651	.3401	.236	0.7192	.3080
.335	0.4261	.3643	.295	0.5681	.3395	.235	0.7225	.3073
.334	0.4289	.3639	.284	0.5710	.3389	.234	0.7257	.3066
.333	0.4316	.3635	.283	0.5740	.3384	.233	0.7290	.3058
.332	0.4344	.3630	.282	0.5769	.3378	.232	0.7323	.3051
.331	0.4372	.3626	.281	0.5799	.3372	.231	0.7356	.3044
.330	0.4399	.3621	.280	0.5828	.3366	.230	0.7388	.3036
.329	0.4427	.3617	.279	0.5858	.3360	.229	0.7421	.3029
.328	0.4454	.3613	.278	0.5888	.3355	.228	0.7454	.3022
.327	0.4482	.3608	.277	0.5918	.3349	.227	0.7488	.3014
.326	0.4510	.3604	.276	0.5948	.3343	.226	0.7521	.3007
.325	0.4538	.3599	.275	0.5978	.3337	.225	0.7554	.2999
.324	0.4565	.3595	.274	0.6008	.3331	.224	0.7588	.2992
.323	0.4593	.3590	.273	0.6038	.3325	.223	0.7621	.2984
.322	0.4621	.3585	.272	0.6068	.3319	.222	0.7655	.2976
.321	0.4649	.3581	.271	0.6098	.3313	.221	0.7688	.2969
.320	0.4677	.3576	.270	0.6128	.3306	.220	0.7722	.2961
.319	0.4705	.3571	.269	0.6158	.3300	.219	0.7756	.2953
.318	0.4733	.3567	.268	0.6189	.3294	.218	0.7790	.2945
.317	0.4761	.3562	.267	0.6219	.3288	.217	0.7824	.2938
.316	0.4789	.3557	.266	0.6250	.3282	.216	0.7858	.2930
.315	0.4817	.3552	.265	0.6280	.3275	.215	0.7892	.2922
.314	0.4845	.3548	.264	0.6311	.3269	.214	0.7926	.2914
.313	0.4874	.3543	.263	0.6341	.3263	.213	0.7961	.2906
.312	0.4902	.3538	.262	0.6372	.3256	.212	0.7995	.2898
.311	0.4930	.3533	.261	0.6403	.3250	.211	0.8030	.2890
.310	0.4959	.3528	.260	0.6433	.3244	.210	0.8064	.2882
.309	0.4987	.3523	.259	0.6464	.3237	.209	0.8099	.2874
.308	0.5015	.3518	.258	0.6495	.3231	.208	0.8134	.2866
.307	0.5044	.3513	.257	0.6526	.3224	.207	0.8169	.2858
.306	0.5072	.3508	.256	0.6557	.3218	.206	0.8204	.2849
.305	0.5101	.3503	.255	0.6588	.3211	.205	0.8239	.2841
.304	0.5129	.3498	.254	0.6620	.3204	.204	0.8274	.2833
.303	0.5158	.3493	.253	0.6651	.3198	.203	0.8310	.2825
.302	0.5187	.3487	.252	0.6682	.3191	.202	0.8345	.2816
.301	0.5215	.3482	.251	0.6713	.3184	.201	0.8381	.2808

TABLE XLIII.—NORMAL PROBABILITY INTEGRAL ORIENTED IN TERMS OF q.
(*Continued*)

q	x/σ_x	z	q	x/σ_x	z	q	x/σ_x	z
.200	0.8416	.2800	.150	1.0364	.2332	.100	1.2816	.1755
.199	0.8452	.2791	.149	1.0407	.2321	.099	1.2873	.1742
.198	0.8488	.2783	.148	1.0450	.2311	.098	1.2930	.1729
.197	0.8524	.2774	.147	1.0494	.2300	.097	1.2988	.1716
.196	0.8560	.2766	.146	1.0537	.2290	.096	1.3047	.1703
.195	0.8596	.2757	.145	1.0581	.2279	.095	1.3106	.1690
.194	0.8633	.2748	.144	1.0625	.2269	.094	1.3165	.1677
.193	0.8669	.2740	.143	1.0669	.2258	.093	1.3225	.1664
.192	0.8705	.2731	.142	1.0714	.2247	.092	1.3285	.1651
.191	0.8742	.2722	.141	1.0758	.2237	.091	1.3346	.1637
.190	0.8779	.2714	.140	1.0803	.2226	.090	1.3408	.1624
.189	0.8816	.2705	.139	1.0848	.2215	.089	1.3469	.1610
.188	0.8853	.2696	.138	1.0893	.2204	.088	1.3532	.1597
.187	0.8890	.2687	.137	1.0939	.2193	.087	1.3595	.1583
.186	0.8927	.2678	.136	1.0985	.2182	.086	1.3658	.1570
.185	0.8965	.2669	.135	1.1031	.2171	.085	1.3722	.1556
.184	0.9002	.2660	.134	1.1077	.2160	.084	1.3787	.1542
.183	0.9040	.2651	.133	1.1123	.2149	.083	1.3852	.1529
.182	0.9078	.2642	.132	1.1170	.2138	.082	1.3917	.1515
.181	0.9116	.2633	.131	1.1217	.2127	.081	1.3984	.1501
.180	0.9154	.2624	.130	1.1264	.2115	.080	1.4051	.1487
.179	0.9192	.2615	.129	1.1311	.2104	.079	1.4118	.1473
.178	0.9230	.2606	.128	1.1359	.2093	.078	1.4187	.1458
.177	0.9269	.2596	.127	1.1407	.2081	.077	1.4255	.1444
.176	0.9307	.2587	.126	1.1455	.2070	.076	1.4325	.1430
.175	0.9346	.2578	.125	1.1503	.2059	.075	1.4395	.1416
.174	0.9385	.2568	.124	1.1552	.2047	.074	1.4466	.1401
.173	0.9424	.2559	.123	1.1601	.2035	.073	1.4538	.1387
.172	0.9463	.2550	.122	1.1650	.2024	.072	1.4611	.1372
.171	0.9502	.2540	.121	1.1700	.2012	.071	1.4684	.1357
.170	0.9542	.2531	.120	1.1750	.2000	.070	1.4758	.1343
.169	0.9581	.2521	.119	1.1800	.1989	.069	1.4833	.1328
.168	0.9621	.2511	.118	1.1850	.1977	.068	1.4909	.1313
.167	0.9661	.2502	.117	1.1901	.1965	.067	1.4985	.1298
.166	0.9701	.2492	.116	1.1952	.1953	.066	1.5063	.1283
.165	0.9741	.2482	.115	1.2004	.1941	.065	1.5141	.1268
.164	0.9782	.2473	.114	1.2055	.1929	.064	1.5220	.1253
.163	0.9822	.2463	.113	1.2107	.1917	.063	1.5301	.1237
.162	0.9863	.2453	.112	1.2160	.1905	.062	1.5382	.1222
.161	0.9904	.2443	.111	1.2212	.1893	.061	1.5464	.1207
.160	0.9945	.2433	.110	1.2265	.1880	.060	1.5548	.1191
.159	0.9986	.2423	.109	1.2319	.1868	.059	1.5632	.1176
.158	1.0027	.2413	.108	1.2372	.1856	.058	1.5718	.1160
.157	1.0069	.2403	.107	1.2426	.1843	.057	1.5805	.1144
.156	1.0110	.2393	.106	1.2481	.1831	.056	1.5893	.1128
.155	1.0152	.2383	.105	1.2536	.1818	.055	1.5982	.1112
.154	1.0194	.2373	.104	1.2591	.1806	.054	1.6072	.1096
.153	1.0237	.2362	.103	1.2646	.1793	.053	1.6164	.1080
.152	1.0279	.2352	.102	1.2702	.1781	.052	1.6258	.1064
.151	1.0322	.2342	.101	1.2759	.1768	.051	1.6352	.1048

TABLE XLIII.—NORMAL PROBABILITY INTEGRAL ORIENTED IN TERMS OF q.*
(Concluded)

q	x/σ_z	z	q	x/σ_z	z	q	x/σ_z	z
.050	1.6449	.1031	.033	1.8384	.0736	.016	2.1444	.0400
.049	1.6546	.1015	.032	1.8522	.0718	.015	2.1701	.0379
.048	1.6646	.0998	.031	1.8663	.0699	.014	2.1973	.0357
.047	1.6747	.0982	.030	1.8808	.0680	.013	2.2262	.0335
.046	1.6849	.0965	.029	1.8957	.0662	.012	2.2571	.0312
.045	1.6954	.0948	.028	1.9110	.0643	.011	2.2904	.0290
.044	1.7060	.0931	.027	1.9268	.0623	.010	2.3263	.0267
.043	1.7169	.0914	.026	1.9431	.0604	.009	2.3656	.0243
.042	1.7279	.0897	.025	1.9600	.0584	.008	2.4089	.0219
.041	1.7392	.0879	.024	1.9774	.0565	.007	2.4573	.0195
.040	1.7507	.0862	.023	1.9954	.0545	.006	2.5121	.0170
.039	1.7624	.0844	.022	2.0141	.0525	.005	2.5758	.0145
.038	1.7744	.0826	.021	2.0335	.0505	.004	2.6521	.0118
.037	1.7866	.0809	.020	2.0537	.0484	.003	2.7478	.0091
.036	1.7991	.0791	.019	2.0749	.0464	.002	2.8782	.0063
.035	1.8119	.0773	.018	2.0969	.0443	.001	3.0902	.0034
.034	1.8250	.0755	.017	2.1201	.0422			

* The above table was adapted from the table by Kondo and Elderton, published in *Biometrika*, Vol. 22, pp. 368–376. The following table (Table XLIV) was adapted from Pearson's "Tables for Statisticians and Biometricians." Both tables are used by arrangements with the publishers through Prof. E. S. Pearson, editor of *Biometrika*.

TABLE XLIV.—Normal Probability Integral, Oriented in Terms of x/σ_x

x/σ_x	.50-q	z	x/σ_x	.50-q	z	x/σ_x	.50-q	z
0.00	.0000	.3989	0.50	.1915	.3521	1.00	.3413	.2420
0.01	.0040	.3989	0.51	.1950	.3503	1.01	.3438	.2396
0.02	.0080	.3989	0.52	.1985	.3485	1.02	.3461	.2371
0.03	.0120	.3988	0.53	.2019	.3467	1.03	.3485	.2347
0.04	.0160	.3986	0.54	.2054	.3448	1.04	.3508	.2323
0.05	.0199	.3984	0.55	.2088	.3429	1.05	.3531	.2299
0.06	.0239	.3982	0.56	.2123	.3410	1.06	.3554	.2275
0.07	.0279	.3980	0.57	.2157	.3391	1.07	.3577	.2251
0.08	.0319	.3977	0.58	.2190	.3372	1.08	.3599	.2227
0.09	.0359	.3973	0.59	.2224	.3352	1.09	.3621	.2203
0.10	.0398	.3970	0.60	.2257	.3332	1.10	3643	.2179
0.11	.0438	.3965	0.61	.2291	.3312	1.11	.3665	.2155
0.12	.0478	.3961	0.62	.2324	.3292	1.12	.3686	.2131
0.13	.0517	.3956	0.63	.2357	.3271	1.13	.3708	.2107
0.14	.0557	.3951	0.64	.2389	.3251	1.14	.3729	.2083
0.15	.0596	.3945	0.65	.2422	.3230	1.15	.3749	.2059
0.16	.0636	.3939	0.66	.2454	.3209	1.16	.3770	.2036
0.17	.0675	.3932	0.67	.2486	.3187	1.17	.3790	.2012
0.18	.0714	.3925	0.68	.2517	.3166	1.18	.3810	.1989
0.19	.0753	.3918	0.69	.2549	.3144	1.19	.3830	.1965
0.20	.0793	.3910	0.70	.2580	.3123	1.20	.3849	.1942
0.21	.0832	.3902	0.71	.2611	.3101	1.21	.3869	.1919
0.22	.0871	.3894	0.72	.2642	.3079	1.22	.3888	.1895
0.23	.0910	.3885	0.73	.2673	.3056	1.23	.3907	.1872
0.24	.0948	.3876	0.74	.2704	.3034	1.24	.3925	.1849
0.25	.0987	.3867	0.75	.2734	.3011	1.25	.3944	.1826
0.26	.1026	.3857	0.76	.2764	.2989	1.26	.3962	.1804
0.27	.1064	.3847	0.77	.2794	.2966	1.27	.3980	.1781
0.28	.1103	.3836	0.78	.2823	.2943	1.28	.3997	.1758
0.29	.1141	.3825	0.79	.2852	.2920	1.29	.4015	.1736
0.30	.1179	.3814	0.80	.2881	.2897	1.30	.4032	.1714
0.31	.1217	.3802	0.81	.2910	.2874	1.31	.4049	.1691
0.32	.1255	.3790	0.82	.2938	.2850	1.32	.4066	.1669
0.33	.1293	.3778	0.83	.2967	.2827	1.33	.4082	.1647
0.34	.1331	.3765	0.84	.2995	.2803	1.34	.4099	.1626
0.35	.1368	.3752	0.85	.3023	.2780	1.35	.4115	.1604
0.36	.1406	.3739	0.86	.3051	.2756	1.36	.4131	.1582
0.37	.1443	.3725	0.87	.3078	.2732	1.37	.4147	.1561
0.38	.1480	.3712	0.88	.3106	.2709	1.38	.4162	.1539
0.39	.1517	.3697	0.89	.3133	.2685	1.39	.4177	.1518
0.40	.1554	.3683	0.90	.3159	.2661	1.40	.4192	.1497
0.41	.1591	.3668	0.91	.3186	.2637	1.41	.4207	.1476
0.42	.1628	.3653	0.92	.3212	.2613	1.42	.4222	.1456
0.43	.1664	.3637	0.93	.3238	.2589	1.43	.4236	.1435
0.44	.1700	.3621	0.94	.3264	.2565	1.44	.4251	.1415
0.45	.1736	.3605	0.95	.3289	.2541	1.45	.4265	.1394
0.46	.1772	.3589	0.96	.3315	.2516	1.46	.4279	.1374
0.47	.1808	.3572	0.97	.3340	.2492	1.47	.4292	.1354
0.48	.1844	.3555	0.98	.3365	.2468	1.48	.4306	.1334
0.49	.1879	.3538	0.99	.3389	.2444	1.49	.4319	.1315

TABLE XLIV.—NORMAL PROBABILITY INTEGRAL, ORIENTED IN TERMS OF x/σ_x.—(Continued)

x/σ_x	.50-q	z	x/σ_x	.50-q	z	x/σ_x	.50-q	z
1.50	.4332	.1295	2.00	.4772	.0540	2.50	.4938	.0175
1.51	.4345	.1276	2.01	.4778	.0529	2.51	.4940	.0171
1.52	.4357	.1257	2.02	.4783	.0519	2.52	.4941	.0167
1.53	.4370	.1238	2.03	.4788	.0508	2.53	.4943	.0163
1.54	.4382	.1219	2.04	.4793	.0498	2.54	.4945	.0158
1.55	.4394	.1200	2.05	.4798	.0488	2.55	.4946	.0154
1.56	.4406	.1182	2.06	.4803	.0478	2.56	.4948	.0151
1.57	.4418	.1163	2.07	.4808	.0468	2.57	.4949	.0147
1.58	.4429	.1145	2.08	.4812	.0459	2.58	.4951	.0143
1.59	.4441	.1127	2.09	.4817	.0449	2.59	.4952	.0139
1.60	.4452	.1109	2.10	.4821	.0440	2.60	.4953	.0136
1.61	.4463	.1092	2.11	.4826	.0431	2.61	.4955	.0132
1.62	.4474	.1074	2.12	.4830	.0422	2.62	.4956	.0129
1.63	.4484	.1057	2.13	.4834	.0413	2.63	.4957	.0126
1.64	.4495	.1040	2.14	.4838	.0404	2.64	.4959	.0122
1.65	.4505	.1023	2.15	.4842	.0396	2.65	.4960	.0119
1.66	.4515	.1006	2.16	.4846	.0387	2.66	.4961	.0116
1.67	.4525	.0989	2.17	.4850	.0379	2.67	.4962	.0113
1.68	.4535	.0973	2.18	.4854	.0371	2.68	.4963	.0110
1.69	.4545	.0957	2.19	.4857	.0363	2.69	.4964	.0107
1.70	.4554	.0940	2.20	.4861	.0355	2.70	.4965	.0104
1.71	.4564	.0925	2.21	.4864	.0347	2.71	.4966	.0101
1.72	.4573	.0909	2.22	.4868	.0339	2.72	.4967	.0099
1.73	.4582	.0893	2.23	.4871	.0332	2.73	.4968	.0096
1.74	.4591	.0878	2.24	.4875	.0325	2.74	.4969	.0093
1.75	.4599	.0863	2.25	.4878	.0317	2.75	.4970	.0091
1.76	.4608	.0848	2.26	.4881	.0310	2.76	.4971	.0088
1.77	.4616	.0833	2.27	.4884	.0303	2.77	.4972	.0086
1.78	.4625	.0818	2.28	.4887	.0297	2.78	.4973	.0084
1.79	.4633	.0804	2.29	.4890	.0290	2.79	.4974	.0081
1.80	.4641	.0790	2.30	.4893	.0283	2.80	.4974	.0079
1.81	.4649	.0775	2.31	.4896	.0277	2.81	.4975	.0077
1.82	.4656	.0761	2.32	.4898	.0270	2.82	.4976	.0075
1.83	.4664	.0748	2.33	.4901	.0264	2.83	.4977	.0073
1.84	.4671	.0734	2.34	.4904	.0258	2.84	.4977	.0071
1.85	.4678	.0721	2.35	.4906	.0252	2.85	.4978	.0069
1.86	.4686	.0707	2.36	.4909	.0246	2.86	.4979	.0067
1.87	.4693	.0694	2.37	.4911	.0241	2.87	.4979	.0065
1.88	.4699	.0681	2.38	.4913	.0235	2.88	.4980	.0063
1.89	.4706	.0669	2.39	.4916	.0229	2.89	.4981	.0061
1.90	.4713	.0656	2.40	.4918	.0224	2.90	.4981	.0060
1.91	.4719	.0644	2.41	.4920	.0219	2.91	.4982	.0058
1.92	.4726	.0632	2.42	.4922	.0213	2.92	.4982	.0056
1.93	.4732	.0620	2.43	.4925	.0208	2.93	.4983	.0055
1.94	.4738	.0608	2.44	.4927	.0203	2.94	.4984	.0053
1.95	.4744	.0596	2.45	.4929	.0198	2.95	.4984	.0051
1.96	.4750	.0584	2.46	.4931	.0194	2.96	.4985	.0050
1.97	.4756	.0573	2.47	.4932	.0189	2.97	.4985	.0048
1.98	.4761	.0562	2.48	.4934	.0184	2.98	.4986	.0047
1.99	.4767	.0551	2.49	.4936	.0180	2.99	.4986	.0046

TABLE XLIV.—NORMAL PROBABILITY INTEGRAL, ORIENTED IN TERMS OF x/σ_x.*—(Concluded)

(Prefix in each column the digits indicated in parentheses.)

x/σ_x	.50-q	z	x/σ_x	.50-q	z	x/σ_x	.50-q	z
	(.49)	(.00)		(.499)	(.000)		(.499)	(.000)
3.00	8650	4432	3.50	7674	8727	4.00	9683	1338
3.01	8694	4301	3.51	7759	8426	4.01	9696	1286
3.02	8736	4173	3.52	7842	8135	4.02	9709	1235
3.03	8777	4049	3.53	7922	7853	4.03	9721	1186
3.04	8817	3928	3.54	7999	7581	4.04	9733	1140
3.05	8856	3810	3.55	8074	7317	4.05	9744	1094
3.06	8893	3695	3.56	8146	7061	4.06	9755	1051
3.07	8930	3584	3.57	8215	6814	4.07	9765	1009
3.08	8965	3475	3.58	8282	6575	4.08	9775	0969
3.09	8999	3370	3.59	8347	6343	4.09	9784	0930
3.10	9032	3267	3.60	8409	6119	4.10	9793	0893
3.11	9065	3167	3.61	8469	5902	4.11	9802	0857
3.12	9096	3070	3.62	8527	5693	4.12	9811	0822
3.13	9126	2975	3.63	8583	5490	4.13	9819	0789
3.14	9155	2884	3.64	8637	5294	4.14	9826	0757
3.15	9184	2794	3.65	8689	5105	4.15	9834	0726
3.16	9211	2708	3.66	8739	4921	4.16	9841	0697
3.17	9238	2623	3.67	8787	4744	4.17	9848	0668
3.18	9264	2541	3.68	8834	4573	4.18	9854	0641
3.19	9289	2462	3.69	8879	4408	4.19	9861	0615
3.20	9313	2384	3.70	8922	4248	4.20	9867	0589
3.21	9336	2309	3.71	8964	4093	4.21	9872	0565
3.22	9359	2236	3.72	9004	3944	4.22	9878	0542
3.23	9381	2165	3.73	9043	3800	4.23	9883	0519
3.24	9402	2096	3.74	9080	3661	4.24	9888	0498
3.25	9423	2029	3.75	9116	3526	4.25	9893	0477
3.26	9443	1964	3.76	9150	3396	4.26	9898	0457
3.27	9462	1901	3.77	9184	3271	4.27	9902	0438
3.28	9481	1840	3.78	9216	3149	4.28	9907	0420
3.29	9499	1780	3.79	9247	3032	4.29	9911	0402
3.30	9517	1723	3.80	9277	2919	4.30	9915	0385
3.31	9534	1667	3.81	9305	2810	4.31	9918	0369
3.32	9550	1612	3.82	9333	2705	4.32	9922	0354
3.33	9566	1560	3.83	9359	2604	4.33	9925	0339
3.34	9581	1508	3.84	9385	2506	4.34	9929	0324
3.35	9596	1459	3.85	9409	2411	4.35	9932	0310
3.36	9610	1411	3.86	9433	2320	4.36	9935	0297
3.37	9624	1364	3.87	9456	2232	4.37	9938	0284
3.38	9638	1319	3.88	9478	2147	4.38	9941	0272
3.39	9651	1275	3.89	9499	2065	4.39	9943	0261
3.40	9663	1232	3.90	9519	1987	4.40	9946	0249
3.41	9675	1191	3.91	9539	1910	4.45	9957	0200
3.42	9687	1151	3.92	9557	1837	4.50	9966	0160
3.43	9698	1112	3.93	9575	1766	4.55	9973	0127
3.44	9709	1075	3.94	9593	1698	4.60	9979	0101
3.45	9720	1038	3.95	9609	1633	4.65	9983	0080
3.46	9730	1003	3.96	9625	1569	4.70	9987	0064
3.47	9740	0969	3.97	9641	1508	4.80	9992	0040
3.48	9749	0936	3.98	9655	1449	4.90	9995	0024
3.49	9759	0904	3.99	9670	1393	5.00	9997	0015

* See footnote on p. 484.

STATISTICAL PROCEDURES

TABLE XLV.—THE DISTRIBUTION OF STUDENT'S t
(Percentage of the Total Area in Tail of Distribution from $t = x/\sigma_x$ to ∞)

t	$n = 1$ $n' = 2$	2 3	3 4	4 5	5 6	6 7	7 8	8 9	9 10	10 11
0	.5000	.5000	.5000	.5000	.5000	.5000	.5000	.5000	.5000	.5000
0.1	.4683	.4647	.4633	.4626	.4621	.4618	.4616	.4614	.4613	.4612
0.2	.4372	.4300	.4271	.4256	.4247	.4240	.4236	.4232	.4230	.4227
0.3	.4072	.3962	.3919	.3896	.3881	.3871	.3864	.3859	.3855	.3852
0.4	.3789	.3639	.3580	3548	.3528	.3515	.3505	.3498	.3492	3488
0.5	.3524	.3333	.3257	.3217	.3191	.3174	.3162	.3153	.3145	.3139
0.6	.3280	.3047	.2954	.2904	.2873	.2852	.2837	.2826	.2817	.2809
0.7	.3056	.2782	.2672	.2613	.2576	.2551	.2533	.2519	.2508	.2499
0.8	.2852	.2538	.2411	.2342	.2300	.2271	.2250	.2234	.2222	.2212
0.9	.2667	.2316	.2172	.2095	.2047	.2014	.1990	.1972	.1958	.1946
1.0	.2500	.2113	.1955	.1870	.1816	.1780	.1753	.1733	.1717	.1704
1.1	.2349	.1930	.1758	.1665	.1607	.1567	.1539	.1517	.1499	.1486
1.2	.2211	.1765	.1581	.1482	.1419	.1377	.1346	.1322	.1304	.1289
1.3	.2087	.1616	.1422	.1317	.1252	.1207	.1174	.1149	.1130	.1114
1.4	.1974	.1482	.1280	.1171	.1102	.1055	.1021	.0995	.0975	.0959
1.5	.1872	.1362	.1153	.1040	.0970	.0921	.0886	.0860	.0839	.0823
1.6	.1778	.1254	.1040	.0924	.0852	.0804	.0768	.0741	.0720	.0703
1.7	.1693	.1156	.0938	.0822	.0749	.0700	.0665	.0638	.0617	.0600
1.8	.1614	.1068	.0848	.0731	.0659	.0610	.0574	.0548	.0527	.0510
1.9	.1542	.0989	.0768	.0651	.0579	.0531	.0496	.0470	.0449	.0433
2.0	.1476	.0918	.0697	.0581	.0510	.0462	.0428	.0403	.0383	.0367
2.1	.1415	.0853	.0633	.0518	.0449	.0402	.0369	.0345	.0326	.0310
2.2	.1358	.0794	.0576	.0463	.0395	.0351	.0319	.0295	.0277	.0262
2.3	.1305	.0741	.0525	.0415	.0349	.0306	.0275	.0252	.0235	.0221
2.4	.1257	.0692	.0479	.0372	.0308	.0266	.0237	.0216	.0199	.0187
2.5	.1211	.0648	.0439	.0334	.0272	.0233	.0205	.0185	.0169	.0157
2.6	.1169	.0608	.0402	.0300	.0242	.0203	.0177	.0158	.0144	.0132
2.7	.1129	.0571	.0369	.0270	.0214	.0178	.0153	.0135	.0122	.0112
2.8	.1092	.0537	.0339	.0244	.0190	.0156	.0133	.0116	.0104	.0094
2.9	.1057	.0506	.0313	.0221	.0169	.0137	.0115	.0099	.0088	.0079
3.0	.1024	.0477	.0288	.0200	.0150	.0120	.0100	.0085	.0075	.0067
3.1	.0993	.0451	.0266	.0181	.0134	.0106	.0087	.0073	.0064	.0056
3.2	.0964	.0427	.0247	.0165	.0120	.0093	.0075	.0063	.0054	.0047
3.3	.0937	.0404	.0229	.0150	.0107	.0082	.0066	.0054	.0046	.0040
3.4	.0911	.0383	.0212	0136	.0096	.0072	.0057	.0047	.0039	.0034

TABLE XLV.—THE DISTRIBUTION OF STUDENT'S t.—(*Continued*)

t	$n = 11$ $n' = 12$	12 13	13 14	14 15	15 16	16 17	17 18	18 19	19 20	20 21	∞
0	.5000	.5000	.5000	.5000	.5000	.5000	.5000	.5000	.5000	.5000	.5000000
0.1	.4611	.4610	.4609	.4609	.4608	.4608	.4608	.4607	.4607	.4607	.4601722
0.2	.4226	.4224	.4223	.4222	4221	.4220	.4219	.4219	.4218	.4218	.4207403
0.3	.3849	.3847	.3845	.3843	.3841	.3840	.3839	.3838	.3837	.3836	.3820886
0.4	.3484	.3481	.3478	.3476	.3474	.3472	.3471	.3469	.3468	.3467	.3445783
0.5	.3135	.3131	.3127	.3124	.3122	.3119	.3117	.3116	.3114	.3113	.3085375
0.6	.2803	.2798	.2794	.2790	.2787	.2785	.2782	.2780	.2778	.2776	.2742531
0.7	.2492	.2486	.2481	.2477	.2473	.2470	.2467	.2464	.2462	2460	.2419637
0.8	.2203	.2196	.2190	.2185	.2181	.2177	.2174	.2171	.2168	.2166	.2118554
0.9	.1937	.1929	.1922	.1917	.1912	.1907	.1903	.1900	.1897	.1894	.1840601
1.0	.1694	.1685	.1678	.1671	.1666	.1661	.1657	.1653	.1649	.1646	.1586553
1.1	.1474	.1465	.1456	.1449	.1443	.1438	.1433	.1429	.1425	.1422	.1356661
1.2	.1277	.1266	.1258	.1250	.1244	.1238	.1233	.1228	.1224	.1221	.1151697
1.3	.1101	.1090	.1081	.1073	.1066	.1060	.1055	.1050	.1046	1042	.0968005
1.4	.0945	.0934	.0925	.0916	.0909	.0903	.0897	.0893	.0888	.0884	.0807567
1.5	.0809	.0797	.0788	.0779	.0772	.0765	.0760	.0755	.0750	.0746	.0668072
1.6	.0690	.0678	.0668	.0660	.0652	.0646	.0640	.0635	.0630	.0626	.0547993
1.7	.0586	.0574	.0565	.0556	.0549	.0542	.0537	.0532	.0527	.0523	.0445655
1.8	.0497	.0485	.0475	.0467	.0460	.0454	.0448	.0443	.0439	.0435	.0359303
1.9	.0420	.0409	.0399	.0391	.0384	.0378	.0373	.0368	.0364	.0360	.0287166
2.0	.0354	.0343	.0334	.0326	.0320	.0314	.0309	.0304	.0300	.0296	.0227501
2.1	.0298	.0288	.0279	.0272	.0265	.0260	.0255	.0250	.0247	.0243	.0178644
2.2	.0250	.0241	.0232	.0226	.0219	.0214	.0210	.0206	.0202	.0199	.0139034
2.3	.0210	.0201	.0193	.0187	.0181	.0176	.0172	.0168	.0165	.0162	.0107241
2.4	.0176	.0168	.0160	.0154	.0149	.0145	.0141	.0137	.0134	.0131	.0081975
2.5	.0148	.0140	.0133	.0127	.0123	.0118	0115	.0112	.0109	.0106	.0062097
2.6	.0123	.0116	.0110	.0105	.0100	.0097	.0093	.0090	.0088	.0086	.0046612
2.7	.0103	.0097	.0091	0086	.0082	.0079	.0076	.0073	.0071	.0069	.0034670
2.8	.0086	.0080	.0075	.0071	.0067	.0064	.0062	.0059	0057	.0055	.0025551
2.9	.0072	.0067	.0062	.0058	.0055	.0055	.0050	.0048	.0046	.0044	.0018658
3.0	.0060	.0055	.0051	0048	0045	.0042	0040	.0038	.0037	.0035	.0013499
3.1	.0051	.0046	.0042	.0039	.0037	.0034	.0033	.0031	0029	.0028	.0009676
3.2	.0042	.0038	.0035	.0032	.0030	.0028	.0026	.0025	.0024	.0022	.0006871
3.3	.0035	.0032	.0029	.0026	.0024	.0023	.0021	.0020	.0019	.0018	.0004834
3.4	.0030	.0026	.0024	.0022	.0020	.0018	.0017	.0016	.0015	.0014	.0003369

STATISTICAL PROCEDURES

TABLE XLV.—THE DISTRIBUTION OF STUDENT'S t.—(*Continued*)

t	$n = 1$ $n' = 2$	2 3	3 4	4 5	5 6	6 7	7 8	8 9	9 10	10 11
3.5	.0886	.0364	.0197	.0124	.0086	.0064	.0050	.0040	.0034	.0029
3.6	.0862	.0346	.0184	.0114	.0078	.0057	.0044	.0035	.0029	.0024
3.7	.0840	.0330	.0171	.0104	.0070	.0050	.0038	.0030	.0025	.0021
3.8	.0819	0314	.0160	0096	.0063	.0045	.0034	.0026	.0021	0017
3.9	.0799	.0299	.0150	.0088	.0057	.0040	.0029	.0023	.0018	.0015
4.0	.0780	.0286	.0140	0081	.0052	.0036	.0026	.0020	.0016	.0013
4.1	.0761	.0273	.0131	.0074	.0047	.0032	.0023	.0017	.0013	.0011
4.2	.0744	.0261	.0123	.0068	.0042	.0028	0020	.0015	.0012	.0009
4.3	.0727	.0250	.0116	.0063	0039	.0025	.0018	.0013	.0010	.0008
4.4	.0711	.0240	.0109	.0058	.0035	.0023	.0016	.0011	.0009	.0007
4.5	.0696	.0230	.0102	.0054	.0032	.0021	.0014	.0010	.0007	.0006
4.6	.0681	.0221	.0097	.0050	.0029	.0018	.0012	.0009	.0006	.0005
4.7	.0667	.0212	.0091	.0047	.0027	.0017	.0011	.0008	.0006	.0004
4.8	.0654	.0204	.0086	.0043	.0024	.0015	.0010	.0007	.0005	.0004
4.9	.0641	.0196	.0081	.0040	.0022	.0014	.0009	.0006	.0004	.0003
5.0	.0628	.0189	.0077	.0037	.0021	.0012	.0008	.0005	.0004	.0003
5.1	.0616	.0182	.0073	.0035	.0019	.0011	.0007	.0005	.0003	.0002
5.2	.0605	.0175	.0069	.0033	.0017	.0010	.0006	.0004	.0003	.0002
5.3	.0594	.0169	.0066	.0030	.0016	.0009	.0006	.0004	.0002	0002
5.4	.0583	.0163	.0062	.0028	.0015	.0008	.0005	.0003	.0002	.0002
5.5	.0572	.0158	.0059	.0027	.0014	.0008	.0005	.0003	.0002	.0001
5.6	.0562	.0152	.0056	.0025	.0013	.0007	.0004	.0003	.0002	.0001
5.7	.0553	.0147	.0054	.0023	.0012	.0006	.0004	.0002	.0001	.0001
5.8	.0543	.0142	.0051	.0022	.0011	.0006	.0003	.0002	.0001	.0001
5.9	.0534	0138	.0049	.0021	.0010	.0005	.0003	.0002	.0001	.0001
6.0	.0526	.0133	.0046	.0019	.0009	.0005	.0003	.0002	.0001	.0001

TABLE XLV.—THE DISTRIBUTION OF STUDENT'S *t.*—(*Continued*)

t	$n = 11$ $n' = 12$	12 13	13 14	14 15	15 16	16 17	17 18	18 19	19 20	20 21	∞
3.5	.0025	.0022	.0020	.0018	.0016	.0015	.0014	.0013	0012	.0011	.0002326
3.6	.0021	.0018	.0016	.0014	.0013	.0012	.0011	.0010	.0010	.0009	.0001591
3.7	.0018	.0015	.0013	.0012	.0011	.0010	.0009	.0008	.0008	.0007	.0001078
3.8	.0015	.0013	.0011	.0010	.0009	.0008	.0007	.0007	.0006	.0006	.0000723
3.9	.0012	.0011	.0009	.0008	.0007	.0006	.0006	.0005	0005	.0004	.0000481
4.0	.0010	.0009	.0008	.0007	0006	.0005	.0005	.0004	.0004	.0004	.0000317
4.1	.0009	.0007	.0006	.0005	.0005	.0004	.0004	.0003	.0003	.0003	.0000207
4.2	.0007	.0006	.0005	.0004	.0004	.0003	.0003	.0003	.0002	.0002	.0000133
4.3	.0006	.0005	.0004	.0004	.0003	.0003	.0002	0002	.0002	.0002	0000085
4.4	.0005	.0004	.0004	.0003	.0003	.0002	.0002	.0002	.0002	0001	.0000054
4.5	.0005	.0004	0003	.0002	.0002	.0002	.0002	.0001	.0001	.0001	.0000034
4.6	.0004	.0003	.0002	.0002	.0002	.0001	.0001	0001	0001	.0001	.0000021
4.7	.0003	.0003	.0002	.0002	.0001	.0001	.0001	.0001	.0001	.0001	.0000013
4.8	0003	.0002	.0001	.0001	.0001	.0001	.0001	.0001	.0001	.0001	0000008
4.9	.0002	.0002	.0001	.0001	.0001	.0001	.0001	.0001	.0000	.0000	.0000005
5.0	.0002	.0002	.0001	.0001	.0001	0001	.0001	0000			.0000003
5.1	.0002	.0001	.0001	.0001	.0001	.0001	.0000	.0000			.0000002
5.2	.0001	.0001	.0001	.0001	.0001	.0000					.0000001
5.3	.0001	.0001	.0001	.0001	.0000						.0000001
5.4	.0001	.0001	.0001	.0000							.0000000
5.5	.0001	.0001	.0001								
5.6	.0001	.0001	.0000								
5.7	.0001	0000									
5.8	.0001										
5.9	.0001										
6.0	.0000										

TABLE XLV.—THE DISTRIBUTION OF STUDENT'S t.*—(Concluded)

t	$n = 3$ $n' = 4$	4 5	5 6	6 7	7 8	8 9	9 10	10 11
6.0	.004636	.001941	.000923	.000482	.000271	.000162	.000101	.000066
6.5	.003697	.001445	.000643	.000316	.000167	.000094		.000034
7.0	.002993	.001096	.000458	.000212	.000106	.000056	.000032	
7.5	.002456	.000845				.000035		
8.0	.002038	.000662	.000246	.000102	.000046			
8.5	.001710							
9.0	.001448	.000422	.000141	.000053				
10.0	.001064	.000281	.000085	.000029				
11.0	.000804							
12.0	.000623	.000138	.000035					
14.0	.000395	.000076						
16.0	.000265	.000045						
20.0	.000137							
24.0	.000079							
28.0	.000050							

* This table, and Table XLVI, were taken from Student's article, "New Tables for Testing the Significance of Observations," *Metron*, Vol. V, pp. 114–120. Student, whose real name was William Sealy Gosset, died in 1937. We were granted permission by his wife and heir, Mrs. Marjory Gosset, to use these tables. We have made a few corrections in this table which Student reported to Prof. Egon S. Pearson of the University of London and which Prof. Pearson passed on to us. In this table we subtracted the entries made by Student from 1.00 so as to give the percentage in the tail of the distribution between $t = x/\sigma_s$ and ∞. Table XLVI we used as it stands in *Metron*.

TABLE XLVI.—STUDENT'S TABLE FOR CORRECTING PROBABILITIES CORRESPONDING TO t's WHEN n EXCEEDS 20*

t	c_1	c_2	c_3	c_4
0.1	.0100231	− .001261	− .00155	+0.0004
0.2	.0203342	− .002616	− .00308	0.0008
0.3	.0311785	− .004177	− .00453	0.0013
0.4	.0427193	− .006087	− .00586	0.0017
0.5	.0550102	− .008509	− .00697	0.0022
0.6	.0679778	− .011595	− .00772	0.0026
0.7	.0814202	− .015432	− .00796	0.0028
0.8	.0950188	− .019991	− .00774	0.0026
0.9	.1083632	− .025066	− .00651	0.0021
1.0	.1209854	− .030246	− .00504	0.0011
1.1	.1323997	− .034907	− .00376	0.0004
1.2	.1421442	− .038248	− .00375	0.0011
1.3	.1498190	− .039363	− .00656	0.0058
1.4	.1551177	− .037344	− .01410	0.0182
1.5	.1578496	− .031399	− .02841	0.0430
1.6	.1579512	− .020971	− .05129	0.0849
1.7	.1554867	− .005832	− .08384	0.1612
1.8	.1506370	+ .013846	− .12609	0.2323
1.9	.1436822	.037483	− .17664	0.3351
2.0	.1349775	.064114	− .23256	0.4466
2.1	.1249244	.092473	− .28945	0.5512
2.2	.1139444	.121099	− .34185	0.6277
2.3	.1024518	.148472	− .38379	0.6522
2.4	.0908322	.173147	− .40950	0.6010
2.5	.0794251	.193877	− .41417	0.4553
2.6	.0685124	.209710	− .39459	+0.2056
2.7	.0583129	.220052	− .34967	−0.1454
2.8	.0489808	.224693	− .28061	−0.5809
2.9	.0406097	.223749	− .19082	−1.0704
3.0	.0332389	.217715	− .08559	−1.5727
3.1	.0268622	.207289	+ .02849	−1.3685
3.2	.0214377	.193351	.14423	−1.6108
3.3	.0168971	.176859	.25458	−1.8372
3.4	.0131552	.158774	.35327	−2.0348
3.5	.0101177	.139969	.43535	−2.7328
3.6	.0076879	.121313	.49749	−2.5031
3.7	.0057722	.103371	.53813	−2.1237
3.8	.0042823	.086649	.55733	−1.6257
3.9	.0031397	.071486	.55667	−1.0501
4.0	.0022751	.058066	.53880	−0.4417
4.1	.0016295	.046453	.50708	+0.1555
4.2	.0011538	.036613	.46519	0.7026
4.3	.0008074	.028438	.41681	1.1692
4.4	.0005586	.021773	.36531	1.5353
4.5	.0003821	.016436	.31356	1.7916
4.6	.0002584	.012235	.26386	1.9387
4.7	.0001728	.008984	.21787	1.9853
4.8	.0001143	.006508	.17663	1.9462
4.9	.0000746	.004652	.14070	1.8394
5.0	.0000483	.003281	.11017	1.6839
5.1	.0000309	.002284	.08485	1.4986
5.2	.0000195	.001570	.06429	1.2995
5.3	.0000122	.001065	.04796	1.1004
5.4	.0000076	.000713	.03527	0.9107
5.5	.0000046	.000472	.02547	0.3799
5.6	.0000028	.000308	.01815	0.5065
5.7	.0000017	.000199	.01274	0.4370
5.8	.0000010	.000127	.00882	0.3495
5.9	.0000006	.000080	.00602	0.2626
6.0	.0000003	.000050	.00405	0.1939

* For acknowledgment, see footnote to Table XLV.   Use with entries in Table XLV:

$$P = P_\infty + \frac{c_1}{n} + \frac{c_2}{n^2} + \frac{c_3}{n^3} + \frac{c_4}{n^4}.$$

TABLE XLVII.—THE DISTRIBUTION OF ϵ^2 WHEN THE TRUE CORRELATION IS ZERO

$$k - 1$$

N−k	1	2	3	4	5	6	7	8	9	10	11	12	14	16	20	24	30	40	50
1	.988 *.9995*																		
2	.854 *.970*	.900 *.980*																	
3	.695 *.892*	.774 *.923*	.805 *.934*																
4	.573 *.802*	.665 *.850*	.706 *.871*	.729 *.892*															
5	.483 *.718*	.578 *.778*	.623 *.806*	.651 *.822*	.669 *.853*														
6	.416 *.645*	.509 *.713*	.556 *.745*	.583 *.765*	.606 *.779*	.621 *.789*													
7	.365 *.584*	.454 *.655*	.501 *.691*	.532 *.714*	.553 *.729*	.570 *.741*	.582 *.750*												
8	.324 *.533*	.409 *.605*	.456 *.643*	.486 *.667*	.509 *.684*	.525 *.697*	.538 *.708*	.550 *.716*											
9	.292 *.489*	.372 *.561*	.417 *.600*	.447 *.625*	.470 *.644*	.487 *.658*	.500 *.669*	.512 *.678*	.522 *.685*										
10	.264 *.451*	.341 *.522*	.385 *.562*	.415 *.588*	.437 *.607*	.454 *.622*	.468 *.634*	.479 *.643*	.489 *.652*	.496 *.658*									
11	.242 *.419*	.314 *.488*	.357 *.528*	.386 *.555*	.407 *.574*	.425 *.590*	.439 *.601*	.451 *.612*	.461 *.620*	.470 *.628*	.476 *.634*								
12	.224 *.391*	.291 *.459*	.332 *.497*	.361 *.524*	.383 *.544*	.400 *.560*	.414 *.574*	.425 *.583*	.435 *.592*	.444 *.600*	.451 *.606*	.458 *.612*							
13	.208 *.366*	.272 *.432*	.311 *.471*	.339 *.507*	.359 *.517*	.377 *.533*	.392 *.546*	.403 *.557*	.413 *.566*	.421 *.574*	.428 *.581*	.434 *.587*							

In the body of this table is given in standard type the maximum ϵ^2 that could be expected 5 times in 100 and, in italics, the maximum ϵ^2 that could be expected 1 time in 100, on the basis of chance fluctuation when the true correlation is zero, the values being given for the number of columns in the correlation table less 1 ($k - 1$) by columns and the total population of the sample less the number of columns ($N - k$) by rows. The reason the section of this table covered by this note is blank is because no valid meaning could attach to ϵ^2 when the average number of items in each column is less than two. This table was made by Charles H. Griffin by the formula derived on pp. 421–422.

TABLE XLVII.—THE DISTRIBUTION OF ϵ^2 WHEN THE TRUE CORRELATION IS ZERO.—(Continued)

N − k	1	2	3	4	5	6	7	8	9	10	11	12	14	16	20	24	30	40	50
14	.194	.255	.292	.319	.340	.357	.371	.382	.392	.400	.407	.414	.425						
	.344	*.408*	*.446*	*.472*	*.493*	*.509*	*.522*	*.533*	*.542*	*.551*	*.557*	*.564*	*.574*						
15	.181	.240	.276	.302	.322	.338	.351	.363	.374	.383	.390	.397	.408	.418					
	.324	*.387*	*.424*	*.450*	*.471*	*.487*	*.500*	*.511*	*.520*	*.528*	*.536*	*.543*	*.553*	*.561*					
16	.170	.226	.261	.287	.306	.322	.336	.346	.357	.364	.371	.378	.390	.399	.415				
	.307	*.368*	*.404*	*.430*	*.450*	*.466*	*.480*	*.491*	*.500*	*.509*	*.516*	*.522*	*.533*	*.542*	*.566*				
17	.161	.214	.248	.272	.291	.307	.321	.332	.342	.349	.356	.363	.375	.385	.399				
	.291	*.350*	*.385*	*.411*	*.432*	*.447*	*.461*	*.471*	*.481*	*.490*	*.497*	*.503*	*.515*	*.524*	*.539*				
18	.152	.203	.236	.260	.278	.293	.307	.317	.327	.335	.342	.349	.361	.370	.385				
	.277	*.334*	*.369*	*.394*	*.414*	*.429*	*.444*	*.455*	*.464*	*.473*	*.481*	*.487*	*.498*	*.508*	*.521*				
19	.145	.193	.225	.248	.266	.281	.294	.305	.315	.322	.329	.336	.348	.356	.371				
	.264	*.320*	*.354*	*.378*	*.398*	*.414*	*.427*	*.438*	*.448*	*.456*	*.464*	*.471*	*.482*	*.492*	*.506*				
20	.138	.185	.215	.238	.255	.270	.283	.293	.303	.310	.317	.324	.336	.344	.359	.371			
	.253	*.306*	*.339*	*.364*	*.383*	*.398*	*.413*	*.422*	*.432*	*.441*	*.449*	*.455*	*.467*	*.477*	*.492*	*.504*			
21	.131	.177	.206	.227	.244	.259	.271	.281	.291	.299	.306	.313	.324	.332	.347	.359			
	.242	*.294*	*.326*	*.350*	*.369*	*.384*	*.398*	*.409*	*.419*	*.427*	*.435*	*.441*	*.453*	*.463*	*.478*	*.490*			
22	.126	.169	.197	.219	.235	.249	.262	.272	.282	.289	.296	.303	.315	.322	.338	.350			
	.232	*.282*	*.314*	*.337*	*.356*	*.372*	*.385*	*.395*	*.406*	*.414*	*.421*	*.428*	*.440*	*.450*	*.466*	*.477*			
23	.120	.162	.190	.211	.227	.240	.253	.263	.271	.279	.286	.291	.301	.311	.326	.338			
	.223	*.272*	*.303*	*.326*	*.344*	*.359*	*.372*	*.383*	*.393*	*.401*	*.409*	*.415*	*.427*	*.437*	*.453*	*.465*			
24	.115	.156	.183	.203	.218	.232	.244	.254	.262	.270	.277	.282	.292	.304	.317	.329			
	.214	*.262*	*.292*	*.315*	*.333*	*.348*	*.361*	*.371*	*.380*	*.390*	*.396*	*.404*	*.416*	*.425*	*.442*	*.454*			
25	.111	.150	.176	.195	.211	.224	.236	.245	.253	.262	.268	.273	.285	.293	.308	.320	.334		
	.207	*.253*	*.283*	*.305*	*.323*	*.337*	*.350*	*.360*	*.369*	*.378*	*.385*	*.392*	*.404*	*.414*	*.430*	*.442*	*.457*		
26	.107	.145	.170	.188	.204	.216	.228	.237	.246	.253	.260	.266	.278	.286	.301	.313	.325		
	.199	*.244*	*.274*	*.295*	*.313*	*.327*	*.339*	*.350*	*.358*	*.367*	*.375*	*.382*	*.394*	*.403*	*.419*	*.431*	*.446*		
27	.103	.139	.164	.182	.197	.210	.220	.229	.238	.245	.251	.258	.269	.277	.292	.304	.317		
	.193	*.236*	*.265*	*.286*	*.304*	*.318*	*.330*	*.341*	*.349*	*.358*	*.364*	*.373*	*.385*	*.393*	*.410*	*.422*	*.436*		

$k - 1$

TABLE XLVII.—THE DISTRIBUTION OF ϵ^2 WHEN THE TRUE CORRELATION IS ZERO.—(Continued)

$k - 1$

$N - k$	1	2	3	4	5	6	7	8	9	10	11	12	14	16	20	24	30	40	50
28	.099 *.186*	.135 *.229*	.159 *.257*	.176 *.277*	.191 *.295*	.203 *.309*	.214 *.321*	.223 *.331*	.231 *.339*	.238 *.348*	.245 *.355*	.251 *.363*	.261 *.375*	.271 *.383*	.286 *.400*	.296 *.412*	.310 *.427*		
29	.096 *.180*	.131 *.222*	.153 *.249*	.171 *.269*	.185 *.286*	.197 *.300*	.208 *.312*	.217 *.322*	.224 *.330*	.232 *.339*	.239 *.346*	.244 *.354*	.255 *.366*	.262 *.374*	.277 *.391*	.290 *.403*	.302 *.418*		
30	.093 *.175*	.127 *.215*	.149 *.243*	.166 *.262*	.179 *.278*	.191 *.292*	.202 *.303*	.211 *.314*	.218 *.322*	.225 *.331*	.231 *.338*	.237 *.345*	.249 *.356*	.256 *.366*	.271 *.383*	.283 *.395*	.296 *.408*		
32	.087 *.165*	.119 *.203*	.140 *.229*	.157 *.248*	.169 *.264*	.181 *.276*	.192 *.288*	.200 *.298*	.207 *.306*	.213 *.316*	.220 *.322*	.226 *.329*	.237 *.341*	.244 *.351*	.259 *.367*	.269 *.378*	.284 *.393*	.297 *.410*	
34	.082 *.155*	.112 *.192*	.132 *.217*	.148 *.236*	.160 *.251*	.171 *.263*	.182 *.274*	.190 *.284*	.197 *.292*	.203 *.300*	.209 *.308*	.215 *.315*	.226 *.326*	.233 *.336*	.248 *.353*	.258 *.363*	.273 *.378*	.286 *.395*	
36	.078 *.147*	.106 *.183*	.125 *.206*	.140 *.224*	.152 *.239*	.163 *.251*	.172 *.262*	.180 *.271*	.187 *.280*	.193 *.288*	.199 *.294*	.205 *.301*	.215 *.312*	.222 *.322*	.237 *.338*	.247 *.351*	.262 *.364*	.275 *.381*	
38	.074 *.140*	.101 *.174*	.119 *.196*	.134 *.214*	.145 *.228*	.155 *.240*	.164 *.251*	.171 *.260*	.179 *.268*	.185 *.275*	.191 *.288*	.197 *.289*	.205 *.300*	.214 *.309*	.227 *.326*	.236 *.338*	.251 *.350*	.267 *.369*	.286 *.394*
40	.069 *.133*	.096 *.166*	.114 *.188*	.128 *.205*	.139 *.218*	.149 *.230*	.157 *.240*	.164 *.249*	.171 *.257*	.176 *.265*	.183 *.272*	.188 *.277*	.198 *.288*	.205 *.299*	.219 *.314*	.229 *.326*	.241 *.340*	.257 *.357*	.268 *.380*
42	.067 *.127*	.092 *.159*	.109 *.180*	.121 *.196*	.133 *.209*	.142 *.220*	.150 *.231*	.158 *.239*	.164 *.247*	.169 *.254*	.175 *.261*	.180 *.267*	.190 *.278*	.197 *.287*	.209 *.303*	.221 *.314*	.233 *.328*	.249 *.345*	.258 *.368*
44	.064 *.123*	.088 *.152*	.104 *.172*	.116 *.188*	.127 *.201*	.136 *.212*	.144 *.221*	.151 *.230*	.157 *.238*	.163 *.245*	.168 *.251*	.174 *.258*	.182 *.268*	.190 *.277*	.202 *.292*	.211 *.304*	.226 *.318*	.239 *.335*	.251 *.357*
46	.061 *.117*	.084 *.146*	.100 *.166*	.112 *.181*	.122 *.193*	.130 *.204*	.139 *.213*	.144 *.221*	.151 *.229*	.157 *.236*	.162 *.243*	.167 *.249*	.175 *.259*	.183 *.268*	.195 *.283*	.204 *.295*	.219 *.308*	.232 *.326*	.244 *.347*
48	.058 *.112*	.081 *.140*	.097 *.159*	.107 *.174*	.117 *.186*	.126 *.196*	.133 *.206*	.140 *.213*	.146 *.221*	.151 *.228*	.156 *.234*	.161 *.240*	.169 *.250*	.177 *.259*	.189 *.274*	.198 *.286*	.212 *.299*	.225 *.317*	.237 *.338*

TABLE XLVII.—THE DISTRIBUTION OF ϵ^2 WHEN THE TRUE CORRELATION IS ZERO.—(Concluded)

$k - 1$

$N - k$	1	2	3	4	5	6	7	8	9	10	11	12	14	16	20	24	30	40	50
50	.056	.077	.092	.104	.113	.121	.128	.135	.140	.145	.150	.155	.164	.171	.182	.194	.206	.219	.231
	.108	.135	.153	.168	.180	.189	.199	.206	.214	.221	.226	.232	.242	.252	.265	.277	.292	.308	.320
55	.051	.071	.084	.095	.103	.111	.118	.124	.129	.133	.139	.143	.152	.158	.169	.179	.191	.204	.216
	.099	.123	.140	.154	.165	.175	.183	.190	.197	.203	.209	.215	.225	.233	.247	.259	.272	.288	.300
60	.047	.065	.077	.087	.095	.102	.109	.115	.119	.124	.128	.133	.140	.146	.158	.167	.178	.191	.203
	.091	.114	.130	.142	.153	.162	.169	.176	.183	.189	.195	.200	.209	.217	.231	.242	.256	.271	.283
65	.043	.060	.072	.080	.089	.095	.101	.106	.110	.116	.120	.123	.131	.136	.147	.155	.166	.178	.190
	.084	.105	.120	.132	.142	.150	.158	.164	.171	.177	.182	.186	.195	.204	.217	.227	.240	.255	.268
70	.040	.056	.067	.075	.083	.089	.094	.099	.103	.108	.112	.115	.123	.128	.138	.146	.157	.169	.181
	.078	.098	.112	.123	.132	.140	.148	.154	.160	.166	.170	.175	.184	.190	.204	.215	.227	.242	.255
80	.035	.049	.059	.066	.073	.078	.083	.087	.091	.095	.099	.103	.109	.114	.123	.130	.141	.153	.164
	.069	.086	.099	.109	.117	.125	.131	.137	.142	.147	.152	.155	.164	.171	.182	.192	.204	.219	.231
100	.028	.039	.047	.053	.058	.063	.067	.071	.074	.077	.080	.083	.088	.094	.102	.109	.116	.127	.138
	.065	.070	.080	.088	.095	.101	.106	.111	.116	.121	.124	.127	.134	.141	.150	.159	.170	.184	.196
125	.023	.032	.038	.043	.047	.051	.054	.057	.060	.063	.065	.068	.072	.076	.082	.088	.096	.106	.114
	.044	.056	.064	.071	.077	.082	.087	.090	.095	.098	.102	.104	.110	.115	.124	.131	.141	.154	.163
150	.019	.026	.032	.036	.039	.043	.046	.048	.051	.053	.055	.057	.061	.064	.070	.075	.083	.090	.099
	.037	.047	.054	.060	.065	.069	.073	.076	.080	.083	.086	.088	.093	.097	.105	.112	.122	.132	.142
200	.014	.020	.024	.027	.030	.032	.034	.036	.038	.040	.041	.043	.046	.049	.053	.058	.064	.070	.077
	.028	.035	.041	.045	.049	.052	.055	.058	.061	.065	.065	.068	.071	.075	.081	.086	.093	.103	.110
400	.007	.010	.012	.014	.015	.016	.017	.018	.019	.020	.021	.022	.024	.025	.028	.030	.033	.037	.041
	.014	.018	.021	.023	.025	.027	.028	.029	.031	.032	.033	.035	.036	.038	.042	.045	.049	.055	.060
1,000	.003	.004	.005	.005	.006	.007	.007	.007	.008	.008	.009	.009	.010	.010	.011	.012	.014	.016	.017
	.006	.007	.008	.009	.010	.011	.011	.012	.013	.013	.014	.014	.015	.016	.017	.019	.020	.023	.025

TABLE XLVIII.—VALUES OF P FOR THE CHI-SQUARE TEST OF GOODNESS OF FIT

χ^2	$n=2$ $n'=3$	$n=3$ $n'=4$	$n=4$ $n'=5$	$n=5$ $n'=6$	$n=6$ $n'=7$	$n=7$ $n'=8$	$n=8$ $n'=9$	$n=9$ $n'=10$	$n=10$ $n'=11$
1	.606531	.801253	.909796	.962566	.985612	.994829	.998249	.999438	.999828
2	.367879	.572407	.735759	.849146	.919699	.959840	.981012	.991468	.996340
3	.223130	.391625	.557825	.699986	.808847	.885002	.934357	.964295	.981424
4	.135335	.261464	.406006	.549416	.676676	.779778	.857123	.911413	.947347
5	.082085	.171797	.287298	.415880	.543813	.659963	.757576	.834308	.891178
6	.049787	.111610	.199148	.306219	.423190	.539750	.647232	.739919	.815263
7	.030197	.071897	.135888	.220640	.320847	.428880	.536632	.637119	.725444
8	.018316	.046012	.091578	.156236	.238103	.332594	.433470	.534146	.628837
9	.011109	.029291	.061099	.109064	.173578	.252656	.342296	.437274	.532104
10	.006738	.018566	.040428	.075235	.124652	.188573	.265026	.350485	.440493
11	.004087	.011726	.026564	.051380	.088376	.138619	.201699	.275709	.357518
12	.002479	.007383	.017351	.034787	.061969	.100558	.151204	.213308	.285057
13	.001503	.004637	.011276	.023379	.043036	.072109	.111850	.162607	.223672
14	.000912	.002905	.007295	.015609	.029636	.051181	.081765	.122325	.172992
15	.000553	.001817	.004701	.010363	.020256	.036000	.059145	.090937	.132061
16	.000335	.001134	.003019	.006844	.013754	.025116	.042380	.066881	.099632
17	.000203	.000707	.001933	.004500	.009283	.017396	.030109	.048716	.074364
18	.000123	.000440	.001234	.002947	.006232	.011970	.021226	.035174	.054964
19	.000075	.000273	.000786	.001922	.004164	.008187	.014860	.025193	.040263
20	.000045	.000170	.000499	.001250	.002769	.005570	.010336	.017913	.029253
21	.000028	.000105	.000317	.000810	.001835	.003770	.007147	.012650	.021093
22	.000017	.000065	.000200	.000524	.001211	.002541	.004916	.008880	.015105
23	.000010	.000040	.000127	.000338	.000796	.001705	.003364	.006197	.010747
24	.000006	.000025	.000080	.000217	.000522	.001139	.002292	.004301	.007600
25	.000004	.000016	.000050	.000139	.000341	.000759	.001554	.002971	.005345
26	.000002	.000010	.000032	.000090	.000223	.000504	.001050	.002043	.003740
27	.000001	.000006	.000020	.000057	.000145	.000333	.000707	.001399	.002604
28	.000001	.000004	.000012	.000037	.000094	.000220	.000474	.000954	.001805
29	.000001	.000002	.000008	.000023	.000061	.000145	.000317	.000648	.001246
30	.000000	.000001	.000005	.000015	.000039	.000095	.000211	.000439	.000857
40	.000000	.000000	.000000	.000000	.000001	.000001	.000003	.000008	.000017
50	.000000	.000000	.000000	.000000	.000000	.000000	.000000	.000000	.000000
60	.000000	.000000	.000000	.000000	.000000	.000000	.000000	.000000	.000000
70	.000000	.000000	.000000	.000000	.000000	.000000	.000000	.000000	.000000

NOTE: This is the Elderton table, taken from Pearson's *Tables for Statisticians and Biometricians* by arrangement with the publishers.

Note:
In using this table do not first divide by d.o.f.

TABLE XLVIII.—VALUES OF P FOR THE CHI-SQUARE TEST OF GOODNESS OF FIT.—(*Continued*)

x^2	$n = 11$ $n' = 12$	$n = 12$ $n' = 13$	$n = 13$ $n' = 14$	$n = 14$ $n' = 15$	$n = 15$ $n' = 16$	$n = 16$ $n' = 17$	$n = 17$ $n' = 18$	$n = 18$ $n' = 19$	$n = 19$ $n' = 20$
1	.999950	.999986	.999997	.999999	1.	1.	1.	1.	1.
2	.998496	.999406	.999774	.999917	.999970	.999990	.999997	.999999	1.
3	.990726	.995544	.997934	.999074	.999598	.999830	.999931	.999972	.999989
4	.969917	.983436	.991191	.995466	.997737	.998903	.999483	.999763	.999894
5	.931167	.957979	.975193	.985813	.992127	.995754	.997771	.998860	.999431
6	.873365	.916082	.946153	.966491	.979749	.988095	.993187	.996197	.997929
7	.799073	.857613	.902151	.934711	.957650	.973260	.983549	.990125	.994213
8	.713340	.785131	.843601	.889327	.923783	.948867	.966547	.978637	.986671
9	.621892	.702931	.772943	.831051	.877517	.913414	.940261	.959743	.973479
10	.530387	.615960	.693934	.762183	.819739	.866628	.903610	.931906	.952946
11	.443263	.528919	.610817	.686036	.752594	.809485	.856564	.894357	.923839
12	.362642	.445680	.527643	.606303	.679028	.743980	.800136	.847327	.885624
13	.293326	.369041	.447812	.526524	.602298	.672758	.736186	.791573	.838571
14	.232993	.300708	.373844	.449711	.525529	.598714	.667102	.729091	.783691
15	.182498	.241436	.307354	.378154	.451418	.524638	.595482	.661967	.722598
16	.141130	.191236	.249129	.313374	.382051	.452961	.523834	.592547	.657277
17	.107876	.149597	.199304	.256178	.318864	.385597	.454366	.523105	.589868
18	.081581	.115691	.157520	.206781	.262666	.323897	.388841	.455653	.522438
19	.061094	.088529	.123104	.164949	.213734	.268663	.328532	.391823	.456836
20	.045341	.067086	.095210	.130141	.171932	.220220	.274229	.332819	.394578
21	.033371	.050380	.072929	.101632	.136830	.178510	.226291	.279413	.336801
22	.024374	.037520	.055362	.078614	.107804	.143191	.184719	.231985	.284256
23	.017676	.027726	.041677	.060270	.084140	.113735	.149251	.190590	.237342
24	.012733	.020341	.031130	.045822	.065093	.089504	.119435	.155028	.196152
25	.009117	.014822	.023084	.034566	.049943	.069824	.094710	.124915	.160542
26	.006490	.010734	.017001	.025887	.038023	.054028	.074461	.099758	.130189
27	.004595	.007727	.012441	.019254	.028736	.041483	.058068	.078995	.104653
28	.003238	.005532	.009050	.014228	.021569	.031620	.044938	.062055	.083428
29	.002270	.003940	.006546	.010450	.016085	.023936	.034526	.048379	.065985
30	.001585	.002792	.004710	.007632	.011921	.018002	.026345	.037446	.051798
40	.000036	.000072	.000138	.000255	.000453	.000778	.001294	.002087	.003272
50	.000001	.000001	.000003	.000006	.000012	.000023	.000042	.000075	.000131
60	.000000	.000000	.000000	.000000	.000000	.000001	.000001	.000002	.000004
70	.000000	.000000	.000000	.000000	.000000	.000000	.000000	.000000	.000000

TABLE XLVIII.—VALUES OF P FOR THE CHI-SQUARE TEST OF GOODNESS OF FIT.—(*Concluded*)

χ^2	$n = 20$ $n' = 21$	$n = 21$ $n' = 22$	$n = 22$ $n' = 23$	$n = 23$ $n' = 24$	$n = 24$ $n' = 25$	$n = 25$ $n' = 26$	$n = 26$ $n' = 27$	$n = 27$ $n' = 28$	$n = 28$ $n' = 29$	$n = 29$ $n' = 30$
1	1.	1.	1.	1.	1.	1.	1.	1.	1.	1.
2	1.	1.	1.	1.	1.	1.	1.	1.	1.	1.
3	.999996	.999998	.999999	1.	1.	1.	1.	1.	1.	1.
4	.999954	.999980	.999992	.999997	.999999	1.	1.	1.	1.	1.
5	.999722	.999868	.999939	.999972	.999987	.999994	.999998	.999999	1.	1.
6	.998898	.999427	.999708	.999855	.999929	.999966	.999984	.999993	.999997	.999999
7	.996685	.998142	.998980	.999452	.999711	.999851	.999924	.999962	.999981	.999991
8	.991868	.995143	.997160	.998371	.999085	.999494	.999726	.999853	.999924	.999960
9	.982907	.989214	.993331	.995957	.997595	.998596	.999194	.999546	.999748	.999863
10	.968171	.978912	.986304	.991277	.994547	.996653	.997981	.998803	.999302	.999599
11	.946223	.962787	.974749	.983189	.989012	.992946	.995549	.997239	.998315	.998988
12	.916076	.939617	.957379	.970470	.979908	.986567	.991173	.994294	.996372	.997728
13	.877384	.908624	.933161	.951990	.966121	.976501	.983974	.989247	.992900	.995384
14	.830496	.869599	.901479	.926871	.946650	.961732	.973000	.981254	.987189	.991377
15	.776408	.822952	.862238	.894634	.920759	.941383	.957334	.969432	.978436	.985015
16	.716624	.769650	.815886	.855268	.888076	.914828	.936203	.952947	.965819	.975536
17	.652974	.711106	.763362	.809251	.848662	.881793	.909083	.931122	.948589	.962181
18	.587408	.649004	.705988	.757489	.803008	.842390	.875773	.903519	.926149	.944272
19	.521826	.585140	.645328	.701224	.751990	.797120	.836430	.870001	.898136	.921288
20	.457930	.521261	.583040	.641912	.696776	.746825	.791556	.830756	.864464	.892927
21	.397132	.458944	.520738	.581087	.638725	.692609	.741964	.786288	.825349	.859149
22	.340511	.399510	.459889	.520252	.579267	.635744	.688697	.737377	.781291	.820189
23	.288795	.343979	.401730	.460771	.519798	.577564	.632947	.685013	.733041	.776543
24	.242392	.293058	.347229	.403808	.461597	.519373	.575965	.630316	.681535	.728932
25	.201431	.247164	.297075	.350285	.405760	.462373	.518975	.574462	.627835	.678248
26	.165812	.206449	.251682	.300866	.353165	.407598	.463105	.518600	.573045	.625491
27	.135264	.170853	.211226	.255967	.304453	.355884	.409333	.463794	.518247	.571705
28	.109399	.140151	.175681	.215781	.260040	.307853	.358458	.410973	.464447	.517913
29	.087759	.114002	.144861	.180310	.220131	.263916	.311082	.360899	.412528	.465066
30	.069854	.091988	.118464	.149402	.184752	.224289	.267611	.314154	.363218	.414004
40	.004995	.007437	.010812	.015369	.021387	.029164	.039012	.051237	.066128	.083937
50	.000221	.000365	.000586	.000921	.001416	.002131	.003144	.004551	.006467	.009032
60	.000007	.000013	.000022	.000038	.000064	.000104	.000168	.000264	.000407	.000618
70	.000000	.000000	.000001	.000001	.000002	.000004	.000007	.000011	.000019	.000030

TABLE XLIX.—COEFFICIENTS OF r'S IN THE TETRACHORIC CORRELATION
SERIES

r_n	Coefficient of r's according to percentage in tail of distribution								
	5%	6%	7%	8%	9%	10%	11%	12%	13%
r^2	1.1631	1.0994	1.0436	.9936	.9841	.9062	.8673	.8309	.7965
r^3	.6963	.5786	.4809	.3977	.3256	.2622	.2059	.1554	.1097
r^4	−.0989	−.1849	−.2476	−.2942	−.3291	−.3552	−.3745	−.3884	−.3981
r^5	−.5398	−.5167	−.4860	−.4517	−.4157	−.3795	−.3435	−.3083	−.2741
r^6	−.2903	−.1929	−.1120	−.0442	.0127	.0608	.1014	.1357	.1646
r^7	.2360	.2853	.3125	.3250	.3272	.3222	.3121	.2982	.2816
r^8	.3640	.3115	.2529	.1969	.1449	.0972	.0540	.0150	−.0199
r^9	.0082	−.0739	−.1334	−.1759	−.2052	−.2243	−.2354	−.2401	−.2398
r^{10}	−.3077	−.2995	−.2755	−.2442	−.2092	−.1729	−.1368	−.1019	−.0686
r^{11}	−.1597	−.0768	−.0081	.0048	.0914	.1256	.1513	.1699	.1824
r^{12}	.1921	.2258	.2363	.2318	.2175	.1970	.1727	.1463	.1191
r^{13}	.2282	.1650	.1039	.0485	.0002	−.0407	−.0745	−.1020	−.1234
r^{14}	−.0705	−.1323	−.1693	−.1880	−.1933	−.1891	−.1784	−.1622	−.1431
r^{15}	−.2347	−.2011	−.1577	−.1117	−.0672	−.0261	.0105	.0423	.0691
r^{16}	−.0328	.0414	.0948	.1306	.1522	.1626	.1641	.1590	.1488
r^{17}	.2004	.1985	.1773	.1461	.1106	.0743	.0392	.0068	−.0222
r^{18}	.1077	.0349	−.0250	−.0711	−.1043	−.1265	−.1388	−.1435	−.1420
r^{19}	−.1436	−.1701	−.1715	−.1572	−.1337	−.1054	−.0751	−.0450	−.0162
r^{20}	−.1522	−.0913	−.0335	.0162	.0562	.0864	.1075	.1207	.1270
r^{21}	.0785	.1267	.1482	.1507	.1404	.1219	.0984	.0726	.0463
r^{22}	.1691	.1270	.0778	.0301	−.0121	−.0471	−.0743	−.0941	−.1071
r^{23}	−.0152	−.0771	−.1144	−.1319	−.1345	−.1263	−.1109	−.0909	−.0684
r^{24}	−.1635	−.1434	−.1073	−.0660	−.0255	.0110	.0418	.0663	.0845
r^{25}	−.0395	.0278	.0758	.1053	.1195	.1215	.1144	.1009	.0832

NOTE: This table was made by H. P. Peters.

TABLE XLIX.—COEFFICIENTS OF r'S IN THE TETRACHORIC CORRELATION SERIES.—(*Continued*)

r_n	Coefficient of r's according to percentage in tail of distribution								
	14%	15%	16%	17%	18%	19%	20%	21%	22%
r^2	.7639	.7329	.7032	.6747	.6473	.6208	.5951	.5703	.5461
r^3	.0682	.0303	−.0045	−.0366	−.0662	−.0936	−.1191	−.1428	−.1648
r^4	−.4042	−.4074	−.4082	−.4070	−.4040	−.3995	−.3937	−.3868	−.3789
r^5	−.2424	−.2092	−.1785	−.1491	−.1210	−.0941	−.0683	−.0437	−.0203
r^6	.1883	.2090	.2256	.2391	.2498	.2580	.2640	.2681	.2703
r^7	.2659	.2433	.2088	.2013	.1798	.1582	.1367	.1154	.0945
r^8	−.0494	−.0785	−.1027	−.1238	−.1421	−.1578	−.1710	−.1820	−.1909
r^9	−.2398	−.2278	−.2176	−.2054	−.1917	−.1767	−.1607	−.1442	−.1271
r^{10}	−.0403	−.0085	.0181	.0425	.0644	.0840	.1014	.1167	.1300
r^{11}	.1956	.1928	.1921	.1884	.1822	.1738	.1636	.1520	.1393
r^{12}	.0961	.0651	.0394	.0150	−.0079	−.0291	−.0485	−.0662	−.0882
r^{13}	−.1470	−.1511	−.1571	−.1620	−.1625	−.1602	−.1554	−.1487	−.1402
r^{14}	−.1279	−.0997	−.0771	−.0547	−.0328	−.0118	−.0082	.0268	.0440
r^{15}	.1001	.1089	.1223	.1319	.1380	.1410	.1412	.1390	.1346
r^{16}	.1426	.1183	.1001	.0809	.0612	.0415	.0223	.0038	−.0138
r^{17}	−.0581	−.0693	−.0871	−.1013	−.1120	−.1194	−.1239	−.1257	−.1208
r^{18}	−.1447	−.1252	−.1120	−.0967	−.0801	−.0627	−.0450	−.0274	−.0101
r^{19}	.0223	.0339	.0545	.0719	.0861	.0972	.1052	.1105	.1131
r^{20}	.1395	.1234	.1156	.1047	.0916	.0770	.0614	.0452	.0289
r^{21}	.0067	−.0035	−.0255	−.0449	−.0615	−.0729	−.0863	−.0945	−1.000
r^{22}	−.1282	−.1156	−.1135	−.1116	−.0971	−.0857	−.0726	−.0583	−.0434
r^{23}	−.0291	−.0217	.0004	.0207	.0389	.0546	.0678	.0784	.0864
r^{24}	.1137	.1037	.1058	.1038	.0983	.0901	.0796	.0675	.0542
r^{25}	.0450	.0419	.0207	.0004	−.0185	−.0355	−.0503	−.0627	−.0728

TABLE XLIX.—COEFFICIENTS OF r'S IN THE TETRACHORIC CORRELATION SERIES.—(*Continued*)

r_n	Coefficient of r's according to percentage in tail of distribution								
	23%	24%	25%	26%	27%	28%	29%	30%	31%
r^2	.5225	.4995	.4770	.4549	.4333	.4122	.3913	.3708	.3506
r^3	−.1854	−.2046	−.2225	−.2393	−.2549	−.2696	−.2832	−.2960	−.3079
r^4	−.3701	−.3606	−.3504	−.3396	−.3283	−.3165	−.3043	−.2917	−.2788
r^5	.0022	.0233	.0436	.0628	.0810	.0983	.1147	.1301	.1447
r^6	.2709	.2701	.2679	.2645	.2600	.2545	.2481	.2409	.2329
r^7	.0737	.0545	.0347	.0159	−.0023	−.0198	−.0366	−.0527	−.0680
r^8	−.1979	−.2030	−.2065	−.2085	−.2090	−.2082	−.2061	−.2029	−.1986
r^9	−.1093	−.0873	−.0750	−.0578	−.0408	−.0241	−.0078	.0080	.0233
r^{10}	.1412	.1506	.1581	.1641	.1683	.1711	.1724	.1724	.1711
r^{11}	.1249	.1114	.0965	.0814	.0661	.0508	.0355	.0204	.0056
r^{12}	−.0961	−.1083	−.1189	−.1277	−.1348	−.1404	−.1444	−.1470	−.1482
r^{13}	−.1294	−.1193	−.1073	−.0945	−.0811	−.0674	−.0534	−.0394	−.0253
r^{14}	.0597	.0739	.0864	.0973	.1066	.1147	.1206	.1253	.1288
r^{15}	.1281	.1205	.1113	.0962	.0854	.0740	.0621	.0498	.0373
r^{16}	−.0303	−.0455	−.0593	−.0717	−.0826	−.0920	−.0999	−.1063	−.1112
r^{17}	−.1208	−.1174	−.1109	−.1030	−.0938	−.0836	−.0727	−.0611	−.0490
r^{18}	.0064	.0220	.0366	.0500	.0620	.0727	.0819	.0897	.0960
r^{19}	.1134	.1115	.1076	.1020	.0950	.0866	.0772	.0669	.0560
r^{20}	.0128	−.0027	−.0176	−.0315	−.0443	−.0558	−.0660	−.0750	−.0824
r^{21}	−.1031	−.1038	−.1026	−.0990	−.0940	−.0874	−.0796	−.0706	−.0608
r^{22}	−.0281	−.0131	.0016	.0157	.0389	.0411	.0521	.0619	.0703
r^{23}	.0919	.0945	.0958	.0945	.0914	.0866	.0803	.0727	.0640
r^{24}	.0402	.0286	.0117	−.0023	−.0156	−.0333	−.0397	−.0502	−.0593
r^{25}	−.0803	−.0855	−.0884	−.0891	−.0878	−.0846	−.0798	−.0735	−.0660

TABLE XLIX.—COEFFICIENTS OF r'S IN THE TETRACHORIC CORRELATION SERIES.—(Concluded)

r_n	Coefficient of r's according to percentage in tail of distribution								
	32%	33%	34%	35%	36%	37%	38%	39%	40%
r^2	.3307	.3111	.2917	.2725	.2535	.2347	.2160	.1975	.1792
r^3	−.3189	−.3292	−.3388	−.3476	−.3558	−.3633	−.3702	−.3764	−.3820
r^4	−.2655	−.2520	−.2383	−.2243	−.2101	−.1958	−.1813	−.1666	−.1518
r^5	.1584	.1713	.1833	.1946	.2050	.2146	.2235	.2317	.2391
r^6	.2242	.2148	.2049	.1944	.1834	.1720	.1602	.1481	.1356
r^7	−.0826	−.0964	−.1095	−.1218	−.1333	−.1440	−.1540	−.1631	−.1715
r^8	−.1934	−.1872	−.1802	−.1725	−.1640	−.1548	−.1451	−.1348	−.1241
r^9	.0380	.0521	.0655	.0783	.0904	.1017	.1122	.1220	.1310
r^{10}	.1687	.1651	.1605	.1550	.1485	.1413	.1332	.1245	.1151
r^{11}	−.0088	−.0228	−.0363	−.0492	−.0615	−.0731	−.0840	−.0942	−.1036
r^{12}	−.1480	−.1466	−.1440	−.1404	−.1356	−.1299	−.1234	−.1159	−.1078
r^{13}	−.0114	.0022	.0155	.0283	.0407	.0524	.0636	.0740	.0837
r^{14}	.1303	.1310	.1302	.1278	.1245	.1202	.1153	.1087	.1015
r^{15}	.0248	.0123	−.0001	−.0121	−.0238	−.0350	−.0457	−.0558	−.0652
r^{16}	−.1147	−.1167	−.1173	−.1167	−.1148	−.1117	−.1075	−.1023	−.0961
r^{17}	−.0366	−.0242	−.0117	.0007	.0127	.0244	.0357	.0463	.0563
r^{18}	.1008	.1042	.1062	.1068	.1061	.1041	.1009	.0966	.0913
r^{19}	.0445	.0327	.0208	.0088	−.0030	−.0145	−.0257	−.0364	−.0465
r^{20}	−.0884	−.0930	−.0961	−.0978	−.0982	−.0972	−.0949	−.0915	−.0869
r^{21}	−.0503	−.0393	−.0279	−.0164	−.0049	.0064	.0175	.0282	.0383
r^{22}	.0773	.0829	.0870	.0897	.0910	.0909	.0895	.0867	.0829
r^{23}	.0545	.0443	.0336	.0225	.0114	.0003	−.0106	−.0212	−.0314
r^{24}	−.0672	−.0736	−.0786	−.0822	−.0844	−.0851	−.0844	−.0825	−.0793
r^{25}	−.0574	−.0480	−.0380	−.0275	−.0167	−.0059	−.0048	.0153	.0254

TABLE L.—FIRST POWER r's CORRESPONDING TO TETRACHORIC r's IN WIDESPREAD CLASSES

Corresponding r' (first power r) according to percentage in tail of distribution

r	9%	10%	11%	12%	13%	14%	15%	16%	17%	18%	19%	20%	21%	22%	23%	24%	25%
.01	.0100	.0100	.0100	.0100	.0100	.0100	.0100	.0100	.0100	.0100	.0100	.0100	.0100	.0100	.0100	.0100	.0100
.02	.0200	.0200	.0200	.0200	.0200	.0200	.0200	.0200	.0200	.0200	.0200	.0200	.0200	.0200	.0200	.0200	.0200
.03	.0300	.0300	.0300	.0300	.0300	.0300	.0300	.0300	.0300	.0300	.0300	.0300	.0300	.0300	.0300	.0300	.0300
.04	.0400	.0400	.0400	.0400	.0400	.0400	.0400	.0400	.0400	.0400	.0400	.0400	.0400	.0400	.0400	.0400	.0400
.05	.0500	.0500	.0500	.0500	.0500	.0500	.0500	.0500	.0500	.0500	.0500	.0500	.0500	.0500	.0500	.0500	.0500
.06	.0600	.0600	.0600	.0600	.0600	.0600	.0600	.0600	.0600	.0600	.0600	.0600	.0600	.0600	.0600	.0600	.0600
.07	.0700	.0700	.0700	.0700	.0700	.0700	.0700	.0700	.0700	.0700	.0700	.0700	.0700	.0700	.0700	.0700	.0700
.08	.0800	.0799	.0799	.0799	.0799	.0799	.0800	.0800	.0800	.0800	.0800	.0800	.0800	.0800	.0800	.0800	.0800
.09	.0900	.0899	.0899	.0899	.0899	.0899	.0900	.0900	.0900	.0900	.0900	.0900	.0900	.0900	.0901	.0901	.0901
.10	.1000	.0999	.0999	.0999	.0999	.0999	.1000	.1000	.1000	.1000	.1000	.1000	.1001	.1001	.1001	.1001	.1001
.11	.1098	.1099	.1099	.1099	.1099	.1099	.1100	.1100	.1100	.1100	.1101	.1101	.1101	.1101	.1101	.1101	.1101
.12	.1198	.1198	.1199	.1199	.1199	.1199	.1200	.1200	.1200	.1200	.1201	.1201	.1201	.1201	.1201	.1201	.1202
.13	.1297	.1298	.1298	.1299	.1299	.1299	.1300	.1300	.1300	.1301	.1301	.1301	.1301	.1301	.1302	.1302	.1302
.14	.1396	.1397	.1398	.1398	.1399	.1399	.1400	.1400	.1400	.1401	.1401	.1401	.1402	.1402	.1402	.1402	.1402
.15	.1495	.1496	.1497	.1498	.1498	.1499	.1500	.1500	.1500	.1501	.1501	.1502	.1502	.1502	.1503	.1503	.1503
.16	.1594	.1596	.1596	.1597	.1598	.1599	.1599	.1600	.1601	.1601	.1602	.1602	.1602	.1603	.1603	.1603	.1604
.17	.1693	.1695	.1696	.1697	.1698	.1699	.1699	.1700	.1701	.1701	.1702	.1702	.1703	.1703	.1704	.1704	.1704
.18	.1792	.1794	.1795	.1796	.1797	.1798	.1799	.1800	.1801	.1802	.1802	.1803	.1803	.1804	.1804	.1805	.1805
.19	.1891	.1892	.1894	.1895	.1897	.1898	.1899	.1900	.1901	.1902	.1903	.1903	.1904	.1905	.1905	.1906	.1906
.20	.1989	.1991	.1993	.1995	.1996	.1998	.1999	.2000	.2001	.2002	.2003	.2004	.2005	.2005	.2006	.2007	.2007
.21	.2087	.2090	.2092	.2094	.2096	.2097	.2099	.2100	.2101	.2102	.2103	.2104	.2105	.2106	.2107	.2108	.2108
.22	.2185	.2188	.2191	.2193	.2195	.2197	.2198	.2200	.2201	.2203	.2203	.2205	.2206	.2207	.2208	.2209	.2210
.23	.2283	.2286	.2289	.2292	.2294	.2296	.2298	.2300	.2302	.2303	.2304	.2306	.2307	.2308	.2309	.2310	.2311
.24	.2381	.2384	.2388	.2391	.2393	.2396	.2398	.2400	.2402	.2403	.2405	.2407	.2408	.2409	.2410	.2412	.2413
.25	.2478	.2482	.2486	.2489	.2492	.2495	.2498	.2500	.2502	.2504	.2506	.2507	.2509	.2510	.2512	.2513	.2514
.26	.2575	.2580	.2584	.2588	.2591	.2594	.2597	.2600	.2602	.2605	.2606	.2608	.2610	.2612	.2613	.2615	.2616
.27	.2672	.2677	.2682	.2686	.2690	.2694	.2697	.2700	.2703	.2705	.2707	.2709	.2711	.2713	.2715	.2717	.2718
.28	.2769	.2775	.2780	.2785	.2789	.2793	.2797	.2800	.2803	.2805	.2808	.2810	.2813	.2814	.2817	.2818	.2820
.29	.2865	.2872	.2877	.2883	.2887	.2892	.2896	.2899	.2903	.2906	.2909	.2911	.2914	.2916	.2918	.2920	.2922
.30	.2961	.2968	.2975	.2981	.2986	.2991	.2995	.2999	.3003	.3006	.3010	.3013	.3015	.3018	.3020	.3023	.3025
.31	.3057	.3065	.3072	.3079	.3084	.3090	.3095	.3099	.3103	.3107	.3111	.3114	.3117	.3120	.3123	.3125	.3127
.32	.3152	.3161	.3169	.3176	.3183	.3188	.3194	.3199	.3203	.3208	.3212	.3215	.3219	.3222	.3225	.3228	.3230
.33	.3247	.3257	.3266	.3274	.3281	.3287	.3293	.3299	.3304	.3308	.3313	.3317	.3320	.3324	.3327	.3330	.3333
.34	.3342	.3353	.3362	.3371	.3379	.3386	.3392	.3398	.3404	.3409	.3414	.3418	.3422	.3426	.3430	.3433	.3436
.35	.3437	.3448	.3459	.3468	.3476	.3484	.3491	.3498	.3504	.3510	.3515	.3520	.3524	.3528	.3532	.3536	.3540

TABLE L.—FIRST POWER r's CORRESPONDING TO TETRACHORIC r's IN WIDESPREAD CLASSES.—(Continued)

Corresponding r' (first power r) according to percentage in tail of distribution

r	9%	10%	11%	12%	13%	14%	15%	16%	17%	18%	19%	20%	21%	22%	23%	24%	25%
.36	.3531	.3543	.3555	.3565	.3574	.3583	.3590	.3598	.3604	.3610	.3616	.3621	.3626	.3631	.3635	.3639	.3643
.37	.3624	.3638	.3650	.3661	.3671	.3681	.3689	.3697	.3704	.3711	.3717	.3723	.3728	.3733	.3738	.3743	.3747
.38	.3717	.3732	.3746	.3758	.3769	.3779	.3788	.3797	.3804	.3812	.3818	.3825	.3831	.3836	.3841	.3846	.3851
.39	.3810	.3826	.3841	.3854	.3866	.3877	.3887	.3896	.3905	.3912	.3920	.3927	.3933	.3939	.3945	.3950	.3955
.40	.3902	.3920	.3935	.3950	.3963	.3974	.3985	.3995	.4005	.4013	.4021	.4029	.4036	.4042	.4048	.4054	.4059
.41	.3994	.4013	.4030	.4045	.4059	.4072	.4084	.4095	.4105	.4114	.4123	.4131	.4138	.4145	.4152	.4158	.4164
.42	.4085	.4105	.4124	.4140	.4155	.4169	.4182	.4194	.4205	.4215	.4224	.4233	.4241	.4249	.4256	.4262	.4269
.43	.4176	.4198	.4217	.4235	.4252	.4266	.4280	.4293	.4304	.4315	.4326	.4335	.4344	.4352	.4360	.4367	.4374
.44	.4266	.4289	.4310	.4330	.4347	.4363	.4378	.4392	.4404	.4416	.4427	.4437	.4447	.4456	.4464	.4472	.4479
.45	.4355	.4380	.4403	.4424	.4443	.4460	.4476	.4490	.4504	.4517	.4529	.4540	.4550	.4559	.4568	.4577	.4585
.46	.4444	.4471	.4496	.4518	.4538	.4556	.4573	.4589	.4604	.4617	.4630	.4642	.4653	.4663	.4673	.4682	.4690
.47	.4532	.4561	.4587	.4611	.4633	.4652	.4671	.4688	.4703	.4718	.4732	.4744	.4756	.4767	.4777	.4787	.4796
.48	.4619	.4651	.4679	.4704	.4727	.4748	.4768	.4786	.4803	.4819	.4833	.4847	.4860	.4871	.4883	.4893	.4903
.49	.4706	.4739	.4769	.4796	.4821	.4844	.4865	.4885	.4902	.4919	.4935	.4949	.4963	.4976	.4988	.4999	.5010
.50	.4792	.4828	.4859	.4888	.4915	.4939	.4962	.4983	.5002	.5020	.5036	.5052	.5067	.5080	.5093	.5105	.5116
.51	.4877	.4915	.4949	.4980	.5008	.5034	.5058	.5081	.5101	.5120	.5138	.5155	.5170	.5185	.5199	.5211	.5224
.52	.4962	.5002	.5038	.5071	.5101	.5128	.5154	.5178	.5200	.5220	.5239	.5257	.5274	.5290	.5304	.5318	.5331
.53	.5045	.5088	.5126	.5161	.5193	.5222	.5250	.5276	.5299	.5320	.5341	.5360	.5377	.5395	.5410	.5425	.5439
.54	.5128	.5173	.5214	.5251	.5285	.5316	.5345	.5373	.5397	.5421	.5442	.5463	.5482	.5500	.5516	.5532	.5547
.55	.5209	.5257	.5301	.5340	.5376	.5409	.5440	.5470	.5496	.5520	.5544	.5565	.5585	.5605	.5623	.5639	.5655
.56	.5290	.5341	.5387	.5428	.5467	.5502	.5535	.5566	.5594	.5620	.5645	.5669	.5690	.5710	.5729	.5747	.5764
.57	.5369	.5423	.5472	.5516	.5557	.5594	.5629	.5662	.5692	.5720	.5746	.5771	.5794	.5815	.5836	.5855	.5873
.58	.5448	.5504	.5556	.5603	.5646	.5686	.5723	.5758	.5789	.5819	.5847	.5873	.5898	.5921	.5943	.5963	.5982
.59	.5525	.5585	.5639	.5689	.5735	.5777	.5816	.5853	.5887	.5918	.5948	.5976	.6002	.6026	.6050	.6071	.6092
.60	.5601	.5664	.5722	.5774	.5823	.5867	.5909	.5948	.5984	.6017	.6049	.6078	.6106	.6132	.6157	.6180	.6201
.61	.5676	.5742	.5803	.5859	.5910	.5957	.6003	.6043	.6080	.6116	.6149	.6181	.6210	.6238	.6264	.6289	.6311
.62	.5749	.5819	.5883	.5942	.5996	.6045	.6093	.6137	.6176	.6214	.6250	.6283	.6314	.6344	.6371	.6397	.6422
.63	.5821	.5895	.5962	.6024	.6081	.6133	.6183	.6230	.6272	.6312	.6350	.6385	.6418	.6449	.6479	.6507	.6533
.64	.5892	.5969	.6040	.6106	.6166	.6221	.6273	.6323	.6367	.6410	.6449	.6487	.6522	.6555	.6587	.6616	.6644
.65	.5961	.6042	.6117	.6185	.6249	.6307	.6362	.6415	.6461	.6507	.6548	.6588	.6626	.6661	.6694	.6726	.6755
.66	.6028	.6114	.6192	.6264	.6331	.6392	.6451	.6507	.6556	.6603	.6648	.6690	.6730	.6767	.6802	.6835	.6867
.67	.6094	.6184	.6266	.6342	.6412	.6476	.6538	.6597	.6649	.6699	.6747	.6791	.6833	.6873	.6910	.6945	.6978
.68	.6157	.6252	.6338	.6417	.6492	.6559	.6625	.6687	.6737	.6794	.6845	.6892	.6936	.6978	.7018	.7055	.7090
.69	.6219	.6318	.6409	.6492	.6570	.6644	.6710	.6776	.6833	.6890	.6942	.6992	.7039	.7084	.7126	.7165	.7202
.70	.6280	.6383	.6477	.6565	.6647	.6721	.6794	.6864	.6924	.6984	.7039	.7092	.7142	.7189	.7234	.7276	.7315

TABLE L.—FIRST POWER r's CORRESPONDING TO TETRACHORIC r's IN WIDESPREAD CLASSES.[1]—(Concluded)

Corresponding r' (first power r) according to percentage in tail of distribution

r	9%	10%	11%	12%	13%	14%	15%	16%	17%	18%	19%	20%	21%	22%	23%	24%	25%
.71	6338	6445	6545	6637	6722	6800	6877	6951	7014	7077	7136	7192	7244	7294	7341	7386	7428
.72	6393	6506	6610	6706	6796	6878	6959	7036	7103	7169	7231	7290	7346	7399	7449	7496	7540
.73	6447	6564	6673	6774	6868	6954	7039	7121	7191	7260	7326	7388	7477	7503	7556	7606	7653
.74	6498	6620	6734	6839	6938	7027	7117	7203	7277	7350	7420	7486	7548	7607	7663	7716	7766
.75	6547	6674	6792	6902	7006	7100	7194	7284	7362	7439	7513	7582	7648	7710	7770	7826	7879
.76	6593	6726	6849	6964	7071	7170	7269	7364	7446	7527	7604	7677	7748	7813	7876	7936	7992
.77	6637	6774	6902	7022	7135	7237	7342	7442	7527	7613	7694	7772	7845	7915	7982	8045	8105
.78	6678	6820	6953	7078	7196	7303	7412	7517	7607	7697	7783	7864	7942	8016	8087	8154	8217
.79	6716	6863	7001	7131	7254	7365	7480	7591	7685	7779	7870	7956	8038	8116	8191	8262	8327
.80	6751	6903	7047	7181	7309	7425	7545	7662	7760	7860	7956	8046	8132	8215	8294	8370	8441
.81	6783	6940	7089	7229	7362	7481	7608	7730	7833	7938	8038	8133	8225	8312	8397	8473	8552
.82	6812	6974	7127	7272	7410	7564	7667	7795	7903	8013	8118	8219	8316	8408	8497	8582	8662
.83	6838	7005	7163	7313	7456	7584	7723	7857	7970	8085	8196	8302	8404	8502	8597	8687	8771
.84	6861	7032	7194	7349	7497	7630	7776	7916	8033	8154	8271	8383	8469	8594	8694	8790	8879
.85	6881	7055	7222	7382	7535	7671	7824	7971	8093	8220	8342	8460	8574	8683	8789	8891	8986
.86	6897	7075	7246	7410	7568	7708	7868	8059	8148	8281	8410	8534	8654	8769	8881	8990	9090
.87	6910	7092	7266	7434	7597	7740	7909	8067	8199	8338	8473	8603	8730	8852	8971	9086	9193
.88	6921	7104	7282	7454	7621	7766	7941	8107	8244	8390	8535	8668	8801	8931	9057	9179	9293
.89	6928	7114	7294	7469	7640	7787	7969	8142	8284	8436	8584	8728	8868	9005	9139	9268	9389
.90	6933	7120	7301	7479	7652	7821	7991	8170	8217	8475	8630	8781	8929	9074	9215	9353	9482
.91	.693	.713	.733	.750	.766	.781	.800	.820	.836	.852	.869	.886	.900	.916	.932	.945	.959
.92	.693	.713	.733	.751	.767	.782	.801	.822	.838	.855	.872	.889	.905	.921	.937	.950	.965
.93	.693	.713	.734	.751	.768	.784	.802	.823	.840	.857	.874	.891	.909	.924	.940	.955	.970
.94	.693	.713	.734	.752	.769	.785	.802	.823	.841	.858	.875	.892	.911	.928	.943	.958	.975
.95	.694	.713	.734	.752	.769	.786	.803	.823	.841	.858	.876	.893	.912	.930	.946	.962	.979
.96	.694	.713	.734	.752	.769	.787	.803	.823	.841	.858	.876	.894	.913	.931	.947	.964	.982
.97	.694	.713	.734	.752	.769	.787	.803	.824	.841	.859	.877	.894	.913	.931	.948	.966	.984
.98	.694	.714	.734	.752	.770	.787	.804	.824	.842	.859	.877	.895	.914	.932	.948	.967	.986
.99	.695	.714	.734	.752	.770	.787	.804	.824	.842	.860	.878	.895	.914	.932	.948	.968	.987
1.00	.695	.714	.734	.752	.770	.787	.804	.824	.842	.860	.878	.895	.914	.932	.949	.968	.987

[1] The r''s for r's above .90 were estimated from a nomograph.

TABLE LI.—THE PREDICTED LOCATION OF AN INDIVIDUAL IN A DEPENDENT MEASUREMENT FROM HIS STANDING IN AN INDEPENDENT ONE

$r = .05$

Tenth independent	Tenth dependent variable								
	9	8	7	6	5	4	3	2	1
I	914	823	728	632	533	432	329	224	115
II	909	814	718	620	521	420	318	215	109
III	906	810	712	613	513	412	312	209	106
IV	904	806	707	608	508	407	307	205	103
V	901	802	702	603	503	402	302	201	101
VI	899	799	698	598	497	397	298	198	99
VII	897	795	693	593	492	392	293	194	96
VIII	894	791	688	587	487	388	288	190	94
IX	891	785	682	580	479	380	282	186	91
X	885	776	671	568	467	368	272	177	86

$r = .15$

Tenth independent	9	8	7	6	5	4	3	2	1
I	939	865	782	694	599	497	389	274	148
II	927	843	754	660	562	461	355	244	127
III	919	830	737	640	541	439	334	227	116
IV	912	819	722	624	523	422	318	214	108
V	906	808	709	608	508	406	305	203	101
VI	899	797	695	594	492	392	291	192	94
VII	892	786	682	578	477	376	278	181	88
VIII	884	773	666	561	459	360	263	170	81
IX	873	756	645	539	438	340	246	157	73
X	852	726	611	503	401	306	218	135	61

$r = .25$

Tenth independent	9	8	7	6	5	4	3	2	1
I	960	902	833	754	664	565	453	328	184
II	944	872	791	702	605	502	392	274	145
III	933	852	763	669	569	465	357	244	125
IV	923	834	739	641	540	436	329	221	110
V	912	816	717	616	513	409	305	201	98
VI	902	799	695	591	487	384	283	184	88
VII	890	779	671	564	460	359	261	166	77
VIII	875	756	643	535	431	331	237	148	67
IX	855	726	608	498	395	298	209	128	56
X	816	672	547	435	336	246	167	98	40

NOTE: Tenths in the independent factor are indicated by the Roman numerals at the left while tenths in the dependent one are at the tops of columns. Example for reading the table: Skeletal development and intelligence test scores are correlated to the extent of +.05. A boy stands in the third tenth in skeletal development (theoretically at the mid-point of that tenth). The chances are 106 in 1,000 that he will be found in the highest tenth in intelligence (no lower than its lower border); they are 209 in 1,000 that he will be in the second tenth or higher; 312 in 1,000 that he will be in the third tenth or better; etc.

This table was made by Richard P. T. Scott.

TABLE LI.—THE PREDICTED LOCATION OF AN INDIVIDUAL IN A DEPENDENT MEASUREMENT FROM HIS STANDING IN AN INDEPENDENT ONE.—(*Continued*)

$$r = .35$$

Tenth independent	Tenth dependent variable								
	9	8	7	6	5	4	3	2	1
I	976	935	880	812	731	635	522	388	226
II	960	901	828	745	651	546	431	305	164
III	947	875	792	699	599	493	379	259	132
IV	935	851	759	661	557	450	339	225	110
V	921	828	728	625	519	412	304	197	93
VI	907	803	696	588	481	375	272	172	79
VII	890	775	661	550	443	339	241	149	65
VIII	868	741	621	507	401	301	208	125	53
IX	836	695	569	454	349	255	172	99	40
X	774	612	478	365	269	188	120	65	24

$$r = .45$$

Tenth independent	9	8	7	6	5	4	3	2	1
I	988	962	922	867	796	707	595	455	272
II	975	928	866	790	699	594	474	337	181
III	962	900	823	734	633	522	402	273	137
IV	948	872	783	684	577	464	347	227	107
V	933	843	742	636	525	413	300	190	85
VI	915	810	700	587	475	364	258	157	67
VII	893	773	653	536	423	316	217	128	52
VIII	863	727	598	478	367	266	177	100	38
IX	819	663	526	406	301	210	134	72	25
X	728	545	405	293	204	133	78	38	12

$$r = .50$$

Tenth independent	9	8	7	6	5	4	3	2	1
I	992	972	940	893	829	744	635	491	298
II	981	942	886	814	725	620	497	354	189
III	969	913	840	752	652	539	414	280	138
IV	956	884	796	697	588	472	351	227	104
V	940	852	751	642	529	413	297	184	80
VI	920	816	703	587	471	358	249	148	60
VII	896	773	649	528	412	303	204	116	44
VIII	862	720	586	461	348	248	160	87	31
IX	811	646	503	380	275	186	114	58	19
X	702	509	365	256	171	107	60	28	8

$$r = .55$$

Tenth independent	9	8	7	6	5	4	3	2	1
I	996	982	956	917	861	782	676	530	326
II	987	955	905	838	753	648	522	373	197
III	976	927	858	773	672	556	427	287	138
IV	963	896	811	711	600	480	354	225	100
V	947	862	761	650	533	413	293	177	73
VI	927	823	707	587	467	350	239	138	53
VII	900	775	646	520	400	289	189	104	37
VIII	862	713	573	444	328	227	142	73	24
IX	803	627	478	352	247	162	95	45	13
X	674	470	324	218	139	83	44	18	4

TABLE LI.—THE PREDICTED LOCATION OF AN INDIVIDUAL IN A DEPENDENT MEASUREMENT FROM HIS STANDING IN AN INDEPENDENT ONE.—(*Concluded*)

$r = .65$

Tenth independent	Tenth dependent variable								
	9	8	7	6	5	4	3	2	1
I	999	994	982	959	920	858	763	618	390
II	995	977	943	889	812	710	578	413	212
III	988	954	897	819	718	596	455	298	134
IV	978	925	846	746	629	498	359	218	87
V	964	888	787	670	543	411	280	159	57
VI	943	841	720	589	457	330	213	112	36
VII	913	782	641	502	371	254	154	75	22
VII	866	702	545	404	282	181	103	46	12
IX	788	587	422	290	188	111	57	23	5
X	610	382	237	142	80	41	18	6	1

$r = .75$

Tenth independent	9	8	7	6	5	4	3	2	1
I	1,000	999	996	988	969	931	858	723	471
II	999	993	975	940	880	786	649	461	223
III	997	979	940	874	778	649	489	306	120
IV	991	956	891	794	669	521	361	202	67
V	981	921	825	700	557	405	258	129	36
VI	964	871	742	595	443	300	175	79	19
VII	933	798	639	479	331	206	109	44	9
VIII	880	694	511	351	222	126	60	21	3
IX	777	539	351	214	120	60	25	7	1
X	529	277	142	69	31	12	4	1	0

$r = .85$

Tenth independent	9	8	7	6	5	4	3	2	1
I	1,000	1,000	1,000	999	996	985	952	855	588
II	1,000	1,000	996	984	953	883	751	530	223
III	1,000	996	981	942	862	728	537	305	90
IV	999	987	947	864	733	556	355	165	35
V	996	964	885	753	580	390	214	82	13
VI	987	918	786	610	420	247	115	36	4
VII	965	835	645	444	267	136	53	13	1
VIII	910	695	463	272	138	58	19	4	0
IX	777	470	249	117	47	16	4	0	0
X	412	145	48	15	4	1	0	0	0

$r = .95$

Tenth independent	9	8	7	6	5	4	3	2	1
I	1,000	1,000	1,000	1,000	1,000	1,000	1,000	990	816
II	1,000	1,000	1,000	1,000	999	990	929	675	171
III	1,000	1,000	1,000	998	980	893	644	261	20
IV	1,000	1,000	998	976	879	641	306	64	2
V	1,000	999	980	883	649	334	97	10	0
VI	1,000	990	903	666	351	117	20	1	0
VII	998	936	694	359	121	24	2	0	0
VIII	980	739	356	107	20	2	0	0	0
IX	829	324	71	10	1	0	0	0	0
X	184	10	0	0	0	0	0	0	0

INDEX

R

Rabold, C. N., 184
Range, 74
  first to ninth decile, 75
  inter-quartile, 75
Ranks correlation, 103–109
  relation to r, 107
Ratio, Fisher's z, 336
  Snedecor's F, 336
  standard error, 130–137, 453, 476–477
  Student's t, 154
Regression, partial, 220–234
  formulas for partial, 243–244
  related table of, 508–510
Regression coefficients, 95–110
Regression equation, simple, 110–112
Regression lines, 97
Reitz, H. L., 158, 444
Replication of experiments, 469–474
Rider, P. R., 351
Rotation of reference axes, 264–268
Rugg, H. O., 115

S

Sample variance, 70–71
  standard error of, 141
Scores, comparable, 80
  discrete and continuous, 48
  standard, 80
  true, 123, 204–208
Scott, R. P. T., 508
Semi-interquartile range, 75
Sheppard, W. F., 73
Sheppard's correction, 72–74, 84–89, 397
Sisk, H. L., 276
Skewness, 79
  β_1 as measure of, 80
  standard error of, 158
  value of, in normal distribution, 291–292
  of z', 155
Small samples, r's from, 153, 154
  reliability of, 165

Small samples, Student's distribution for, 171–176
  variance of, 70–71, 114
Smith, H. L., 359
Snedecor, G. W., 336, 339, 342, 351, 420, 423
Sones, E., 363, 364
Soper, H. E., 152, 365, 390, 391
Spearman, C., 103, 104, 109, 191, 248, 249, 250, 251, 252, 276
Spearman prophecy formula, 191–196
Standard deviation, 67–74, 81
  for combined samples, 81
  correcting for grouping, 72–74, 84–89
  correlation between, 182
  effect of adding a constant, 77–78
  effect of multiplying by constant, 77
  of a mutilated distribution, 385
  partial, 241–243
  of the population, 69–71
  of a rectangular distribution, 107
  of a set of n ranks, 106
  standard error of, 139–143
  standard error of difference between, 180–182
Standard error, of any difference, 176–177
  of any sum, 177
  of β_1 and β_2, 158
  of biserial r, 365
  from widespread classes, 388–391
  of a cell frequency, 143–145
  of the difference between means, 160–176, 452–455
  of the difference between proportions, 182–185
  of the difference between r's, 185–188
  of the difference between standard deviations, 180–182, 455–456
  of the difference between z's, 188–189
  of estimate, 112–117, 207
  of interpoint ranges, 148